Instructor's Solutions Manual

BO LOU

COLLEGE
PHYSICS

FOURTH EDITION

WILSON
BUFFA

PRENTICE HALL, Upper Saddle River, NJ 07458

Executive Editor: Alison Reeves
Project Manager: Elizabeth Kell
Special Projects Manager: Barbara A. Murray
Production Editor: Jonathan Boylan
Supplement Cover Manager: Paul Gourhan
Supplement Cover Designer: Liz Nemeth
Manufacturing Manager: Trudy Pisciotti

Printed in the United States of America

10 9 8 7 6 5 4 3 2 1

ISBN   0-13-084168-4

Prentice-Hall International (UK) Limited, London
Prentice-Hall of Australia Pty. Limited, Sydney
Prentice-Hall Canada, Inc., Toronto
Prentice-Hall Hispanoamericana, S.A., Mexico
Prentice-Hall of India Private Limited, New Delhi
Prentice-Hall (Singapore) Pte. Ltd.
Prentice-Hall of Japan, Inc., Tokyo
Editora Prentice-Hall do Brazil, Ltda., Rio de Janeiro

PREFACE

This instructor's solutions manual is written to accompany "**COLLEGE PHYSICS**" third edition by Jerry D. Wilson and Anthony J. Buffa, fourth edition. It contains detailed solutions to all end-of-chapter exercises. At the end of the solution, you can find comparison grids that tell you whether the exercises are new for the fourth edition, unchanged from the third edition, or modified from the third edition.

Correctness and accuracy of the solutions and answers are of paramount importance to both instructors and students. Every possible effort has been taken to ensure an error free and accurate solutions manual. Every exercise has been worked out, checked, rechecked, and rechecked by the authors of the text and myself during the four stages (manuscripts, revised manuscripts, page proofs and second page proofs) of the book. Every exercise was also checked for accuracy by at least two other physics professors at other institutions.

Since this manual is written mainly for instructors, verbal explanations in the solutions have been kept to a minimum and some algebraic procedures are only outlined.

The answers given here were reached by working the exercises step-by-step and rounding the result at each step following the general rules of thumb of significant figures (an extra digit or two are carried in intermediate results). If you work the exercises fully and then round only your final result, your *correct* answer may differ slightly from the answer you find here. Variations may be due to rounding or to calculator differences.

This manual was typeset with Microsoft Word for Windows Version 7.0. The diagrams are drafted either with Word 7.0 or Coreldraw 6.0. Since I typed all the solutions and drafted all the diagrams, I bear the final and ultimate responsibilities for any error. Should you find any error, I would be grateful if you could notify me.

Please contact the publisher (liz_kell@prenhall.com) to get a copy.

I certainly hope you find this manual helpful in your teaching.

Bo Lou, Ph.D., Professor of Physics (http://instruction.ferris.edu/loub)
Department of Physical Sciences
Ferris State University
Big Rapids, MI 49307

ACKNOWLEDGMENT

I would like to thank the following people and organizations for their enormous help and support.

First to the authors, Jerry D. Wilson and Anthony J. Buffa, for their meticulous checking of my work and numerous constructive and helpful comments and discussions.

To John Kinard and Jerry Wilson for their solutions manual of the second edition Wilson book. Although this is the fourth edition, some of the solutions are from their work.

To David Curott (University of North Alabama) and Willam McCorkle (West Luberty State College) for checking the solutions and answers.

To Prentice Hall for the financial support and the editors, Paul Corey, Alison Reeves, Karen Karlin, Wendy Rivers, Liz Kell, for their guidance, and Gillian Kieff for assistance.

To Carolyn Gauntt for proof-reading this manual.

Last but not the least, to my family, Lingfei and Alina, for their essential and generous support and love. I dedicate this manual to them.

TABLE OF CONTENTS

CHAPTER 1

UNITS AND PROBLEM SOLVING

1. (b).

2. (c).

3. (c).

4. (a) Since 1 gal = 3.785 L, $300 \text{ L} = (300 \text{ L}) \times \dfrac{1 \text{ gal}}{3.785 \text{ L}} = 79.3 \text{ gal.}$ $\boxed{\text{Not reasonable}}$.

   (b) Since 1 in. = 2.54 cm, $225 \text{ cm} = (225 \text{ cm}) \times \dfrac{1 \text{ in.}}{2.54 \text{ cm}} = 88.6 \text{ in.} = 7'5''.$ $\boxed{\text{Yes}}$.

   (c) Since 1 m = 3.28 ft, $120 \text{ m}^2 = (120 \text{ m}^2) \times \left(\dfrac{3.28 \text{ ft}}{1 \text{ m}}\right)^2 = 1.29 \times 10^3 \text{ ft}^2.$ $\boxed{\text{Not reasonable}}$.

5. Decimal (base 10) has a dime worth 10¢ and a dollar worth 10 dimes or 100¢. By analogy a duodecimal system would have a dime worth 12¢ and a dollar worth 12 "dimes" or $1.44 in current dollars. Then a penny would be $\dfrac{1}{144}$ of a dollar.

6. (a) Different ounces are used for volume and weight measurements.
   (b) Two different pound units are used. Avoirdupois lb = 16 oz, troy lb = 12 oz.

7. 1 nautical mile = 6076 ft = 1.15 mi.

8. (d).

9. (d).

10. $\boxed{\text{No}}$, it only tells if the equation is dimensionally correct.

11. (d).

12. $[L] = [L] + \dfrac{[L]}{[T]} \times [T] = [L] + [L].$

13. (d).

14. $$\left(\frac{[L]}{[T]}\right)^2 = \left(\frac{[L]}{[T]}\right)^2 - 2\frac{[L]}{[T]^2} \times [L] = \left(\frac{[L]}{[T]}\right)^2 - 2\left(\frac{[L]}{[T]}\right)^2 = \left(\frac{[L]}{[T]}\right)^2.$$

15. $m^2 = (m)^2 = m^2$.

16. $\boxed{\text{Yes}}$, since $[m^3] = [m]^3 = [m^3]$.

17. $\boxed{\text{No}}$, it should be $\boxed{V = \pi d^3/6}$.

18. $x = \dfrac{gt^2}{2}$ ☞ $g = \dfrac{2x}{t^2}$.   So the units of g are $\boxed{\text{m/s}^2}$.

19. $\boxed{\text{Yes}}$, because $\text{m/s} = \text{m/s} - (\text{m/s}^2)(\text{s}) = \text{m/s} - \text{m/s}$.

20. (a) $\boxed{\text{Yes}}$, because $s = \sqrt{\dfrac{m}{m/s^2}} = \sqrt{s^2} = s$.

    (b) $\boxed{\text{No}}$, because $\text{m/s} \neq (\text{m/s} + \text{m/s}^2)\, s = m + \text{m/s}$.

21. $\boxed{\text{Yes}}$, because $[L^2] = \frac{1}{2}[L]([L] + [L]) = [L^2] + [L^2]$.

22. $\boxed{\text{The first student}}$, because $\text{m/s} = \sqrt{(\text{m/s}^2)(\text{m})} = \text{m/s}$.

23. Since $f = \dfrac{1}{2\pi}\sqrt{\dfrac{g}{L}}$, hertz $= \sqrt{\dfrac{m/s^2}{m}} = \boxed{1/\text{s or s}^{-1}}$.

24. (a) Since $F = ma$, newton $= (\text{kg})(\text{m/s}^2) = \boxed{\text{kg·m/s}^2}$.

    (b) $\boxed{\text{Yes}}$, because $(\text{kg}) \times \dfrac{m^2/s^2}{m} = \text{kg·m/s}^2$ $(F = m\dfrac{v^2}{r})$

25. (a) Since $E = mc^2$, the units of energy $= (\text{kg})(\text{m/s})^2 = \boxed{\text{kg·m}^2/\text{s}^2}$.

    (b) $\boxed{\text{Yes}}$, because $(\text{kg})(\text{m/s}^2)(\text{m}) = \text{kg·m}^2/\text{s}^2$ $(E = mgh)$.

26. (c).

27. (a).

28. $130 \text{ ft} = (130 \text{ ft}) \times \dfrac{1 \text{ m}}{3.281 \text{ ft}} = \boxed{39.6 \text{ m}}$.

29.   (a) $\boxed{\text{yd}}$.   (b) $\boxed{\text{dm}}$.   (c) $\boxed{\text{cm}}$.

30.   (a) $100 \text{ m} = (100 \text{ m}) \times \dfrac{3.28 \text{ ft}}{1 \text{ m}} = \boxed{328 \text{ ft}}$.

         (b) $2.4 \text{ m} = (2.4 \text{ m}) \times \dfrac{3.28 \text{ ft}}{1 \text{ m}} = \boxed{7.9 \text{ ft}}$.

31. $40\,000 \text{ mi} = (40\,000 \text{ mi}) \times \dfrac{1609 \text{ m}}{1 \text{ mi}} = 64\,400\,000 \text{ m}$. So $\dfrac{64\,400\,000 \text{ m}}{1.75 \text{ m}} = \boxed{37\,000\,000 \text{ times}}$.

32. $1454 \text{ ft} = (1454 \text{ ft}) \times \dfrac{1 \text{ m}}{3.281 \text{ ft}} = \boxed{443.2 \text{ m}}$.

33. $209 \text{ ft}, 1 \text{ in.} = 2059 \text{ in.} = (2059 \text{ in.}) \times \dfrac{0.0254 \text{ m}}{1 \text{ in.}} = \boxed{63.7 \text{ m}}$.

         $199 \text{ ft}, 11 \text{ in.} = 2399 \text{ in.} = (2399 \text{ in.}) \times \dfrac{0.0254 \text{ m}}{1 \text{ in.}} = \boxed{60.9 \text{ m}}$.

         $20 \text{ ft}, 4 \text{ in.} = 244 \text{ in.} = (244 \text{ in.}) \times \dfrac{0.0254 \text{ m}}{1 \text{ in.}} = \boxed{6.20 \text{ m}}$.

         The circumference of the fuselage is $c = \pi d = \pi(6.20 \text{ m}) = \boxed{19.5 \text{ m}}$.

34.   (a) $0.5 \text{ gal} = (0.5 \text{ gal}) \times \dfrac{3.785 \text{ L}}{1 \text{ gal}} = 1.89 \text{ L}$. $2 \text{ L} - 1.89 \text{ L} = 0.11 \text{ L}$.   So $\boxed{2 \text{ L by } 0.11 \text{ L}}$.

         (b) $16 \text{ oz} = (1 \text{ pt}) \times \dfrac{946 \text{ mL}}{2 \text{ pt}} = 473 \text{ mL}$. $500 \text{ mL} - 473 \text{ mL} = 27 \text{ mL}$.   So $\boxed{27 \text{ mL in } 500 \text{ mL}}$.

35. $18 \text{ gal} = (18 \text{ gal}) \times \dfrac{3.785 \text{ L}}{1 \text{ gal}} = \boxed{68 \text{ L}}$.

36.   (a) $300 \text{ ft} = (300 \text{ ft}) \times \dfrac{1 \text{ m}}{3.28 \text{ ft}} = 91.5 \text{ m}$. $160 \text{ ft} = (160 \text{ ft}) \times \dfrac{1 \text{ m}}{3.28 \text{ ft}} = 48.8 \text{ m}$.

         So the dimensions are $\boxed{91.5 \text{ m by } 48.8 \text{ m}}$.

         (b) $11 \text{ in.} = (11 \text{ in.}) \times \dfrac{2.54 \text{ cm}}{1 \text{ in.}} = 27.9 \text{ cm}$. $11.25 \text{ in.} = (11.25 \text{ in.}) \times \dfrac{2.54 \text{ cm}}{1 \text{ in.}} = 28.6 \text{ cm}$.

         So the length is $\boxed{27.9 \text{ cm to } 28.6 \text{ cm}}$.

37. From Exercise 1.36, the $\boxed{\text{metric field}}$ is larger.

$A_{\text{current}} = (91.4 \text{ m})(48.8 \text{ m}) = 4.46 \times 10^3 \text{ m}^2.$ $A_{\text{metric}} = (100 \text{ m})(54 \text{ m}) = 5.4 \times 10^3 \text{ m}^2.$

So the difference is $5.4 \times 10^3 \text{ m}^2 - 4.46 \times 10^3 \text{ m}^2 = \boxed{9.4 \times 10^2 \text{ m}^2}.$

38. $15 \text{ m/s} = (15 \text{ m/s}) \times \dfrac{1 \text{ mi}}{1609 \text{ m}} \times \dfrac{3600 \text{ s}}{1 \text{ h}} = 34 \text{ mi/h}.$ So $\boxed{34 \text{ mi}}.$

39. $763 \text{ mi/h} = (763 \text{ mi/h}) \times \dfrac{1609 \text{ m}}{1 \text{ mi}} \times \dfrac{1 \text{ h}}{3600 \text{ s}} = \boxed{341 \text{ m/s}}.$

(b) $300 \text{ ft} = (300 \text{ ft}) \times \dfrac{1 \text{ m}}{3.28 \text{ ft}} = 91.46 \text{ m}.$ So the time is $\dfrac{91.46 \text{ m}}{341 \text{ m/s}} = \boxed{0.268 \text{ s}}.$

40. $1 \text{ km/h} = (1 \text{ km/h}) \times \dfrac{1000 \text{ m}}{1 \text{ km}} \times \dfrac{1 \text{ h}}{3600 \text{ s}} = 0.8 \text{ m/s} < 1 \text{ m/s}$

$1 \text{ ft/s} = (1 \text{ ft/s}) \times \dfrac{1 \text{ m}}{3.28 \text{ ft}} = 0.30 \text{ m/s} < 1 \text{ m/s}$

$1 \text{ mi/h} = (1 \text{ mi/h}) \times \dfrac{1609 \text{ m}}{1 \text{ mi}} \times \dfrac{1 \text{ h}}{3600 \text{ s}} = 0.45 \text{ m/s} < 1 \text{ m/s}.$

So (a) represents the greatest speed.

41. (a) $10 \text{ mi/h} = (10 \text{ mi/h}) \times \dfrac{1.609 \text{ km}}{1 \text{ mi}} = \boxed{16 \text{ km/h for each } 10 \text{ mi/h}}.$

(b) $65 \text{ mi/h} = (65 \text{ mi/h}) \times \dfrac{1.609 \text{ km}}{1 \text{ mi}} = \boxed{105 \text{ km/h}}.$

42. (a) $25.0 \text{ mi/gal} = (25.0 \text{ mi/gal}) \times \dfrac{1.609 \text{ km}}{1 \text{ mi}} \times \dfrac{1 \text{ gal}}{3.785 \text{ L}} = \boxed{10.6 \text{ km/L}}.$

(b) 6000 km requires $(6000 \text{ km}) \times \dfrac{1 \text{ L}}{10.6 \text{ km}} = 565 \text{ L},$

which costs $(565 \text{ L}) \times \dfrac{1 \text{ gal}}{3.785 \text{ L}} \times \dfrac{\$5.00}{1 \text{ gal}} = \boxed{\$746}.$

43. (a) $2.0 \text{ fl. oz} = (2.0 \text{ fl. oz}) \times \dfrac{473 \text{ mL}}{16 \text{ fl. oz}} = \boxed{59 \text{ mL}}.$

(b) $100 \text{ g} = (100 \text{ g}) \times \dfrac{14.5 \text{ oz}}{411 \text{ g}} = \boxed{3.5 \text{ oz}}.$

44. $12 \text{ fl. oz} = \tfrac{3}{8} \text{ qt} = (\tfrac{3}{8} \text{ qt}) \times \dfrac{1 \text{ L}}{1.057618 \text{ qt}} = 355 \text{ mL}.$ The correct one is $\boxed{12 \text{ fl. oz} = 355 \text{ mL}}.$

45. $18 \text{ in.} = (18 \text{ in.}) \times \dfrac{2.54 \text{ cm}}{1 \text{ in.}} = 45.7 \text{ cm.}$ $5 \text{ ft, 6 in.} = 66 \text{ in.} = (66 \text{ in.}) \times \dfrac{2.54 \text{ cm}}{1 \text{ in.}} = 167.6 \text{ cm.}$

So the growth per year is $\dfrac{167.6 \text{ cm} - 45.7 \text{ cm}}{20} = \boxed{6.1 \text{ cm}}$.

46.   (a) $x = (19 \text{ in.}) \cos 37° = 15.2 \text{ in.}$ and $y = (19 \text{ in.}) \sin 37° = 11.4 \text{ in.}$

So the area $= xy = (15.2 \text{ in.})(11.4 \text{ in.}) = \boxed{1.7 \times 10^2 \text{ in}^2}$.

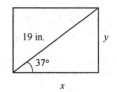

(b) $1.7 \times 10^2 \text{ in.}^2 = (1.7 \times 10^2 \text{ in.}^2) \times \left(\dfrac{2.54 \text{ cm}}{1 \text{ in.}}\right)^2 = \boxed{1.1 \times 10^3 \text{ cm}^2}$.

47.   (a) $W = 3.2 \text{ yd} = (3.2 \text{ yd}) \times \dfrac{3 \text{ ft}}{1 \text{ yd}} \times \dfrac{1 \text{ m}}{3.28 \text{ ft}} = 2.93 \text{ m.}$ $L = 4.0 \text{ yd} = 3.66 \text{ m.}$

$H = 8.0 \text{ ft} = (8.0 \text{ ft}) \times \dfrac{1 \text{ m}}{3.28 \text{ ft}} = 2.44 \text{ m.}$

The volume $V = LWH = (3.66 \text{ m})(2.93 \text{ m})(2.44 \text{ m}) = \boxed{26 \text{ m}^3}$.

(b) $V = 26.2 \text{ m}^3 = (26.2 \text{ m}^3) \times \left(\dfrac{3.28 \text{ ft}}{1 \text{ m.}}\right)^3 = \boxed{9.2 \times 10^2 \text{ ft}^3}$.

48.   (a) $13.6 \text{ g/cm}^3 = (13.6 \text{ g/cm}^3) \times \dfrac{1 \text{ kg}}{1000 \text{ g}} \times \left(\dfrac{100 \text{ cm}}{1 \text{ m}}\right)^3 = \boxed{1.36 \times 10^4 \text{ kg/m}^3}$.

(b) $\rho = \dfrac{m}{V}$,   ☞ $m = \rho V = (13.6 \text{ g/cm}^3)(0.250 \text{ L}) \times \dfrac{1000 \text{ cm}^3}{1 \text{ L}} = 3.40 \times 10^3 \text{ g} = \boxed{3.40 \text{ kg}}$.

49.   (a) The volume of a sphere $V = \dfrac{4\pi r^3}{3} = \dfrac{4\pi (0.10 \text{ m})^3}{3} = 4.19 \times 10^{-3} \text{ m}^3$.

$\rho = \dfrac{m}{V} = \dfrac{10 \text{ kg}}{4.19 \times 10^{-3} \text{ m}^3} = \boxed{2.4 \times 10^3 \text{ kg/m}^3}$.

(b) $m = \rho V = (2.4 \times 10^3 \text{ kg/m}^3) \times \dfrac{4\pi (0.20 \text{ m})^3}{3} = \boxed{80 \text{ kg}}$.

50. $L = 300 \text{ cubits} = (300 \text{ cubits}) \times \dfrac{0.5 \text{ yd}}{1 \text{ cubit}} \times \dfrac{3 \text{ ft}}{1 \text{ yd}} \times \dfrac{1 \text{ m}}{3.28 \text{ ft}} = 137 \text{ m.}$

$W = 50.0 \text{ cubits} = 22.9 \text{ m},$ $H = 30.0 \text{ cubits} = 13.7 \text{ m.}$

So the dimensions are $\boxed{137 \text{ m by } 22.9 \text{ m by } 13.7 \text{ m}}$.

(b) $V = LWH = (137 \text{ m})(22.9 \text{ m})(13.7 \text{ m}) = \boxed{4.30 \times 10^4 \text{ m}^3}$.

51.   (a).

52.   (b).

53. $50\,500\ \mu\text{m} = (50\,500\ \mu\text{m}) \times \dfrac{1\ \text{cm}}{10\,000\ \mu\text{m}} = \boxed{5.05\ \text{cm}} = \boxed{5.05 \times 10^{-1}\ \text{dm}} = \boxed{5.05 \times 10^{-2}\ \text{m}}$.

54. $\boxed{0.001\ \text{m or 1 mm}}$.

55. $\boxed{\text{No}}$, only one doubtful digit (1/10 mm or 1/100 cm) can be measured. The best measurement is 25.48 cm.

56.   (a) $\boxed{4}$.   (b) $\boxed{3}$.   (c) $\boxed{5}$.   (d) $\boxed{2}$.

57.   (a) $\boxed{1.0\ \text{m}}$.   (b) $\boxed{8.0\ \text{cm}}$.   (c) $\boxed{16\ \text{kg}}$.   (d) $\boxed{1.5 \times 10^{-2}\ \mu\text{s}}$.

58. $\boxed{\text{(b) and (d)}}$. (a) has 4 and (c) has 6.

59.   (a) $\boxed{10.1\ \text{m}}$.   (b) $\boxed{775\ \text{km}}$.   (c) $\boxed{2.55 \times 10^{-3}\ \text{kg}}$.   (d) $\boxed{9.30 \times 10^{7}\ \text{mi}}$.

60. $A = LW = (3.7\ \text{m})(2.37\ \text{m}) = \boxed{8.8\ \text{m}^2}$.

61. $A = \pi r^2 = \pi (6.36 \times 10^{6}\ \text{m})^2 = \boxed{1.27 \times 10^{14}\ \text{m}^2}$.

62. $V = a^3$,   ☞ $a = \sqrt[3]{V} = \sqrt[3]{2.5 \times 10^{2}\ \text{cm}^3} = \boxed{6.3\ \text{cm}}$.

63.   The area is the sum of that of the top, the bottom, and the side. The side of the can is a rectangle with a length equal to the circumference and width equal to the height of the can.

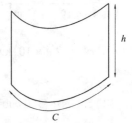

$$A = \frac{\pi d^2}{4} + \frac{\pi d^2}{4} + Ch = \frac{\pi d^2}{4} + \frac{\pi d^2}{4} + (\pi d)h$$

$$= \frac{\pi (12.559\ \text{cm})^2}{4} + \frac{\pi (12.559\ \text{cm})^2}{4} + \pi (12.559\ \text{cm})(5.62\ \text{cm}) = \boxed{470\ \text{cm}^2}.$$

64. $46.9\ \text{m} + 5.72\ \text{m} - 38\ \text{m} = \boxed{15\ \text{m}}$.

65. (a) $v = \dfrac{x}{t} = \dfrac{8.5 \text{ m}}{2.7 \text{ s}} = 3.1 \text{ m/s}, \quad p = mv = (0.66 \text{ kg})(3.1 \text{ m/s}) = \boxed{2.0 \text{ kg}\cdot\text{m/s}}.$

(b) $p = \dfrac{mx}{t} = \dfrac{(0.66 \text{ kg})(8.5 \text{ m})}{2.7 \text{ s}} = \boxed{2.1 \text{ kg}\cdot\text{m/s}}.$ The difference comes from $\boxed{\text{rounding}}$.

66. (a).

67. (c).

68. $\rho = \dfrac{m}{V} = \dfrac{6.0 \times 10^{25} \text{ kg}}{1.1 \times 10^{21} \text{ m}^3} = \boxed{5.5 \times 10^3 \text{ kg/m}^3}.$

69. $\rho = \dfrac{m}{V}, \quad \text{☞} \quad m = \rho V = (1.03 \text{ g/cm}^3)(1 \text{ L}) \times \dfrac{1000 \text{ cm}^3}{1 \text{ L}} = \boxed{1.03 \times 10^3 \text{ g} = 1.03 \text{ kg}}.$

70. (a) $\boxed{\text{Yes}}$. 1000 kg is equivalent to $(1000 \text{ kg}) \times \dfrac{2.2 \text{ lb}}{1 \text{ kg}} = 2200 \text{ lb}.$

(b) $\boxed{\text{No}}$. 283 cm $= (283 \text{ cm}) \times \dfrac{3.28 \text{ ft}}{100 \text{ cm}} = 9.3 \text{ ft}.$

(c) $\boxed{\text{Yes}}$. $3.00 \times 10^8 \ \mu s = (3.00 \times 10^8 \ \mu s) \times \dfrac{1 \text{ s}}{10^6 \ \mu s} = 3.00 \times 10^2 \text{ s} = 5.00 \text{ min}.$

(d) $\boxed{\text{Yes}}$. 25 m/s $= (25 \text{ m/s}) \times \dfrac{1 \text{ mi}}{1609 \text{ m}} \times \dfrac{3600 \text{ s}}{1 \text{ h}} = 56 \text{ mi/h}.$

(e) $\boxed{\text{No}}$. 10 dm $= (10 \text{ dm}) \times \dfrac{1 \text{ in.}}{0.254 \text{ dm}} = 40 \text{ in}.$

(f) $\boxed{\text{No}}$. 40 cm $= (40 \text{ cm}) \times \dfrac{1 \text{ in.}}{2.54 \text{ cm}} = 16 \text{ in}.$

71. (a) The percentage is $\dfrac{(18 \text{ g})(9 \text{ cal/g})}{310 \text{ cal}} = 0.52 = \boxed{52\%}.$

(b) Total fat $= \dfrac{18 \text{ g}}{0.28} = \boxed{64 \text{ g}}; \quad$ saturated fat $= \dfrac{7 \text{ g}}{0.35} = \boxed{20 \text{ g}}.$

72. One sheet has two pages. The average thickness per sheet is $\dfrac{3.75 \text{ cm}}{430 \text{ sheets}} = \boxed{8.72 \times 10^{-3} \text{ cm}}.$

73. 1 ly $= (365.25 \text{ d})(86400 \text{ s/d})(3.00 \times 10^8 \text{ m/s}) = \boxed{9.47 \times 10^{15} \text{ m}}.$

74. $d = \sqrt{(1000 \text{ m})^2 + (500 \text{ m})^2} = \boxed{1.12 \times 10^3 \text{ m}}$.

Exercise 1.74

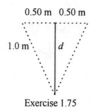

Exercise 1.75

75. $d = \sqrt{(1.0 \text{ m})^2 - (0.50 \text{ m})^2} = \boxed{0.87 \text{ m}}$.

76. A better buy gives you more *AREA* (more pepperoni) per dollar. Calculating the ratio of area to dollar.

For the 9.0-inch: $\dfrac{\pi(4.5 \text{ in})^2}{\$7.95} = 8.0 \text{ in.}^2/\text{dollar}$.   For the 12-inch: $\dfrac{\pi(6.0 \text{ in})^2}{\$13.50} = 8.4 \text{ in.}^2/\text{dollar}$.

So the $\boxed{\text{12-inch is the better buy}}$.

77. For the center circle: $A = \pi r^2 = \pi(0.64 \text{ cm})^2 = 1.3 \text{ cm}^2$.

For the outer ring: $A = \pi(r_2^2 - r_1^2) = \pi[(1.78 \text{ cm})^2 - 1.66 \text{ cm})^2] = 1.3 \text{ cm}^2$.

So $\boxed{\text{same area for both}}$ if calculated to 2 significant figures.

78. $d = \sqrt{(90 \text{ ft})^2 + (90 \text{ ft})^2} = 127 \text{ ft} = (127 \text{ ft}) \times \dfrac{1 \text{ m}}{3.28 \text{ ft}} = \boxed{39 \text{ m}}$.

79. $t = \dfrac{x}{v} = \dfrac{31 \text{ mi}}{75 \text{ mi/h}} = 0.41 \text{ h} = \boxed{25 \text{ min}}$.

80. $V = AL = \pi r^2 L = \pi\left[(12 \text{ in.}) \times \dfrac{0.0254 \text{ m}}{1 \text{ in.}}\right]^2 (300 \text{ mi}) \times \dfrac{1609 \text{ m}}{1 \text{ mi}} = 1.41 \times 10^5 \text{ m}^3$.

$\rho = \dfrac{m}{V}$,   ☞ $m = \rho V = (1.0 \times 10^3 \text{ kg/m}^3)(1.41 \times 10^5 \text{ m}^3) = 1.41 \times 10^8 \text{ kg}$

$= (1.41 \times 10^8 \text{ kg}) \times \dfrac{1 \text{ ton}}{1000 \text{ kg}} = \boxed{1.4 \times 10^5 \text{ tons}}$.

81. $d = x \tan 30° = (50 \text{ m} - x) \tan 40° = (50 \text{ m}) \tan 40° - x \tan 40°$.

So $x = \dfrac{(50 \text{ m}) \tan 40°}{\tan 30° + \tan 40°} = 29.6 \text{ m}$.

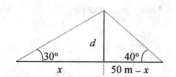

Therefore $d = (29.6 \text{ m}) \tan 30° = \boxed{17 \text{ m}}$.

82.	(a) $12.634 + 2.1 = \boxed{14.7}$.

(b) $13.5 - 2.134 = \boxed{11.4}$.

(c) $\pi(0.25 \text{ m})^2 = \boxed{0.20 \text{ m}^2}$.

(d) $\sqrt{2.37/3.5} = \boxed{0.82}$.

83.	$\$0.32/\text{L} = (\$0.32/\text{L}) \times \dfrac{3.785 \text{ L}}{1 \text{ gal}} = \$1.21/\text{gal.}$ So the answer is $\boxed{\text{yes}}$.

84.	The number of beats $= (70 \text{ times/min})(70 \text{ y})(365 \text{ d/y})(24 \text{ h/d})(60 \text{ min/h}) = \boxed{2.6 \times 10^9 \text{ times}}$.

85.	$A = \frac{1}{2}LH = \frac{1}{2}(11.2 \text{ cm})(7.5 \text{ cm}) = \boxed{42 \text{ cm}^2}$.

86.	Since ax^2 is in meters, $a = \dfrac{\text{m}}{\text{m}^2} = \boxed{1/\text{m}}$.

Since bx is in meters, $b = \dfrac{\text{m}}{\text{m}} = \boxed{\text{dimensionless}}$. c is in $\boxed{\text{m}}$.

87.	$V = LWH = (4.85 \text{ cm})(6.5 \text{ cm})(15.51 \text{ cm}) = \boxed{4.9 \times 10^2 \text{ cm}^3}$.

88.	(a) $A = 4\pi r^2 = 4\pi(12 \text{ cm})^2 = \boxed{1.8 \times 10^3 \text{ cm}^2}$.

(b) $1.8 \times 10^3 \text{ cm}^2 = (1.8 \times 10^3 \text{ cm}^2) \times \left(\dfrac{1 \text{ m}}{100 \text{ cm}}\right)^2 = \boxed{0.18 \text{ m}^2}$.

(c) $V = \dfrac{4\pi r^3}{3} = \dfrac{4\pi(0.12 \text{ m})^3}{3} = 7.24 \times 10^{-3} \text{ m}^3.$ So $\rho = \dfrac{m}{V} = \dfrac{9.0 \text{ kg}}{7.24 \times 10^{-3} \text{ m}} = \boxed{1.2 \times 10^3 \text{ kg/m}^3}$.

89.	$V = AH = (\pi r^2)H = \pi(4.0 \text{ cm})^2(12 \text{ cm}) = 6.03 \times 10^2 \text{ cm}^3 = (6.03 \times 10^2 \text{ cm}^3) \times \dfrac{1 \text{ L}}{1000 \text{ cm}^3} = \boxed{0.60 \text{ L}}$.

90.	(a) $\boxed{0.01 \text{ m} = 1 \text{ cm}}$.

(b) $A = LW = (1.245 \text{ m})(0.760 \text{ m}) = \boxed{0.946 \text{ m}^2}$.

91.	$\boxed{\text{No}}$, because $25 \text{ m/s} = (25 \text{ m/s}) \times \dfrac{1 \text{ mi}}{1609 \text{ m}} \times \dfrac{3600 \text{ s}}{1 \text{ h}} = 56 \text{ mi/h}$.

92. $3.36 \text{ g/cm}^3 = (3.36 \text{ g/cm}^3) \times \dfrac{1 \text{ kg}}{1000 \text{ g}} \times \left(\dfrac{100 \text{ cm}}{1 \text{ m}}\right)^3 = 3.36 \times 10^3 \text{ kg/m}^3.$

$\rho = \dfrac{m}{V}, \quad \text{☞} \quad m = \rho V = (3.36 \times 10^3 \text{ kg/m}^3) \times \dfrac{4\pi}{3} \times [(1080 \text{ mi})(1609 \text{ m/mi})]^3 = \boxed{7.39 \times 10^{22} \text{ kg}},$

which is very close to 7.4×10^{22} kg listed in the inside back cover.

93. $V = \dfrac{4\pi}{3}\,(r_1^3 - r_2^3) = \dfrac{4\pi}{3}\,[(12.3 \text{ cm})^3 - (9.25 \text{ cm})^3] = \boxed{4.48 \times 10^3 \text{ cm}^3}.$

94. $d = \sqrt{(200 \text{ mi})^2 + (300 \text{ mi} - 100 \text{ mi})^2} = \boxed{283 \text{ mi}}.$

$\theta = \tan^{-1}\left(\dfrac{300 \text{ mi} - 100 \text{ mi}}{200 \text{ mi}}\right) = \boxed{45° \text{ north of east}}.$

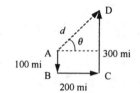

CHAPTER 2

KINEMATICS: DESCRIPTION OF MOTION

1.   (c).

2. $\boxed{\text{Yes}}$, the coordinates of the object depend on the reference point. $\boxed{\text{No}}$, displacement is independent of reference point.

3.   (a).

4. $\boxed{\text{Yes}}$, for a round trip. $\boxed{\text{No}}$; distance is always greater than or equal to the magnitude of displacement.

5.   No final position can be given. The position could be anywhere from 0 to 500 m.

6.   Speed is the magnitude of velocity.

7. $\boxed{\text{No}}$. The average velocity could be zero (for a round trip) while the average speed is never zero.

8.   Displacement is the change in position.

So the magnitude of the displacement is $\boxed{300 \text{ m}}$.

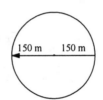

9.   Displacement is the change in position.

So it is $\boxed{1.65 \text{ m down}}$.

10. $avg. \ sp. = \dfrac{d}{t}$, ☞ $t = \dfrac{d}{avg. \ sp.} = \dfrac{250 \text{ km}}{150 \text{ km/h}} = \boxed{1.67 \text{ h}}$.

11. $avg. \ sp. = \dfrac{d}{t}$, ☞ $d = (avg. \ sp.)t = (90 \text{ km/h})(\tfrac{1}{3}\text{ h}) = \boxed{30 \text{ km}}$.

$\boxed{\text{Yes}}$, this is the actual distance.

12.   (a) First trip: $avg. \ sp. = \dfrac{d}{t} = \dfrac{150 \text{ km}}{2.5 \text{ h}} = \boxed{60 \text{ km/h}}$.

Return trip: $avg. \ sp. = \dfrac{150 \text{ km}}{2.0 \text{ h}} = \boxed{75 \text{ km/h}}$.

(b) Total trip: $avg. \ sp. = \dfrac{150 \text{ km} + 150 \text{ km}}{2.5 \text{ h} + 2.0 \text{ h}} = \boxed{67 \text{ km/h}}$.

13.   (a) $avg.\ sp. = \dfrac{d}{t} = \dfrac{(0.30\ \text{km})(1000\ \text{m/km})}{(10\ \text{min})(60\ \text{s/min})} = \boxed{0.50\ \text{m/s}}$.

        (b) $avg.\ sp._1 = 1.20(avg.\ sp.) = 1.20(0.50\ \text{m/s}) = 0.60\ \text{m/s}$.

        So $t = \dfrac{d}{avg.\ sp._1} = \dfrac{300\ \text{m}}{0.60\ \text{m/s}} = 500\ \text{s} = \boxed{8.3\ \text{min}}$.

14.   (a) $avg.\ sp. = \dfrac{d}{t} = \dfrac{500\ \text{m}}{50\ \text{s}} = \boxed{0.50\ \text{m/s}}$.

        (b) The displacement is zero for a round trip, so the average velocity is $\boxed{\text{zero}}$.

15. $d = \sqrt{(40\ \text{m})^2 + (50\text{m} - 30\ \text{m})^2} = \boxed{45\ \text{m}}$.

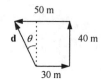

        $\theta = \tan^{-1}\left(\dfrac{50\ \text{m} - 30\ \text{m}}{40\ \text{m}}\right) = \boxed{27°\ \text{west of north}}$.

16.   (a) $avg.\ sp. = \dfrac{d}{t} = \dfrac{2(10\ \text{m})}{2.4\ \text{s}} = \boxed{8.3\ \text{m/s}}$.

        (b) Since the ball is caught at the initial height, the displacement is zero.

        So the average velocity is $\boxed{\text{zero}}$.

17.   (a) $avg.\ sp. = \dfrac{d}{t} = \dfrac{27\ \text{m} + 21\ \text{m}}{(30\ \text{min})(60\ \text{s/min})} = \boxed{2.7\ \text{cm/s}}$.

        (b) The displacement is $\Delta x = \sqrt{(27\ \text{m})^2 + (21\ \text{m})^2} = 34.2\ \text{m}$.

        $v = \dfrac{\Delta x}{\Delta t} = \dfrac{34.2\ \text{m}}{(30\ \text{min})(60\ \text{s/min})} = \boxed{1.9\ \text{cm/s}}$.

18.   (a) $avg.\ sp. = \dfrac{d}{t} = \dfrac{(1.50\ \text{km})(1000\ \text{m/km})}{(1.10\ \text{min})(60\ \text{s/min})} = \boxed{22.7\ \text{m/s}}$.

        $\boxed{\text{Velocity is not constant}}$ because its direction changes.

19.   (a) $avg.\ sp. = \dfrac{d}{t}$, ☞ $t_\text{L} = \dfrac{2500\ \text{m}}{3.00 \times 10^8\ \text{m/s}} = 8.33 \times 10^{-6}\ \text{s}$, $t_\text{S} = \dfrac{2500\ \text{m}}{340\ \text{m/s}} = 7.35\ \text{s}$.

        So the time elapse is $\Delta t = t_\text{S} - t_\text{L} = \boxed{7.35\ \text{s}}$.

        (b) $\boxed{\text{No}}$, the speed of light is already so much greater than that of sound.

20.   (a) $\bar{v} = \dfrac{\Delta x}{\Delta t}$,   So

        $\bar{v}_\text{AB} = \dfrac{1.0\ \text{m} - 1.0\ \text{m}}{1.0\ \text{s} - 0} = \boxed{0}$; $\bar{v}_\text{BC} = \dfrac{7.0\ \text{m} - 1.0\ \text{m}}{3.0\ \text{s} - 1.0\ \text{s}} = \boxed{3.0\ \text{m/s}}$;

$$\bar{v}_{CD} = \frac{9.0 \text{ m} - 7.0 \text{ m}}{4.5 \text{ s} - 3.0 \text{ s}} = \boxed{1.3 \text{ m/s}}; \qquad \bar{v}_{DE} = \frac{7.0 \text{ m} - 9.0 \text{ m}}{6.0 \text{ s} - 4.5 \text{ s}} = \boxed{-1.3 \text{ m/s}};$$

$$\bar{v}_{EF} = \frac{2.0 \text{ m} - 7.0 \text{ m}}{9.0 \text{ s} - 6.0 \text{ s}} = \boxed{-1.7 \text{ m/s}}; \qquad \bar{v}_{FG} = \frac{2.0 \text{ m} - 2.0 \text{ m}}{11.0 \text{ s} - 9.0 \text{ s}} = \boxed{0};$$

$$\bar{v}_{BG} = \frac{2.0 \text{ m} - 1.0 \text{ m}}{11.0 \text{ s} - 1.0 \text{ s}} = \boxed{0.10 \text{ m/s}}.$$

(b) $\boxed{\text{The motion of BC, CD, and DE are not uniform}}$ since they are not straight lines.

(c) The object changes its direction of motion at point D. So it has to stop momentarily and $v = \boxed{0}$.

21.   Use $\quad avg.\ sp. = \dfrac{d}{t} \quad$ and $\quad \bar{v} = \dfrac{\Delta x}{\Delta t}.$

(a) $avg.\ sp._{0\text{-}2.0\text{ s}} = \dfrac{2.0 \text{ m} - 0}{2.0 \text{ s} - 0} = \boxed{1.0 \text{ m/s}}; \qquad avg.\ sp._{2.0\text{ s-}3.0\text{ s}} = \dfrac{2.0 \text{ m} - 2.0 \text{ m}}{3.0 \text{ s} - 2.0} = \boxed{0};$

$avg.\ sp._{3.0\text{ s-}4.5\text{ s}} = \dfrac{4.0 \text{ m} - 2.0}{4.5 \text{ s} - 3.0 \text{ s}} = \boxed{1.3 \text{ m/s}}; \qquad avg.\ sp._{4.5\text{ s-}6.5\text{ s}} = \dfrac{4.0 \text{ m} - (-1.5 \text{ m})}{6.5 \text{ s} - 4.5 \text{ s}} = \boxed{2.8 \text{ m/s}};$

$avg.\ sp._{6.5\text{ s-}7.5\text{ s}} = \dfrac{-1.5 \text{ m} - (-1.5 \text{ m})}{7.5 \text{ s} - 6.5 \text{ s}} = \boxed{0}; \qquad avg.\ sp._{7.5\text{ s-}9.0\text{ s}} = \dfrac{0 - (-1.5 \text{ m})}{9.0 \text{ s} - 7.5 \text{ s}} = \boxed{1.0 \text{ m/s}};$

(b) $\bar{v}_{0\text{-}2.0\text{ s}} = \dfrac{2.0 \text{ m} - 0}{2.0 \text{ s} - 0} = \boxed{1.0 \text{ m/s}}; \qquad \bar{v}_{2.0\text{ s-}3.0\text{ s}} = \dfrac{2.0 \text{ m} - 2.0 \text{ m}}{3.0 \text{ s} - 2.0} = \boxed{0};$

$\bar{v}_{3.0\text{ s-}4.5\text{ s}} = \dfrac{4.0 \text{ m} - 2.0}{4.5 \text{ s} - 3.0 \text{ s}} = \boxed{1.3 \text{ m/s}}; \qquad \bar{v}_{4.5\text{ s-}6.5\text{ s}} = \dfrac{-1.5 \text{ m} - 4.0 \text{ m}}{6.5 \text{ s} - 4.5 \text{ s}} = \boxed{-2.8 \text{ m/s}};$

$\bar{v}_{6.5\text{ s-}7.5\text{ s}} = \dfrac{-1.5 \text{ m} - (-1.5 \text{ m})}{7.5 \text{ s} - 6.5 \text{ s}} = \boxed{0}; \qquad \bar{v}_{7.5\text{ s-}9.0\text{ s}} = \dfrac{0 - (-1.5 \text{ m})}{9.0 \text{ s} - 7.5 \text{ s}} = \boxed{1.0 \text{ m/s}}.$

(c) $v_{1.0\text{ s}} = avg.\ sp._{0\text{-}2.0\text{ s}} = \boxed{1.0 \text{ m/s}}; \qquad v_{2.5\text{ s}} = avg.\ sp._{2.0\text{ s-}3.0\text{ s}} = \boxed{0};$

$v_{4.5\text{ s}} = \boxed{0}$ since the object reverses its direction of motion; $\quad v_{6.0\text{ s}} = avg.\ sp._{4.5\text{ s-}6.5\text{ s}} = \boxed{-2.8 \text{ m/s}}.$

(d) $v_{4.5\text{ s-}9.0\text{ s}} = \dfrac{0 - 4.0 \text{ m}}{9.0 \text{ s} - 4.5 \text{ s}} = \boxed{-0.89 \text{ m/s}}.$

22.   (a) $avg.\ sp. = \dfrac{d}{t}$, ☞ $t = \dfrac{1 \text{ mi}}{65 \text{ mi/h}} = 0.0154 \text{ h} = \boxed{55 \text{ s}}.$

(b) $avg.\ sp. = \dfrac{1 \text{ mi}}{(65 \text{ s})(1 \text{ h}/3600 \text{ s})} = \boxed{55 \text{ mi/h}}.$

23.   From $avg.\ sp. = \dfrac{d}{t}$, we have $t_{\text{transverse}} = \dfrac{d}{8.9 \text{ km/s}}; \quad t_{\text{longitudinal}} = \dfrac{d}{5.1 \text{ km/s}}.$

$\Delta t = t_{\text{longitudinal}} - t_{\text{transverse}} = \dfrac{d}{5.1 \text{ km/s}} - \dfrac{d}{8.9 \text{ km/s}} = 73 \text{ s}.$

Solving, $d = \boxed{8.7 \times 10^2 \text{ km}}.$

24.   (a) 6 h, 42 min, and 8 s = (6 + 42/60 + 8/3600) h = 6.70 h,   2 h, 41 min, and 18 s = 2.69 h.

$avg.\ sp._{1911} = \dfrac{\Delta d}{\Delta t} = \dfrac{500\ \text{mi}}{6.70\ \text{h}} = \boxed{74.6\ \text{mi/h}}$; $avg.\ sp._{1990} = \dfrac{500\ \text{mi}}{2.69\ \text{h}} = \boxed{186\ \text{mi/h}}$.

(b) The percentage change is $\dfrac{186\ \text{mi/h} - 74.6\ \text{mi/h}}{74.6\ \text{mi/h}} = 1.49 = \boxed{149\%}$.

25.   The minimum speed is $avg.\ sp. = \dfrac{d}{t} = \dfrac{675\ \text{km}}{7.00\ \text{h}} = 96\ \text{km/h} = \boxed{60\ \text{mi/h; no}}$.

26.   To the runner on right, the runner on left is running at a velocity of +4.50 m/s − (−3.50 m/s) = +8.00 m/s.

So it takes $\Delta t = \dfrac{\Delta x}{\bar{v}} = \dfrac{100\ \text{m}}{8.00\ \text{m/s}} = \boxed{12.5\ \text{s}}$.

They meet at (4.50 m/s)(12.5 s) = $\boxed{56.3\ \text{m from the initial position of the runner on left}}$.

27.   Let the distance to school be d, t_1 be the time to school, t_2 be the time to home,

and $avg.\ sp._2$ be the average speed to home. Apply $avg.\ sp. = \dfrac{d}{t}$,   ☞ $t = \dfrac{d}{avg.\ sp.}$.

To school: $t_1 = \dfrac{d}{30\ \text{km/h}}$;   to home: $t_2 = \dfrac{d}{avg.\ sp._2}$;   total trip: $t_1 + t_2 = \dfrac{2d}{60\ \text{km/h}}$.

So $\dfrac{d}{30\ \text{km/h}} + \dfrac{d}{avg.\ sp._2} = \dfrac{2d}{60\ \text{km/h}}$,   or $\dfrac{1}{30\ \text{km/h}} + \dfrac{1}{avg.\ sp._2} = \dfrac{2}{60\ \text{km/h}}$,

$\dfrac{1}{avg.\ sp._2} = \dfrac{2}{60\ \text{km/h}} - \dfrac{1}{30\ \text{km/h}} = 0$.

Thus $avg.\ sp._2$ has to be infinity. Hence it is $\boxed{\text{impossible}}$.

28.   (d). Any change in either magnitude or direction results in a change in velocity. The brakes and gear shift change the magnitude and the steering wheel and changes the direction.

29. $\boxed{\text{Yes}}$. Although the speed of the car is constant, its velocity is not because of the change in direction. A change in velocity results in acceleration.

30.   (b).

31. $\boxed{v_0}$. Since an equal amount of time is spent on acceleration and deceleration of the same magnitude.

32.   In Figure 2.22(a), the object accelerates uniformly first, maintains constant velocity for a while, and then accelerates uniformly at the same rate again as in the first segment .
In Figure 2.22(b), the object accelerates uniformly.

33. $25.0 \text{ km/h} = (25.0 \text{ km/h}) \times \dfrac{1000 \text{ m}}{1 \text{ km}} \times \dfrac{1 \text{ h}}{3600 \text{ s}} = 6.944 \text{ m/s}, \quad 65.0 \text{ km/h} = 18.06 \text{ m/s}.$

So $\bar{a} = \dfrac{\Delta v}{\Delta t} = \dfrac{18.06 \text{ m/s} - 6.944 \text{ m/s}}{6.00 \text{ s}} = \boxed{1.85 \text{ m/s}^2}.$

34. $60 \text{ mi/h} = (60 \text{ mi/h}) \times \dfrac{1609 \text{ m}}{1 \text{ mi}} \times \dfrac{1 \text{ h}}{3600 \text{ s}} = 26.8 \text{ m/s}.$

$\bar{a} = \dfrac{\Delta v}{\Delta t} = \dfrac{26.8 \text{ m/s} - 0}{3.9 \text{ s}} = \boxed{6.9 \text{ m/s}^2}$

35. $\Delta t = \dfrac{26.8 \text{ m/s} - 0}{7.2 \text{ m/s}^2} = \boxed{3.7 \text{ s}}.$

36. $40.0 \text{ km/h} = (40 \text{ km/h}) \times \dfrac{1000 \text{ m}}{1 \text{ km}} \times \dfrac{1 \text{ h}}{3600 \text{ s}} = 11.1 \text{ m/s}.$

So $\bar{a} = \dfrac{\Delta v}{\Delta t} = \dfrac{0 - 11.1 \text{ m/s}}{5.0 \text{ s}} = -2.2 \text{ m/s}^2$ or $\boxed{-2.2 \text{ m/s in each s}}.$

The negative sign indicates that the acceleration vector is in opposite direction of motion.

37. $\bar{a} = \dfrac{\Delta v}{\Delta t}, \quad ☞ \quad \Delta v = v - v_0 = \bar{a}\Delta t = (3.00 \text{ m/s}^2)(3.50 \text{ s}) = 10.5 \text{ m/s}.$

So $v = v_0 + \Delta v = 5.00 \text{ m/s} + 10.5 \text{ m/s} = \boxed{15.5 \text{ m/s}}.$

38. The initial velocity is $v_0 = +3.5 \text{ m/s}$. Before the object can have a negative velocity, it must change its direction of motion or it must experience a zero velocity. The acceleration is negative since it is in the negative x direction. $\bar{a} = \dfrac{\Delta v}{\Delta t}, \quad ☞ \quad \Delta t = \dfrac{\Delta v}{\bar{a}} = \dfrac{0 - 3.5 \text{ m/s}}{-0.50 \text{ m/s}^2} = \boxed{7.0 \text{ s}}$, i.e., any time after 7.0 s.

39. $\bar{a}_{0-4.0s} = \dfrac{\Delta v}{\Delta t} = \dfrac{8.0 \text{ m/s} - 0}{4.0 \text{ s} - 0} = \boxed{2.0 \text{ m/s}^2}; \qquad \bar{a}_{4.0\,s-10.0s} = \dfrac{8.0 \text{ m/s} - 8.0 \text{ m/s}}{10.0 \text{ s} - 4.0 \text{ s}} = \boxed{0};$

$\bar{a}_{10.0\,s-18.0\,s} = \dfrac{0 - 8.0 \text{ m/s}}{18.0 \text{ s} - 10.0 \text{ s}} = \boxed{-1.0 \text{ m/s}^2}.$

The object accelerates at 2.0 m/s² first, then moves with constant velocity, then decelerates at 1.0 m/s².

40. (a) $\bar{a}_{0-1.0\,s} = \dfrac{\Delta v}{\Delta t} = \dfrac{0 - 0}{1.0 \text{ s} - 0} = \boxed{0}; \qquad \bar{a}_{1.0\,s-3.0\,s} = \dfrac{8.0 \text{ m/s} - 0}{3.0 \text{ s} - 1.0 \text{ s}} = \boxed{4.0 \text{ m/s}^2};$

$\bar{a}_{3.0\,s-8.0\,s} = \dfrac{-12 \text{ m/s} - 8.0 \text{ m/s}}{8.0 \text{ s} - 3.0 \text{ s}} = \boxed{-4.0 \text{ m/s}^2}; \qquad \bar{a}_{8.0\,s-9.0\,s} = \dfrac{-4 \text{ m/s} - (-12.0 \text{ m/s})}{9.0 \text{ s} - 8.0 \text{ s}} = \boxed{8.0 \text{ m/s}^2};$

$\bar{a}_{9.0\,s-13.0\,s} = \dfrac{-4.0 \text{ m/s} - 4.0 \text{ m/s}}{13.0 \text{ s} - 9.0 \text{ s}} = \boxed{0}. \qquad$ (b) $\boxed{\text{Constant velocity of } -4.0 \text{ m/s}}.$

41. $$72 \text{ km/h} = (72 \text{ km/h}) \times \frac{1000 \text{ m}}{1 \text{ km}} \times \frac{1 \text{ h}}{3600 \text{ s}} = 20 \text{ m/s}.$$

During deceleration, $$\Delta t_1 = \frac{\Delta v}{\bar{a}} = \frac{0 - 20 \text{ m/s}}{-1.0 \text{ m/s}^2} = 20 \text{ s};$$

$$\Delta x_1 = \bar{v}_1 \Delta t_1 = \frac{20 \text{ m/s} + 0}{2} (20 \text{ s}) = 200 \text{ m}.$$

It would have taken the train $\dfrac{200 \text{ m}}{20 \text{ m/s}} = 10 \text{ s}$ to travel 200 m.

So it lost only $20 \text{ s} - 10 \text{ s} = 10 \text{ s}$ during deceleration.

During acceleration, $$\Delta t_2 = \frac{20 \text{ m/s} - 0}{0.50 \text{ m/s}^2} = 40 \text{ s};$$

$$\Delta x_2 = \frac{0 + 20 \text{ m/s}}{2} (40 \text{ s}) = 400 \text{ m}.$$

It would have taken the train $\dfrac{400 \text{ m}}{20 \text{ m/s}} = 20 \text{ s}$ to travel 400 m. So it lost only $40 \text{ s} - 20 \text{ s} = 20 \text{ s}$ during

acceleration. Therefore the train lost $2 \text{ min} + 10 \text{ s} + 20 \text{ s} = \boxed{150 \text{ s}}$ in stopping at the station.

42.   (c).

43.   (a). Since $v = v_0 + at = 0 + at,$ $\bar{v} = \dfrac{v_0 + v}{2} = \tfrac{1}{2} at.$

44. $\boxed{\text{No}}$. If the object has a negative initial velocity or $v_0 = 0$, it will accelerate in the negative direction.

45.   The average velocity is $\bar{v} = \dfrac{\Delta x}{\Delta t} = \dfrac{100 \text{ m}}{4.5 \text{ s}} = 22.2 \text{ m/s}.$

$$\bar{v} = \frac{v_0 + v}{2} = \frac{v}{2}.$$

So the final velocity must be $v = 2(22.2 \text{ m/s}) = 44.4 \text{ m/s}.$

$$\bar{a} = \frac{\Delta v}{\Delta t}, \quad \text{☞} \quad \Delta t = \frac{\Delta v}{\bar{a}} = \frac{44.4 \text{ m/s} - 0}{9.0 \text{ m/s}^2} = 4.9 \text{ s} > 4.5 \text{ s}.$$

So $\boxed{\text{no}}$, the driver did not do it.

The acceleration must be $\dfrac{44.4 \text{ m/s} - 0}{4.5 \text{ s}} = \boxed{9.9 \text{ m/s}^2}.$

46.   Given: $v_0 = 0$, $a = 2.0 \text{ m/s}^2$, $t = 5.00 \text{ s}$.   Find: v and x.

(a) $v = v_0 + at = 0 + (2.0 \text{ m/s}^2)(5.0 \text{ s}) = \boxed{10 \text{ m/s}}.$

(b) $x = v_0 t + \tfrac{1}{2} a t^2 = 0 + \tfrac{1}{2}(2.0 \text{ m/s}^2)(5.0 \text{ s})^2 = \boxed{25 \text{ m}}.$

47. Given: $v_0 = 35$ mi/h $= 15.6$ m/s, $v = 0$, $x = 35$ m.   Find: a.

$$v^2 = v_0^2 + 2ax, \quad \text{☞} \quad a = \frac{v^2 - v_0^2}{2x} = \frac{(0)^2 - (15.6 \text{ m/s})^2}{2(35 \text{ m})} = \boxed{-3.5 \text{ m/s}^2}.$$

The negative sign indicates that the acceleration vector is in opposite direction of velocity.

48. Given: $v_0 = 75$ km/h $= 20.8$ m/s, $v = 40$ km/h $= 11.1$ m/s, $x = 50$ m.   Find: a.

$$v^2 = v_0^2 + 2ax, \quad \text{☞} \quad a = \frac{v^2 - v_0^2}{2x} = \frac{(11.1 \text{ m/s})^2 - (20.8 \text{ m/s})^2}{2(50 \text{ m})} = \boxed{-3.1 \text{ m/s}^2}.$$

49. (a) Given: $v_0 = 100$ km/h $= 27.78$ m/s, $a = -6.50$ m/s^2, $x = 20.0$ m.   Find: v.

$$v^2 = v_0^2 + 2ax = (27.78 \text{ m/s})^2 + 2(-6.50 \text{ m/s}^2)(20.0 \text{ m}) = 511.6 \text{ m}^2/\text{s}^2,$$

So $v = 22.62$ m/s $= \boxed{81.4 \text{ km/h}}$.

(b) $v = v_0 + at$,   ☞ $t = \dfrac{v - v_0}{a} = \dfrac{22.62 \text{ m/s} - 27.78 \text{ m/s}}{-6.50 \text{ m/s}^2} = \boxed{0.794 \text{ s}}$.

50. Given: $v_0 = 0$, $v = 560$ km/h $= 155.6$ m/s, $x = 400$ m.   Find: t.

$$x = \overline{v}t = \frac{v_0 + v}{2}t, \quad \text{☞} \quad t = \frac{2x}{v_0 + v} = \frac{2(400 \text{ m})}{0 + 155.6 \text{ m/s}} = \boxed{5.14 \text{ s}}.$$

51. Given: $v_0 = 250$ km/h $= 69.44$ m/s, $a = -8.25$ m/s^2, $x = 175$ m.   Find: t.

$x = v_0 t + \frac{1}{2}at^2$,   ☞ 175 m $= (69.44 \text{ m/s})t + \frac{1}{2}(-8.25 \text{ m/s}^2)t^2$.

Reduce to quadratic equation $4.125 \, t^2 - 69.44 \, t + 175 = 0$.

Solving, $t = \boxed{3.09 \text{ s}}$ or 13.7 s.

The 13.7 s answer is physically possible but not likely in reality. After 3.09 s, it is 175 m from where the reverse thrust was applied, but the rocket keeps traveling forward while slowing down. Finally it stops. However, if the

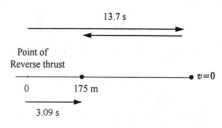

reverse thrust is continuously applied (possible, but not likely) it will reverse its direction and be back to 175 m from the point where the initial reverse thrust was applied, it had taken 13.7 s.

52. (a) Given: Car A: $a_A = 3.00$ m/s^2, $v_0 = 2.50$ m/s, $t = 10$ s.

        Car B: $a_B = 3.00$ m/s^2, $v_0 = 5.00$ m/s, $t = 10$ s.   Find: Δx.

From $x = v_0 t + \frac{1}{2}at^2$, $x_A = (2.50 \text{ m/s})(10 \text{ s}) + \frac{1}{2}(3.00 \text{ m/s})^2(10 \text{ s})^2 = 175$ m,

        $x_B = (5.00 \text{ m/s})(10 \text{ s}) + \frac{1}{2}(3.00 \text{ m/s})^2(10 \text{ s})^2 = 200$ m.

So $\Delta x = x_B - x_A = 200$ m $- 175$ m $= \boxed{25 \text{ m}}$.

(b) From $v = v_0 + at$, $v_A = 2.50$ m/s + (3.00 m/s)(10 s) = 32.5 m/s,

$v_B = 5.00$ m/s + (3.00 m/s)(10 s) = 35.0 m/s. So $\boxed{\text{car B}}$ is faster.

53. Given: $v_0 = 40$ m/s, $a = -3.5$ m/s^2, $x = 0$ ("returns to the origin"). Find: t.

$x = v_0 t + \frac{1}{2} at^2$, ☞ $0 = (40 \text{ m/s})t + \frac{1}{2}(-3.5 \text{ m/s}^2)t^2$.

Reduce to quadratic equation: $1.75t^2 - 40t = 0$. Solving for $t = 0$ or 23 s.

The $t = 0$ answer corresponds to the initial time. So the answer is $t = \boxed{23 \text{ s}}$.

54. Given: $v_0 = 330$ m/s, $v = 0$, $x = 30$ cm = 0.30 m. Find: a.

$v^2 = v_0^2 + 2ax$, ☞ $a = \dfrac{v^2 - v_0^2}{2x} = \dfrac{(0)^2 - (330 \text{ m/s})^2}{2(0.30 \text{ m})} = -\boxed{1.8 \times 10^5 \text{ m/s}^2}$.

The negative sign here indicates that the acceleration vector is in opposite direction of velocity.

55. Given: $v_0 = 350$ m/s, $v = 210$ m/s, $x = 4.00$ cm = 0.0400 m. Find: t.

$x = \bar{v}\, t = \dfrac{v_0 + v}{2}\, t$, ☞ $t = \dfrac{2\, x}{v_0 + v} = \dfrac{2(0.0400 \text{ m})}{350 \text{ m/s} + 210 \text{ m/s}} = \boxed{1.43 \times 10^{-4} \text{ s}}$.

56. Given: $v_0 = 10$ m/s, $v = 0$, $x = 25$ cm = 0.25 m. Find: a.

$v^2 = v_0^2 + 2\,ax$, ☞ $a = \dfrac{v^2 - v_0^2}{2x} = \dfrac{(0 \text{ m/s})^2 - (10 \text{ m/s})^2}{2(0.25 \text{ m})} = -\boxed{2.0 \times 10^2 \text{ m/s}^2}$.

The negative sign here indicates that the acceleration vector is in opposite direction of velocity.

57. Given: $v_0 = 0$, $x = 94$ m, $t = 2.5$ s. Find: v.

$x = \bar{v}\, t = \dfrac{v_0 + v}{2}\, t = \dfrac{0 + v}{2}\, t$, ☞ $v = \dfrac{2\, x}{t} = \dfrac{2(94 \text{ m})}{2.5 \text{ s}} = \boxed{75 \text{ m/s}}$.

58. 40 km/h = (40 km/h) $\times \dfrac{1000 \text{ m}}{1 \text{ km}} \times \dfrac{1 \text{ h}}{3600 \text{ s}} = 11.11$ m/s.

During reaction, the car travels $d = (11.11 \text{ m/s})(0.25 \text{ s}) = 2.78$ m.

So the car really has only 13 m – 2.78 m = 10.2 m to come to rest.

Let's calculate the stopping distance of the car.

Given: $v_0 = 11.1$ m/s, $v = 0$, $a = -8.0$ m/s^2. Find: x.

$v^2 = v_0^2 + 2ax$, ☞ $x = \dfrac{v^2 - v_0^2}{2a} = \dfrac{0 - (11.1 \text{ m/s})^2}{2(-8.0 \text{ m/s}^2)} = 7.70$ m.

So it takes the car only 2.78 m + 7.70 m = $\boxed{10.5 \text{ m} < 13 \text{ m}}$ to stop.

$\boxed{\text{Yes}}$, the car will stop before hitting the child.

59. Repeat the calculation of Exercise 2.58.

$d = (11.1 \text{ m/s})(0.50 \text{ s}) = 5.55 \text{ m}.$

$5.55 \text{ m} + 7.70 \text{ m} = \boxed{13.3 \text{ m} > 13 \text{ m}}.$ $\boxed{\text{No}}$, the car will not stop before hitting the child.

60. For constant acceleration, the v vs. t plot is a straight line.

Point p has coordinates of $(0, v_o)$ and point q has coordinates of

$(t, v_o + at)$. The distance from point q to point o is therefore at.

The area under the curve is the area of the triangle $\frac{1}{2}(at)t$ plus the

area of the rectangle $v_o t$.

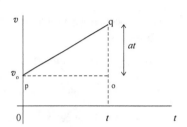

So $A = v_o t + \frac{1}{2} at^2 = x.$

(a) $A = v_o t + 0 = \boxed{v_o t}.$ (b) $A = 0 + \frac{1}{2} at^2 = \boxed{\frac{1}{2} at^2}.$ (c) $A = \boxed{v_o t + \frac{1}{2} at^2}.$

61. Use the result of Exercise 2.60. The total area is consisted of two triangles from 0 to 4.0 s and from 10.0 s to 18.0 s and a rectangle from 4.0 s to 10.0 s.

$x = A = \frac{1}{2}(4.0 \text{ s} - 0)(8.0 \text{ m/s}) + (10.0 \text{ s} - 4.0 \text{ s})(8.0 \text{ m/s}) + \frac{1}{2}(18.0 \text{ s} - 10.0 \text{ s})(8.0 \text{ m/s}) = \boxed{96 \text{ m}}.$

62. (a) $v(8.0 \text{ s}) = \boxed{-12 \text{ m/s}};$ $v(11.0 \text{ s}) = \boxed{-4.0 \text{ m/s}}.$

(b) Use the result of Exercise 2.60. The total area consists of a rectangle from 0 to 1.0 s, a triangle from 1.0 s to 5.0 s, a trapezoid from 5.0 s to 11.0 s, and a triangle from 6.0 s to 9.0 s with baseline at –4.0 m/s.

$x = A = 0 + \frac{1}{2}(5.0 \text{ s} - 1.0 \text{ s})(8.0 \text{ m/s}) + \dfrac{(11.0 \text{ s} - 6.0 \text{ s}) + (11.0 \text{ s} - 5.0 \text{ s})}{2} \times (-4.0 \text{ m/s})$

$+ \frac{1}{2}(9.0 \text{ s} - 6.0 \text{ s})[(-12.0 \text{ m/s}) - (-4.0 \text{ m/s})] = \boxed{-18 \text{ m}}.$

(c) The total distance (not displacement) is the addition of the absolute values of the areas.

$d = \Sigma A_i = 0 + \frac{1}{2}(5.0 \text{ s} - 1.0 \text{ s})(8.0 \text{ m/s}) + \dfrac{(11.0 \text{ s} - 6.0 \text{ s}) + (11.0 \text{ s} - 5.0 \text{ s})}{2} \times (4.0 \text{ m/s})$

$+ \frac{1}{2}(9.0 \text{ s} - 6.0 \text{ s})[(12.0 \text{ m/s} - 4.0 \text{ m/s}] = \boxed{50 \text{ m}}.$

63. Now $\Delta x = x - x_o$ and $\Delta t = t - t_o.$ So the kinematic equations become:

$x - x_o = \dfrac{v_o + v}{2}(t - t_o);$ $v = v_o + a(t - t_o);$

$x - x_o = v_o(t - t_o) + \frac{1}{2} a(t - t_o)^2;$ $v^2 = v_o^2 + 2a(x - x_o).$

The x in Eq. 2.9 stands for displacement from initial location, the x in the equations here stands for position.

64. Given: $x = 65$ m $- 5.0$ m $= 60$ m, $\quad v_0 = 10$ m/s, $\quad t = 2.5$ s. Find: a.

$$x = v_0 t + \tfrac{1}{2}at^2, \quad \text{☞} \quad a = \frac{x - v_0 t}{\tfrac{1}{2}t^2} = \frac{60 \text{ m} - (10 \text{ m/s})(2.5 \text{ s})}{\tfrac{1}{2}(2.5 \text{ s})^2} = \boxed{11 \text{ m/s}^2}.$$

65. (d).

66. (c). It accelerates at 9.80 m/s^2 so it increases its speed by 9.80 m/s in each second.

67. After the object is thrown, it will experience the acceleration due to gravity during its entire motion in the air. So the acceleration at the highest point is still $\boxed{9.80 \text{ m/s}^2 \text{ downward}}$. The velocity at the highest point is zero, but the acceleration is not zero. That is why the object falls back down after reaching the highest point.

68. $\boxed{\text{Yes, two answers}}$. One for on the way up and the other for on the way down.

69. First find the gravitational acceleration (the Exercise did not say that it happens on the Earth).

Given: $v_0 = 0$, $\quad y = -19.6$ m, $\quad t = 2.00$ s. Find: g.

$$y = v_0 t - \tfrac{1}{2}gt^2 = -\tfrac{1}{2}gt^2, \quad \text{☞} \quad g = -\frac{2y}{t^2} = -\frac{2(-19.6 \text{ m})}{(2.00 \text{ s})^2} = 9.80 \text{ m/s}^2.$$

Therefore $y(4.00 \text{ s}) = -\tfrac{1}{2}(9.80 \text{ m/s}^2)(4.00 \text{ s})^2 = -78.4$ m. It will fall $\boxed{78.4 \text{ m}}$.

70. (a) A straight line, slope $= -g$.   (b) A parabola.

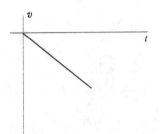 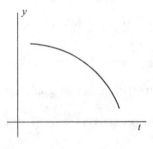

71. (a)   (b)

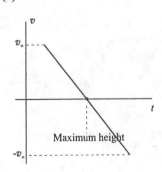 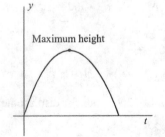

72.   (a) Given: $v_0 = 0$, $t = 2.8$ s.   Find: v.

        $v = v_0 - gt = 0 - (9.80 \text{ m/s}^2)(2.8 \text{ s}) = -\boxed{27 \text{ m/s}}$.

        (b) $y = v_0 t - \frac{1}{2}gt^2 = 0 - \frac{1}{2}(9.80 \text{ m/s}^2)(2.8 \text{ s})^2 = -\boxed{38 \text{ m}}$.

73.   Given: $v_0 = 0$, $t = 1.80$ s.   Find: y.

        $y = v_0 t - \frac{1}{2}gt^2 = 0 - \frac{1}{2}(9.80 \text{ m/s}^2)(1.80 \text{ s})^2 = -15.9$ m.

        So the height above the water is $\boxed{15.9 \text{ m}}$.

74.   Given: $v_0 = 15$ m/s, $v = 0$ (maximum height).   Find: y.

        $v^2 = v_0^2 - 2gy$,   ☞ $y = \dfrac{v_0^2 - v^2}{2g} = \dfrac{(15 \text{ m/s})^2 - (0)^2}{2(9.80 \text{ m/s}^2)} = \boxed{11 \text{ m}}$.

75.   From Exercise 2.74, $y = \dfrac{v_0^2 - v^2}{2g} = \dfrac{(15 \text{ m/s})^2 - (0)^2}{2(1.67 \text{ m/s}^2)} = \boxed{67 \text{ m}}$.

76.   (a) Given: $v_0 = 21$ m/s, $t = 3.0$ s.   Find: y.

        $y = v_0 t - \frac{1}{2}gt^2 = (21 \text{ m/s})(3.0 \text{ s}) - \frac{1}{2}(9.80 \text{ m/s}^2)(3.0 \text{ s})^2 = \boxed{19 \text{ m}}$.

        (b) $12 \text{ m} = (21 \text{ m/s})t - \frac{1}{2}(9.80 \text{ m/s}^2)t^2$,   or $4.90t^2 - 21t + 12 = 0$.

        Solve the quadratic equation for $t = \boxed{0.68 \text{ s (on the way up) or } 3.6 \text{ s (on the way down)}}$.

77.   The maximum initial velocity which can be given is for the apple to reach maximum height just below the ceiling.

        Given: $v = 0$ (max height), $y = 3.75 \text{ m} - 0.50 \text{ m} = 3.25$ m.   Find: v_0.

        $v^2 = v_0^2 - 2gy$,   ☞ $v_0 = \sqrt{v^2 + 2gy} = \sqrt{0 + 2(9.80 \text{ m/s}^2)(3.25 \text{ m})} = 7.98$ m/s.

        Therefore it is $\boxed{\text{slightly less than 8.0 m/s}}$.

78.   (a) $y = v_0 t - \frac{1}{2}gt^2 = 0 - \frac{1}{2}gt^2 = -\frac{1}{2}gt^2$,   so $t = \sqrt{\dfrac{-2y}{g}}$.

        For $y = -417$ m, $t = 9.225$ s;   for $y = -381$ m, $t = 8.818$ s.

        So $\Delta t = 9.225 \text{ s} - 8.818 \text{ s} = \boxed{0.407 \text{ s}}$.

        (b) For $y = 443$ m, $t = \boxed{9.51 \text{ s}}$.

79.   (a) Given: $v_0 = -14$ m/s, $t = 2.00$ s.   Find: y.

$y = v_0 t - \frac{1}{2}gt^2 = (-14$ m/s$)(2.00$ s$) - \frac{1}{2}(9.80$ m/s$^2)(2.00$ s$)^2 = -\boxed{48 \text{ m}}$.

(b) Given: $v_0 = -14$ m/s, $y = -65.0$ m.   Find: v.

$v^2 = v_0^2 - 2gy = (-14$ m/s$)^2 - 2(9.80$ m/s$^2)(-65.0$ m$) = 1.47 \times 10^3$ m^2/s^2.

So $v = -\sqrt{1.47 \times 10^3 \text{ m}^2/\text{s}^2} = -38$ m/s $= \boxed{38 \text{ m/s downward}}$.

80.   (a) Given: $v_0 = -4.00$ m/s, $t = 1.80$ s.   Find: y.

$y = v_0 t - \frac{1}{2}gt^2 = (-4.00$ m/s$)(1.80$ s$) - \frac{1}{2}(9.80$ m/s$^2)(1.80$ s$)^2 = -\boxed{23.1 \text{ m/s}}$.

(b) $v = v_0 - gt = -4.00$ m/s $- (9.80$ m/s$^2)(1.80$ s$) = -21.6$ m/s $= \boxed{21.6 \text{ m/s downward}}$.

81.   (a) From Example 2.12(b), $t_{up} = 1.14$ s. Consider the downward motion using the highest spot as the starting point.   Given: $v_0 = 0$, $y = -6.40$ m.   Find: t.

$y = v_0 t - \frac{1}{2}gt^2 = -\frac{1}{2}gt^2$,   ☞ $t_{down} = \sqrt{\dfrac{-2y}{g}} = \sqrt{\dfrac{-2(-6.40 \text{ m})}{9.80 \text{ m/s}^2}} = 1.14$ s.

So the travel times are the $\boxed{\text{same}}$.

(b) Given: $v_0 = 11.2$ m/s, $y = 0$ (back to starting position),   Find: v.

$v^2 = v_0^2 - 2gy$,   ☞ $v = -v_0 = -11.2$ m/s. So the two velocities are $\boxed{\text{equal but opposite}}$.

82.   (a)

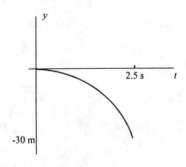
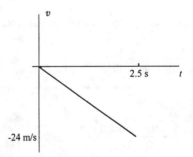

(b)

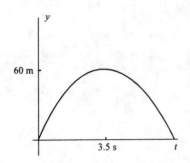
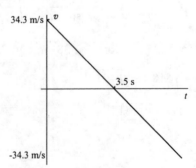

(c) For both motions the acceleration is a constant equal to $-g = -9.80$ m/s^2.

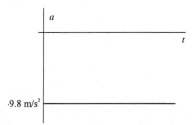

83.   First calculate the speed just before impact.

Given: $v_0 = 0$, $y = -4.00$ m.   Find: v.

$v^2 = v_0^2 - 2gy = 0^2 - 2(9.80 \text{ m/s}^2)(-4.00 \text{ m}) = 78.4 \text{ m}^2/\text{s}^2$,

so $v = -\sqrt{78.4 \text{ m}^2/\text{s}^2} = -8.85$ m/s.

Therefore the speed right after rebound is $0.950(8.85 \text{ m/s}) = 8.41$ m/s.

Now consider the rising motion.   Given: $v_0 = 8.41$ m/s, $v = 0$ (max height).   Find: y.

$$v^2 = v_0^2 - 2gy, \quad \text{☞} \quad y = \frac{v_0^2 - v^2}{2 g} = \frac{(8.41 \text{ m/s})^2 - 0^2}{2(9.80 \text{ m/s}^2)} = \boxed{3.61 \text{ m}}.$$

$\boxed{\text{No}}$, not 95% of the initial height.

84.   (a) Ball A: Given: $v_0 = 10.0$ m/s, $y = -60.0$ m.   Find: t.

Ball B: Given: $v_0 = -10.0$ m/s, $y = -60.0$ m.   Find: t.

Use $y = v_0 t - \frac{1}{2}g t^2$.

For ball A: $-60.0 \text{ m} = (10.0 \text{ m/s})t - \frac{1}{2}(9.80 \text{ m/s}^2)t^2$,   or $4.90 t^2 - 10.0 t - 60.0 = 0$.

Solving the quadratic equation for $t_A = 4.665$ s.

For ball B: $-60.0 \text{ m} = (-10.0 \text{ m/s})t - \frac{1}{2}(9.80 \text{ m/s}^2)t^2$,   or $4.90 t^2 + 10.0 t - 60.0 = 0$.

Solving the quadratic equation for $t_B = 2.625$ s.

So $\boxed{\text{ball B}}$ will hit the ground first.

(b) $\Delta t = t_A - t_B = 4.665$ s $- 2.625$ s $= \boxed{2.04 \text{ s}}$.

(c) $\boxed{\text{No}}$, mass does not matter in free fall if air resistance is ignored.

85.   First find the time it takes for the ball to reach the level of the prof's head.

Given: $y = -(18.0 \text{ m} - 1.70 \text{ m}) = -16.3$ m, $v_0 = 0$.   Find: t.

From $y = v_0 t - \frac{1}{2}g t^2 = -\frac{1}{2}g t^2$,

$$t = \sqrt{-\frac{2 y}{g}} = \sqrt{-\frac{2(-16.3 \text{ m})}{9.80 \text{ m/s}^2}} = 1.824 \text{ s}.$$

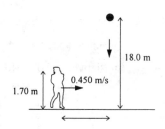

During this time, the prof advances a distance equal to

$(0.450 \text{ m/s})(1.824 \text{ s}) = 0.821 \text{ m} < 1.00 \text{ m}.$ No , it does not hit her.

Now calculate the time it takes for the ball to hit the ground.

$$t = \sqrt{-\frac{2(-18.0 \text{ m})}{9.80 \text{ m/s}^2}} = 1.917 \text{ s}.$$

During this time, the prof advances $(0.450 \text{ m/s})(1.917 \text{ s}) = 0.862 \text{ m} < 1.00 \text{ m}.$

So the ball hits $1.00 \text{ m} - 0.862 \text{ m} = 0.14 \text{ m} =$ 14 cm in front of the prof .

86. (a) Given: $v_0 = 12.50 \text{ m/s}$ (ascending), $y = -60.0 \text{ m}.$ Find: $t.$

$y = v_0 t - \frac{1}{2}gt^2,$ ☞ $-60.0 \text{ m} = (12.50 \text{ m/s})t - (4.90 \text{ m/s}^2)t^2.$

Reduce to a quadratic equation: $4.90t^2 - 12.50t - 60.0 = 0.$

Solve for $t =$ 5.00 s or -2.45 s which is physically meaningless.

(b) $v = v_0 - gt = 12.50 \text{ m/s} - (9.80 \text{ m/s}^2)(5.00 \text{ s}) = -36.5 \text{ m/s} =$ 36.5 m/s downward .

87. (a) $y = v_0 t - \frac{1}{2}gt^2 = -\frac{1}{2}gt^2,$ ☞ $t = \sqrt{-\frac{2y}{g}}.$

So $\dfrac{t_\text{M}}{t_\text{E}} = \dfrac{\sqrt{1/g_\text{M}}}{\sqrt{1/g_\text{E}}} = \sqrt{\dfrac{g_\text{E}}{g_\text{M}}} = \sqrt{6} =$ 2.45 .

(b) Given: $v_0 = 18.0 \text{ m/s},$ $v = 0$ ("max height"). Find: y and $t.$

$v^2 = v_0^2 - 2gy,$ ☞ $y = \dfrac{v_0^2 - v^2}{2g} = \dfrac{v_0^2}{2g}.$ So $\dfrac{y_\text{M}}{y_\text{E}} = \dfrac{g_\text{E}}{g_\text{M}} = 6.$

For the total trip (up and down), the displacement is zero ($y = 0$).

So $y = v_0 t - \frac{1}{2}gt^2 = 0,$ ☞ $t = \dfrac{2v_0}{g}.$

Therefore $\dfrac{t_\text{M}}{t_\text{E}} = \dfrac{g_\text{E}}{g_\text{M}} = 6.$

On Earth, $y_\text{E} = \dfrac{(18.0 \text{ m/s})^2}{2(9.80 \text{ m/s}^2)} =$ 16.5 m . $t_\text{E} = \dfrac{2(18.0 \text{ m/s})}{9.80 \text{ m/s}^2} =$ 3.67 s .

So $y_\text{M} = 6\,y_\text{E} =$ 99.2 m and $t_\text{M} = 6\,t_\text{E} =$ 22.0 s .

88. The key to this Exercise is to find the velocity of the object when it reaches the top of the window (it is not zero), This velocity is the initial velocity for Motion 1 and the final velocity for Motion 2. Consider Motion 2 first.

Given: $y = -1.35 \text{ m},$ $t = 0.210 \text{ s}.$ Find: $v_0.$

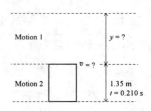

Apply $y = v_o t - \frac{1}{2}gt^2$, ☞ $v_o = \frac{x}{t} + \frac{1}{2}gt = \frac{-1.35 \text{ m}}{0.210 \text{ s}} + (4.90 \text{ m/s}^2)(0.210 \text{ s}) = -5.40 \text{ m/s}$.

Now consider Motion 1. Given: $v_o = 0$, $v = -5.40$ m. Find: y.

$v^2 = v_o^2 - 2gy$, ☞ $y = \frac{v_o^2 - v^2}{2g} = \frac{0 - (-5.40 \text{ m/s})^2}{2(9.80 \text{ m/s}^2)} = \boxed{1.49 \text{ m}}$.

89. (a) Since 25.0 m is a distance, we need to find the maximum height first.

Given: $v_o = 7.25$ m/s, $v = 0$. Find: y.

$v^2 = v_o^2 - 2gy$, ☞ $y = \frac{v_o^2 - v^2}{2g} = \frac{(7.25 \text{ m/s})^2 - 0}{2(9.80 \text{ m/s}^2)} = 2.68$ m.

So if it has traveled a distance of 25.0 m, it has traveled

25.0 m − 2.68 m = 22.3 m downward after reaching maximum height.

So the displacement is $y = -(22.3 \text{ m} - 2.68 \text{ m}) = -19.6$ m.

Now $v^2 = v_o^2 - 2gy = (7.25 \text{ m/s})^2 - 2(9.80 \text{ m/s}^2)(-19.6 \text{ m})$

$= 4.37 \times 10^2 \text{ m}^2/\text{s}^2$. So $v = -\sqrt{v^2} = \boxed{-20.9 \text{ m/s}}$.

(b) $v = v_o - gt$, ☞ $t = \frac{v_o - v}{g} = \frac{7.25 \text{ m/s} - (-20.9 \text{ m/s})}{9.80 \text{ m/s}^2} = \boxed{2.87 \text{ s}}$.

90. $\bar{v} = \frac{v + v_o}{2} = \frac{v_o + 0}{2}$, ☞ $v_o = 2\bar{v} = -70.0 \text{ km/h} = -19.4 \text{ m/s}$.

$a = \frac{v - v_o}{t} = \frac{0 - (-19.4 \text{ m/s})}{7.00 \text{ s}} = \boxed{2.78 \text{ m/s}^2}$.

In this case, the positive 2.78 m/s^2 indicates deceleration because the velocity is negative.

91. (a) Given: $v = 0$ ("max height"), $y = 23$ m. Find: v_o.

$v^2 = v_o^2 - 2gy = 0$, ☞ $v_o = \sqrt{2gy} = \sqrt{2(9.80 \text{ m/s}^2)(23 \text{ m})} = \boxed{21 \text{ m/s}}$.

(b) $y = v_o t - \frac{1}{2}gt^2 = (21 \text{ m/s})(1.3 \text{ s}) - \frac{1}{2}(9.80 \text{ m/s}^2)(1.3 \text{ s})^2 = \boxed{19 \text{ m}}$.

92. (a) Given: $v_o = 200$ km/h = 55.6 m/s, $v = 20$ km/h = 5.56 m/s, $t = 12$ s. Find: a.

$a = \frac{v - v_o}{g} = \frac{5.56 \text{ m/s} - 55.6 \text{ m/s}}{12 \text{ s}} = \boxed{-4.2 \text{ m/s}^2}$.

(b) $x = \bar{v}\,t = \frac{v + v_o}{2}\,t = \frac{55.6 \text{ m/s} + 5.56 \text{ m/s}}{2} \times (12 \text{ s}) = \boxed{3.7 \times 10^2 \text{ m}}$.

93. $avg. \ sp. = \frac{d}{t} = \frac{500 \text{ mi} + 380 \text{ mi} + 600 \text{ mi}}{10 \text{ h} + 8.0 \text{ h} + 15 \text{ h}} = \boxed{45 \text{ mi/h}}$.

94.   Given: $v_0 = 25$ mi/h $= 11.2$ m/s, $v = 0$, $a = -7.0$ m/s^2.   Find: t.

$v = v_0 + at$,   ☞ $t = \dfrac{0 - 11.2 \text{ m/s}}{-7.0 \text{ m/s}^2} = = 1.6$ s > 1.5 s. So the answer is $\boxed{\text{no}}$.

95. $d = \sqrt{(50 \text{ m})^2 + (50 \text{ m})^2} = \boxed{71 \text{ m}}$.

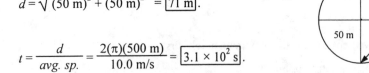

96. $t = \dfrac{d}{avg.\ sp.} = \dfrac{2(\pi)(500 \text{ m})}{10.0 \text{ m/s}} = \boxed{3.1 \times 10^2 \text{ s}}$.

97.   Given: $v = 0$ (max height), $y = 14.0$ m.   Find: v_0.

$v^2 = v_0^2 - 2gy$,   ☞ $v_0 = \sqrt{v^2 + 2gy} = \sqrt{0 + 2(9.80 \text{ m/s}^2)(14.0 \text{ m})} = \boxed{16.6 \text{ m/s}}$.

98.   (a) Given: $v_0 = 45.0$ km/h $= 12.5$ m/s, $a = 1.50$ m/s^2, $x = 200$ m.   Find: v.

$v^2 = v_0^2 + 2ax = (12.5 \text{ m/s})^2 + 2(1.6 \text{ m/s}^2)(200 \text{ m}) = 756$ m^2/s^2,   ☞ $v = \boxed{27.5 \text{ m/s}}$.

(b) $v = v_0 + at$,   ☞ $t = \dfrac{v - v_0}{a} = \dfrac{27.5 \text{ m/s} - 12.5 \text{ m/s}}{1.50 \text{ m/s}^2} = \boxed{10.0 \text{ s}}$.

99.   Given: $v_0 = 85$ km/h $= 23.6$ m/s, $v = 0$, $t = 10$ s.   Find: x.

$x = \bar{v}\, t = \dfrac{v + v_0}{2}\, t = \dfrac{23.6 \text{ m/s} + 0}{2} \times (10 \text{ s}) = \boxed{1.2 \times 10^2 \text{ m}}$.

100.   (a) Use $x = v_0 t + \frac{1}{2} at^2$.

For car: $d = 0 + \frac{1}{2}(3.70 \text{ m/s}^2)t^2$,   Eq. (1)

For motorcycle: $d + 25.0 \text{ m} = 0 + \frac{1}{2}(4.40 \text{ m/s}^2)t^2$.   Eq. (2)

Eq. (2) − Eq. (1) gives: 25.0 m $= (0.35 \text{ m/s}^2)t^2$,   ☞ $t = \boxed{8.45 \text{ s}}$.

(b) For car: $x_c = \frac{1}{2}(3.70 \text{ m/s}^2)(8.45 \text{ s})^2 = \boxed{132 \text{ m}}$.

For motorcycle: $x_m = x_c + 25.0 \text{ m} = \boxed{157 \text{ m}}$.

(c) During 8.45 s $+ 2.00$ s $= 10.45$ s, the motorcycle will be ahead of the car by

$\Delta x = x_m - x_c = \frac{1}{2}[(4.40 \text{ m/s}^2) - (3.70 \text{ m/s}^2)](10.45 \text{ s})^2 - 25.0 \text{ m} = \boxed{13 \text{ m}}$.

101.   (a) Given: $v_0 = 15$ m/s, $y = -25$ m.   Find: v.

$v^2 = v_0^2 - 2gy = (15 \text{ m/s})^2 - 2(9.80 \text{ m/s}^2)(-25 \text{ m}) = 715$ m^2/s^2.

So $v = -\sqrt{715 \text{ m}^2/\text{s}^2} = \boxed{-27 \text{ m/s}}$.

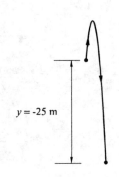

$y = -25$ m

(b) $v = v_0 - gt$,   ☞ $t = \dfrac{v_0 - v}{g} = \dfrac{15 \text{ m/s} - (-27 \text{ m/s})}{9.80 \text{ m/s}^2} = \boxed{4.3 \text{ s}}$.

102. During acceleration: $v_0 = 0$, $a = 1.5$ m/s^2, $t = 6.0$ s.

$x_1 = v_0 t + \frac{1}{2} at^2 = 0 + \frac{1}{2}(1.5 \text{ m/s}^2)(6.0 \text{ s})^2 = 27$ m, $v = v_0 + at = 0 + (1.5 \text{ m/s}^2)(6.0 \text{ s}) = 9.0$ m/s.

During constant velocity: $x_2 = (9.0 \text{ m/s})(8.0 \text{ s}) = 72$ m.

So $\bar{v} = \dfrac{\Delta x}{\Delta t} = \dfrac{27 \text{ m} + 72 \text{ m}}{14 \text{ s}} = \boxed{7.1 \text{ m/s}}$.

103. The time for the stone and sound to travel is 3.65 s $- 0.250$ s $= 3.40$ s. Assume the depth of the well is d and it takes t_1 for the stone to reach the bottom and t_2 for sound to travel to the top.

For the stone: $y = d = v_0 t - \frac{1}{2} gt^2 = -\frac{1}{2} gt^2$,   ☞ $t_1 = \sqrt{\dfrac{2d}{g}}$.

For sound: $t_2 = \dfrac{d}{v_s}$.   So $3.40 \text{ s} = t_1 + t_2 = \sqrt{\dfrac{2d}{9.80 \text{ m/s}^2}} + \dfrac{d}{340 \text{ m/s}}$.

Simplify to a quadratic equation: $d^2 - (2.590 \times 10^4)d + 1.336 \times 10^6 = 0$.

Solve for $d = \boxed{51.5 \text{ m}}$.   (Using 5 significant figures.)

104. (a) Consider the upward motion.

Given: $v_0 = 50.0$ m/s, $v = 0$ ("max height").   Find: y.

$v^2 = v_0^2 - 2gy$,   ☞ $y = \dfrac{v_0^2 - v^2}{2g} = \dfrac{(50.0 \text{ m/s})^2 - 0}{2(9.80 \text{ m/s}^2)} = \boxed{128 \text{ m}}$.

(b) Consider the downward motion.   Given: $v_0 = 0$, $y = -128$ m.   Find: t.

$y = v_0 t - \frac{1}{2} gt^2 = -\frac{1}{2} gt^2$,   ☞ $t = \sqrt{-\dfrac{2y}{g}} = \sqrt{-\dfrac{2(-128 \text{ m})}{9.80 \text{ m/s}^2}} = 5.11$ s.

So the total time for up and down is $2(5.11 \text{ s}) = \boxed{10.2 \text{ s}}$.

105. (a) It is a motion with constant acceleration. In each second the velocity increases by 5.0 m/s.

So the acceleration is $\boxed{5.0 \text{ m/s}^2}$.

(b) $\bar{v} = \dfrac{v + v_0}{2} = \dfrac{0 + 25 \text{ m/s}}{2} = \boxed{13 \text{ m/s}}$.

(c)   (d)

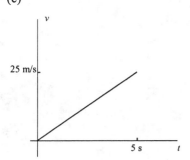

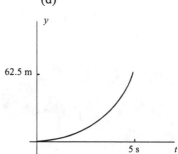

106.   (a) $\bar{v}_1 = \dfrac{\Delta x}{\Delta t} = \dfrac{1.80 \text{ km}}{(20.0/60) \text{ h}} = \boxed{5.40 \text{ km/h east}}$ and $\bar{v}_2 = \dfrac{2.40 \text{ km}}{(35.0/60) \text{ h}} = \boxed{4.11 \text{ km/h north}}$.

     (b) $avg. \; sp. = \dfrac{d}{t} = \dfrac{1.80 \text{ km} + 2.40 \text{ km}}{(20.0 + 35.0)/60 \text{ h}} = \boxed{4.58 \text{ km/h}}$.

     (c) $d_3 = \sqrt{(1.80 \text{ km})^2 + (2.40 \text{ km})^2} = 3.00 \text{ km}$.

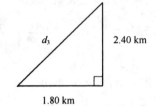

    So $avg. \; sp. = \dfrac{1.80 \text{ km} + 2.40 \text{ km} + 3.00 \text{ km}}{(20.0 + 35.0 + 25.0)/60 \text{ h}} = \boxed{5.40 \text{ km/h}}$.

     $\bar{v} = \boxed{0}$ since the displacement $\Delta x = 0$

CHAPTER 3

MOTION IN TWO DIMENSIONS

1. (a).

2. (c).

3. (a) Linear velocity increases or decreases in magnitude only.

    (b) Moves in a parabolic path.

    (c) Moves in a circular path.

4. Horizontal component: $v_x = v \cos\theta = (35 \text{ m/s}) \cos 37° = \boxed{28 \text{ m/s}}$.

    Vertical component: $v_y = v \sin\theta = (35 \text{ m/s}) \sin 37° = \boxed{21 \text{ m/s}}$.

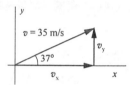

5. $v = \sqrt{v_x^2 + v_y^2} = \sqrt{(3.0 \text{ m/s}^2)^2 + (4.0 \text{ m/s}^2)^2} = \boxed{5.0 \text{ m/s}^2}$.

    $\theta = \tan^{-1}\left(\dfrac{4.0 \text{ m m/s}}{3.0 \text{ m/s}}\right) = \boxed{53° \text{ above } +x \text{ axis}}$.

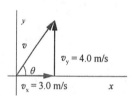

6. $v^2 = v_x^2 + v_y^2$, ☞ $v_y = \pm\sqrt{v^2 - v_x^2} = \pm\sqrt{(7.0 \text{ m/s})^2 - (3.0 \text{ m/s})^2} = \boxed{\pm 6.3 \text{ m/s}}$.

    There are two possible answers because the vector could be either in the first or the fourth quadrant.

7. (a) $\cos 37° = \dfrac{v_x}{v} = \dfrac{4.8 \text{ m/s}}{v}$,

    so $v = \dfrac{4.8 \text{ m/s}}{\cos 37°} = \boxed{6.0 \text{ m/s}}$.

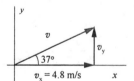

    (b) $v_y = v \sin 37° = (6.0 \text{ m/s}) \sin 37° = \boxed{3.6 \text{ m/s}}$.

8. The displacement that will bring the student back to the starting point is pointing from the finishing point to

    the starting point. $d = \sqrt{(50 \text{ m})^2 + (100 \text{ m})^2} = \boxed{1.1 \times 10^2 \text{ m}}$,

    $\theta = \tan^{-1}\left(\dfrac{50 \text{ m}}{100 \text{ m}}\right) = \boxed{27° \text{ north of east}}$.

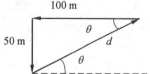

9.   (a) $x = (50 \text{ m}) \cos 37° = 40 \text{ m}$, $y = (50 \text{ m}) \sin 37° = 30 \text{ m}$.

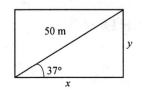

So the distance is $40 \text{ m} + 30 \text{ m} = \boxed{70 \text{ m}}$.

(b) avg. sp. $= \dfrac{d}{t} = \dfrac{70 \text{ m}}{60 \text{ s}} = 1.17 \text{ m/s}$.

The time on each leg is $\dfrac{40 \text{ m}}{1.17 \text{ m/s}} = 34.2 \text{ s} = \boxed{0.57 \text{ min}}$,   and $\dfrac{30 \text{ m}}{1.17 \text{ m/s}} = 25.6 \text{ s} = \boxed{0.43 \text{ min}}$.

10. $x = -(12.5 \text{ cm}) \cos 30° = \boxed{-10.8 \text{ cm}}$,

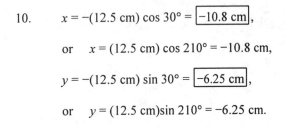

or $x = (12.5 \text{ cm}) \cos 210° = -10.8 \text{ cm}$,

$y = -(12.5 \text{ cm}) \sin 30° = \boxed{-6.25 \text{ cm}}$,

or $y = (12.5 \text{ cm}) \sin 210° = -6.25 \text{ cm}$.

11. $v_x = v_o \cos\theta = (1.50 \text{ m/s}) \cos 45° = 1.06 \text{ m/s}$,

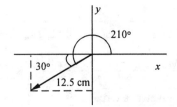

$v_y = v_o \sin\theta = -(1.50 \text{ m/s}) \sin 45° = -1.06 \text{ m/s}$.

$x = v_x t = (1.06 \text{ m/s})(1.65 \text{ s}) = \boxed{1.75 \text{ m}}$,

$y = v_y t = (-1.06 \text{ m/s})(1.65 \text{ s}) = \boxed{-1.75 \text{ m}}$.

12. $x = v_x t = (0.60 \text{ m/s})(2.5 \text{ s}) = 1.5 \text{ m}$, $y = v_y t = (0.80 \text{ m/s})(2.5 \text{ s}) = 2.0 \text{ m}$.

$d = \sqrt{x^2 + y^2} = \sqrt{(1.5 \text{ m})^2 + (2.0 \text{ m})^2} = \boxed{2.5 \text{ m}}$. $\theta = \tan^{-1}\left(\dfrac{2.0 \text{ m}}{1.5 \text{ m}}\right) = \boxed{53° \text{ above} +x \text{ axis}}$.

13.   (a) $x = v_{ox} t + \frac{1}{2} a_x t^2 = 0 + \frac{1}{2}(2.10 \text{ m/s}^2)(2.50 \text{ s})^2 = \boxed{6.56 \text{ m}}$.

$y = v_{oy} t + \frac{1}{2} a_y t^2 = (1.30 \text{ m/s})(2.50 \text{ s}) + 0 = \boxed{3.25 \text{ m}}$.

(b) $v_x = v_{ox} + a_x t = 0 + (2.10 \text{ m/s}^2)(2.50 \text{ s}) = 5.25 \text{ m/s}$, $v_y = v_{oy} + a_y t = 1.30 \text{ m/s} + 0 = 1.30 \text{ m/s}$.

$v = \sqrt{(5.25 \text{ m/s})^2 + (1.30 \text{ m/s})^2} = \boxed{5.41 \text{ m/s}}$. $\theta = \tan^{-1}\left(\dfrac{1.30 \text{ m/s}}{5.25 \text{ m/s}}\right) = \boxed{13.9° \text{ above} +x \text{ axis}}$.

14. $150 \text{ km/h} = (150 \text{ km/h})(1000 \text{ m/km})(1 \text{ h}/3600\text{s}) = 41.67 \text{ m/s}$.

$v_x = v_o \cos\theta = (41.67 \text{ m/s}) \cos 37° = 33.28 \text{ m/s}$,

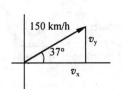

$v_y = v_o \sin\theta = (41.67 \text{ m/s}) \sin 37° = 25.08 \text{ m/s}$.

(a) $y = v_y t = (25.08 \text{ m/s})(3.00 \text{ s}) = \boxed{75.2 \text{ m}}$.

(b) $x = v_x t = (33.28 \text{ m/s})(3.00 \text{ s}) = \boxed{99.8 \text{ m}}$.

15. $\sqrt{(3.0 \text{ m})^2 + (4.0 \text{ m})^2} = 5.0 \text{ m}.$

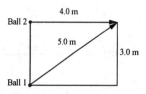

For ball 1, $\quad t = \dfrac{5.0 \text{ m}}{0.75 \text{ m/s}} = 6.67 \text{ s}.$

For ball 2, $\quad v = \dfrac{4.0 \text{ m}}{6.67 \text{ s}} = \boxed{0.60 \text{ m/s}}.$

16. $x = v_x t = (2.5 \text{ m/s})(4.0 \text{ s}) = 10 \text{ m}, \quad y = v_{yo} t + \frac{1}{2} a_y t^2 = 0 + \frac{1}{2}(-0.75 \text{ m/s}^2)(4.0 \text{ s})^2 = -6.0 \text{ m}.$

So the position is $\boxed{(10 \text{ m}, -6.0 \text{ m})}$.

17. (a) 60 km/h = 16.7 m/s.

$v_y = v \sin\theta = (16.7 \text{ m/s}) \sin 15° = \boxed{4.3 \text{ m/s}}.$

(b) $y = (800 \text{ m}) \sin 15° = \boxed{2.1 \times 10^2 \text{ m}}.$

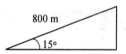

18. (c).

19. The magnitude of the resultant is equal to 1 when the vectors are in $\boxed{\text{opposite directions}}$ and equal to 7 when they are in the $\boxed{\text{same direction}}$.

20. (d).

21. $v_x = v_o \cos\theta = (10.0 \text{ m/s}) \cos 30° = \boxed{8.66 \text{ m/s}}, \quad v_y = v_o \sin\theta = (10.0 \text{ m/s}) \sin 30° = \boxed{5.00 \text{ m/s}}.$

22. (a)   (b)

23. $\boxed{\text{Yes}}$, vector addition is associative.

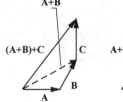 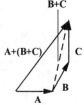

24. $B = \sqrt{(-2.5 \text{ m})^2 + (4.2 \text{ m})^2} = \boxed{4.9 \text{ m}}$.

$\theta = \tan^{-1}\left(\dfrac{4.2 \text{ m}}{-2.5 \text{ m}}\right) = \boxed{59° \text{ above } -x \text{ axis}}$.

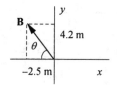

25.

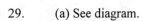

26.   (a) $\mathbf{x}_1 + \mathbf{x}_2 = (20 \text{ m}) \hat{\mathbf{x}} + (15 \text{ m}) \hat{\mathbf{x}} = \boxed{(35 \text{ m}) \hat{\mathbf{x}}}$.   (b) $\mathbf{x}_1 - \mathbf{x}_2 = (20 \text{ m } \hat{\mathbf{x}} - 15 \text{ m}) \hat{\mathbf{x}} = \boxed{(5 \text{ m}) \hat{\mathbf{x}}}$.

(c) $\mathbf{x}_2 - \mathbf{x}_1 = (15 \text{ m}) \hat{\mathbf{x}} - (20 \text{ m}) \hat{\mathbf{x}} = \boxed{(-5 \text{ m}) \hat{\mathbf{x}}}$.

27.   The ground speed is magnitude of the horizontal component of velocity.

$v_g = (120 \text{ mi/h}) \cos 25° = \boxed{109 \text{ mi/h}}$.

28.   (a) See diagram.

(b) For the 15 m vector:

$d_{1x} = (15 \text{ m}) \cos 45° = 10.6 \text{ m}$,

$d_{1y} = (15 \text{ m}) \sin 45° = 10.6 \text{ m}$.

For the 25 m vector:

$d_{2x} = 25 \text{ m}$, $d_{2y} = 0$.

So $d_x = d_{1x} + d_{2x} = 10.6 \text{ m} + 25 \text{ m} = 35.6 \text{ m}$, $d_y = d_{1y} + d_{2y} = 10.6 \text{ m} + 0 = 10.6 \text{ m}$.

Therefore $d = \sqrt{(35.6 \text{ m})^2 + (10.6 \text{ m})^2} = \boxed{37 \text{ m}}$ and $\theta = \tan^{-1}\left(\dfrac{10.6 \text{ m}}{35.6 \text{ m}}\right) = \boxed{17° \text{ north of east}}$.

29.   (a) See diagram.

(b) For the 250 mi vector:

$d_{1x} = -(250 \text{ mi}) \cos 45° = -176.8 \text{ mi}$,

$d_{1y} = (250 \text{ mi}) \sin 45° = 176.8 \text{ mi}$.

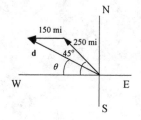

For the 150 mi vector: $d_{2x} = -150$ mi, $\qquad d_{2y} = 0$.

So $d_x = d_{1x} + d_{2x} = -176.8$ mi $+ (-150$ mi$) = -326.8$ mi, $\quad d_y = d_{1y} + d_{2y} = 176.8$ mi $+ 0 = 176.8$ mi.

Therefore $d = \sqrt{(-326.8 \text{ mi})^2 + (176.8 \text{ mi})^2} = \boxed{372 \text{ mi}}$, $\theta = \tan^{-1}\left(\dfrac{10.6 \text{ m}}{35.6 \text{ m}}\right) = \boxed{28.4° \text{ north of west}}$.

30.   (a) See diagram.

(b) For the 50.0 N force:

$F_{1x} = (50.0 \text{ N}) \cos 30° = 43.3$ N,

$F_{1y} = (50.0 \text{ N}) \sin 30° = 25.0$ N.

For the 100 N force:

$F_{2x} = (100 \text{ N}) \cos 60° = 50.0$ N,

$F_{2y} = (100 \text{ N}) \sin 60° = 86.6$ N.

So $F_x = F_{1x} + F_{2x} = 43.3$ N $+ 50.0$ N $= 93.3$ N, $\quad F_y = F_{1y} + F_{2y} = 25.0$ N $+ 86.6$ N $= 111.6$ N.

Therefore $F = \sqrt{(93.3 \text{ N})^2 + (111.6 \text{ N})^2} = \boxed{145 \text{ N}}$ and $\theta = \tan^{-1}\left(\dfrac{111.6 \text{ N}}{93.3 \text{ N}}\right) = \boxed{50.1° \text{ north of east}}$.

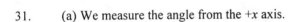

31.   (a) We measure the angle from the $+x$ axis.

$A_x = A \cos\theta = (4.5 \text{ cm}) \cos 40° = 3.45$ cm, $\quad A_y = A \sin\theta = (4.5 \text{ cm}) \sin 40° = 2.89$ cm.

The vector which will yield a null vector is $-\mathbf{A}$, because $\mathbf{A} + (-\mathbf{A}) = 0$.

So it is $\boxed{(-3.4 \text{ cm}) \hat{\mathbf{x}} + (-2.9 \text{ cm}) \hat{\mathbf{y}}}$.

(b) $B = \sqrt{(2.0 \text{ cm}) + (-4.0 \text{ cm})^2} = 4.47$ cm, $\qquad \theta = \tan^{-1}\left(\dfrac{-4.0}{2.0}\right) = -63.4°$.

So the vector is $\boxed{4.5 \text{ cm, } 63° \text{ above } -x \text{ axis}}$.

(c) The angle that $\mathbf{C}$ makes with $+x$ axis is $180° - 60° = 120°$.

$C_x = C \cos\theta = (8.0 \text{ cm}) \cos 120° = -4.0$ cm, $\quad C_y = C \sin\theta = (8.0 \text{ cm}) \sin 120° = 6.93$ cm.

So the vector $-\mathbf{C}$ is $\boxed{(4.0 \text{ cm}) \hat{\mathbf{x}} + (-6.9 \text{ cm}) \hat{\mathbf{y}}}$.

32. $\mathbf{R} = \mathbf{A} + \mathbf{B} + \mathbf{C} = [(-4.0 \text{ m}) \hat{\mathbf{x}} + (2.0 \text{ m}) \hat{\mathbf{y}}[+ [(6.0 \text{ m}) \hat{\mathbf{x}} + (3.5 \text{ m}) \hat{\mathbf{y}}] + (-5.5 \text{ m}) \hat{\mathbf{y}} = \boxed{(2.0 \text{ m}) \hat{\mathbf{x}}}$.

33.   (a) $\mathbf{F}_1 = [(12.0 \text{ N}) \cos 37°] \hat{\mathbf{x}} + [(12.0 \text{ N}) \sin 37°] \hat{\mathbf{y}} = (9.58 \text{ N}) \hat{\mathbf{x}} + (7.22 \text{ N}) \hat{\mathbf{y}}$.

$\mathbf{F}_2 = [-(12.0 \text{ N}) \cos 37°] \hat{\mathbf{x}} + [(12.0 \text{ N}) \sin 37°] \hat{\mathbf{y}} = (-9.58 \text{ N}) \hat{\mathbf{x}} + (7.22 \text{ N}) \hat{\mathbf{y}}$.

So $\mathbf{F}_1 + \mathbf{F}_2 = \boxed{(14.4 \text{ N}) \hat{\mathbf{y}}}$.

(b) $\mathbf{F}_1 = [(12.0 \text{ N}) \cos 27°] \; \hat{\mathbf{x}} + [(12.0 \text{ N}) \sin 27°] \; \hat{\mathbf{y}} = (10.7 \text{ N}) \; \hat{\mathbf{x}} + (5.45 \text{ N}) \; \hat{\mathbf{y}}.$

So $\quad \mathbf{F}_1 + \mathbf{F}_2 = (1.1 \text{ N}) \; \hat{\mathbf{x}} + (12.7 \text{ N}) \; \hat{\mathbf{y}}.$

$F_1 + F_2 = \sqrt{(1.1 \text{ N})^2 + (12.7 \text{ N})^2} = \boxed{12.7 \text{ N}}. \quad \theta = \tan^{-1}\left(\dfrac{12.7 \text{ N}}{1.1 \text{ N}}\right) = \boxed{85.0° \text{ above } +x \text{ axis}}.$

34.   (a) $\mathbf{F} = \mathbf{F}_1 - \mathbf{F}_2 = \boxed{(19.2 \text{ N}) \; \hat{\mathbf{x}}}.$ (b) $\mathbf{F} = \mathbf{F}_2 - \mathbf{F}_1 = \boxed{(-19.2 \text{ N}) \; \hat{\mathbf{x}}}.$ (c) $\boxed{\text{Yes}}.$

35. $A_x = 5.0 \text{ m/s},$ $A_y = 0.$

$B_x = (10 \text{ m/s}) \cos 60° = 5.0 \text{ m/s},$ $B_y = (10.0 \text{ m/s}) \sin 60° = 8.66 \text{ m/s}.$

$C_x = -(15 \text{ m/s}) \cos 30° = -13.0 \text{ m/s},$ $C_y = (15 \text{ m/s}) \sin 30° = 7.5 \text{ m/s}.$

$(A + B + C)_x = 5.0 \text{ m/s} + 5.0 \text{ m/s} + (-13.0 \text{ m/s}) = -3.0 \text{ m/s},$

$(A + B + C)_y = 0 + 8.66 \text{ m/s} + 7.5 \text{ m/s} = 16 \text{ m/s}.$

So $A + B + C = \sqrt{(-3.0 \text{ m/s})^2 + (16 \text{ m/s})^2} = \boxed{16 \text{ m/s}}. \quad \theta = \tan^{-1}\left(\dfrac{16 \text{ m/s}}{3.0 \text{ m/s}}\right) = \boxed{79° \text{ above the } -x \text{ axis}}.$

36.   From Exercise 3.35:

$(A - B - C)_x = 5.0 \text{ m/s} - 5.0 \text{ m/s} - (-13.0 \text{ m/s}) = 13 \text{ m/s},$

$(A - B - C)_y = 0 - 8.66 \text{ m/s} - 7.5 \text{ m/s} = -16 \text{ m/s}.$

So $A - B - C = \sqrt{(13 \text{ m/s})^2 + (-16 \text{ m/s})^2} = \boxed{21 \text{ m/s}}. \quad \theta = \tan^{-1}\left(\dfrac{16 \text{ m/s}}{13 \text{ m/s}}\right) = \boxed{51° \text{ above the } +x \text{ axis}}.$

37.   From Exercise 3.35:

$(A + B - C)_x = 5.0 \text{ m/s} + 5.0 \text{ m/s} - (-13.0 \text{ m/s}) = 23 \text{ m/s},$

$(A + B - C)_y = 0 + 8.66 \text{ m/s} - 7.5 \text{ m/s} = 1.16 \text{ m/s}.$

So $A - B - C = \sqrt{(23 \text{ m/s})^2 + (1.16 \text{ m/s})^2} = \boxed{23 \text{ m/s}}. \quad \theta = \tan^{-1}\left(\dfrac{1.16 \text{ m/s}}{23 \text{ m/s}}\right) = \boxed{2.9° \text{ above the } +x \text{ axis}}.$

38.   From $\mathbf{F}_1 + \mathbf{F}_2 + \mathbf{F}_3 = 0,$

$\mathbf{F}_3 = -\mathbf{F}_1 - \mathbf{F}_2 = (-3.0 \text{ N}) \; \hat{\mathbf{x}} + (-3.0 \text{ N}) \; \hat{\mathbf{y}} - [(-6.0 \text{ N}) \; \hat{\mathbf{x}} + (4.5 \text{ N}) \; \hat{\mathbf{y}}] = (3.0 \text{ N}) \; \hat{\mathbf{x}} + (1 - .5 \text{ N}) \; \hat{\mathbf{y}}.$

So $\quad F_3 = \sqrt{(3.0 \text{ N})^2 + (-1.5 \text{ N})^2} = \boxed{3.4 \text{ N}}. \quad \theta = \tan^{-1}\left(\dfrac{-1.5 \text{ N}}{3.0 \text{ N}}\right) = \boxed{27° \text{ below the } +x \text{ axis}}.$

39. $\mathbf{F}_1 = [(8.0 \text{ N}) \cos 60°] \; \hat{\mathbf{x}} + [(8.0 \text{ N}) \sin 60°] \; \hat{\mathbf{y}} = (4.0 \text{ N}) \; \hat{\mathbf{x}} + (6.93 \text{ N}) \; \hat{\mathbf{y}},$

$\mathbf{F}_2 = (5.5 \text{ N})[(\cos 45°) \; \hat{\mathbf{x}} - (\sin 45°) \; \hat{\mathbf{y}}] = (3.89 \text{ N}) \; \hat{\mathbf{x}} - (3.89 \text{ N}) \; \hat{\mathbf{y}},$

From $\mathbf{F}_1 + \mathbf{F}_2 + \mathbf{F}_3 = 0$,

$\mathbf{F}_3 = -\mathbf{F}_1 - \mathbf{F}_2 = -[(4.0\text{ N})\,\hat{\mathbf{x}} + (6.93\text{ N})\,\hat{\mathbf{y}}] - [(3.89\text{ N})\,\hat{\mathbf{x}} - (3.89\text{ N})\,\hat{\mathbf{y}}] = (-7.9\text{ N})\,\hat{\mathbf{x}} - (3.0\text{ N})\,\hat{\mathbf{y}}$.

So $\quad F_3 = \sqrt{(-7.9\text{ N})^2 + (-3.0\text{ N})^2} = \boxed{8.5\text{ N}}$. $\quad \theta = \tan^{-1}\left(\dfrac{-3.0\text{ N}}{-7.9\text{ N}}\right) = \boxed{21°\text{ below }-x\text{ axis}}$.

40.   (a) $\boxed{\text{In the same direction}}$.   (b) $\boxed{\text{In the opposite direction}}$.   (c) $\boxed{\text{At right angles}}$.

41. $F_{\parallel} = (50\text{ N})\sin 37° = \boxed{30\text{ N}}$,

        $F_{\perp} = (50\text{ N})\cos 37° = \boxed{40\text{ N}}$.

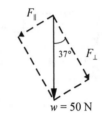

42. $\mathbf{d}_1 = (50.0\text{ m})\,\hat{\mathbf{x}}$,

        $\mathbf{d}_2 = (25.0\text{ m})[(\cos 30°)\,\hat{\mathbf{x}} + (\sin 30°)\,\hat{\mathbf{y}}]$

        $\quad = (21.65\text{ m})\,\hat{\mathbf{x}} + (12.5\text{ m})\,\hat{\mathbf{y}}$,

        $\mathbf{d}_3 = (15.0\text{ m})[(\cos 40°)\,\hat{\mathbf{x}} - (\sin 40°)\,\hat{\mathbf{y}}]$

        $\quad = (11.49\text{ m})\,\hat{\mathbf{x}} + (-9.64\text{ m})\,\hat{\mathbf{y}}$.

So $\mathbf{d} = \mathbf{d}_1 + \mathbf{d}_2 + \mathbf{d}_3 = (83.1\text{ m})\,\hat{\mathbf{x}} + (2.9\text{ m})\,\hat{\mathbf{y}}$.

Therefore $d = \sqrt{(83.1\text{ m})^2 + (2.9\text{ m})^2} = \boxed{83.2\text{ m}}$. $\theta = \tan^{-1}\left(\dfrac{2.9\text{ m}}{83.1\text{ m}}\right) = \boxed{2.0°\text{ above the horizontal}}$

43. $\mathbf{d}_1 = (20\text{ m})[(\cos 30°)\,\hat{\mathbf{x}} + (\sin 30°)\,\hat{\mathbf{y}}] = (17.3\text{ m})\,\hat{\mathbf{x}} + (10.0\text{ m})\,\hat{\mathbf{y}}$

        $\mathbf{d}_2 = (30\text{ m})\,\hat{\mathbf{y}}$, $\mathbf{d}_3 = (-40\text{ m})\,\hat{\mathbf{x}}$,

        $\mathbf{d}_4 = [(20\text{ m})\cos 45°]\,\hat{\mathbf{x}} - [(20\text{ m})\sin 45°]\,\hat{\mathbf{y}} = (14.1\text{ m})\,\hat{\mathbf{x}} + (-14.1\text{ m})\,\hat{\mathbf{y}}$.

So $\mathbf{d} = \mathbf{d}_1 + \mathbf{d}_2 + \mathbf{d}_3 + \mathbf{d}_4 = (-8.6\text{ m})\,\hat{\mathbf{x}} + (25.9\text{ m})\,\hat{\mathbf{y}}$.

Therefore $d = \sqrt{(-8.6\text{ m})^2 + (25.9\text{ m})^2} = \boxed{27\text{ m}}$. $\theta = \tan^{-1}\left(\dfrac{25.9\text{ m}}{-8.6\text{ m}}\right) = \boxed{72°\text{ above the }-x\text{ axis}}$

44. $\mathbf{d}_1 = (60\text{ mi})[(\cos 45°)\,\hat{\mathbf{x}} + (\sin 45°)\,\hat{\mathbf{y}}] = (42.4\text{ mi})\,\hat{\mathbf{x}} + (42.4\text{ mi})\,\hat{\mathbf{y}}$. $\mathbf{d}_2 = (75\text{ mi})\,\hat{\mathbf{y}}$.

        $\mathbf{d} = \mathbf{d}_2 - \mathbf{d}_1 = (75\text{ mi})\,\hat{\mathbf{y}} - [(42.4\text{ mi})\,\hat{\mathbf{x}} + (42.4\text{ mi})\,\hat{\mathbf{y}}] = (-42.4\text{ mi})\,\hat{\mathbf{x}} + (32.6\text{ mi})\,\hat{\mathbf{y}}$.

So $d = \sqrt{(-42.4\text{ mi})^2 + (32.6\text{ mi})^2} = 53.48\text{ mi}$.

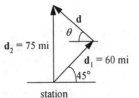

Therefore $v = \dfrac{53.48\text{ mi}}{2.0\text{ h}} = \boxed{26.7\text{ mi/h}}$.

$\theta = \tan^{-1}\left(\dfrac{32.6\text{ mi}}{-42.4\text{ mi}}\right) = \boxed{37.6°\text{ north of west}}$.

45. $\mathbf{d}_1 = (-20.0 \text{ mi}) \hat{\mathbf{y}}.$

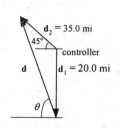

$\mathbf{d}_2 = (35.0 \text{ mi})[(-\cos 45°) \hat{\mathbf{x}} + (\sin 45°) \hat{\mathbf{y}}] = (-24.7 \text{ mi}) \hat{\mathbf{x}} + (24.7 \text{ mi}) \hat{\mathbf{y}}.$

$\mathbf{d} = \mathbf{d}_2 - \mathbf{d}_1 = (-24.7 \text{ mi}) \hat{\mathbf{x}} + (24.7 \text{ mi}) \hat{\mathbf{y}} - (-20.0 \text{ mi}) \hat{\mathbf{y}} = (-24.7 \text{ mi}) \hat{\mathbf{x}} + (44.7 \text{ mi}) \hat{\mathbf{y}}.$

So $d = \sqrt{(-24.7 \text{ mi})^2 + (44.7 \text{ mi})^2} = 51.1 \text{ mi}.$

Therefore $v = \dfrac{51.1 \text{ mi}}{0.50 \text{ h}} = \boxed{102 \text{ mi/h}}.$

$\theta = \tan^{-1}\left(\dfrac{44.7 \text{ mi}}{-24.7 \text{ mi}}\right) = \boxed{61.1° \text{ north of west}}.$

46. $\mathbf{d}_1 = (10 \text{ km}) \hat{\mathbf{x}}.$

$\mathbf{d}_2 = (15 \text{ km})[(-\cos 45°) \hat{\mathbf{x}} + (\sin 45°) \hat{\mathbf{y}}] = (-10.6 \text{ km}) \hat{\mathbf{x}} + (10.6 \text{ km}) \hat{\mathbf{y}}.$

$\mathbf{d} = \mathbf{d}_2 - \mathbf{d}_1 = (-10.6 \text{ km}) \hat{\mathbf{x}} + (10.6 \text{ km}) \hat{\mathbf{y}} - (10 \text{ km}) \hat{\mathbf{y}}$

$\quad = (-20.6 \text{ km}) \hat{\mathbf{x}} + (10.6 \text{ km}) \hat{\mathbf{y}}.$

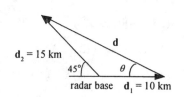

So $d = \sqrt{(-20.6 \text{ km})^2 + (10.6 \text{ km})^2} = \boxed{23 \text{ km}}.$

$\theta = \tan^{-1}\left(\dfrac{10.6 \text{ km}}{-20.6 \text{ km}}\right) = \boxed{27° \text{ north of west}}.$

47. $\mathbf{F}_1 = (100 \text{ N})[(\cos 30°) \hat{\mathbf{x}} + (\sin 30°) \hat{\mathbf{y}}] = (86.6 \text{ N}) \hat{\mathbf{x}} + (50.0 \text{ N}) \hat{\mathbf{y}}.$

$\mathbf{F}_2 = (150 \text{ N})[(\cos 60°) \hat{\mathbf{x}} + (\sin 60°) \hat{\mathbf{y}}] = (75.0 \text{ N}) \hat{\mathbf{x}} + (129.9 \text{ N}) \hat{\mathbf{y}}.$

From $\mathbf{F}_1 + \mathbf{F}_1 + \mathbf{F}_3 = 0,$

$\mathbf{F}_3 = -\mathbf{F}_1 - \mathbf{F}_2 = -[(86.6 \text{ N}) \hat{\mathbf{x}} + (50.0 \text{ N}) \hat{\mathbf{y}}] - [(75.0 \text{ N}) \hat{\mathbf{x}} + (129.9 \text{ N}) \hat{\mathbf{y}}] = -(161.6 \text{ N}) \hat{\mathbf{x}} - (179.9 \text{ N}) \hat{\mathbf{y}}.$

So $F_3 = \sqrt{(-161.6 \text{ N})^2 + (-179.9 \text{ N})^2} = \boxed{242 \text{ N}}.$

$\theta = \tan^{-1}\left(\dfrac{-179.9 \text{ N}}{-161.6 \text{ N}}\right) = \boxed{48° \text{ below the } -x \text{ axis}}.$

48. (a) $\boxed{\text{Zero}}.$

(b) Use the following subscripts: s = student, t = treadmill, and g = ground.

$\mathbf{v}_{sg} = \mathbf{v}_{st} + \mathbf{v}_{tg},$ ☞ $\mathbf{v}_{st} = \mathbf{v}_{sg} - \mathbf{v}_{tg} = 0 - (-4.0 \text{ m/s}) = \boxed{4.0 \text{ m/s}}.$

49. (a) $\boxed{\text{Face}}.$ (b) $\boxed{\text{Back and face}}.$ (c) $\boxed{\text{Back}}.$

50. Use the following subscripts: o = other driver, y = you, and g = ground.

So $\mathbf{v}_{og} = 120 \text{ km/h},$ $\mathbf{v}_{yg} = 90 \text{ km/h}$

(a) $\mathbf{v}_{yg} = \mathbf{v}_{yo} + \mathbf{v}_{og}$, ☞ $\mathbf{v}_{yo} = \mathbf{v}_{yg} - \mathbf{v}_{og} = 90$ km/h − 120 km/h = $\boxed{-30 \text{ km/h}}$.

(b) $\mathbf{v}_{oy} = -\mathbf{v}_{yo} = -(-30 \text{ km/h}) = \boxed{30 \text{ km/h}}$.

51.   Use the following subscripts: s = shopper, e = escalator, and f = floor.

So $\mathbf{v}_{se} = 1.0$ m/s, $\mathbf{v}_{ef} = 0.50$ m/s.

$\mathbf{v}_{sf} = \mathbf{v}_{se} + \mathbf{v}_{ef} = 1.0$ m/s + 0.50 m/s = 1.50 m/s.

Therefore the time is $\dfrac{20 \text{ m}}{1.50 \text{ m/s}} = \boxed{13 \text{ s}}$

52.   Use the following subscripts: t = truck, b = ball, and o = observer.

So $\mathbf{v}_{tg} = 70$ km/h, $\mathbf{v}_{bt} = -15$ km/h.

(a) $\mathbf{v}_{bo} = \mathbf{v}_{bt} + \mathbf{v}_{to} = -15$ km/h + 70 km/h = $\boxed{+55 \text{ km/h}}$.

(b) $\mathbf{v}_{bt} = \mathbf{v}_{bo} - \mathbf{v}_{to} = 55$ km/h − 90 km/h = $\boxed{-35 \text{ km/h}}$.

53.   (a) From Exercise 3.52,

(a) $\mathbf{v}_{bo} = \mathbf{v}_{bt} + \mathbf{v}_{to} = 15$ km/h + 70 km/h = $\boxed{+85 \text{ km/h}}$.

(b) $\mathbf{v}_{bt} = \mathbf{v}_{bo} - \mathbf{v}_{to} = 85$ km/h − 90 km/h = $\boxed{-5 \text{ km/h}}$.

54.   Use the following subscripts: b = boat, c = current, and w = water.

So $\mathbf{v}_{bc} = 5.0$ m/s, $\mathbf{v}_{cw} = -3.0$ m/s. $\mathbf{v}_{bw} = \mathbf{v}_{bc} + \mathbf{v}_{cw} = 5.0$ m/s + (−3.0 m/s) = 2.0 m/s.

So the distance is (2.0 m/s)(30 s) = $\boxed{60 \text{ m}}$.

55.   Use the following subscripts: b = boat, c = current, and w = water.

Upstream: $\mathbf{v}_{bc} = 7.5$ m/s, $\mathbf{v}_{cw} = -5.0$ m/s.

$\mathbf{v}_{bw} = \mathbf{v}_{bc} + \mathbf{v}_{cw} = 7.5$ m/s + (−5.0 m/s) = 2.5 m/s.   So $t_{up} = \dfrac{500 \text{ m}}{2.5 \text{ m/s}} = 200$ s.

Downstream: $\mathbf{v}_{bc} = 7.5$ m/s, $\mathbf{v}_{cw} = 5.0$ m/s.

$\mathbf{v}_{bw} = \mathbf{v}_{bc} + \mathbf{v}_{cw} = 7.5$ m/s + 5.0 m/s = 12.5 m/s.

So $t_{down} = \dfrac{500 \text{ m}}{12.5 \text{ m/s}} = 40$ s.

Therefore $t = 200$ s + 40 s = 240 s = $\boxed{4.0 \text{ min}}$.

56.   Use the following subscripts: o = other train, p = passenger, and g = ground.

The velocity of the other train relative to the passenger is $\dfrac{180 \text{ m}}{4.0 \text{ s}} = 45$ m/s.

So $v_{op} = \pm 45$ m/s since the direction of the other train is not given.

Therefore the velocity of the other train relative to the ground is

$v_{pg} = v_{op} + v_{pg} = \pm 45$ m/s $+ 20$ m/s $= \boxed{70 \text{ m/s or } -20 \text{ m/s}}$.

57. The velocity of the passenger relative to the ground is 0.30 m/s for the first 25 m and

(0.30 m/s + 0.50 m/s) = 0.80 m/s for the rest.

So the total time is $\dfrac{25 \text{ m}}{0.30 \text{ m/s}} + \dfrac{50 \text{ m}}{0.80 \text{ m/s}} = 146$ s $= \boxed{2.43 \text{ min}}$.

58. Use the following subscripts: s = swimmer, c = current, and b = bank.

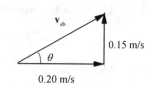

$\mathbf{v}_{sb} = \mathbf{v}_{sc} + \mathbf{v}_{cb}$.

So $v_{sb} = \sqrt{(0.20 \text{ m/s})^2 + (0.15 \text{ m/s})^2} = \boxed{0.25 \text{ m/s}}$.

$\theta = \tan^{-1}\left(\dfrac{0.15 \text{ m/s}}{0.20 \text{ m/s}}\right) = \boxed{37° \text{ north of east}}$.

59. (a) $d = vt = (0.75 \text{ m/s})(1.50 \text{ min})(60 \text{ s/min}) = \boxed{68 \text{ m}}$.

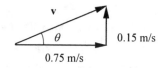

(b) $v = \sqrt{(0.15 \text{ m/s})^2 + (0.75 \text{ m/s})^2} = \boxed{0.76 \text{ m/s}}$,

$\theta = \tan^{-1}\left(\dfrac{0.15 \text{ m/s}}{0.75 \text{ m/s}}\right) = \boxed{11° \text{ relative to shore}}$.

60. (a) $\theta = \tan^{-1}\left(\dfrac{100 \text{ m}}{50 \text{ m}}\right) = 63.4°$

$\tan\theta = \dfrac{v_{sb}}{v_{cb}}$,   ☞ $v_{cb} = \dfrac{v_{sb}}{\tan\theta} = \dfrac{0.15 \text{ m/s}}{\tan 63.4°} = \boxed{0.075 \text{ m/s}}$.

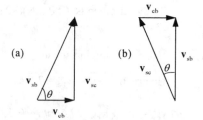

(b) $\theta = \sin^{-1}\left(\dfrac{0.075 \text{ m/s}}{0.15 \text{ m/s}}\right) = \boxed{30°}$.

61. (a) The relative velocity of the rain to that of the car is $\mathbf{v}_{rc} = \mathbf{v}_{rg} - \mathbf{v}_{cg}$, where the

subscripts r, c, and g stands for rain, car, and ground, respectively, and the symbol $\mathbf{v}_{cg}$

denotes the relative velocity of the car to the ground, etc. It is clear in the vector

diagram that $\mathbf{v}_{rc}$ is not vertical, but at an angle.

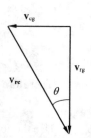

(b) $v_{cg} = v_{rg} \tan\theta = (10 \text{ m/s}) \tan 25° = \boxed{4.7 \text{ m/s}}$.

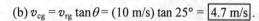

62. Use the following subscripts: b = boat, w = water, and g = ground.

(a) Same both ways, $\theta_1 = \theta_2 = \sin^{-1}\left(\dfrac{0.50}{6.75}\right) = \boxed{4.25°}$.

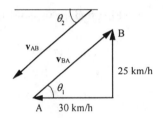

(b) For trip 1 (cross):

$v_{bg} = v_{bw}\,\theta_1 = (6.75 \text{ m/s}) \cos 4.25° = 6.73 \text{ m/s}$,

so the time is $t_1 = \dfrac{150 \text{ m}}{6.73 \text{ m/s}} = 22.3 \text{ s}$.

For trip 2 (back): $v_{bg} = v_{bw} \cos\theta_2 = (6.75 \text{ m/s}) \cos 4.25° = 6.73 \text{ m/s}$,

so the time is $t_2 = \dfrac{150 \text{ m}}{6.73 \text{ m/s}} = 22.3 \text{ s}$.   Therefore the total time is 22.3 s + 22.3 s = $\boxed{44.6 \text{ s}}$.

63. (a) $v_{BA} = \sqrt{(25 \text{ km/h})^2 + (30 \text{ km/h})^2} = \boxed{39 \text{ km/h}}$,

$\theta = \tan^{-1}\left(\dfrac{25}{30}\right) = \boxed{40° \text{ north of east}}$.

(b) $v_{AB} = \boxed{39 \text{ km/h}}$, $\theta = \boxed{40° \text{ south of west}}$.

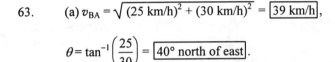

64. (b).

65. See Figure 3.17.

66. The horizontal motion does not affect the vertical motion. The vertical motion of the ball projected horizontally is identical to that of the ball dropped.

67. The vertical motion does not affect the horizontal motion. The horizontal motion of the ball projected vertically is identical to that of the car.

68. Given: $v_{xo} = 1.5 \text{ m/s}$, $v_{yo} = 0$, $y = -2.00 \text{ m}$.   Find: (a) t, (b) x.

(a) $y = v_{yo}\,t - \frac{1}{2}gt^2 = 0 - \frac{1}{2}gt^2$,   ☞ $t = \sqrt{-\dfrac{2y}{g}} = \sqrt{-\dfrac{2(-2.00 \text{ m})}{9.80 \text{ m/s}^2}} = \boxed{0.64 \text{ s}}$.

(b) $x = v_{xo}\,t = (1.5 \text{ m/s})(0.64 \text{ s}) = \boxed{0.96 \text{ m}}$.

69. Given: $v_{xo} = 1.5 \times 10^6 \text{ m/s}$, $v_{yo} = 0$, $x = 0.35 \text{ m}$.   Find: y.

First find the time of flight from the horizontal motion.

$x = v_{xo}\,t$,   ☞ $t = \dfrac{x}{v_{xo}} = \dfrac{0.35 \text{ m}}{1.5 \times 10^6 \text{ m/s}} = 2.33 \times 10^{-7} \text{ s}$.

$y = v_{yo}\,t - \frac{1}{2}gt^2 = 0 - (4.9 \text{ m/s}^2)(2.33 \times 10^{-7} \text{ s})^2 = -2.7 \times 10^{-13} \text{ m}$. So it falls $\boxed{2.7 \times 10^{-13} \text{ m}}$.

70. Given: $v_{xo} = 15$ m/s, $v_{yo} = 0$, $y = -6.0$ m. Find: x.

First find the time of flight from the vertical motion.

$$y = v_{yo}t - \tfrac{1}{2}gt^2 = 0 - \tfrac{1}{2}gt^2, \quad \text{☞} \quad t = \sqrt{-\frac{2y}{g}} = \sqrt{-\frac{2(-6.0 \text{ m})}{9.80 \text{ m/s}^2}} = 1.11 \text{ s.}$$

$$x = v_{xo}t = (15 \text{ m/s})(1.11 \text{ s}) = \boxed{17 \text{ m}}.$$

71. From Exercise 3.70, $t = \sqrt{-\dfrac{2y}{g}} = \sqrt{-\dfrac{2(-6.0 \text{ m})}{1.67 \text{ m/s}^2}} = 2.68$ s.

$$x = v_{xo}t = (15 \text{ m/s})(2.68 \text{ s}) = \boxed{40 \text{ m}}.$$

72. Given: $v_{yo} = 0$, $x = 8.7$ m, $y = -6.5$ m. Find: v_{xo}.

First find the time of flight from the vertical motion.

$$y = v_{yo}t - \tfrac{1}{2}gt^2 = 0 - \tfrac{1}{2}gt^2, \quad \text{☞} \quad t = \sqrt{-\frac{2y}{g}} = \sqrt{-\frac{2(-6.5 \text{ m})}{9.80 \text{ m/s}^2}} = 1.15 \text{ s.}$$

$$x = v_{xo}t, \quad \text{☞} \quad v_{xo} = \frac{x}{t} = \frac{8.7 \text{ m}}{1.15 \text{ s}} = \boxed{7.6 \text{ m/s}}.$$

73. $v_{xo} = v_o \cos\theta = (30 \text{ m/s}) \cos 30° = \boxed{26 \text{ m/s}}$, $\quad v_{yo} = v_o \sin\theta = (30 \text{ m/s}) \sin 30° = \boxed{15 \text{ m/s}}$.

74. 140 km/h = 38.89 m/s.

(a) $x = v_{xo}t, \quad \text{☞} \quad t = \dfrac{x}{v_{xo}} = \dfrac{18.4 \text{ m}}{38.89 \text{ m/s}} = 0.473$ s. The time to watch is 0.473 s $-$ 0.350 s = $\boxed{0.123 \text{ s}}$.

(b) $y = v_{yo}t - \tfrac{1}{2}gt^2 = 0 - \tfrac{1}{2}(9.80 \text{ m/s}^2)(0.473 \text{ s})^2 = -1.10$ m. So it drops by $\boxed{1.10 \text{ m}}$, or about 3.6 ft.

75. $\boxed{\text{Yes}}$. $y = v_{yo}t - \tfrac{1}{2}gt^2 = 0 - \tfrac{1}{2}gt^2, \quad \text{☞} \quad t = \sqrt{-\dfrac{2y}{g}} = \sqrt{-\dfrac{2(-1.00 \text{ m})}{9.80 \text{ m/s}^2}} = 0.452$ s.

$$x = v_{xo}t = (0.25 \text{ m/s})(0.452 \text{ s}) = \boxed{0.11 \text{ m}}.$$

76. (a) 140 km/h = 38.9 m/s. First find the range.

$$y = v_{yo}t - \tfrac{1}{2}gt^2 = 0 - \tfrac{1}{2}gt^2,$$

so $\quad t = \sqrt{-\dfrac{2y}{g}} = \sqrt{-\dfrac{2(-500 \text{ m})}{9.80 \text{ m/s}^2}} = 10.1$ s.

$$R = x = v_{xo}t = (38.9 \text{ m/s})(10.1 \text{ s}) = 393 \text{ m}. \quad \text{So} \quad \theta = \tan^{-1}\left(\frac{500}{393}\right) = \boxed{51.8°}.$$

(b) $\boxed{\text{Directly over the impact point}}$ since they have the same horizontal velocity.

77.　(a) The horizontal velocities of the cart and the ball are the same.

(b) First calculate the time of flight of the ball. When the ball returns, $y = 0$.

$$y = v_{yo}\, t - \tfrac{1}{2}gt^2, \qquad \text{☞} \qquad t = \frac{v_{yo}}{\tfrac{1}{2}g} = \frac{5.0 \text{ m/s}}{4.90 \text{ m/s}^2} = 1.02 \text{ s.}$$

So　$x = v_{xo}\, t = (0.75 \text{ m/s})(1.02 \text{ s}) = \boxed{0.77 \text{ m}}$.

(c) The ball would $\boxed{\text{not fall back in}}$.

78.　$v_{xo} = v_o \cos\theta = (20.0 \text{ m/s}) \cos 15.0° = 19.32 \text{ m/s,}$

$v_{yo} = v_o \sin\theta = (20.0 \text{ m/s}) \sin 15.0° = 5.176 \text{ m/s.}$

(a) At maximum height, $v_y = 0$.　$v_y^2 = v_{yo}^2 - 2gy, \qquad \text{☞} \qquad y = \frac{(5.176 \text{ m/s})^2}{2(9.80 \text{ m/s}^2)} = \boxed{1.37 \text{ m}}$.

(b) At impact, $y = 0$.　$y = v_{yo}\, t - \tfrac{1}{2}gt^2, \qquad \text{☞} \qquad t = \frac{5.176 \text{ m/s}}{\tfrac{1}{2}(9.80 \text{ m/s}^2)} = 1.056 \text{ s.}$

So　$R = x = v_{xo}\, t = (19.32 \text{ m/s})(1.056 \text{ s}) = \boxed{20.4 \text{ m}}$.

(c) Kick the ball harder to increase v_o and/or increase the angle to as close to 45° as possible.

79.　$v_{xo} = v_o \cos\theta = (250 \text{ m/s}) \cos 37° = 199.66 \text{ m/s,}$

$v_{yo} = v_o \sin\theta = (250 \text{ m/s}) \sin 37° = 150.45 \text{ m/s.}$

(a) At maximum height, $v_y = 0$.　$v_y^2 = v_{yo}^2 - 2gy, \qquad \text{☞} \qquad y = \frac{(150.45 \text{ m/s})^2}{2(9.80 \text{ m/s}^2)} = \boxed{1.15 \text{ km}}$.

(b) At impact, $y = 0$.　$y = v_{yo}\, t - \tfrac{1}{2}gt^2, \qquad \text{☞} \qquad t = \frac{150.45 \text{ m/s}}{\tfrac{1}{2}(9.80 \text{ m/s}^2)} = \boxed{30.7 \text{ s}}$.

(c) $R = x = v_{xo}\, t = (199.66 \text{ m/s})(30.7 \text{ s}) = \boxed{6.13 \text{ km}}$.

80.　$v_{xo} = v_o \cos\theta = (30.0 \text{ m/s}) \cos 37° = 23.96 \text{ m/s,}$

$v_{yo} = v_o \sin\theta = (30.0 \text{ m/s}) \sin 37° = 18.05 \text{ m/s.}$

$y = v_{yo}\, t - \tfrac{1}{2}gt^2 = (18.05 \text{ m/s})(3.00 \text{ s}) - \tfrac{1}{2}(9.80 \text{ m/s}^2)(3.00 \text{ s})^2 = 10.05 \text{ m.}$

So　$10.05 \text{ m} = (18.05 \text{ m/s})t - \tfrac{1}{2}(9.80 \text{ m/s}^2)t^2$.

Simplifying to quadratic equation:　$4.9t^2 - 18.05t + 10.05 = 0$.　Solving for　$t = \boxed{0.68 \text{ s}}$.

81.　$R = \dfrac{v_o^2 \sin 2\theta}{g}$,　☞　$\sin 2\theta = \dfrac{Rg}{v_o^2} = \dfrac{(31 \text{ m})(9.80 \text{ m/s}^2)}{(18 \text{ m/s})^2} = 0.937$.

So　$2\theta = \sin^{-1}(0.938) = 69.7°$ or $110°$.　Therefore　$\theta = \boxed{35° \text{ or } 55°}$.

82. $g = (9.80 \text{ m/s}^2)/6$ on the surface of the Moon.

$$R = \frac{v_o^2 \sin2\theta}{g} = \frac{(25 \text{ m})^2 \sin(2\times45°)}{(9.80 \text{ m/s}^2)/6} = \boxed{3.8 \times 10^2 \text{ m}}.$$

83. (a) $v_{xo} = v_o \cos\theta = (12 \text{ m/s}) \cos 45° = 8.485 \text{ m/s}$,

$v_{yo} = v_o \sin\theta = (12 \text{ m/s}) \sin 45° = 8.485 \text{ m/s}$.

$y = v_{yo} t - \frac{1}{2} gt^2 = 0 - \frac{1}{2} gt^2$, ☞ $-20 \text{ m} = (8.485 \text{ m/s})t - \frac{1}{2}(9.80 \text{ m/s}^2)t^2$.

Simplifying to quadratic equation: $4.9t^2 - 8.485t - 20 = 0$.

Solving for $t = 3.06 \text{ s}$ (negative time discarded). $R = x = v_{xo} t = (8.485 \text{ m/s})(3.06 \text{ s}) = \boxed{26 \text{ m}}$.

(b) $v_y = v_{yo} - gt = 8.485 \text{ m/s} - (9.80 \text{ m/s}^2)(3.06 \text{ s}) = -21.5 \text{ m/s}$.

So $v = \sqrt{(8.485 \text{ m/s})^2 + (-21.5 \text{ m/s})^2} = \boxed{23 \text{ m/s}}$.

$$\theta = \tan^{-1}\left(\frac{-21.5 \text{ m/s}}{8.485 \text{ m/s}}\right) = \boxed{68° \text{ below horizontal}}.$$

84. The range $R = 15 \text{ m}$. So $R = \frac{v_o^2 \sin2\theta}{g} = 15 \text{ m}$.

or $R = \frac{(55 \text{ m/s})^2 \sin2\theta}{9.80 \text{ m/s}^2} = 15 \text{ m}$, ☞ $\sin2\theta = 0.0486$.

Therefore $2\theta = \sin^{-1}(0.0486) = 2.79°$, hence $\theta = \boxed{1.4°}$.

85. $x = v_{xo} t$, ☞ $v_{xo} = \frac{x}{t} = \frac{20.0 \text{ m}}{0.500 \text{ s}} = 40.0 \text{ m/s}$.

$y = v_{yo} t - \frac{1}{2} gt^2$, ☞ $v_{yo} = \frac{y}{t} + \frac{1}{2} gt = \frac{(4.00 \text{ m} - 1.00 \text{ m})}{0.500 \text{ s}} + (4.90 \text{ m/s}^2)(0.500 \text{ s}) = 8.45 \text{ m/s}$.

So $v_o = \sqrt{(40.0 \text{ m/s})^2 + (8.45 \text{ m/s})^2} = \boxed{40.9 \text{ m/s}}$, $\theta = \tan^{-1}\left(\frac{8.45}{40.0}\right) = \boxed{11.9° \text{ above horizontal}}$.

86. $R = \frac{v_o^2 \sin2\theta}{g}$, ☞ $v_o = \sqrt{\frac{Rg}{\sin2\theta}} = \sqrt{\frac{(2.5 \text{ m} + 1.4 \text{ m})(9.80 \text{ m/s}^2)}{\sin(2\times15°)}} = \boxed{8.7 \text{ m/s}}$.

87. Let's just calculate the range of the ball assuming it would have been caught at a height of 5.0 ft above the ground.

$$R = \frac{v_o^2 \sin2\theta}{g} = \frac{(50 \text{ ft})^2 \sin(2\times40°)}{32 \text{ ft/s}} = 77 \text{ ft} \approx 26 \text{ yd}. \quad \text{So } \boxed{\text{the pass is short}}.$$

88. $v_x = v_{xo} = v_o \cos\theta, \quad v_y^2 = v_{yo}^2 - 2gy = (v_o \sin\theta)^2 - 2g(-h), \quad \text{☞} \quad v_y = \sqrt{(v_o \sin\theta)^2 + 2gh}$.

So the speed is $v = \sqrt{v_x^2 + v_y^2} = \sqrt{v_o^2 \cos^2\theta + v_o^2 \sin^2\theta + 2gh} = \sqrt{v_o^2 (\sin^2\theta + \cos^2\theta) + 2gh}$

$$= \sqrt{v_o^2 + 2gh}, \text{ which is independent of } \theta \text{ (we used the identity } \sin^2\theta + \cos^2\theta = 1).$$

Thus all three have the same speed .

89.   (a) $\alpha = \tan^{-1}\left(\dfrac{12.0 \text{ m}}{150 \text{ m}}\right) = 45.7°,$ so the launch angle $\theta = 4.57° + 10.0° = 14.6°.$

$x = v_{xo} t = (v_o \cos\theta)t, \quad \text{☞} \quad t = \dfrac{x}{v_{xo}} = \dfrac{x}{v_o \cos\theta},$

$y = v_{yo} t - \tfrac{1}{2}gt^2 = v_o \sin\theta \times \dfrac{x}{v_o \cos\theta} - \tfrac{1}{2}g\left(\dfrac{x}{v_o \cos\theta}\right)^2$

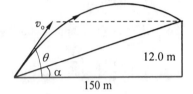

$= x \tan\theta - \dfrac{gx^2}{2v_o^2\cos^2\theta}.$

$v_o = \dfrac{x}{\cos\theta}\sqrt{\dfrac{g}{2(x\tan\theta - y)}} = \dfrac{150 \text{ m}}{\cos 14.57°}\sqrt{\dfrac{9.80 \text{ m/s}^2}{2[(150 \text{ m})\tan 14.57° - 12.0 \text{ m}]}} = \boxed{66.0 \text{ m/s}}.$

(b) $\theta = 4.57° + 10.5° = 15.07°.$

First find the time of flight.

$12.0 \text{ m} = (66.0 \text{ m/s})(\sin 15.07°)t - (4.90 \text{ m/s}^2)t^2,$

or $4.90 \, t^2 - 17.16 \, t + 12.0 = 0.$ Solving, $t = 0.97 \text{ s or } 2.54 \text{ s}.$

The 0.97 s answer is the time it takes to reach 12 m on the way up.

Therefore $x = (66.0 \text{ m/s})(\cos 15.07°)(2.54 \text{ s}) = 162 \text{ m} > 150 \text{ m},$

$y = (66.0 \text{ m/s})(\sin 15.07°)(2.54 \text{ s}) - (4.90 \text{ m/s}^2)(2.54 \text{ s})^2 = 12.0 \text{ m}.$

So the shot is too long for the hole .

90.   When the bullet travels a horizontal distance x, it takes $t = \dfrac{x}{v_{xo}} = \dfrac{x}{v_o \cos\theta}.$

During this time, the vertical position of the bullet is

$y_b = v_{yo} t - \tfrac{1}{2}gt^2 = v_o \sin\theta \, \dfrac{x}{v_o \cos\theta} - \tfrac{1}{2}g\dfrac{x^2}{v_o^2 \cos^2\theta} = x \tan\theta - \tfrac{1}{2}g\dfrac{x^2}{v_o^2\cos^2\theta}.$

During the same time, the monkey drops by $-\tfrac{1}{2}gt^2 = -\tfrac{1}{2}g\dfrac{x^2}{v_o^2\cos^2\theta}.$

So the vertical position of the monkey is $y_m = y_0 - \tfrac{1}{2}g\dfrac{x^2}{v_o^2\cos^2\theta} = x \tan\theta - \tfrac{1}{2}g\dfrac{x^2}{v_o^2\cos^2\theta} = y_b.$

Therefore when the bullet travels a horizontal distance x, its vertical height is the same as the vertical height of the monkey. Thus the bullet will hit the monkey.

91. $\mathbf{v} = \mathbf{v}_1 + \mathbf{v}_2 + \mathbf{v}_3 = (3.0 \text{ m/s}) \,\hat{\mathbf{x}} + (4.0 \text{ m/s}) \,\hat{\mathbf{y}} + (-4.0 \text{ m/s}) \,\hat{\mathbf{x}} + (5.0 \text{ m/s}) \,\hat{\mathbf{y}} + (5.0 \text{ m/s}) \,\hat{\mathbf{x}} + (-7.0 \text{ m/s}) \,\hat{\mathbf{y}}$

$= \boxed{(4.0 \text{ m/s}) \,\hat{\mathbf{x}} + (2.0 \text{ m/s}) \,\hat{\mathbf{y}}}$.

$v = \sqrt{(4.0 \text{ m/s})^2 + (2.0 \text{ m/s})^2} = \boxed{4.5 \text{ m/s}}$.

$\theta = \tan^{-1}\left(\dfrac{2.0 \text{ m/s}}{4.0 \text{ m/s}}\right) = \boxed{27° \text{ above the } +x \text{ axis}}$.

92. $v = \sqrt{(40.0 \text{ km/h})^2 + (15.0 \text{ km/h})^2} = 42.72 \text{ km/h} = 11.87 \text{ m/s}$.

So $d = vt = (11.87 \text{ m/s})(5.00 \text{ s}) = \boxed{59.3 \text{ m}}$.

$\theta = \tan^{-1}\left(\dfrac{15.0}{40.0}\right) = \boxed{20.6°}$ from its straight line path.

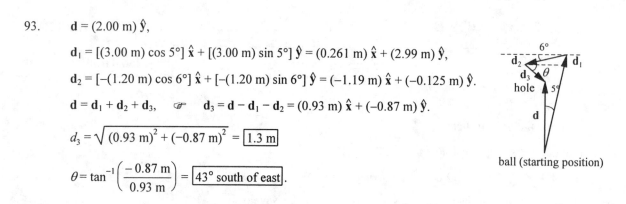

93. $\mathbf{d} = (2.00 \text{ m}) \,\hat{\mathbf{y}}$,

$\mathbf{d}_1 = [(3.00 \text{ m}) \cos 5°] \,\hat{\mathbf{x}} + [(3.00 \text{ m}) \sin 5°] \,\hat{\mathbf{y}} = (0.261 \text{ m}) \,\hat{\mathbf{x}} + (2.99 \text{ m}) \,\hat{\mathbf{y}}$,

$\mathbf{d}_2 = [-(1.20 \text{ m}) \cos 6°] \,\hat{\mathbf{x}} + [-(1.20 \text{ m}) \sin 6°] \,\hat{\mathbf{y}} = (-1.19 \text{ m}) \,\hat{\mathbf{x}} + (-0.125 \text{ m}) \,\hat{\mathbf{y}}$.

$\mathbf{d} = \mathbf{d}_1 + \mathbf{d}_2 + \mathbf{d}_3$,   ☞ $\mathbf{d}_3 = \mathbf{d} - \mathbf{d}_1 - \mathbf{d}_2 = (0.93 \text{ m}) \,\hat{\mathbf{x}} + (-0.87 \text{ m}) \,\hat{\mathbf{y}}$.

$d_3 = \sqrt{(0.93 \text{ m})^2 + (-0.87 \text{ m})^2} = \boxed{1.3 \text{ m}}$

$\theta = \tan^{-1}\left(\dfrac{-0.87 \text{ m}}{0.93 \text{ m}}\right) = \boxed{43° \text{ south of east}}$.

94.   Use the following subscripts: b = boat, w = water, and g = ground.

For the boat to make the trip straight across, v_{bw} must be the hypotenuse of the

right-angle triangle. So it must be greater in magnitude than v_{wg}. So if the reverse

is true, that is, if $v_{wg} > v_{bw}$, the boat cannot make the trip directly across the river.

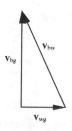

95.   From $y = v_{yo} t - \frac{1}{2} g t^2 = 0 - \frac{1}{2} g t^2$,

$t = \sqrt{-\dfrac{2y}{g}} = \sqrt{-\dfrac{2[-(15.0 \text{ m} - 1.50 \text{ m})]}{9.80 \text{ m/s}^2}} = 1.66 \text{ s}$,.

$x = v_{xo} t$,   ☞ $v_{xo} = \dfrac{x}{t} = \dfrac{10.0 \text{ m}}{1.66 \text{ s}} = \boxed{6.02 \text{ m/s}}$.

96. $R = \dfrac{v_o^2 \sin 2\theta}{g}$,   ☞ $\dfrac{R_{35}}{R_{60}} = \dfrac{\sin[2(35°)]}{\sin[2(60°)]} = 1.1$.   So the $\boxed{35° \text{ throw by } 1.1 \text{ times}}$.

97.   (a) $v_x = v_o \cos\theta = (20.0 \text{ m/s}) \cos 45° = 14.14 \text{ m/s}, \quad v_{yo} = v_o \sin\theta = (20.0 \text{ m/s}) \sin 45° = 14.14 \text{ m/s}.$

Find the time of flight to maximum height where $v_y = 0$.

$$v_y = v_{yo} - gt = 0, \quad \text{☞} \quad t = \frac{v_{yo}}{g} = \frac{14.14 \text{ m/s}}{9.80 \text{ m/s}^2} = 1.44 \text{ s}.$$

So $\quad y_{max} = v_{yo} t - \frac{1}{2} gt^2 = (14.14 \text{ m/s})(1.44 \text{ s}) - \frac{1}{2}(9.80 \text{ m/s}^2)(1.44 \text{ s})^2 = \boxed{10.2 \text{ m}},$

and $\quad x = v_{xo} t = (14.14 \text{ m/s})(1.44 \text{ s}) = \boxed{20.4 \text{ m}}.$

(b) $v_x = (20.0 \text{ m/s}) \cos 50° = 12.86 \text{ m/s}, \quad v_{yo} = (20.0 \text{ m/s}) \sin 50° = 15.32 \text{ m/s}.$

For the stream to reach the window, $x = 25.0$ m.

$t = \dfrac{25.0 \text{ m}}{12.86 \text{ m/s}} = 1.94 \text{ s}.$ So $\quad y = (15.32 \text{ m/s})(1.94 \text{ s}) - \frac{1}{2}(9.80 \text{ m/s}^2)(1.94 \text{ s})^2 = 11.3 \text{ m} > 11.0 \text{ m}.$

Therefore the stream can barely reach the window.

98.   First find the time of flight.

$$y = v_{yo} t + \frac{1}{2} gt^2, \quad \text{☞} \quad -30 \text{ m} = -[(25 \text{ m/s}) \sin 40°) t - \frac{1}{2}(9.80 \text{ m/s}^2) t^2.$$

Reduce to quadratic equation: $\quad 4.90 t^2 + 16.1 t - 30 = 0.$

Solve for $\quad t = 1.33$ s or -4.61 s. Discard the negative answer.

So $\quad x = v_{xo} t = (25 \text{ m/s})(\cos 40°)(1.33 \text{ s}) = \boxed{25 \text{ m}}.$

99.   (a) $R = \dfrac{v_o^2 \sin 2\theta}{g}, \quad \text{☞} \quad \sin 2\theta = \dfrac{Rg}{v_o^2} = \dfrac{(2.00 \times 10^3 \text{ m})(9.80 \text{ m/s}^2)}{(1.50 \times 10^2 \text{ m/s})^2} = 0.871.$

$2\theta = 60.6°$ or $119.4°$. So $\quad \theta = \boxed{30.3° \text{ or } 59.7°}.$

(b) $R_{max} = \dfrac{v_o^2 \sin 90°}{g} = \dfrac{(1.50 \times 10^2 \text{ m/s})^2}{9.80 \text{ m/s}^2} = 2.30 \text{ km}.$ So $\boxed{\text{no}}$, the target could not be hit.

100.   (a) $v_y = v_{yo} = 2.5 \text{ m/s}, \quad v_x = v_{xo} + a_x t = 0 + (0.45 \text{ m/s}^2)(4.0 \text{ s}) = 1.8 \text{ m/s}.$

So $\quad \mathbf{v} = \boxed{(1.8 \text{ m/s}) \, \hat{\mathbf{x}} + (2.5 \text{ m/s}) \, \hat{\mathbf{y}}}.$

(b) $x = v_{xo} t + \frac{1}{2} a_x t^2 = 0 + \frac{1}{2}(0.45 \text{ m/s}^2)(4.0 \text{ s})^2 = 3.6 \text{ m}, \quad y - 1.0 \text{ m} = v_{yo} t = (2.5 \text{ m/s})(4.0 \text{ s}) = 10 \text{ m}.$

So the position is at $\boxed{(3.6 \text{ m}, 11 \text{ m})}.$

101.   (a) First calculate the time of flight.

$$y = v_{yo} t - \frac{1}{2} gt^2 = 0 - \frac{1}{2} gt^2, \quad \text{☞} \quad t = \sqrt{-\frac{2y}{g}} = \sqrt{-\frac{2(-32.5 \text{ m})}{9.80 \text{ m/s}^2}} = 2.575 \text{ s}.$$

$x = v_{xo} t, \quad \text{☞} \quad v_{xo} = \dfrac{x}{t} = \dfrac{56.0 \text{ m}}{2.575 \text{ s}} = \boxed{21.7 \text{ m/s}}.$

(b) $v_x = 21.7$ m/s, $\quad v_y = v_{yo} - gt = 0 - (9.80 \text{ m/s}^2)(2.575 \text{ s}) = -25.2$ m/s.

So $\quad v = \sqrt{(21.7 \text{ m/s})^2 + (-25.2 \text{ m/s})^2} = \boxed{33.3 \text{ m/s}}$,

$\theta = \tan^{-1}\left(\dfrac{-25.2 \text{ m/s}}{21.7 \text{ m/s}}\right) = \boxed{49.3° \text{ below horizontal}}$.

102.   First calculate the time it takes for the ball to travel a horizontal distance of 40 yd = 120 ft.

$x = v_{xo} t = (v_o \cos\theta)t, \quad \text{☞} \quad t = \dfrac{x}{v_o \cos\theta} = \dfrac{120 \text{ ft}}{(70.0 \text{ ft/s}) \cos 45°} = 2.424$ s.

During this time $\quad y = v_{yo} t - \tfrac{1}{2}gt^2 = (70.0 \text{ ft/s})(\sin 45°)(2.424 \text{ s}) - \tfrac{1}{2}(32 \text{ ft/s}^2)(2.424 \text{ s})^2 = 26 \text{ ft} > 10$ ft.

So $\boxed{\text{the field goal is good}}$.

103.   (a) A positive x component could be

$\theta = \pm\cos^{-1}\left(\dfrac{6.0}{10}\right) = \boxed{\pm 53°}$.

(b) $v_y = v \sin\theta = (10 \text{ m/s}) \sin(\pm 53°) = \boxed{\pm 8.0 \text{ m/s}}$.

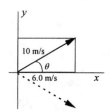

104.   (a) $R = \dfrac{v_o^2 \sin 2\theta}{g}, \quad \text{☞} \quad v_o = \sqrt{\dfrac{Rg}{\sin 2\theta}} = \sqrt{\dfrac{(8.20 \text{ m})(9.80 \text{ m/s}^2)}{\sin(2\times 37°)}} = \boxed{9.14 \text{ m/s}}$.

(b) $R = \dfrac{(4.57 \text{ m/s})^2 \sin(2\times 37°)}{(9.80 \text{ m/s}^2)/6} = \boxed{12.3 \text{ m}}$. There is no air on the Moon!

105. $d_{\text{north}} = (150 \text{ km/h})(4.0 \text{ h}) = 600 \text{ km}, \quad d_{\text{west}} = (30 \text{ km/h})(4.0 \text{ h}) = 120$ km.

So the distance $\quad d = \sqrt{(600 \text{ km})^2 + (120 \text{ km})^2} = \boxed{6.1 \times 10^2 \text{ km}}$.

CHAPTER 4

FORCE AND MOTION

1. $\boxed{\text{No}}$. If an object remains at rest, the *net force* is zero. There could still be forces acting on it as long as the net force is zero.

2. (c).

3. (c).

4. (c).

5. $\boxed{\text{No}}$, same mass, same inertia.

6. $\boxed{\text{Forward}}$ in the direction of velocity or acceleration, because the inertia of the liquid will resist the forward acceleration. So the bubble of negligible mass or inertia moves forward relative to the liquid. Then it moves $\boxed{\text{backward}}$ opposite the velocity (or in the direction of acceleration) for the same reason.

   (b) The principle is based on the $\boxed{\text{inertia of the liquid}}$.

7. (a) For the same reason as in Exercise 4.6 (now it's the inertia of the air that dominates; since helium has much smaller inertia that air), the balloon moves $\boxed{\text{forward}}$ in the direction of acceleration.

   (b) $\boxed{\text{backward}}$ in the direction of acceleration again.

8. Even though objects have no weight in deep space, they still have mass. You can distinguish their masses by moving them up and down several times to accelerate them — those that accelerate less have more mass.

9. According to Newton's first law or the law of inertia, the dishes at rest tend to remain at rest.

10. $\boxed{\text{Zero}}$. If the car is travelling at constant velocity, then its acceleration is zero, so is the net force.

11. $m = \rho V$, ☞ $\dfrac{m_{Al}}{m_{water}} = \dfrac{(2.7 \text{ g/cm}^3)(10 \text{ cm}^3)}{(1.0 \text{ g/cm}^3)(20 \text{ cm}^3)} = \boxed{1.35}$.

12.   (a) $\mathbf{F}_1 = (3.6\ \text{N})[(\cos 74°)\ \hat{\mathbf{x}} - (\sin 74°)\ \hat{\mathbf{y}}] = (0.99\ \text{N})\ \hat{\mathbf{x}} - (3.46\ \text{N})\ \hat{\mathbf{y}}$.

$\mathbf{F}_2 = (3.6\ \text{N})[(-\cos 34°)\ \hat{\mathbf{x}} + (\sin 34°)\ \hat{\mathbf{y}}] = -(2.98\ \text{N})\ \hat{\mathbf{x}} + (2.01\ \text{N})\ \hat{\mathbf{y}}$.

If $a = 0$, then $\Sigma\mathbf{F} = 0$ from Newton's first law.

$\Sigma\mathbf{F} = \mathbf{F}_1 + \mathbf{F}_2 = -(1.99\ \text{N})\ \hat{\mathbf{x}} - (1.45\ \text{N})\ \text{y} \neq 0$, so there must be a third force to make $\Sigma\mathbf{F} = 0$.

$\Sigma\mathbf{F} = \mathbf{F}_1 + \mathbf{F}_2 + \mathbf{F}_3 = 0$, ☞ $\mathbf{F}_3 = -(\mathbf{F}_1 + \mathbf{F}_2) = (1.99\ \text{N})\ \hat{\mathbf{x}} + (1.45\ \text{N})\ \text{y}$.

$F_3 = \sqrt{(1.99\ \text{N})^2 + (1.45\ \text{N})^2} = \boxed{2.5\ \text{N}}$. $\theta = \tan^{-1}\left(\dfrac{1.45\ \text{N}}{1.99\ \text{N}}\right) = \boxed{36°\ \text{above the} +x\ \text{axis}}$.

(b) $\boxed{\text{No}}$, all we can say is that the acceleration is zero. The object could be at rest or moving with constant velocity.

13. $\mathbf{F}_1 = (5.5\ \text{N})[(\cos 30°)\ \hat{\mathbf{x}} - (\sin 30°)\ \text{y}] = (4.76\ \text{N})\ \hat{\mathbf{x}} - (2.75\ \text{N})\ \hat{\mathbf{y}}$,

$\mathbf{F}_2 = (3.5\ \text{N})[(\cos 37°)\ \hat{\mathbf{x}} + (\sin 37°)\ \text{y}] = (2.80\ \text{N})\ \hat{\mathbf{x}} + (2.11\ \text{N})\ \hat{\mathbf{y}}$.

$\Sigma\mathbf{F} = \mathbf{F}_1 + \mathbf{F}_2 + \mathbf{F}_3 = 0$, ☞ $\mathbf{F}_3 = -(\mathbf{F}_1 + \mathbf{F}_2) = -(7.6\ \text{N})\ \hat{\mathbf{x}} + (0.64\ \text{N})\ \hat{\mathbf{y}}$.

So the x-component of $\mathbf{F}_3$ is $\boxed{(-7.6\ \text{N})\ \hat{\mathbf{x}}}$.

14.   (a) $\mathbf{F}_1 = (5.0\ \text{N})[(\cos 37°)\ \hat{\mathbf{x}} + (\sin 37°)\ \hat{\mathbf{y}}] = (3.99\ \text{N})\ \hat{\mathbf{x}} + (3.01\ \text{N})\ \hat{\mathbf{y}}$,

$\mathbf{F}_2 = (2.5\ \text{N})\ \hat{\mathbf{x}}$,

$\mathbf{F}_3 = -(3.5\ \text{N})[(\cos 45°)\ \hat{\mathbf{x}} + (\sin 45°)\ \hat{\mathbf{y}}] = -(2.47\ \text{N})\ \hat{\mathbf{x}} - (2.47\ \text{N})\ \hat{\mathbf{y}}$,

$\mathbf{F}_4 = -(1.5\ \text{N})\ \hat{\mathbf{y}}$.

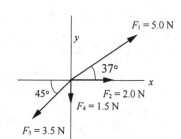

$\Sigma\mathbf{F} = \mathbf{F}_1 + \mathbf{F}_2 + \mathbf{F}_3 + \mathbf{F}_4 = (4.02\ \text{N})\ \hat{\mathbf{x}} - (0.96\ \text{N})\ \hat{\mathbf{y}} \neq 0$.

So the answer is $\boxed{\text{no}}$.

(b) $\Sigma\mathbf{F} = \mathbf{F}_1 + \mathbf{F}_2 + \mathbf{F}_3 + \mathbf{F}_4 + \mathbf{F}_5 = 0$,

so $\mathbf{F}_5 = -(\mathbf{F}_1 + \mathbf{F}_2 + \mathbf{F}_3 + \mathbf{F}_4) = -(4.0\ \text{N})\ \hat{\mathbf{x}} + (0.96\ \text{N})\ \hat{\mathbf{y}}$,

or $F_5 = \sqrt{(-4.0\ \text{N})^2 + (0.96\ \text{N})^2} = \boxed{4.1\ \text{N}}$, $\theta = \tan^{-1}\left(\dfrac{0.96\ \text{N}}{-4.0\ \text{N}}\right) = \boxed{13°\ \text{above the} -x\ \text{axis}}$.

15.   (b).

16.   There will be $\boxed{\text{extra acceleration}}$. A pickup truck in snow and a launched rocket are examples.

17.   Soft hands here result in longer contact time between the ball and the hands. The increase in contact time decreases the magnitude of acceleration. From Newton's second law, this in turn decreases the force required to stop the ball and its reaction force, the force on the hands.

18. $\Sigma F = ma,$ ☞ $a = \dfrac{\Sigma F}{m} = \dfrac{3.0\text{ N}}{1.5\text{ kg}} = \boxed{2.0\text{ m/s}^2}.$

19. $\Sigma F = ma,$ ☞ $m = \dfrac{\Sigma F}{a} = \dfrac{5.0\text{ N}}{3.0\text{ m/s}^2} = \boxed{1.7\text{ kg}}.$

20. $\Sigma F = ma,$ ☞ $m = \dfrac{\Sigma F}{a} = \dfrac{75\text{ N}}{0.50\text{ m/s}^2} = 150\text{ kg}.$

So $w = mg = (150\text{ kg})(9.80\text{ m/s}^2) = \boxed{1.5 \times 10^3\text{ N}}.$

21. $\Sigma F = ma = (7.0 \times 10^7\text{ kg})(0.10\text{ m/s}^2) = \boxed{7.0 \times 10^6\text{ N}}.$

22.   (b). Mass is a measure of inertia and it does not change.

23. $m = \dfrac{w}{g} = \dfrac{740\text{ N}}{9.80\text{ m/s}^2} = \boxed{75.5\text{ kg}}.$

24. $w = mg = (1.0\text{ kg})(9.80\text{ m/s}^2) = \boxed{9.8\text{ N}}.$

25. $w = mg = (8.0\text{ kg})(9.80\text{ m/s}^2) = \boxed{78\text{ N}} = (78\text{ N}) \times \dfrac{1\text{ lb}}{4.45\text{ N}} = \boxed{18\text{ lb}}.$

26. $150\text{ lb} = (150\text{ lb}) \times \dfrac{4.45\text{ N}}{1\text{ lb}} = \boxed{668\text{ N}}.$ $m = \dfrac{w}{g} = \dfrac{668\text{ N}}{9.80\text{ m/s}^2} = \boxed{68.2\text{ kg}}.$

27.   (a) $\boxed{\text{Yes}}$. 1 lb is equivalent to 454 g, or 454 g weighs 1 lb.

(b) $\boxed{\text{No}}$. The acceleration on the Moon is only about one-sixth of that on the Earth. So it takes six times

the mass to weigh 1 lb. $6(0.454\text{ kg}) = \boxed{2.7\text{ kg (1 lb)}}.$

28.   (a) The total force $= 18(600\text{ N}) = 1.08 \times 10^4\text{ N} = $ weight of car (why?).

$m = \dfrac{w}{g} = \dfrac{1.08 \times 10^4\text{ N}}{9.80\text{ m/s}^2} = \boxed{1.10 \times 10^3\text{ kg}}.$

(b) $w = (1.08 \times 10^4\text{ N}) \times \dfrac{1\text{ lb}}{4.45\text{ N}} = \boxed{2.43 \times 10^3\text{ lb}}.$

29.   (a) $m = \dfrac{w}{g} = \dfrac{98\text{ N}}{9.80\text{ m/s}^2} = 10\text{ kg}.$ So $a = \dfrac{\Sigma F}{m} = \dfrac{12\text{ N}}{10\text{ kg}} = \boxed{1.2\text{ m/s}^2}.$

(b) For the same object, the mass is still 10 kg. So the acceleration is also the $\boxed{\text{same}}$.

30. The resistive force is opposite the forward force. $a = \dfrac{\Sigma F}{m} = \dfrac{15\text{ N} - 8.0\text{ N}}{1.0\text{ kg}} = \boxed{7.0\text{ m/s}^2}$.

31. The friction force is opposite the horizontal force. $a = \dfrac{\Sigma F}{m} = \dfrac{300\text{ N} - 120\text{ N}}{75\text{ kg}} = \boxed{2.40\text{ m/s}^2}$.

32. First find acceleration from kinematics.

$v_0 = 15$ knots $= (15)(1.15\text{ mi/h}) = 17.25\text{ mi/h} = 7.71\text{ m/s}, \quad v = 0, \quad x = 5.0\text{ km} = 5000\text{ m}.$

$v^2 = v_0^2 + 2ax, \quad \mathscr{F} \quad a = \dfrac{v^2 - v_0^2}{2x} = \dfrac{0 - (7.71\text{ m/s})^2}{2(5000\text{ m})} = -0.0594\text{ m/s}^2.$

So $\Sigma F = ma = (6.4 \times 10^7\text{ kg})(-0.00594\text{ m/s}^2) = -\boxed{3.8 \times 10^5\text{ N}}$.

The negative sign indicates that the force is opposite the motion or the velocity.

33. (a) $a = \dfrac{\Sigma F}{m} = \dfrac{200\text{ N} + 300\text{ N} - 300\text{ N}}{1500\text{ kg}} = \boxed{0.133\text{ m/s}^2}$.

(b) Once the car is moving, ΣF would be zero for constant velocity.

So $\Sigma F = F - 300\text{ N} = 0$, we have $F = \boxed{300\text{ N}}$.

34. First find acceleration from kinematics.

$v_0 = 90\text{ km/h} = 25\text{ m/s}, \quad v = 0, \quad t = 5.5\text{ s}. \quad$ So $\quad a = \dfrac{v - v_0}{t} = \dfrac{0 - 25\text{ m/s}}{5.5\text{ s}} = -4.56\text{ m/s}^2.$

$\Sigma F = ma = (60\text{ kg})(-4.55\text{ m/s}^2) = -\boxed{2.7 \times 10^2\text{ N}}$.

The negative sign indicates that the force is opposite the motion or the velocity.

35. First find acceleration from kinematics.

$v_0 = 0, \quad v = 320 \times 0.278\text{ m/s} = 88.96\text{ m/s}, \quad t = 2.0\text{ s}. \quad a = \dfrac{v - v_0}{t} = \dfrac{88.96\text{ m/s} - 0}{2.0\text{ s}} = 44.48\text{ m/s}^2.$

Therefore $\Sigma F = ma = (2000\text{ kg})(44.48\text{ m/s}^2) = \boxed{8.9 \times 10^4\text{ N}}$.

36. First find acceleration from kinematics. $v_0 = 0, \quad v = 35\text{ m/s}, \quad x = 0.50\text{ m}.$

$v^2 = v_0^2 + 2ax, \quad \mathscr{F} \quad a = \dfrac{v^2 - v_0^2}{2x} = \dfrac{(35\text{ m/s})^2 - 0}{2(0.50\text{ m})} = 1.23 \times 10^3\text{ m/s}^2.$

$\Sigma F = ma = (0.056\text{ kg})(1.23 \times 10^3\text{ m/s}^2) = \boxed{69\text{ N}}$.

37. (c).

38.   (d).

39. $\boxed{\text{Yes}}$. The two forces mentioned are on two different objects. The force by the bat is on the ball and the force by the ball is on the bat. Forces on different objects cannot cancel.

40.   The reaction of w is an upward force on the Earth by the book and the reaction force of N is a downward force on the horizontal surface by the book.

41.   If a brick is hit by a fist with a force of 800 N, the fist is also "hit" by the brick with a force of 800 N. No, this is not something you can try at home.

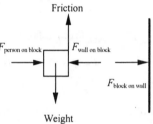

42.   The force on the block by the wall $F_{\text{wall on block}}$ and the force on the wall by the block $F_{\text{block on wall}}$ are action-reaction pairs.

43.   The force on the female by the male $F = ma = (45\ \text{kg})(2.0\ \text{m/s}^2) = 90\ \text{N}$.

       The force on the male by the female is also 90 N according to Newton's third law.

       So $a_{\text{male}} = \dfrac{90\ \text{N}}{60\ \text{kg}} = \boxed{1.5\ \text{m/s}^2}$ opposite to hers.

44.   (a) For Jane: $T = ma = (50\ \text{kg})(0.92\ \text{m/s}^2) = 46\ \text{N}$.

       The force on John is also 46 N by Newton's third law.

       $a_{\text{John}} = \dfrac{46\ \text{N}}{60\ \text{kg}} = \boxed{0.77\ \text{m/s}^2}$ toward Jane.

       (b) $x_{\text{John}} = \frac{1}{2} a_{\text{John}}\, t^2$, $x_{\text{Jane}} = \frac{1}{2} a_{\text{Jane}}\, t^2$.   So $\dfrac{x_{\text{Jane}}}{x_{\text{John}}} = \dfrac{a_{\text{Jane}}}{a_{\text{John}}} = \dfrac{0.92}{0.767} = 1.2$.

       Also $x_{\text{John}} + x_{\text{Jane}} = 10\ \text{m}$,   or $x_{\text{John}} + 1.2\, x_{\text{John}} = 10\ \text{m}$,

       therefore $x_{\text{John}} = \boxed{4.5\ \text{m from John's original position}}$.

45. $\boxed{\text{Yes}}$ if it accelerates downward. The scale reading is equal to the normal force on the object. From $\Sigma F = w - N = ma$,

       $a = \dfrac{w - N}{m} = \dfrac{(500\ \text{kg})(9.80\ \text{m/s}^2) - 4000\ \text{N}}{500\ \text{kg}} = \boxed{1.8\ \text{m/s}^2}$ downward.

46.   (a) The scale reading is equal to the normal force on the person.

$\Sigma F = w - N = ma = 0,$ ☞ $N = w = mg = (75.0 \text{ kg})(9.80 \text{ m/s}^2) = \boxed{735 \text{ N}}$.

(b) a is still zero. So $N = \boxed{735 \text{ N}}$.

(c) From $\Sigma F = N - w = ma,$

$N = w + ma = mg + ma = m(g + a) = (75.0 \text{ kg})(9.80 \text{ m/s}^2 + 2.00 \text{ m/s}^2) = \boxed{885 \text{ N}}$.

47.   From Exercise 4.46:

(a) $N = \boxed{735 \text{ N}}$.

(b) $N = \boxed{735 \text{ N}}$.

(c) From $\Sigma F = w - N = ma,$

$N = w - ma = mg - ma = m(g - a) = (75.0 \text{ kg})(9.80 \text{ m/s}^2 - 2.00 \text{ m/s}^2) = \boxed{585 \text{ N}}$.

48.   (a) $\mathbf{F}_1 = (600 \text{ N})[(\cos 45°)\, \hat{\mathbf{x}} + (\sin 45°)\, \hat{\mathbf{y}}] = (424 \text{ N})\, \hat{\mathbf{x}} + (424 \text{ N})\, \hat{\mathbf{y}},$

$\mathbf{F}_2 = (600 \text{ N})[(\cos 45°)\, \hat{\mathbf{x}} + (-\sin 45°)\, \hat{\mathbf{y}}] = (424 \text{ N})\, \hat{\mathbf{x}} + (-424 \text{ N})\, \hat{\mathbf{y}},$

$\Sigma \mathbf{F} = \mathbf{F}_1 + \mathbf{F}_2 + \mathbf{F}_3 = 0,$ ☞ $\mathbf{F}_3 = -(\mathbf{F}_1 + \mathbf{F}_2) = (-849 \text{ N})\, \hat{\mathbf{x}}.$ So it is $\boxed{849 \text{ N}}$.

(b) Now $\mathbf{F}_1 = (495 \text{ N})\, \hat{\mathbf{x}} + (495 \text{ N})\, \hat{\mathbf{y}},$ $\mathbf{F}_2 = (495 \text{ N})\, \hat{\mathbf{x}} + (-495 \text{ N})\, \hat{\mathbf{y}},$ $\mathbf{F}_3 = (-849 \text{ N})\, \hat{\mathbf{x}}.$

So $\Sigma F = 141 \text{ N},$ therefore $a = \dfrac{141 \text{ N}}{75.0 \text{ kg}} = \boxed{1.88 \text{ m/s}^2}$.

49.   (a) $\mathbf{F}_1 = (400 \text{ N})\, \hat{\mathbf{x}},$ $\mathbf{F}_2 = (-300 \text{ N})\, \hat{\mathbf{x}},$

$\mathbf{F}_3 = (50 \text{ N})[(\cos 60°)\, \hat{\mathbf{x}} + (\sin 60°)\, \hat{\mathbf{y}}] = (25.0 \text{ N})\, \hat{\mathbf{x}} + (43.3 \text{ N})\, \hat{\mathbf{y}}.$

$\Sigma \mathbf{F} = \mathbf{F}_1 + \mathbf{F}_2 + \mathbf{F}_3 = (125 \text{ N})\, \hat{\mathbf{x}} + (43.3 \text{ N})\, \hat{\mathbf{y}}.$

So $\mathbf{a} = \dfrac{\Sigma \mathbf{F}}{m} = \dfrac{(125 \text{ N})\, \hat{\mathbf{x}} + (43.3 \text{ N})\, \hat{\mathbf{y}}}{65 \text{ kg}} = (1.92 \text{ m/s}^2)\, \hat{\mathbf{x}} + (0.67 \text{ m/s}^2)\, \hat{\mathbf{y}}.$

Therefore $a = \sqrt{(1.92 \text{ m/s}^2)^2 + (0.67 \text{ m/s}^2)^2} = \boxed{2.0 \text{ m/s}^2},$

$\theta = \tan^{-1}\left(\dfrac{0.67}{1.92}\right) = \boxed{19° \text{ north of east}}$.

(b) Now the wind and current force is opposite to that of Part (a).

$\mathbf{F}_3 = -[(25.0 \text{ N})\, \hat{\mathbf{x}} + (43.3 \text{ N})\, \hat{\mathbf{y}}].$ $\Sigma \mathbf{F} = \mathbf{F}_1 + \mathbf{F}_2 + \mathbf{F}_3 = (75 \text{ N})\, \hat{\mathbf{x}} + (-43.3 \text{ N})\, \hat{\mathbf{y}}.$

$\mathbf{a} = (1.15 \text{ m/s}^2)\, \hat{\mathbf{x}} + (-0.67 \text{ m/s}^2)\, \hat{\mathbf{y}}.$

$a = \sqrt{(1.15 \text{ m/s}^2)^2 + (-0.67 \text{ m/s}^2)^2} = \boxed{1.3 \text{ m/s}^2}.$ $\theta = \tan^{-1}\left(\dfrac{-0.67}{1.15}\right) = \boxed{30° \text{ south of east}}$.

50. (a) $\Sigma F_x = F \cos 30° = (25 \text{ N}) \cos 30° = 21.65 \text{ N} = ma_x$,

so $a_x = \dfrac{21.65 \text{ N}}{30 \text{ kg}} = \boxed{0.72 \text{ m/s}^2}$.

(b) $\Sigma F_y = N + F \sin 30° - w = ma_y = 0$,

so $N = w - F \sin 30° = (30 \text{ kg})(9.80 \text{ m/s}^2) - (25 \text{ N}) \sin 30° = \boxed{2.8 \times 10^2 \text{ N}}$.

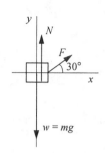

51. (a) $\Sigma F_x = F \cos\theta = (30 \text{ N}) \cos 37° = 23.96 \text{ N} = ma_x$,

so $a_x = \dfrac{23.96 \text{ N}}{25 \text{ kg}} = \boxed{0.96 \text{ m/s}^2}$.

(b) $\Sigma F_y = N - F \sin\theta - w = ma_y = 0$,

so $N = w + F \sin 37° = (25 \text{ kg})(9.80 \text{ m/s}^2) + (30 \text{ N}) \sin 37° = \boxed{2.6 \times 10^2 \text{ N}}$.

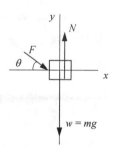

52. (a) The x-component of the weight is the side opposite to the angle θ shown,

so sine is used. $\Sigma F_x = mg \sin\theta = ma_x$,

So $a_x = g \sin\theta = (9.80 \text{ m/s}^2) \sin 37° = \boxed{5.9 \text{ m/s}^2}$.

(b) From $v^2 = v_o^2 + 2ax$,

$v = \sqrt{(5.0 \text{ m/s})^2 + 2(5.9 \text{ m/s}^2)(35 \text{ m})} = \boxed{21 \text{ m/s}}$.

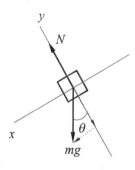

53. From Exercise 4.52(a), $a_x = g \sin\theta = (9.80 \text{ m/s}^2) \sin 30° = 4.9 \text{ m/s}^2$ down the slope.

If up the slope is chosen as positive, then $a = -4.9 \text{ m/s}^2$.

$v^2 = v_o^2 + 2ax$, $\quad x = \dfrac{(0)^2 - (25 \text{ m/s})^2}{2(-4.9 \text{ m/s}^2)} = \boxed{64 \text{ m}}$.

54. First find the mass of the first block. $\quad m_1 = \dfrac{\Sigma F}{a} = \dfrac{40 \text{ N}}{2.5 \text{ m/s}^2} = 16 \text{ kg}$.

Now $\quad a' = \dfrac{40 \text{ N}}{16 \text{ kg} + 4.0 \text{ kg}} = \boxed{2.0 \text{ m/s}^2}$.

55. (a) $m_1 = \dfrac{w}{g} = \dfrac{80 \text{ N}}{9.80 \text{ m/s}^2} = 8.16 \text{ kg}$, $\quad m_2 = \dfrac{50 \text{ N}}{9.80 \text{ m/s}^2} = 5.10 \text{ kg}$,

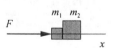

The two objects can be considered as a single system with a mass of

$M = m_1 + m_2 = 8.16 \text{ kg} + 5.10 \text{ kg} = 13.26 \text{ kg}$.

$$\Sigma F_x = 40 \text{ N} = Ma, \quad \text{☞} \quad a = \frac{40 \text{ N}}{13.26 \text{ kg}} = \boxed{3.0 \text{m/s}^2}.$$

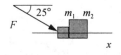

(b) $\Sigma F_x = (40 \text{ N}) \cos 25° = 36.25 \text{ N}, \quad a = \dfrac{36.25 \text{ N}}{13.26 \text{ kg}} = \boxed{2.7 \text{ m/s}^2}.$

56.   (a) There are two rings. $\Sigma F_y = T + T - w = 0.$

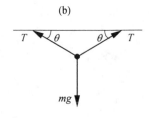

So $\quad T = \dfrac{w}{2} = \dfrac{mg}{2} = \dfrac{(50 \text{ kg})(9.80 \text{ m/s}^2)}{2} = \boxed{2.5 \times 10^2 \text{ N}}.$

(b) In the vertical direction: $\quad \Sigma F_y = T \sin\theta + T \sin\theta - mg = 0.$

So $\quad T = \dfrac{mg}{2 \sin\theta} = \dfrac{(50 \text{ kg})(9.80 \text{ m/s}^2)}{2 \sin 45°} = \boxed{3.5 \times 10^2 \text{ N}}.$

57.   (a) For the truck: $\Sigma F_x = 3200 \text{ N} - T = (3000 \text{ kg})a.$ (1)

For the car: $\quad \Sigma F_x = T = (1500 \text{ kg})a.$ (2)

(1) + (2) results $\quad 3200 \text{ N} = (3000 \text{ kg} + 1500 \text{ kg})a.$

So $\quad a = \boxed{0.711 \text{ m/s}^2}.$

Alternate method: Consider the car and truck as a system of mass 3000 kg + 1500 kg = 4500 kg.

$\Sigma F = 3200 \text{ N} = (4500 \text{ kg})a, \quad \text{☞} \quad a = 0.711 \text{ m/s}^2.$

(b) From (1) in (a), $T = (1500 \text{ kg})(0.711 \text{ m/s}^2) = \boxed{1067 \text{ N}}.$

58.   (a) Consider the three blocks as a system with mass of

$$M = m_1 + m_2 + m_3 = 1.0 \text{ kg} + 2.0 \text{ kg} + 3.0 \text{ kg} = 6.0 \text{ kg}. \quad a = \frac{\Sigma F}{M} = \frac{18.0 \text{ N}}{6.0 \text{ kg}} = \boxed{3.0 \text{ m/s}^2}.$$

(b) For m_1: $\quad F_{net} = T_1 = m_1 a = (1.0 \text{ kg})(3.0 \text{ m/s}^2) = \boxed{3.0 \text{ N}},$

For m_2: $\quad F_{net} = T_2 - T_1 = m_2 a = (2.0 \text{ kg})(3.0 \text{ m/s}^2) = 6.0 \text{ N},$

so $\quad T_2 = 6.0 \text{ N} + T_1 = \boxed{9.0 \text{ N}}.$

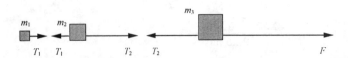

59.   The free-body diagrams of the three objects.

For m_1: $T_1 - m_1 g = m_1 a,$ (1)

For m_3: $T_2 - T_1 = m_3 a,$ (2)

For m_2: $m_2 g - T_2 = m_2 a,$ (3)

(1) + (2) + (3) gives $\quad (m_2 - m_1)g = (m_1 + m_2 + m_3)a,$

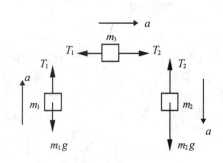

so $a = \dfrac{(m_2 - m_1)g}{m_1 + m_2 + m_3}$.

(a) $a = \dfrac{(0.50 \text{ kg} - 0.25 \text{ kg})(9.80 \text{ m/s}^2)}{0.25 \text{ kg} + 0.50 \text{ kg} + 0.25 \text{ kg}} = \boxed{2.5 \text{ m/s}^2 \text{ to right}}$.

(b) $a = \dfrac{(0.15 \text{ kg} - 0.35 \text{ kg})(9.80 \text{ m/s}^2)}{0.35 \text{ kg} + 0.15 \text{ kg} + 0.50 \text{ kg}} = -2.0 \text{ m/s}^2.$ So it is $\boxed{2.0 \text{ m/s}^2 \text{ to left}}$.

60.   From Example 4.6, $a = \dfrac{(m_2 - m_1)g}{m_1 + m_2} = \dfrac{(0.25 \text{ kg} - 0.20 \text{ kg})(9.80 \text{ m/s}^2)}{0.25 \text{ kg} + 0.20 \text{ kg}} = \boxed{1.2 \text{ m/s}^2, \text{ up}}$.

61.   First find acceleration from kinematics. $v_0 = 0,$ $t = 2.4$ s, $x = 1.0$ m.

$x = v_0 t + \tfrac{1}{2}at^2 = \tfrac{1}{2}at^2,$ ☞ $a = \dfrac{2x}{t^2} = \dfrac{2(1.0 \text{ m})}{(2.4 \text{ s})^2} = 0.347 \text{ m/s}^2$.

From Example 4.6, $a = \dfrac{(m_2 - m_1)g}{m_1 + m_2}$,

so $g = \dfrac{(m_1 + m_2)a}{m_2 - m_1} = \dfrac{(0.150 \text{ kg} + 0.140 \text{ kg})(0.347 \text{ m/s}^2)}{0.150 \text{ kg} - 0.140 \text{ kg}} = \boxed{10 \text{ m/s}^2}$.

62.   (a) First find the acceleration from dynamics.

From Example 4.6, $a = \dfrac{(m_2 - m_1)g}{m_1 + m_2} = \dfrac{(0.255 \text{ kg} - 0.215 \text{ kg})(9.80 \text{ m/s}^2)}{0.215 \text{ kg} + 0.255 \text{ kg}} = 0.834 \text{ m/s}^2$.

Now $x = v_0 t + \tfrac{1}{2}at^2 = \tfrac{1}{2}at^2,$ ☞ $t = \sqrt{\dfrac{2x}{a}} = \sqrt{\dfrac{2(1.10 \text{ m})}{0.834 \text{ m/s}^2}} = \boxed{1.62 \text{ s}}$.

(b) When m_2 hits the floor, m_1 has traveled up a distance of 1.10 m and has a velocity of v which is obtained

from: $v^2 = v_0^2 + 2ax = 0 + 2(0.834 \text{ m/s}^2)(1.10 \text{ m}) = 1.835 \text{ m}^2/\text{s}^2$,

so $v = 1.35$ m/s.

Now m_1 will move up as a "free fall" with an initial velocity of 1.35 m/s.

The height from that point is from $v^2 = 0 = v_0^2 - 2gy$,

therefore $y = \dfrac{v_0^2}{2g} = \dfrac{(1.35 \text{ m/s})^2}{2(9.80 \text{ m/s}^2)} = 0.0936 \text{ m}$.

Therefore m_1 will ascend from the floor by 1.10 m + 0.0936 m = $\boxed{1.19 \text{ m}}$ before stopping.

63.   First calculate the speed of the ball when it hits the beach.

Given: $v_0 = 0,$ $y = -10$ m.   Find: v.

$v^2 = v_0^2 - 2gy = (0)^2 - 2(9.80 \text{ m/s}^2)(-10 \text{ m}) = 196 \text{ m}^2/\text{s}^2$.

So $v = -14$ m/s. The negative sign simply indicates that the velocity is downward.

Now consider the impact. Note that the final velocity of the fall is the initial velocity of the impact.

Given: $v_0 = -14$ m/s, $v = 0,$ $x = 5.0$ cm $= 0.050$ m.   Find: a.

$$v^2 = v_o^2 + 2ax, \quad \text{☞} \quad a = \frac{v^2 - v_o^2}{2a} = \frac{(0)^2 - (-14 \text{ m/s})^2}{2(0.050 \text{ m})} = 1690 \text{ m/s}^2.$$

Finally, $\quad \Sigma F = ma = (0.20 \text{ kg})(1690 \text{ m/s}^2) = \boxed{3.9 \times 10^2 \text{ N}}$.

The force is positive so it is upward.

64. For m_1: $\Sigma F_x = T - m_1 g \sin\theta = m_1 a_x = 0, \quad \text{☞} \quad T = m_1 g \sin\theta.$

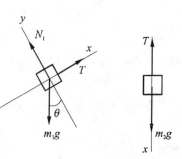

For m_2: $\Sigma F_y = m_2 g - T = m_2 a_y = 0, \quad \text{☞} \quad m_2 g = T = m_1 g \sin\theta.$

So $\quad m_2 = m_1 \sin\theta = (2.0 \text{ kg}) \sin 37° = \boxed{1.2 \text{ kg}}$.

If both are moving at constant velocity, the answer is the $\boxed{\text{same}}$

1.2 kg because the acceleration is still zero and the forces must still

balance out.

65. (a) For m_1: $\qquad \Sigma F_x = T - m_1 g \sin\theta = m_1 a_x.$ $\qquad$ (1)

For m_2: $\qquad \Sigma F_y = m_2 g - T = m_2 a_y.$ $\qquad$ (2)

$a_x = a_y = a$ in magnitude. $\quad$ (1) + (2) results $\quad (m_2 - m_1 \sin\theta)g = (m_1 + m_2)a.$

So $\quad a = \frac{m_2 - m_1 \sin\theta}{m_1 + m_2} g = \frac{2.5 \text{ kg} - (3.0 \text{ kg}) \sin 37°}{2.5 \text{ kg} + 3.0 \text{ kg}} \times (9.80 \text{ m/s}^2) = \boxed{1.2 \text{ m/s}^2}$ (m_1 up and m_2 down).

(b) From (2) in (a), $T = m_2 (g - a) = (2.5 \text{ kg})(9.80 \text{ m/s}^2 - 1.24 \text{ m/s}^2) = \boxed{21 \text{ N}}$.

66. (c).

67. (a) There is $\boxed{\text{no friction}}$ in this case.

(b) The direction of the friction force is $\boxed{\text{opposite the direction of velocity}}$.

(c) It is $\boxed{\text{sideways}}$ or perpendicular to the direction of velocity.

(d) It is $\boxed{\text{forward}}$ or in the direction of velocity.

68. (c).

69. This is because kinetic friction (sliding) is less than static friction (rolling). A greater friction force can

decrease the stopping distance.

70. When it is pushed, the normal force equals the sum of the weight and the vertical component of the pushing force, i.e., $N = w + F \sin\theta$. When it is pulled, $N = w - F \sin\theta$. Since friction force is directly proportional to normal force it is easier to $\boxed{\text{pull}}$ than to push.

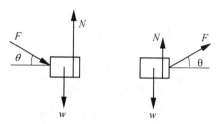

71. The down force will increase the normal force on the car to more than the weight of the car. Since friction force is directly proportional to the normal force, this will increase friction or "grip." If a car is simply made more massive to get more normal force, it will be more difficult to accelerate according to Newton's second law. So the wings can make the car grip better without significantly increasing the weight of the car—net result is more acceleration.

72. (a) $\boxed{\text{No}}$, there is no inconsistency. Here the friction force OPPOSES slipping.

(b) Wind can increase or decrease air friction depending on wind directions.

73. The treads are designed to displace water so cars with regular tires can drive in the rain. However, the wide and smooth drag race tires increase friction. These tires cannot be used in rain.

74. (a) $\Sigma F_y = N - mg = ma_y = 0$, $\quad\mathbb{F}\quad N = mg$.

$\Sigma F_x = F - f_s = ma_x = 0$ (on the verge of moving),

so $f_{smax} = \mu_s N = F$,

or $\mu_s = \dfrac{F}{mg} = \dfrac{275 \text{ N}}{(35.0 \text{ kg})(9.80 \text{ m/s}^2)} = \boxed{0.802}$.

(b) Similarly, $\mu_k = \dfrac{195 \text{ N}}{(35.0 \text{ kg})(9.80 \text{ m/s}^2)} = \boxed{0.569}$.

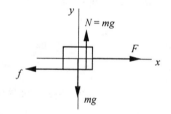

75. Refer to the diagram in Exercise 4.74.

$F = f_{smax} = \mu_s N = \mu_s mg = 0.69(40 \text{ kg})(9.80 \text{ m/s}^2) = \boxed{2.7 \times 10^2 \text{ N}}$.

76. $\Sigma F_y = N - mg = ma_y = 0$, $\quad\mathbb{F}\quad N = mg$.

$f_{smax} = 150 \text{ N} = \mu_s N = \mu_s mg$, $\quad\mathbb{F}\quad \mu_s = \dfrac{f_{smax}}{mg} = \dfrac{150 \text{ N}}{(20 \text{ kg})(9.8 \text{ m/s}^2)} = \boxed{0.77}$.

Similarly, $\mu_k = \dfrac{f_k}{mg} = \dfrac{120 \text{ N}}{(20 \text{ kg})(9.8 \text{ m/s}^2)} = \boxed{0.61}$.

77. $\Sigma F_y = N - mg = ma_y = 0,$ $N = mg.$

$f_{s\,max} = \mu_s N = \mu_s mg = 0.60(50\text{ kg})(9.80\text{ m/s}^2) = 294\text{ N}.$

$f_k = \mu_k mg = 0.40(50\text{ kg})(9.80\text{ m/s}^2) = 196\text{ N}.$

(a) Since $250\text{ N} < f_{s\,max} = 294\text{ N}$, the object won't move. So $a = \boxed{0}$.

(b) Since $350 > f_{s\,max} = 294\text{ N}$, the object will move and f_k is used.

$\Sigma F_x = 350\text{ N} - 196\text{ N} = 154\text{ N} = ma = (50\text{ kg})a.$ So $a = \boxed{3.1\text{ m/s}^2}.$

78. (a) First find acceleration from dynamics and use μ_k from Table 4.1.

$\Sigma F_x = -f_k = -\mu_k mg = ma,$ $\mu_k = -\dfrac{a}{g}.$

So $a = -\mu_k g = -0.85(9.80\text{ m/s}^2) = -8.33\text{ m/s}^2,$

and $v_0 = 90\text{ km/h} = 25\text{ m/s}, \quad v = 0.$

$v^2 = v_0^2 + 2ax,$ $x = \dfrac{v^2 - v_0^2}{2a} = \dfrac{0 - (25\text{ m/s})^2}{2(-8.33\text{ m/s}^2)} = \boxed{38\text{ m}}.$

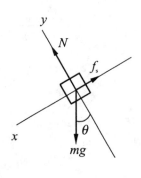

(b) $a = -0.60(9.80\text{ m/s}^2) = -5.88\text{ m/s}^2.$ So $x = \dfrac{0 - (25\text{ m/s})^2}{2(-5.88\text{ m/s}^2)} = \boxed{53\text{ m}}.$

79. Use the result of 4.78(a), $\mu_k = -\dfrac{a}{g}.$

$a = \dfrac{0 - (5.0\text{ m/s})^2}{2(20\text{ m})} = -0.625\text{ m/s}^2,$ so $\mu_k = -\dfrac{-0.625\text{ m/s}^2}{9.80\text{ m/s}^2} = \boxed{0.064}.$

80. (a) First find the minimum angle of inclination required for an object to slide.

$\Sigma F_y = N - mg\cos\theta = ma_y = 0,$ $N = mg\cos\theta.$

For on the verge of sliding, $a_x = 0.$ So $\Sigma F_x = mg\sin\theta - f_s = 0.$

So $mg\sin\theta = \mu_s N = \mu_s(mg\cos\theta).$ Therefore $\mu_s = \dfrac{\sin\theta}{\cos\theta} = \tan\theta,$

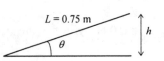

$\theta = \tan^{-1}\mu_s = \tan^{-1}0.65 = \boxed{33° > 20°}.$ So it will not move.

81. Use the result from Exercise 4.80(a).

$\mu_k = \tan\theta$ for object moving with constant velocity down incline.

So $\theta = \tan^{-1}(0.40) = 21.8°\ (\mu_k = 0.40\text{ from Table 4.1}).$

So the height $h = L\sin\theta = (0.75\text{ m})\sin 21.8° = \boxed{0.28\text{ m}}.$

82. $\Sigma F_y = N - mg\cos\theta = ma_y = 0,$ ☞ $N = mg\cos\theta.$

For constant velocity, $a_x = 0.$ So $\Sigma F_x = mg\sin\theta - f_k = 0.$

Or $mg\sin\theta = \mu_k N = \mu_k (mg\cos\theta).$

Therefore $\mu_k = \dfrac{\sin\theta}{\cos\theta} = \boxed{\tan\theta}.$

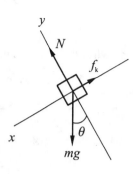

83.   (a) Use the result of Exercise 4.80(a).   When the object starts sliding down the plane,

$\mu_s = \dfrac{\sin\theta}{\cos\theta} = \tan\theta,$ so $\theta = \tan^{-1}0.58 = \boxed{30°}$ (μ_s from Table 4.1).

(b) Replace μ_s with μ_k (or see Exercise 4.82), $\theta = \tan^{-1}0.40 = \boxed{22°}.$

84.   Use the result from Exercise 4.80(a). $\mu_s = \tan\theta,$ independent of m, size, etc.

So it is still $\boxed{30°}$ and $\mu_s = \tan 30° = \boxed{0.58}.$

85. $\Sigma F_y = N - mg\cos\theta = ma_y = 0,$ ☞ $N = mg\cos\theta.$

$\Sigma F_x = mg\sin\theta - f_k = ma_x.$

Or $mg\sin\theta - \mu_k N = mg\sin\theta - \mu_k (mg\cos\theta) = ma_x.$

So $\mu_k = \dfrac{g\sin\theta - a_x}{g\cos\theta} = \dfrac{(9.80\text{ m/s}^2)\sin 37° - 0.15\text{ m/s}^2}{(9.80\text{ m/s}^2)\cos 37°} = \boxed{0.73}.$

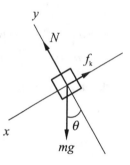

86. $\Sigma F_y = N - mg - F_1\sin 30° + F_2\sin 37° = 0,$

or $N = mg + F_1\sin 30° - F_2\sin 37°.$

$N = (5.0\text{ kg})(9.80\text{ m/s}^2) + (5.0\text{ N})\sin 30° - (4.0\text{ N})\sin 37° = 49.1\text{ N}.$

$\Sigma F_x = F_1\cos 30° + F_2\cos 37° - f_{smax} = 0,$

or $F_1\cos 30° + F_2\cos 37° - \mu_s N = 0.$

$\mu_s = \dfrac{F_1\cos 30° + F_2\cos 37°}{N} = \dfrac{(5.0\text{ N})\cos 30° + (4.0\text{ N})\cos 37°}{49.1\text{ N}} = \boxed{0.15}.$

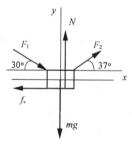

87.   Consider all three objects as a single system and refer to Exercise 4.58.

The total friction force is $f = f_1 + f_2 + f_3 = \mu (N_1 + N_2 + N_3) = \mu (m_1 + m_2 + m_3)g.$

(a) $F = f_{smax} = \mu_s (m_1 + m_2 + m_3)g = 0.45(1.0\text{ kg} + 2.0\text{ kg} + 3.0\text{ kg})(9.80\text{ m/s}^2) = \boxed{26\text{ N}}.$

(b) $F = f_k = \mu_k (m_1 + m_2 + m_3)g = 0.35(1.0\text{ kg} + 2.0\text{ kg} + 3.0\text{ kg})(9.80\text{ m/s}^2) = \boxed{21\text{ N}}.$

88. (a) When the system is on the verge of (but not quite) moving, the acceleration is still zero.

For m_1: $\Sigma F_y = N - m_1 g = 0$, ☞ $N = m_1 g$.

$\Sigma F_x = T - f_{smax} = T - \mu_s N = T - \mu_s m_1 g = 0$, ☞ $T = \mu_s m_1 g$.

For m_2: $\Sigma F = m_2 g - T = 0$, ☞ $T = m_2 g = \mu_s m_1 g$.

So $m_2 = \mu_s m_1 = 0.60(10 \text{ kg}) = \boxed{6.0 \text{ kg}}$.

(b) Once the system starts moving, the kinetic friction force is used.

For m_1: $\Sigma F_x = T - f_k = T - \mu_k N = T - \mu_k m_1 g = m_1 a$. (1)

For m_2: $\Sigma F = m_2 g - T = m_2 a$. (2)

(1) + (2) gives $m_2 g - \mu_k m_1 g = (m_1 + m_2)a$.

So $a = \dfrac{(m_2 - \mu_k m_1)g}{m_1 + m_2} = \dfrac{[6.0 \text{ kg} - 0.40(10 \text{ kg})](9.80 \text{ m/s}^2)}{10 \text{ kg} + 6.0 \text{ kg}} = \boxed{1.2 \text{ m/s}^2}$.

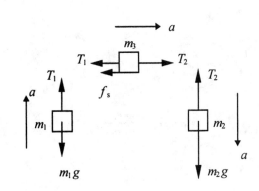

89. For m_1: $\Sigma F = T_1 - m_1 g = 0$, (1)

For m_3: $\Sigma F = T_2 - T_1 - f_{smax} = 0$, (2)

For m_2: $\Sigma F = m_2 g - T_2 = 0$, (3)

(1) + (2) + (3) gives $(m_2 - m_1)g - f_s = 0$,

or $(m_2 - m_1)g - \mu_s N_3 = (m_2 - m_1)g - \mu_s m_3 g = 0$,

so $\mu_s = \dfrac{m_2 - m_1}{m_3} = \dfrac{0.50 \text{ kg} - 0.25 \text{ kg}}{0.75 \text{ kg}} = \boxed{0.33}$.

Alternate method (more conceptual).

Since $a = 0$, $T_1 = m_1 g$ and $T_2 = m_2 g$.

So for m_3, $m_2 g - m_1 g - f_s = 0$, or $m_2 g - m_1 g - \mu_s m_3 g = 0$.

Therefore $\mu_s = \dfrac{m_2 - m_1}{m_3}$.

90. Use the diagram in Exercise 4.89 but with f_k replacing f_s.

For m_1: $\Sigma F = T_1 - m_1 g = m_1 a$, Eq. (1)

For m_3: $\Sigma F = T_2 - T_1 - f_k = m_3 a$, Eq. (2), where $f_k = \mu_k N_3 = \mu_k m_3 g$.

For m_2: $\Sigma F = m_2 g - T_2 = m_2 a$, Eq. (3)

Eq. (1) + Eq. (2) + Eq. (3) gives $(m_2 - m_1 - \mu_k m_3)g = (m_1 + m_2 + m_3)a$,

so $a = \dfrac{(m_2 - m_1 - \mu_k m_3)g}{m_1 + m_2 + m_3}$.

(a) For constant speed, $a = 0$.

So $m_3 = \dfrac{m_2 - m_1}{\mu_k} = \dfrac{0.250 \text{ kg} - 0.150 \text{ kg}}{0.560} = \boxed{0.179 \text{ kg}}$.

(b) $a = \dfrac{0.250 \text{ kg} - 0.150 \text{ kg} - (0.560)(0.100 \text{ kg})}{0.150 \text{ kg} + 0.250 \text{ kg} + 0.100 \text{ kg}} (9.80 \text{ m/s}^2) = \boxed{0.862 \text{ m/s}^2}$.

91. (a) First assume that m_1 has the tendency to move up the incline.

For m_1:

$\Sigma F_y = N_1 - m_1 g \cos\theta = 0$, ☞ $N_1 = m_1 g \cos\theta$.

$\Sigma F_x = T - m_1 g \sin\theta - f_{smax} = T - m_1 g \sin\theta - \mu_s N_1$

$\quad = T - m_1 g \sin\theta - \mu_s m_1 g \cos\theta = 0$.

So $T = m_1 g \sin\theta + \mu_s m_1 g \cos\theta = m_1 g(\sin\theta + \mu_s \cos\theta)$.

For m_2:

$\Sigma F_x = m_2 g - T = 0$, ☞ $m_2 g = T = m_1 g(\sin\theta + \mu_s \cos\theta)$.

Therefore $m_2 = m_1(\sin\theta + \mu_s \cos\theta) = (2.0 \text{ kg})(\sin 37° + 0.30 \cos 37°) = 1.7 \text{ kg}$.

Next assume the other extreme, that m_1 has the tendency to move down the incline.

The static friction force will now be pointing up the incline, so the term $\mu_s m_1 g \cos\theta$ becomes negative.

Repeating the calculation: $m_2 = m_1(\sin\theta - \mu_s \cos\theta) = (2.0 \text{ kg})(\sin 37° - 0.30 \cos 37°) = 0.72 \text{ kg}$.

Therefore m_2 can be anywhere between $\boxed{0.72 \text{ kg and } 1.7 \text{ kg}}$.

(b) When both are moving at constant velocity, the acceleration is still zero. However, μ_s is replace by μ_k. Assume that m_1 has the tendency to move up the incline.

$m_2 = m_1(\sin\theta + \mu_k \cos\theta) = (2.0 \text{ kg})(\sin 37° + 0.20 \cos 37°) = 1.5 \text{ kg}$.

Assume that m_1 has the tendency to move down the incline.

$m_2 = m_1(\sin\theta - \mu_k \cos\theta) = (2.0 \text{ kg})(\sin 37° - 0.20 \cos 37°) = 0.88 \text{ kg}$.

Therefore m_2 can be anywhere between $\boxed{0.88 \text{ kg and } 1.5 \text{ kg}}$.

92. $a = \dfrac{F}{m}$, ☞ $\dfrac{a_2}{a_1} = \dfrac{F_2}{F_1} \times \dfrac{m_1}{m_1} = \dfrac{1}{2} \times \dfrac{1}{2} = \boxed{1/4 \text{ as great}}$.

93. First find the acceleration from kinematics.

Given: $x = 0.750 \text{ m}$, $v_o = 0$, $v = 300 \text{ m/s}$. Find: a.

$v^2 = v_o^2 + 2ax$, ☞ $a = \dfrac{(300 \text{ m/s})^2 - (0)^2}{2(0.750 \text{ m})} = 6.0 \times 10^4 \text{ m/s}^2$.

Then $F = ma = (0.0250 \text{ kg})(6.0 \times 10^4 \text{ m/s}^2) = \boxed{1.5 \times 10^3 \text{ N}}$.

94. $\Sigma F = T - mg = ma,$ ☞ $a = \dfrac{T}{m} - g = \dfrac{400 \text{ N}}{25 \text{ kg}} - 9.80 \text{ m/s}^2 = \boxed{6.2 \text{ m/s}^2}.$

95. (a) $f_{smax} = \mu_s N = \mu_s mg = 0.45(9.0 \text{ kg})(9.80 \text{ m/s}^2) = 39.7 \text{ N} > 35 \text{ N}.$

So the answer is $\boxed{\text{no}}$.

96. First calculate the acceleration from dynamics. Choose north as the positive direction.

$a = \dfrac{\Sigma F}{m} = \dfrac{6.5 \text{ N} - 8.5 \text{ N}}{2.0 \text{ kg}} = -1.0 \text{ m/s}^2.$

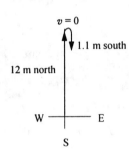

(a) The object continues to move north with a deceleration.

Given: $v_0 = 4.8 \text{ m/s},$ $v = 0,$ $a = -1.0 \text{ m/s}^2.$ Find: $x.$

$v^2 = 0 = v_0^2 + 2ax,$ ☞ $x = -\dfrac{(4.8 \text{ m/s})^2}{2(-1.0 \text{ m/s}^2)} = \boxed{12 \text{ m north}}.$

(b) Now the object turns around and move south with an acceleration.

Given: $v_0 = 0,$ $t = 1.5 \text{ s},$ $a = -1.0 \text{ m/s}^2.$ Find: $x.$

$x = v_0 t + \frac{1}{2} at^2 = 0 + \frac{1}{2}(-1.0 \text{ m/s}^2)(1.5 \text{ s})^2 = -1.1 \text{ m} = \boxed{1.1 \text{ m south}}$ of where its velocity is zero.

97. $\Sigma F_y = N - mg - F \sin\theta = 0,$ so $N = mg + F \sin\theta.$

$\Sigma F_x = F \cos\theta - f_{smax} = 0,$

or $F \cos\theta - \mu_s N = F \cos\theta - \mu_s (mg + F \sin\theta) = 0.$

Therefore $F = \dfrac{\mu_s mg}{\cos\theta - \mu_s \sin\theta}.$

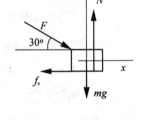

(a) $\mu_s = 0.75$ (Table 4.1),   so $F = \dfrac{0.75(5.0 \text{ kg})(9.80 \text{ m/s}^2)}{\cos 30° - (0.75) \sin 30°} = \boxed{75 \text{ N}}.$

(b) $\mu_s = 0.12,$ so $F = \dfrac{0.12(5.0 \text{ kg})(9.80 \text{ m/s}^2)}{\cos 30° - (0.12) \sin 30°} = \boxed{7.3 \text{ N}}.$

98. $\Sigma F_y = N - mg \cos\theta = 0,$ ☞ $N = mg \cos\theta.$

$\Sigma F_x = F - mg \sin\theta - f_k = 0,$

or $F - mg \sin\theta - \mu_k N = F - mg \sin\theta - \mu_k (mg \cos\theta) = 0.$

So $F = mg(\sin\theta + \mu_k \cos\theta)$

$= (9.80 \times 10^3 \text{ N})[\sin 37° + 0.750 \cos 37°] = \boxed{1.18 \times 10^4 \text{ N}}.$

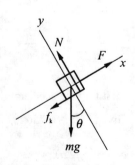

99. Use the result in Example 4.6, $a = \dfrac{(m_2 - m_1)g}{m_1 + m_2}$, which could be considered as $a = \dfrac{\Sigma F}{M}$.

So after the modification with friction, the result is $a = \dfrac{(m_2 - m_1)g - f}{m_1 + m_2}$,

so $f = (m_2 - m_1)g - (m_1 + m_2)a$

$= (0.40 \text{ kg} - 0.30 \text{ kg})(9.80 \text{ m/s}^2) - (0.40 \text{ kg} + 0.30 \text{ kg})(0.95 \text{ m/s}^2) = \boxed{0.32 \text{ N}}$.

100. First find the acceleration with dynamics. $m = \dfrac{w}{g} = \dfrac{2.75 \times 10^6 \text{ N}}{9.80 \text{ m/s}^2} = 2.806 \times 10^5 \text{ kg}$.

$a = \dfrac{F}{m} = \dfrac{6.35 \times 10^6 \text{ N}}{2.806 \times 10^5 \text{ kg}} = 22.63 \text{ m/s}^2$.

Now given: $v_0 = 0$, $v = 285 \times 0.278 \text{ m/s} = 79.23 \text{ m/s}$, $a = 22.63 \text{ m/s}^2$. Find: x.

$v^2 = v_0^2 + 2ax = 2ax$, ☞ $x = \dfrac{v^2 - v_0^2}{2a} = \dfrac{(79.23 \text{ m/s})^2 - (0)^2}{2(22.63 \text{ m/s}^2)} = \boxed{139 \text{ m}}$.

101. First find acceleration from dynamics.

Use the result of Exercise 4.78(a), $\mu_k = -\dfrac{a}{g}$.

$a = -\mu_k g = -(0.20)((9.80 \text{ m/s}^2) = -1.96 \text{ m/s}^2$.

Now given: $v_0 = 4.5 \text{ m/s}$, $v = 0$, $a = -1.96 \text{ m/s}^2$. Find: x.

$v^2 = 0 = v_0^2 + 2ax$, ☞ $x = -\dfrac{v_0^2}{2a} = -\dfrac{(4.5 \text{ m/s})^2}{2(-1.96 \text{ m/s}^2)} = \boxed{5.2 \text{ m}}$.

102. First find acceleration from kinematics.

Given: $x = 135 \text{ m}$, $v_0 = 0$, $v = 24 \text{ m/s}$. Find: a.

$v^2 = v_0^2 + 2ax$, ☞ $a = \dfrac{v^2 - v_0^2}{2x} = \dfrac{(24 \text{ m/s})^2 - (0)^2}{2(135 \text{ m})} = 2.13 \text{ m/s}^2$.

From Exercise 4.52, $a = g\sin\theta$. So $\sin\theta = \dfrac{a}{g} = \dfrac{2.13 \text{ m/s}^2}{9.80 \text{ m/s}^2} = 0.217$.

Therefore $\theta = \sin^{-1} 0.217 = \boxed{13°}$.

103. Similar to Exercise 4.78,

$a = -0.25(9.80 \text{ m/s}^2) = -2.45 \text{ m/s}^2$, $v_0 = 35 \text{ km/h} = 9.71 \text{ m/s}$, $v = 0$.

$x = \dfrac{v^2 - v_0^2}{2a} = \dfrac{0 - (9.71 \text{ m/s})^2}{2(-2.45 \text{ m/s}^2)} = 19 \text{ m} < 26 \text{ m}$. So the answer is $\boxed{\text{no}}$.

104.   First find the acceleration from kinematics. $v_o = 15$ m/s, $v = 0$, $x = 25$ cm $= 0.25$ m.

$$v^2 = 0 = v_o^2 + 2ax, \quad \text{☞} \quad x = -\frac{v_o^2}{2a} = -\frac{(15 \text{ m/s})^2}{2(0.25 \text{ m})} = -450 \text{ m/s}^2.$$

Then $F = ma = 0.14$ kg$(-450$ m/s$^2) = -\boxed{63 \text{ N}}$.

The negative sign indicates that the force is opposite to the velocity of the baseball or in the direction of acceleration.

CHAPTER 5

WORK AND ENERGY

1. (d).

2. $\boxed{\text{No}}$, you are not doing any work because there is no displacement.

3. (a) $\boxed{\text{No}}$, the weight is not moving, so there is no displacement and therefore, no work.

    (b) $\boxed{\text{Yes}}$, positive work in done by the force exerted by the weightlifter.

    (c) $\boxed{\text{No}}$, as in (a), no work is done.

    (d) $\boxed{\text{Yes}}$, but the positive work is done by gravity, not the weightlifter.

4. The work done by the carrying force is $\boxed{\text{zero}}$ because the angle between the force (upward) and the

    displacement (horizontal) is $90°$ and $W = F \cos\theta\, d = F \cos 90°\, d = 0$.

5. $\boxed{\text{Positive on the way down and negative on the way up}}$.

    $\boxed{\text{No, it is not constant}}$.

    Maximum at points B and D ($\theta = 0°$ or $180°$)

    and minimum at points A and C ($\theta = 90°$).

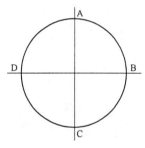

6. $W = F \cos\theta\, d$, ☞ $F = \dfrac{W}{d\cos\theta} = \dfrac{50 \text{ J}}{(10 \text{ m}) \cos 0°} = \boxed{5.0 \text{ N}}$.

7. The friction force is $f_k = \mu_k N = \mu_k mg$ and the angle between the friction force and displacement is $180°$.

    So $W = F \cos\theta\, d = \mu_k mg \cos\theta\, d = 0.20(5.0 \text{ kg})(9.80 \text{ m/s}^2) \cos 180° (10 \text{ m}) = \boxed{-98 \text{ J}}$.

8. At constant speed, the upward force is equal to gravity.

    $W = F \cos\theta\, d = (mg) \cos\theta\, d = (15 \text{ kg})(9.80 \text{ m/s}^2) \cos 0° (10 \text{ m}) = \boxed{1.5 \times 10^3 \text{ J}}$.

9. $W = F \cos\theta\, d$, ☞ $d = \dfrac{W}{F\cos\theta} = \dfrac{1.44 \times 10^3 \text{ J}}{(250 \text{ N}) \cos 30°} = \boxed{6.65 \text{ m}}$.

10. $\boxed{\text{Gravity}}$ does work. $W = F_{\parallel}d = mgd\sin\theta = (3.00\ \text{kg})(9.80\ \text{m/s}^2)(1.50\ \text{m})\cos 20° = \boxed{15.1\ \text{J}}$.

11. The friction force $f_k = \mu_k N = \mu_k\ (mg\cos 20°) = 0.275(3.00\ \text{kg})(9.80\ \text{m/s}^2)\cos 20° = 7.597\ \text{N}$.

So $W_{\text{net}} = 15.1\ \text{J} + (7.597\ \text{N})(1.5\ \text{m})\cos 180° = \boxed{3.7\ \text{J}}$, where the 180° angle is between f_k and displacement.

12. $W = F\cos\theta\,d = (F\cos\theta)\,d = F_{\parallel}d = F(d\cos\theta) = F\,d_{\parallel}$.

13. $W = F\cos\theta\,d = (mg)\cos\theta\,d = (500\ \text{kg})(9.80\ \text{m/s}^2)(\cos 0°)[(1.50\ \text{m/s})(20.0\ \text{s})] = \boxed{1.47\times 10^5\ \text{J}}$.

14. $\Sigma F_y = N + F\sin\theta - mg = 0, \quad N = mg - F\sin\theta.$

$\Sigma F_x = F\cos\theta - f_k = 0, \quad$ or $\quad F\cos\theta = \mu_k N = \mu_k\ (mg - F\sin\theta) = 0.$

So $F = \dfrac{\mu_k\,mg}{\cos\theta + \mu_k\sin\theta} = \dfrac{0.20(35\ \text{kg})(9.80\ \text{m/s}^2)}{\cos 30° + 0.20\sin 30°} = 71.0\ \text{N}.$

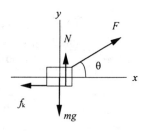

Therefore $W = F\cos\theta\,d = (71.0\ \text{N})\cos 30°\ (10\ \text{m}) = \boxed{6.1\times 10^2\ \text{J}}$.

15. $\Sigma F_y = N - F\sin\theta - mg\cos\theta = 0, \quad$ so $\quad N = mg\cos\theta + F\sin\theta.$

$\Sigma F_x = F\cos\theta - mg\sin\theta - f_k = 0,$

or $\quad F\cos\theta - mg\sin\theta - \mu_k\ (mg\cos\theta + F\sin\theta) = 0.$

So $F = \dfrac{mg(\sin\theta + \mu_k)}{\cos\theta - \mu_k\sin\theta}$

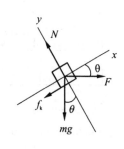

$= \dfrac{(35\ \text{kg})(9.80\ \text{m/s}^2)(\sin 15° + 0.20)}{\cos 15° - 0.20\sin 15°} = 172.2\ \text{N}.$

Therefore $W = F\cos\theta\,d = (172.2\ \text{N})\cos 15°\left(\dfrac{3.6\ \text{m}}{\sin 15°}\right) = \boxed{2.4\times 10^3\ \text{J}}$.

16. (a) $W = F\cos\theta\,d = (50\ \text{N})\cos 37°\ (25\ \text{m}) = 998\ \text{J} = \boxed{1.0\times 10^3\ \text{J}}$.

(b) Refer to the diagram in the solution of 5.14.

$\Sigma F_y = N + F\sin\theta - mg = 0, \quad N = mg - F\sin\theta.$

So $f_k = \mu_k N = \mu_k\ (mg - F\sin\theta) = 0.15[(20\ \text{kg})(9.80\ \text{m/s}^2) - (50\ \text{N})\sin 37°] = 24.89\ \text{N}.$

Therefore $W = (24.89\ \text{N})\cos 180°\ (25\ \text{m}) = -622\ \text{J} = \boxed{-6.2\times 10^2\ \text{J}}$.

(c) $W_{\text{net}} = 998\ \text{J} + (-622\ \text{J}) = 376\ \text{J} = \boxed{3.8\times 10^2\ \text{J}}$.

17.   (a) $\Sigma F = F - mg = ma$,

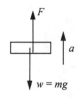

   so $F = m(g + a) = (500\text{ kg})(9.80\text{ m/s}^2 + 2.00\text{ m/s}^2) = 5.90 \times 10^3\text{ N}$.

   In 5.0 s, $d = v_o t + \frac{1}{2}at^2 = \frac{1}{2}(2.00\text{ m/s}^2)(5.00\text{ s}) = 25.0\text{ m}$.

   Therefore $W = F\cos\theta\, d = (5.90 \times 10^3\text{ N})\cos 0°\ (25.0\text{ m}) = 1.475 \times 10^5\text{ J} = \boxed{1.48 \times 10^5\text{ J}}$.

   (b) $W = (500\text{ kg})(9.80\text{ m/s}^2)\cos 180°\ (25.0\text{ m}) = -1.225 \times 10^5\text{ J} = \boxed{-1.23 \times 10^5\text{ J}}$.

   (c) $W_{net} = 1.475 \times 10^5\text{ J} + (-1.225 \times 10^5\text{ J}) = \boxed{2.50 \times 10^4\text{ J}}$.

18. $\Sigma F_y = N - mg\cos\phi = 0$,   ☞ $N = mg\cos\phi$.

   $\Sigma F_x = mg\sin\phi - F - f_k = 0$,   or $mg\sin\phi - F - \mu_k(mg\cos\phi) = 0$.

   $F = mg(\sin\phi - \mu_k\cos\phi) = (50\text{ kg})(9.80\text{ m/s}^2)[\sin 25° - (0.33)\cos 25°] = 60.5\text{ N}$.

   $f_k = 0.33(50\text{ kg})(9.80\text{ m/s}^2)\cos 25° = 146.5\text{ N}$.

   (a) $W = F\cos\theta\, d = (60.5\text{ N})\cos 180°\ (5.0\text{ m}) = \boxed{-3.0 \times 10^2\text{ J}}$.

   (b) $W = (146.5\text{ N})\cos 180°\ (5.0\text{ m}) = \boxed{-7.3 \times 10^2\text{ J}}$.

   (c) $W = (50\text{ kg})(9.80\text{ m/s}^2)\cos 65°\ (5.0\text{ m}) = \boxed{1.0 \times 10^3\text{ J}}$.

   (d) $W_{net} = (\Sigma F)\cos\theta\, d = \boxed{0}$, where $\Sigma F = 0$ for constant velocity.

19.   (c).

20.   (d) since $W = \frac{1}{2}k\,(x^2 - x_o^2)$,   ☞ $\dfrac{W_2}{W_1} = \dfrac{x_2^2 - x_1^2}{x_1^2 - x_o^2} = \dfrac{6.0^2 - 2.0^2}{2.0^2 - 0^2} = \boxed{8\text{ times}}$.

21. $\boxed{\text{No}}$, more work, because the force increases as the spring stretches from Hooke's law: $F_s = -kx$.

22. $F_s = -kx$,   ☞ $k = \left|\dfrac{F_s}{x}\right| = \dfrac{4.0\text{ N}}{0.050\text{ m}} = \boxed{80\text{ N/m}}$.

23. $F_s = -kx$,   ☞ $x = \left|\dfrac{F_s}{k}\right| = \dfrac{10\text{ N}}{4.0 \times 10^2\text{ N/m}} = 0.025\text{ m} = \boxed{2.5\text{ cm}}$.

24. $W = \frac{1}{2}kx^2 = \frac{1}{2}(40\text{ N/m})(0.020\text{ m})^2 = \boxed{8.0 \times 10^{-3}\text{ J}}$.

25. $W = \frac{1}{2}kx^2$,   ☞ $k = \dfrac{2W}{x^2} = \dfrac{2(400\text{ J})}{(0.0800\text{ m})^2} = \boxed{1.25 \times 10^5\text{ N/m}}$.

26. $F_s = -kx$, ☞ $k = \left| \dfrac{F_s}{x} \right| = \dfrac{(0.25\ \text{kg})(9.80\ \text{m/s}^2)}{0.050\ \text{m}} = 49\ \text{N/m}$.

$W = \frac{1}{2}kx^2$, ☞ $x = \sqrt{\dfrac{2W}{k}} = \sqrt{\dfrac{2(10\ \text{J})}{49\ \text{N/m}}} = \boxed{0.64\ \text{m}}$.

27. $F_s = -kx$, ☞ $k = \left| \dfrac{F_s}{x_1 - x_o} \right| = \dfrac{(0.075\ \text{kg})(9.80\ \text{m/s}^2)}{0.070\ \text{m} - 0.040\ \text{m}} = 24.5\ \text{N/m}$.

$W = \frac{1}{2}k(x_2^2 - x_o^2) = \frac{1}{2}(24.5\ \text{N/m})(0.10\ \text{m} + 0.030\ \text{m})^2 = \boxed{0.21\ \text{J}}$.

28. (a) $W = \frac{1}{2}kx^2 = \frac{1}{2}(2.5 \times 10^3\ \text{N/m})(0.060\ \text{m})^2 = \boxed{4.5\ \text{J}}$.

(b) $W = \frac{1}{2}k(x_2^2 - x_1^2) = \frac{1}{2}(2.5 \times 10^3\ \text{N/m})[(0.080\ \text{m})^2 - (0.060\ \text{m})^2] = \boxed{3.5\ \text{J}}$.

29. (a) $m = \dfrac{w}{g} = \dfrac{F}{g} = \dfrac{kx}{g} = \dfrac{(2.5 \times 10^3\ \text{N/m})(0.060\ \text{m})}{9.80\ \text{m/s}^2} = \boxed{15\ \text{kg}}$.

(b) $m = \dfrac{k(x_2 - x_1)}{g} = \dfrac{(2.5 \times 10^3\ \text{N/m})(0.020\ \text{m})}{9.80\ \text{m/s}^2} = \boxed{5.1\ \text{kg more}}$.

30. (a) $F = kx = (60\ \text{N/m})x$, ☞ $k = 60\ \text{N/m}$.

$W = \frac{1}{2}k(x^2 - x_o^2) = \frac{1}{2}(60\ \text{N/m})[(0.15\ \text{m})^2 - 0] = \boxed{0.68\ \text{J}}$.

(b) $W = \frac{1}{2}(60\ \text{N/m})[(0.25\ \text{m})^2 - (0.15\ \text{m})^2] = \boxed{1.2\ \text{J}}$.

31. $W = \text{area} = \frac{1}{2}(6.0\ \text{N})(2.0\ \text{m}) + \frac{1}{2}(-6.0\ \text{N})(5.0\ \text{m} - 2.0\ \text{m}) = \boxed{-3.0\ \text{J}}$.

32. (b), because $\cos\theta < 0$ for $90° < \theta < 270°$ and $W = F\cos\theta\, d$.

33. Because the heel can lift from the blade, the blade will be in contact with the ice longer. This will make the displacement a bit greater (longer stride) so that the work done is greater. Greater work translates to faster speed according to the work-energy theorem.

34. (a) $K = \frac{1}{2}mv^2 = \frac{1}{2}(4m)v^2 = 2mv^2$.

(b) $K = \frac{1}{2}(3m)(2v)^2 = 6mv^2$.

(c) $K = \frac{1}{2}(2m)(3v)^2 = 9mv^2$.

(d) $K = \frac{1}{2}(m)(4v)^2 = 8mv^2$.

So the answer is (a).

35. $K_o = \frac{1}{2} m v_o^2 = \frac{1}{2}(0.50 \text{ kg})(10 \text{ m/s})^2 = 25 \text{ J}.$ $K = \frac{1}{2}(0.50 \text{ kg})(5.0 \text{ m/s})^2 = 6.25 \text{ J}.$

So the kinetic energy lost $= 25 \text{ J} - 6.25 \text{ J} = \boxed{19 \text{ J}}$.

36. $W_{net} = \frac{1}{2} m v^2 - \frac{1}{2} m v_o^2 = 0 - \frac{1}{2} m v_o^2.$ $W_{net} = -f d = -\mu_k N d = -\mu_k m g d.$

So $d = \dfrac{v_o^2}{2 \mu_k g}$ independent of m. Therefore the stopping distance is $\boxed{\text{the same}}$.

37. From Exercise 5.36, $d = \dfrac{v_o^2}{2 \mu_k g}$.

For the large car: $d_1 = \dfrac{v_o^2}{2 \mu_k g}$, for the small car: $d_2 = \dfrac{(2v)^2}{2 \mu_k g} = 4 \dfrac{v_o^2}{2 \mu_k g}$.

So the distance for the $\boxed{\text{small car is four times as long}}$.

38. $90 \text{ km/h} = 25 \text{ m/s}.$

(a) $K_o = \frac{1}{2} m v^2 = \frac{1}{2}(1.2 \times 10^3 \text{ kg})(25 \text{ m/s})^2 = \boxed{3.8 \times 10^5 \text{ J}}$.

(b) $W_{net} = \frac{1}{2} m v^2 - \frac{1}{2} m v_o^2 = 0 - 3.8 \times 10^5 \text{ J} = \boxed{-3.8 \times 10^5 \text{ J}}$.

39. (a) $W_{net} = \frac{1}{2} m v^2 - \frac{1}{2} m v_o^2 = K - 0,$ ☞ $K = W_{net} = Fd = (75 \text{ N})(0.60 \text{ m}) = \boxed{45 \text{ J}}$.

(b) $K = \frac{1}{2} m v,$ ☞ $v = \sqrt{\dfrac{2K}{m}} = \sqrt{\dfrac{2(45 \text{ J})}{0.20 \text{ kg}}} = \boxed{21 \text{ m/s}}$.

40. $W_{net} = \frac{1}{2} m v^2 - \frac{1}{2} m v_o^2 = 0 - \frac{1}{2}(3.0 \times 10^{-3} \text{ kg})(350 \text{ m/s})^2 = -1.84 \times 10^2 \text{ J}.$

So $F = \dfrac{W_{net}}{d} = \dfrac{-1.84 \times 10^2 \text{ J}}{0.12 \text{ m}} = -\boxed{1.5 \times 10^3 \text{ N}}$, opposite to direction of velocity.

41. $W_{net} = \frac{1}{2} m v^2 - \frac{1}{2} m v_o^2,$

So $v = \sqrt{\dfrac{2 W_{net}}{m} + v_o^2} = \sqrt{\dfrac{2(2.5 \text{ J})}{0.60 \text{ kg}} + (3.0 \text{ m/s})^2} = \boxed{4.2 \text{ m/s}}$ in $+x$.

42. $W_{net} = \frac{1}{2} m v^2 - \frac{1}{2} m v_o^2 = 0 - \frac{1}{2} m v_o^2.$ $W_{net} = -f d.$ So $d = \dfrac{v_o^2}{2f} \propto v_o^2.$

$\dfrac{d_2}{d_1} = \dfrac{(90 \text{ km/h})^2}{(45 \text{ km/h})^2} = 4,$ ☞ $d_2 = 4 d_1 = 4(50 \text{ m}) = \boxed{200 \text{ m}}$.

43. $W = \frac{1}{2}mv^2 - \frac{1}{2}mv_o^2 = \frac{1}{2}m(v^2 - v_o^2)$, ☞ $\dfrac{W_2}{W_1} = \dfrac{(30 \text{ km/h})^2 - (20 \text{ km/h})^2}{(20 \text{ km/h})^2 - (10 \text{ km/h})^2} = 1.67$.

So $W_2 = 1.67 W_1 = 1.67(5.0 \times 10^3 \text{ J}) = \boxed{8.3 \times 10^3 \text{ J}}$.

44. (d). $U = \frac{1}{2}kx^2$, so $\Delta U = \frac{1}{2}k(x^2 - x_o^2) \propto x^2 - x_o^2$.

45. (d).

46. See diagram on the right.

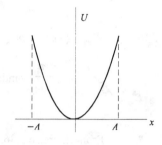

47. $U = mgh = (1.0 \text{ kg})(9.80 \text{ m/s}^2)(50 \text{ m}) = \boxed{4.9 \times 10^2 \text{ J}}$.

48. $U = \frac{1}{2}kx^2$, ☞ $x = \sqrt{\dfrac{2U}{k}} = \sqrt{\dfrac{2(1.0 \text{ J})}{45 \text{ N.m}}} = \boxed{0.21 \text{ m}}$.

49. $U = mgh$, ☞ $\Delta U = mg\Delta h = (1.0 \text{ kg})(9.80 \text{ m/s}^2)(1.5 \text{ m} - 0.90 \text{ m}) = \boxed{5.9 \text{ J}}$.

50. $U = mgh$, ☞ $\Delta U = mg\Delta h$, so $\Delta h = \dfrac{\Delta U}{mg} = \dfrac{-10 \text{ J}}{(2.0 \text{ kg})(9.80 \text{ m/s}^2)} = -0.51 \text{ m}$.

Therefore it is $\boxed{\text{lowered by 0.51 m}}$.

$\boxed{\text{No}}$, the height cannot be determined. Only the change in height Δh can be determined.

51. First find the maximum height from kinematics.

$v^2 = 0 = v_o^2 - 2gy$, ☞ $y_{max} = \dfrac{v_o^2}{2g} = \dfrac{(7.5 \text{ m/s})^2}{2(9.80 \text{ m/s}^2)} = 2.87 \text{ m}$.

(a) $U = mgh = (0.20 \text{ kg})(9.80 \text{ m/s}^2)(1.2 \text{ m} + 2.87 \text{ m}) = \boxed{8.0 \text{ J}}$.

(b) $\Delta U = mg\Delta h = (0.20 \text{ kg})(9.80 \text{ m/s}^2)(2.87 \text{ m}) = \boxed{5.6 \text{ J}}$.

52. (a) On the board: $\quad U = mgh = (60 \text{ kg})(9.80 \text{ m/s}^2)(5.0 \text{ m}) = \boxed{2.9 \times 10^3 \text{ J}}$.

At the bottom of pool: $\quad U = (60 \text{ kg})(9.80 \text{ m/s}^2)(-3.0 \text{ m}) = \boxed{-1.8 \times 10^3 \text{ J}}$.

(b) To the board: $\quad \Delta U = mg\Delta h = (60 \text{ kg})(9.80 \text{ m/s}^2)(-8.0 \text{ m} - 0) = \boxed{-4.7 \times 10^3 \text{ J}}$.

To the surface: $\quad \Delta U = (60 \text{ kg})(9.80 \text{ m/s}^2)(-3.0 \text{ m} - 5.0 \text{ m}) = \boxed{-4.7 \times 10^3 \text{ J}}$.

To the bottom of pool: $\quad \Delta U = (60 \text{ kg})(9.80 \text{ m/s}^2)(0 - 8.0 \text{ m}) = \boxed{-4.7 \times 10^3 \text{ J}}$.

53. (a) $U_b = mgh = (1.5 \text{ kg})(9.80 \text{ m/s}^2)(-3.0 \text{ m}) = \boxed{-44 \text{ J}}$,

$U_a = (1.5 \text{ kg})(9.80 \text{ m/s}^2)(4.5 \text{ m}) = \boxed{66 \text{ J}}$.

(b) To the attic:

$\Delta U = mg\Delta h = (1.5 \text{ kg})(9.80 \text{ m/s}^2)(-7.5 \text{ m} - 0) = \boxed{-1.1 \times 10^2 \text{ J}}$.

To the ground:

$\Delta U = (1.5 \text{ kg})(9.80 \text{ m/s}^2)(-3.0 \text{ m} - 4.5 \text{ m}) = \boxed{-1.1 \times 10^2 \text{ J}}$.

To the basement: $\Delta U = (1.5 \text{ kg})(9.80 \text{ m/s}^2)(0 - 7.5 \text{ m}) = \boxed{-1.1 \times 10^2 \text{ J}}$.

54. Assume the first book is already on a surface. To put the second book on top of the first, the student has to raise its center of gravity a distance of 0.020 m + 0.040 m = 0.060 m. Similarly the heights for the 3rd, 4th, 5th, and 6th books are 0.10 m, 0.14 m, 0.18m, and 0.22 m.

So the total work is $W = \Delta U = (30 \text{ N})(0.060 \text{ m} + 0.10 \text{ m} + 0.14 \text{ m} + 0.18 \text{ m} + 0.22 \text{ m}) = \boxed{21 \text{ J}}$.

55. (d).

56. (c).

57. Due to the conservation of energy, the initial potential energy is equal to the final potential energy so the final height is equal to the initial height.

58. Before starting to run, the vaulter has chemical potential energy stored in the molecules in the muscles. When the muscles contract before he runs, some of the chemical energy is converted to kinetic energy of the muscles. When he is running, he has kinetic energy. Part of that kinetic energy and some chemical potential energy in the muscles will bend the pole and store elastic potential energy in the pole. The rest of the kinetic energy and the elastic potential energy will be converted to gravitational potential energy when he is on the way up. At the maximum height, almost all the energy is in gravitational potential energy (he still has some kinetic energy due to some horizontal motion). On the way down, potential energy is converted to kinetic energy and when the vaulter lands, negative work in done on him to "consume" most of the kinetic energy. Some kinetic energy will be converted to heat and sound and cause permanent deformation on the mattress.

59. Each time you land on the trampoline, you coil your legs on the way down, then push down on the trampoline as you land, thereby compressing it more; storing more energy, you rebound and go higher. The limit is determined by the "spring constant" of the trampoline and how much you can compress it.

60.   (a) $E_o = K_o + U_o = 0 + (0.250 \text{ kg})(9.80 \text{ m/s}^2)(115 \text{ m}) = \boxed{282 \text{ J}}$.

(b) $U_1 = (0.250 \text{ kg})(9.80 \text{ m/s}^2)(115 \text{ m} - 75.0 \text{ m}) = \boxed{98.0 \text{ J}}$.

Since $E = E_o$ is conserved, $K_1 = E_o - U_1 = 282 \text{ J} - 98.0 \text{ J} = \boxed{184 \text{ J}}$.

(c) $E_2 = K_2 + 0 = \boxed{282 \text{ J}}$. $K_2 = \frac{1}{2}mv^2$,   ☞ $v = \sqrt{\dfrac{2K_2}{m}} = \dfrac{2(282 \text{ J})}{0.250 \text{ kg}} = \boxed{47.5 \text{ m/s}}$.

(d) For (a) $E_o = 0 + 0 = \boxed{0}$.

For (b) $U_1 = (0.250 \text{ kg})(9.80 \text{ m/s}^2)(-75.0 \text{ m}) = \boxed{-184 \text{ J}}$. $K_1 = 0 - (-184 \text{ J}) = \boxed{184 \text{ J}}$.

For (c) $E_2 = K_2 + U_2 = \boxed{0}$. $K_2 = 0 - (0.250 \text{ kg})(9.80 \text{ m/s}^2)(-115 \text{ m}) = 282 \text{ J}$.

So $v = \dfrac{2(282 \text{ J})}{0.250 \text{ kg}} = \boxed{47.5 \text{ m/s}}$.

61.   (a) $K_o = \frac{1}{2}mv_o^2 = \frac{1}{2}(0.300 \text{ kg})(10.0 \text{ m/s})^2 = \boxed{15.0 \text{ J}}$, $U_o = mgh_o = \boxed{0}$, $E_o = K_o + U_o = \boxed{15.0 \text{ J}}$.

(b) From the conservation of energy, $E = E_o = 15.0 \text{ J}$. $U = (0.300 \text{ kg})(9.80 \text{ m/s}^2)(2.50 \text{ m}) = 7.35 \text{ J}$.

So $K = E - U = 15.0 \text{ J} - 7.35 \text{ J} = \boxed{7.65 \text{ J}}$, $U = \boxed{7.35 \text{ J}}$, $E = \boxed{15.0 \text{ J}}$.

(c) At maximum height, $v = 0$.

So $K = \boxed{0}$, $U = \boxed{15.0 \text{ J}}$, $E = \boxed{15.0 \text{ J}}$.

62. $U = mgh$,   ☞ $h = \dfrac{U}{mg} = \dfrac{15.0 \text{ J}}{(0.300 \text{ kg})(9.80 \text{ m/s}^2)} = \boxed{5.10 \text{ m}}$.

63.   (a) The mechanical energy ($E = K + U$) is 80 J. From the conservation of energy, the potential energy at the maximum height is 80 J because the kinetic energy is zero there. At three-fourth of the distance to the maximum height, the potential energy is

$U = \frac{3}{4}(80 \text{ J}) = 60 \text{ J}$.   So $K = 80 \text{ J} - 60 \text{ J} = \boxed{20 \text{ J}}$, $U = \boxed{60 \text{ J}}$.

(b) $K = \frac{1}{2}mv^2$,   ☞ $v = \sqrt{\dfrac{2K}{m}} = \sqrt{\dfrac{2(20 \text{ J})}{0.50 \text{ kg}}} = \boxed{8.9 \text{ m/s}}$.

(c) The kinetic energy is zero at the maximum height so $U = \boxed{80 \text{ J}}$.

64. $\frac{1}{2}mv^2 + U = \frac{1}{2}mv_o^2 + U_o$,   ☞ $\frac{1}{2}mv^2 + mg(0.500 \text{ m}) = 0 + mg\,(2.00 \text{ m})$,

so $v = \sqrt{2(9.80 \text{ m/s}^2)(1.50 \text{ m})} = \boxed{5.42 \text{ m/s at bottom of swing}}$.

65. (a) $\dfrac{h_1}{h_o} = \dfrac{E_1}{E_o} = 0.820,$ ☞ $h_1 = 0.820\, h_o = (0.82)(1.25\text{ m}) = \boxed{1.03\text{ m}}.$

(b) $h_2 = 0.82\, h_1 = (0.820)(1.025\text{ m}) = \boxed{0.841\text{ m}}.$

(c) The kinetic energy of the ball must be equal to the lost mechanical energy.

$K_o = 0.180\, E_o = 0.180\,(K_o + U_o),$ ☞ $K_o = \dfrac{0.180\, U_o}{0.820} = 0.2195\, U_o = 0.2195\, mg\,(1.25\text{ m}) = \tfrac{1}{2}mv^2,$

so $v = \sqrt{2(0.2195)(9.80\text{ m/s}^2)(1.25\text{ m})} = \boxed{2.32\text{ m/s}}.$

66. Choose the bottom of the slope (point B) as the reference for height ($h_o = 0$).

$\tfrac{1}{2}mv_B^{\,2} + U_B = \tfrac{1}{2}mv_A^{\,2} + U_A,$ ☞ $\tfrac{1}{2}mv_B^{\,2} + mg(0) = \tfrac{1}{2}m(5.0\text{ m/s})^2 + mg\,(10\text{ m}),$

so $v_B = \sqrt{(5.0\text{ m/s})^2 + 2(9.80\text{ m/s}^2)(10\text{ m})} = \boxed{15\text{ m/s}}.$

67. Choose the lowest point on the course (point B) as the reference for height ($h_o = 0$).

(a) $\tfrac{1}{2}mv_B^{\,2} + U_B = \tfrac{1}{2}mv_A^{\,2} + U_A,$ ☞ $\tfrac{1}{2}mv_B^{\,2} + mg(0) = \tfrac{1}{2}m(5.0\text{ m/s})^2 + mg(5.0\text{ m}),$

so $v_B = \sqrt{(5.0\text{ m/s})^2 + 2(9.80\text{ m/s}^2)(5.0\text{ m})} = \boxed{11\text{ m/s}}.$

(b) $E_A = E_B = \tfrac{1}{2}m\,(11\text{ m/s})^2 = 60.5m.$ $E_C = mg(8.0\text{ m}) = m(9.80\text{ m/s}^2)(8.0\text{ m}) = 78.4m > E_A.$

So $\boxed{\text{no}}$, it will not reach point C.

(c) $\tfrac{1}{2}mv_A^{\,2} + mg(5.0\text{ m}) = \tfrac{1}{2}m(0)^2 + mg(8.0\text{ m}),$ ☞ $v_A = \boxed{7.7\text{ m/s}}.$

68. (a) $L - h = L\cos 25°,$ ☞ $h = L(1 - \cos 25°).$

(b) $K + U = K_o + U_o = 0 + U_o,$

so $K = U_o - U = mg\,(h_o - h) = mg\,L[(1 - \cos 25°) - (1 - \cos 9.0°)]$

$= (0.15\text{ kg})(9.80\text{ m/s}^2)(0.75\text{ m})(\cos 9.0° - \cos 25°) = \boxed{9.0 \times 10^{-2}\text{ J}}.$

(c) $K = (0.15\text{ kg})(9.80\text{ m/s}^2)(0.75\text{ m})(\cos 0° - \cos 25°) = 0.103\text{ J} = \tfrac{1}{2}mv^2,$

so $v = \sqrt{\dfrac{2(0.103\text{ J})}{0.15\text{ kg}}} = \boxed{1.2\text{ m/s}}.$

69. (a) $K = (0.15\text{ kg})(9.80\text{ m/s}^2)(0.75\text{ m})(\cos 0° - \cos 60°) = 0.551\text{ J} = \tfrac{1}{2}mv^2,$

so $v = \sqrt{\dfrac{2(0.551\text{ J})}{0.15\text{ kg}}} = \boxed{2.7\text{ m/s}}.$

(b) Final height = initial height. $h = L(1 - \cos 60°) = (0.75\text{ m})(1 - \cos 60°) = \boxed{0.38\text{ m}}.$

(c) Half the speed means $\tfrac{1}{4}$ of the kinetic energy because $K = \tfrac{1}{2}mv^2.$

$\frac{1}{4}K = \frac{1}{4}$ (0.15 kg)(9.80 m/s^2)(0.75 m)(cos 0° − cos 60°) = (0.15 kg)(9.80 m/s^2)(0.75 m)(cos 0° − cos θ).

Solving,   cos θ = 0.875,   ☞ $\theta = \boxed{29°}$.

70.   (a) $\frac{1}{2}mv^2 + U = \frac{1}{2}mv_0^2 + U_0$ ☞ $0 + \frac{1}{2}kx^2 = \frac{1}{2}mv_0^2 + 0$.

So $x = \sqrt{\dfrac{m}{k}}\, v_0 = \sqrt{\dfrac{1.5 \text{ kg}}{2.0 \times 10^3 \text{ N/m}}} \times (12 \text{ m/s}) = \boxed{0.33 \text{ m}}$.

(b) $\frac{1}{2}mv^2 + \frac{1}{2}kx^2 = \frac{1}{2}mv_0^2 + 0$,   ☞ $x = \sqrt{\dfrac{1.5 \text{ kg}}{2.0 \times 10^3 \text{ N/m}} \times [(12 \text{ m/s})^2 - (6.0 \text{ m.s})^2]} = \boxed{0.28 \text{ m}}$.

71. $W_{nc} = \Delta E = E_0 - E = [\frac{1}{2}m(5.0 \text{ m/s})^2 + mg(10 \text{ m})] - [\frac{1}{2}mv_B^2 + mg(0)]$.

So   2500 J = $[\frac{1}{2}(60 \text{ kg})(5.0 \text{ m/s})^2 + (60 \text{ kg})(9.80 \text{ m/s}^2)(10 \text{ m})] - [\frac{1}{2}(60 \text{ kg})v_B^2 + mg(0)]$.

Solving $v_B = \boxed{12 \text{ m/s}}$.

72.   (b).

73. $\boxed{\text{No, paying for energy}}$ because kWh is the unit of Power × Time = Energy.

74.   (a) $\boxed{\text{No}}$, efficiency is only a measure of how much work is done for each unit of energy input (or the ration of work output to energy input).

(b) Again, $\boxed{\text{no}}$. It depends on the amount of energy input into the machines. If the energy input is the same to two machines, then the one with a higher efficiency will do more work.

75.   They are doing the same amount of work (same mass, same height). So the $\boxed{\text{one that arrives first}}$ will have expended more power due to shorter time interval.

76.   1/4 hp = (1/4 hp) $\times \dfrac{746 \text{ W}}{1/4 \text{ hp}} = \boxed{187 \text{ W}}$.

77. $\overline{P} = \dfrac{E}{t} = \dfrac{8.4 \times 10^6 \text{ J}}{24 \times 3600 \text{ s}} = \boxed{97 \text{ W}}$.

78.   90 km/h = 25 m/s. $W = \Delta K = \frac{1}{2}mv^2 - 0$.

$\overline{P} = \dfrac{W}{t} = \dfrac{mv^2}{2t} = \dfrac{(1500 \text{ kg})(25 \text{ m/s})^2}{2(5.0 \text{ s})} = \boxed{9.4 \times 10^4 \text{ W} = 1.3 \times 10^2 \text{ hp}}$.

79. $P = \dfrac{W}{t} = \dfrac{2mgd}{t} = \dfrac{2(0.50 \text{ kg})(9.80 \text{ m/s}^2)(1.5 \text{ m})}{3 \times 24 \times 2600 \text{ s}}$) = $\boxed{5.7 \times 10^{-5} \text{ W}}$.

80.   (a) $P = \dfrac{W}{t} = \dfrac{mgd}{t} = \dfrac{(60 \text{ kg})(9.80 \text{ m/s}^2)(15 \text{ m})}{20 \text{ s}}$) = $\boxed{4.4 \times 10^{2} \text{ W}}$.

    (b) $(4.4 \times 10^{2} \text{ W}) = (4.4 \times 10^{2} \text{ W}) \times \dfrac{1 \text{ hp}}{746 \text{ W}} = \boxed{0.59 \text{ hp}}$.

81. $P = (0.45)(2.0 \text{ hp})(746 \text{ W/hp}) = 6.7 \times 10^{2} \text{ W} = 6.7 \times 10^{2} \text{ J/s}$. In one second the energy is $\boxed{6.7 \times 10^{2} \text{ J}}$.

82.   1 L of water has a mass of 1 kg.

    In one minute, $E = P\,t = (1.00 \text{ hp})(746 \text{ W/hp})(60 \text{ s}) = 4.476 \times 10^{4} \text{ J}$.

    The work required is $W = Fd = mgd = E$.

    So $m = \dfrac{E}{gd} = \dfrac{4.476 \times 10^{4} \text{ J}}{(9.80 \text{ m/s}^2)(30.0 \text{ m})} = \boxed{1.5 \times 10^{2} \text{ kg}}$.

83.   With an efficiency of 83%, the useful power is $0.83P$, where P is the power rating of the motor.

    Repeating the calculation of Exercise 5.82, $230 \text{ kg} = \dfrac{0.83P(746 \text{ W/hp})(60 \text{ s})}{(9.80 \text{ m/s}^2)(30.0 \text{ m})}$.   So $P = \boxed{1.8 \text{ hp}}$.

84.   850 km/h = 236.1 m/s.   The work required is

    $W = \Delta E = K + U = \frac{1}{2}(3.25 \times 10^{3} \text{ kg})(236.1 \text{ m/s})^2 + (3.25 \times 10^{3} \text{ kg})(9.80 \text{ m/s}^2)(10.0 \times 10^{3} \text{ m})$

      $= 4.091 \times 10^{8} \text{ J}$.

    The energy output is $E = Pt = (1500 \text{ hp})(746 \text{ W/hp})(12.5 \text{ min})(60 \text{ s/min}) = 8.393 \times 10^{8} \text{ J}$.

    So the efficiency is $\varepsilon = \dfrac{4.091}{8.393} = \boxed{48.7\%}$.

85.   (a) $\Sigma F_x = F - f - mg \sin\theta = 0$,

    so $F = f + mg \sin\theta = 950 \text{ N} + (120 \text{ kg})(9.80 \text{ m/s}^2) \sin 15° = 1254 \text{ N}$.

    Also $v = 5.0 \text{ km/h} = 1.389 \text{ m/s}$.

    So $P = Fv = (1254 \text{ N})(1.389 \text{ m/s}) = 1742 \text{ W} = \boxed{2.3 \text{ hp}}$.

    $\boxed{\text{The horse is working hard}}$ (it is working as hard as 2.3 horses. In spurts a

    horse can be more than 1 hp).

    (b) 20 km/h = 5.556 m/s. $a = \dfrac{5.556 \text{ m/s} - 1.389 \text{ m/s}}{5.0 \text{ s}} = 0.833 \text{ m/s}^2$.

    Now $\Sigma F_x = F - f - mg \sin\theta = ma$,   ☞ $F = 1254 \text{ N} + (120 \text{ kg})(0.833 \text{ m/s}^2) = 1354 \text{ N}$.

    $P = (1354 \text{ N})(5.556 \text{ m/s}) = 7522 \text{ W} = \boxed{10 \text{ hp}}$.

c

86. $K = \frac{1}{2}mv^2$,   ☞ $v = \sqrt{\dfrac{2K}{m}} = \sqrt{\dfrac{2(8.00 \times 10^{-17} \text{ J})}{9.11 \times 10^{-31} \text{ kg}}} = \boxed{1.33 \times 10^7 \text{ m/s}}$.

87.   Power input $= \dfrac{1.5 \text{ hp}}{0.75} = 2.0 \text{ hp} = 2(746 \text{ W}) = 1492 \text{ W} = 1.492 \text{ kW}$.

     $E = Pt = (1.492 \text{ kW})(2.0 \text{ h}) = 2.984 \text{ kWh}$.   So it costs $(2.984 \text{ kWh})(\$0.12 / \text{kWh}) = \boxed{\$0.36}$.

88. $W_{\text{nc}} = K_o + U_o - K - U = 0 + mgh_o - \frac{1}{2}mv^2 - 0 = (28 \text{ kg})(9.80 \text{ m/s}^2)(3.0 \text{ m}) - \frac{1}{2}(28 \text{ kg})(2.5 \text{ m/s})^2$

     $= \boxed{7.4 \times 10^2 \text{ J}}$.

89. $W = F \cos\theta\, d = (40 \text{ N}) \cos 25° (0.35 \text{ m}) = \boxed{13 \text{ J}}$.

90. $W_{0\text{-}1} = \frac{1}{2}k(x_1^2 - x_o^2) = \frac{1}{2}(50 \text{ N/m})[(0.10 \text{ m})^2 - 0] = 0.25 \text{ J}$,

     $W_{1\text{-}2} = \frac{1}{2}k(x_2^2 - x_1^2) = \frac{1}{2}(50 \text{ N/m})[(0.20 \text{ m})^2 - (0.10 \text{ m})^2] = 0.75 \text{ J}$.

     So the answer is $\boxed{\text{yes, 0.50 J more}}$.

91.   (a) $F = f_k = \mu_k N = \mu_k mg = 0.25(120 \text{ kg})(9.80 \text{ m/s}^2) = 294 \text{ N}$.

     $W_F = Fd = (294 \text{ N})(750 \text{ m}) = \boxed{+2.2 \times 10^5 \text{ J}}$.

     (b) $W_f = F \cos 180° \, d = - (294 \text{ N})(750 \text{ m}) = \boxed{-2.2 \times 10^5 \text{ J}}$.

92.   First calculate the speed at the bottom of the slide from conservation of mechanical energy.

     Choose bottom of the slide as $h_o = 0$. $\frac{1}{2}mv^2 + U = \frac{1}{2}mv_o^2 + U_o$,   ☞ $\frac{1}{2}mv^2 + 0 = 0 + mgh$,

     so $v = \sqrt{2gh} = \sqrt{2(9.80 \text{ m/s}^2)(4.0 \text{ m})} = 8.85 \text{ m/s}$.

     Now the slider is a horizontal projectile with $y = -1.5$ m.

     The time of flight is from: $y = v_{yo}t - \frac{1}{2}gt^2 = -\frac{1}{2}gt^2$,

     so $t = \sqrt{-\dfrac{2y}{g}} = \sqrt{-\dfrac{2(-1.5 \text{ m})}{9.80 \text{ m/s}^2}} = 0.553 \text{ s}$.

     Therefore $x = (8.85)(0.553 \text{ s}) = \boxed{4.9 \text{ m}}$. $\boxed{\text{No, it is independent of mass}}$.

93.   (a) Refer to Figure 5.30 and Exercise 5.68. $\theta = \sin^{-1}\left(\dfrac{1.8}{4.0}\right) = 26.7°$.

     So $h = L(1 - \cos\theta) = (4.0 \text{ m})(1 - \cos 26.7°) = 0.427 \text{ m}$. $\frac{1}{2}mv^2 + U = \frac{1}{2}mv_o^2 + U_o$,

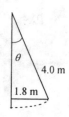

or $\quad 0 + mgh = \frac{1}{2}mv_o^2 + 0$. $\quad$ So $\quad v_o = \sqrt{2gh} = \sqrt{2(9.80 \text{ m/s}^2)(0.427 \text{ m})} = 2.9 \text{ m/s}$.

Therefore the speed has to be $\boxed{\text{at least 2.9 m/s}}$.

(b) $\boxed{\text{Yes, if starting with } v_o < 2.9 \text{ m/s}}$ because of insufficient energy.

94. (a) $20.0 \times 0.278 \text{ m/s} = 5.56 \text{ m/s}$. $\quad P = Fv = (700 \text{ N})(5.556 \text{ m/s}) = 3892 \text{ W}$.

$W = Pt = (3892 \text{ W})(3.50 \text{ min})(60 \text{ s/min}) = \boxed{8.17 \times 10^5 \text{ J}}$.

(b) As in (a) $P = \boxed{3.90 \times 10^3 \text{ W}}$.

95. (a) $K = \frac{1}{2}mv^2$, $\quad \mathbb{G} \quad \dfrac{v_2}{v_1} = \sqrt{\dfrac{m_1}{m_2}} = \dfrac{1}{\sqrt{3}}$. $\quad$ So $\quad v_2 = \dfrac{1}{\sqrt{3}}(90 \text{ km/h}) = \boxed{52 \text{ km/h} = 14 \text{ m/s}}$.

(b) $\frac{1}{2}\left(\frac{1}{2}m_1v_1^2\right) = \frac{1}{2}m_2v_2^2$, $\quad \mathbb{G} \quad v_2 = \sqrt{\dfrac{m_1}{2\,m_2}}\,v_1 = \dfrac{1}{\sqrt{6}}(90 \text{ km/h}) = \boxed{37 \text{ km/h} = 10 \text{ m/s}}$.

96. (a) Choose the stopped position as $h = 0$ and assume the ball compresses the spring by x. Then the initial height $h_o = (1.20 \text{ m} + x)$ high. From conservation of mechanical energy:

$mgh_o + 0 = 0 + \frac{1}{2}kx^2$, so $mg(1.20 \text{ m} + x) = \frac{1}{2}kx^2$, $\quad \mathbb{G} \quad 175x^2 - 3.53x - 4.23 = 0$.

Solving, $\quad x = \boxed{0.166 \text{ m}}$ or -0.150 m. The $-$ answer has no physical meaning.

(b) $mg(1.20 \text{ m} + 0.0500 \text{ m}) = \frac{1}{2}k(0.0500 \text{ m})^2 + \frac{1}{2}m\,v^2$,

or $\quad 4.41 \text{ J} = 0.438 \text{ J} + \frac{1}{2}(0.360 \text{ kg})\,v^2$, $\quad \mathbb{G} \quad v = \boxed{4.70 \text{ m/s}}$.

97. $E_{\text{top}} = 0 + mg(25 \text{ m}) = 25mg \text{ J} = 245m \text{ J}$. $\quad E_{\text{bottom}} = \frac{1}{2}m(20 \text{ m/s})^2 + 0 = 200m \text{ J}$.

So because $\quad E_{\text{top}} > E_{\text{bottom}}$, it is $\boxed{\text{not conserved}}$.

98. (a) $P = Fv$, $\quad \mathbb{G} \quad v = \dfrac{P}{F} = \dfrac{50 \text{ W}}{30 \text{ N}} = \boxed{1.7 \text{ m/s}}$.

(b) $W = Pt = (50 \text{ W})(2.5 \text{ s}) = \boxed{1.3 \times 10^2 \text{ W}}$.

99. (a) $P = \dfrac{W}{t} = \dfrac{Fd}{t} = \dfrac{mgd}{t} = \dfrac{(70 \text{ kg})(9.80 \text{ m/s}^2)(8.0 \text{ m})}{10 \text{ s}} = \boxed{5.5 \times 10^2 \text{ W}}$.

(b) $(5.5 \times 10^2 \text{ W}) \times \dfrac{1 \text{ hp}}{746 \text{ W}} = \boxed{0.74 \text{ hp}}$.

CHAPTER 6

MOMENTUM AND COLLISIONS

1.   (b).

2.   (c).

3.   No , mass is also a factor since momentum is mass times velocity.

4.   (a) 90 km/h = 25 m/s. $p = mv = (60 \text{ kg})(25 \text{ m/s}) = \boxed{1.5 \times 10^3 \text{ kg·m/s}}$.

      (b) The relative velocity is zero, so $p = \boxed{0}$.

5. $p = mv,$ ☞ $m = \dfrac{p}{v} = \dfrac{7.5 \times 10^2 \text{ kg·m/s}}{10 \text{ m/s}} = \boxed{75 \text{ kg}}$.

6.   (a) $p = mv = (7.1 \text{ kg})(12 \text{ m/s}) = \boxed{85 \text{ kg·m/s}}$.

      (b) 90 km/h = 25 m/s. $p = (1200 \text{ kg})(25 \text{ m/s}) = \boxed{3.0 \times 10^4 \text{ kg·m/s}}$.

7.   Running back: $p = mv = (70 \text{ kg})(8.5 \text{ m/s}) = 595 \text{ kg·m/s}$.

      Lineman: $p = (120 \text{ kg})(5.0 \text{ m/s}) = 600 \text{ kg·m/s}$.

      So the lineman has more momentum.

8.   90 km/h = 25 m/s. $p = m_1 v_1 = m_2 v_2,$ ☞ $v_2 = \dfrac{m_1 v_1}{m_2} = \dfrac{(1500 \text{ kg})(25 \text{ m/s})}{1200 \text{ kg}} = \boxed{31 \text{ m/s}}$.

9. $K = \frac{1}{2} mv^2 = \dfrac{m^2 v^2}{2m} = \dfrac{p^2}{2m} = \dfrac{(12 \text{ kg·m/s})^2}{2(3.0 \text{ kg})} = \boxed{24 \text{ J}}$.

10.   Since the ball moves in the opposite direction, $v = -34.7$ m/s   and $v_o = 4.50$ m/s.

      $\Delta p = mv - mv_o = (0.150 \text{ kg})(-34.7 \text{ m/s}) - (0.150 \text{ kg})(4.50 \text{ m/s}) = -5.88 \text{ kg·m/s}$

          $= \boxed{5.88 \text{ kg·m/s in the direction opposite } v_o}$.

11.   Since the bullet moves in the opposite direction, $v = -120$ m/s   and $v_o = 150$ m/s.

      $\Delta p = mv - mv_o = (0.0150 \text{ kg})(-120 \text{ m/s}) - (0.0150 \text{ kg})(150 \text{ m/s}) = -4.05 \text{ kg·m/s}$

          $= \boxed{4.05 \text{ kg·m/s in the direction opposite } v_o}$.

12. Since they approach each other, $v_1 = 340$ m/s and $v_2 = -450$ m/s.

$P = p_1 + p_2 = (1.67 \times 10^{-27}$ kg$)(340$ m/s $- 450$ m/s$) = -1.84 \times 10^{-25}$ kg·m/s

$= \boxed{1.84 \times 10^{-25} \text{ kg·m/s in the direction of the faster proton}}$.

13. (a) $p = mv = m(v_o - gt) = (0.50$ kg$)[0 - (9.80$ m/s$^2)(0.75$ s$)] = -1.8$ kg·m/s $= \boxed{3.7 \text{ kg·m/s down}}$.

(b) $v^2 = v_o^2 - 2gy = 0 - 2(9.80$ m/s$^2)(-10$ m$) = 196$ m^2/s^2, ☞ $v = -14$ m/s.

So $p = (0.50$ kg$)(-14$ m/s$) = -7.0$ kg·m/s $= \boxed{7.0 \text{ kg·m/s down}}$.

14. (a) 36 km/h = 10 m/s. $p = mv = (1.29$ kg/m$^3)(1.0$ m$^3)(10$ m/s$) = \boxed{13 \text{ kg·m/s}}$.

(b) 74 mi/h = 33.1 m/s. $p = (1.29$ kg/m$^3)(1.0$ m$^3)(33.1$ m/s$) = \boxed{43 \text{ kg·m/s}}$.

15. $P = p_1 + p_2 = \pm 350$ kg·m/s. It can be either positive or negative because the Exercise does not specify the direction of the momentum.

± 350 kg·m/s $= (70$ kg$)(2.0$ m/s$) + (60$ kg$)v_2$, ☞ $v_2 = +3.5$ m/s or -8.2 m/s.

The velocity of the light runner is $\boxed{3.5 \text{ m/s in the same direction or 8.2 m/s in the opposite direction}}$.

16. $\Delta p_x = m\Delta v_x = (0.20$ kg$)[(15$ m/s$) \sin 60° - (15$ m/s$) \sin 60°] = 0$,

$\Delta p_y = m\Delta v_y = (0.20$ kg$)[-(15$ m/s$) \cos 60° - (15$ m/s$) \cos 60°] = -3.0$ kg·m/s.

So $\Delta \mathbf{p} = \boxed{(-3.0 \text{ kg·m/s) } \hat{\mathbf{y}}}$.

17. $\Delta p_x = m\Delta v_x = (0.20$ kg$)[(10$ m/s$) \sin 50° - (15$ m/s$) \sin 60°] = -1.1$ kg·m/s,

$\Delta p_y = m\Delta v_y = (0.20$ kg$)[-(10$ m/s$) \cos 50° - (15$ m/s$) \cos 60°] = -2.8$ kg·m/s.

So $\Delta \mathbf{p} = \boxed{(-1.1 \text{ kg·m/s) } \hat{\mathbf{x}} + (-2.8 \text{ kg·m/s) } \hat{\mathbf{y}}}$.

18. $\bar{F} = \dfrac{\Delta p}{\Delta t} = \dfrac{mv - mv_o}{\Delta t} = \dfrac{(10 \text{ kg})(4.0 \text{ m/s} - 0)}{2.5 \text{ s}} = \boxed{16 \text{ N}}$.

19. $v_o = 3.0$ km/h = 0.833 m/s.

$\bar{F} = \dfrac{\Delta p}{\Delta t} = \dfrac{mv - mv_o}{\Delta t} = \dfrac{(5.0 \times 10^3 \text{ kg})(0 - 0.833 \text{ m/s})}{0.64 \text{ s}} = -\boxed{6.5 \times 10^3 \text{ N}}$.

20.   First calculate the speed of the ball hitting the ground.

$v^2 = v_0^2 - 2gy = (0)^2 - 2(9.80 \text{ m/s}^2)(-15 \text{ m}) = 294 \text{ m}^2/\text{s}^2$, so $v = -17.1$ m/s.

For the impact $\bar{F} = \dfrac{\Delta p}{\Delta t} = \dfrac{mv - mv_0}{\Delta t} = \dfrac{(2.0 \text{ kg})[0 - (-17.1 \text{ m/s})]}{0.50 \text{ s}} = \boxed{68 \text{ N}}$.

21.   The final velocity is equal in magnitude but opposite in direction to the initial velocity.

(a) $\Delta p = m\Delta v = m(v - v_0) = m(-v_0 - v_0) = -2mv_0 = -2(120 \text{ lb}) \times \dfrac{1 \text{ kg}}{2.2 \text{ lb}} \times (4.50 \text{ m/s}) = \boxed{-491 \text{ kg·m/s}}$.

(b) $\boxed{\text{Yes}}$. $v^2 = v_0^2 - 2gy = (4.50 \text{ m/s})^2 - 2(9.80 \text{ m/s}^2)(-0.25 \text{ m}) = 25.15 \text{ m}^2/\text{s}^2$, ☞ $v = -5.01$ m/s.

So $\Delta p = (120 \text{ lb}) \times \dfrac{1 \text{ kg}}{2.2 \text{ lb}} \times (-5.01 \text{ m/s} - 4.50 \text{ m/s}) = \boxed{-519 \text{ kg·m/s}}$.

22.   (c).

23.   According to the impulse momentum theorem ($\bar{F}\Delta t = \Delta p = mv - mv_0$), a shorter contact time will result in a greater force if all other factors (m, v_0, v) remain the same.

24.   (a) Drive: large impulse (large $\bar{F}$ and Δt); chip shot: small impulse (small $\bar{F}$ and Δt).
        (b) Jab: small impulse (small $\bar{F}$ and Δt); knock-out punch: large impulse (large $\bar{F}$ and Δt).
        (c) Bunting: small impulse (small F and Δt); home-run swing: large impulse (large $\bar{F}$ and Δt).

25.   In both (a) and (b), it is $\boxed{\text{to increase contact time}}$ Δt so to reduce the average force F because

$\bar{F}\Delta t = \Delta p = mv - mv_0$. It can also decrease the pressure on the body because the force is spread over a larger area.

26.   Consider the horizontal motion.

$\bar{F}\Delta t = mv - mv_0 = mv$, ☞ $v = \dfrac{\bar{F}\Delta t}{m} = \dfrac{3.0 \text{ N·s}}{0.20 \text{ kg}} = \boxed{15 \text{ m/s}}$.

27. $\bar{F}\Delta t = mv - mv_0 = -mv_0$, ☞ $\bar{F} = -\dfrac{mv_0}{\Delta t} = -\dfrac{3.0 \times 10^4 \text{ kg·m/s}}{5.0 \text{ s}} = -\boxed{6.0 \times 10^3 \text{ N}}$.

28. $\bar{F}\Delta t = mv - mv_0 = mv$, ☞ $v = \dfrac{\bar{F}\Delta t}{m} = \dfrac{3.2 \text{ N·s}}{0.25 \text{ kg}} = \boxed{13 \text{ m/s}}$.

29. (a) $\bar{F}\Delta t = mv - mv_0 = -mv_0,$ ☞ $\bar{F} = -\dfrac{mv_0}{\Delta t} = -\dfrac{(0.35\text{ kg})(10\text{ m/s})}{3.0\times 10^{-3}\text{ s}} = \boxed{-1.2\times 10^3\text{ N}}.$

(b) $\bar{F} = -\dfrac{mv_0}{\Delta t} = -\dfrac{(0.35\text{ kg})(10\text{ m/s})}{0.30\times 10^{-3}\text{ s}} = \boxed{-1.2\times 10^4\text{ N}}.$

30. 1 liter of water has a mass of 1 kg. Assume $v_0 = 0.$

$v^2 = v_0^2 - 2gy = 0 - 2(9.80\text{ m/s}^2)(-7.0\text{ m}) = 13726\text{ m}^2/\text{s}^2.$ ☞ $v = -11.7\text{ m/s}.$

$\bar{F} = \dfrac{\Delta p}{\Delta t} = \dfrac{mv - mv_0}{\Delta t} = \dfrac{m}{\Delta t}(v - v_0) = (3.0\text{ kg/s})(-11.7\text{ m/s} - 0) = \boxed{-35\text{ N}}.$

31. The final velocity is opposite to the initial velocity ("hits it back").

$\bar{F} = \dfrac{\Delta p}{\Delta t} = \dfrac{mv - mv_0}{\Delta t} = \dfrac{(0.45\text{ kg})(-7.0\text{ m/s} - 4.0\text{ m/s})}{0.040\text{ s}} = -1.2\times 10^2\text{ N}.$

So it is $\boxed{1.2\times 10^2\text{ N in the direction opposite } v_0}.$

32. The final velocity is opposite to the initial velocity ("rebounds").

$\bar{F} = \dfrac{\Delta p}{\Delta t} = \dfrac{mv - mv_0}{\Delta t} = \dfrac{(1.0\text{ kg})(-13\text{ m/s} - 15\text{ m/s})}{0.020\text{ s}} = -1.4\times 10^3\text{ N}.$

So it is $\boxed{1.4\times 10^3\text{ N in the direction opposite } v_0}.$

33. $\bar{F}\Delta t = mv - mv_0 = -mv_0,$ ☞ $\bar{F} = -\dfrac{mv_0}{\Delta t}.$ So the magnitude is $\dfrac{mv_0}{\Delta t}.$

$\bar{F}_1 = \dfrac{(0.16\text{ kg})(25\text{ m/s})}{3.5\times 10^{-3}\text{ s}} = \boxed{1.1\times 10^3\text{ N}};$ $\bar{F}_2 = \dfrac{(0.16\text{ kg})(25\text{ m/s})}{8.5\times 10^{-3}\text{ s}} = \boxed{4.7\times 10^3\text{ N}}.$

34. (a) Impulse = area of the trapezoid $= \frac{1}{2}(0.30\text{ s} + 0.14\text{ s})(900\text{ N}) = \boxed{77\text{ N·s}}.$

(b) $\bar{F} = \dfrac{\text{impulse}}{\Delta t} = \dfrac{76.5\text{ N·s}}{0.14\text{ s}} = \boxed{5.5\times 10^2\text{ N}}.$

(c) $\bar{F}\Delta t = mv - mv_0,$ ☞ $v = v_0 + \dfrac{\bar{F}\Delta t}{m} = -6.0\text{ m/s} + \dfrac{76.5\text{ N·s}}{3.0\text{ kg}} = \boxed{20\text{ m/s}}.$

35. The velocity of the putty right before impact is (from energy conservation)

$v = -\sqrt{2gh} = -\sqrt{2(9.80\text{ m/s}^2)(2.5\text{ m})} = -7.0\text{ m/s}.$

$\bar{F}\Delta t = mv - mv_0 = -mv_0,$ ☞ $\bar{F} = -\dfrac{mv_0}{\Delta t} = -\dfrac{(0.35\text{ kg})(-7.0\text{ m/s})}{0.30\text{ s}} = \boxed{8.2\text{ N upward}}.$

36. $\bar{F}\Delta t = \Delta p = -3.0\text{ kg·m/s},$ ☞ $\bar{F} = \dfrac{-3.0\text{ N·s}}{0.010\text{ s}} = \boxed{-3.0\times 10^2\text{ N}}.$

37.   40 km/h = 11.1 m/s,   240 lb = 1068 N. The force on the infant is opposite to velocity.

$$F\Delta t = mv - mv_0, \quad \Rightarrow \quad \Delta t = \frac{mv - mv_0}{F} = \frac{(5.5 \text{ kg})(0 - 11.1 \text{ m/s})}{-1068 \text{ N}} = \boxed{0.057 \text{ s}}.$$

38.   (d).

39.   Air moves backwards and the boat moves forward according to momentum conservation. If a sail were installed behind the fan on the boat, the boat would not go forward because the forces between the fan and the sail are internal forces of the system.

40.   (a).

41.   Throw something or even blow a strong breath of air out of your mouth.

42.   According to the conservation of momentum, the astronaut moves in the opposite direction.

$m_1 = 0.50 \text{ kg}, \quad m_2 = 60 \text{ kg}, \quad v_{1o} = 0, \quad v_{2o} = 0, \quad v_1 = 10 \text{ m/s}, \quad v_2 = ?.$

$\mathbf{P_o} = \mathbf{P}, \quad \Rightarrow \quad m_1 v_{1o} + m_2 v_{2o} = m_1 v_1 + m_2 v_2.$

$$v_2 = \frac{m_1 v_{1o} + m_2 v_{2o} - m_1 v_1}{m_2} = \frac{0 + 0 - (0.50 \text{ kg})(10 \text{ m/s})}{60 \text{ kg}} = \boxed{0.083 \text{ m/s}}.$$

43. $m_1 = 45 \text{ kg}, \quad m_2 = 65 \text{ kg}, \quad v_{1o} = 0, v_{2o} = 0, \quad v_1 = 1.5 \text{ m/s}, \quad v_2 = ?$

$\mathbf{P_o} = \mathbf{P}, \quad \Rightarrow \quad m_1 v_{1o} + m_2 v_{2o} = m_1 v_1 + m_2 v_2.$

$$v_2 = \frac{m_1 v_{1o} + m_2 v_{2o} - m_1 v_1}{m_2} = \frac{0 + 0 - (45 \text{ kg})(1.5 \text{ m/s})}{65 \text{ kg}} = -1.0 \text{ m/s} = \boxed{1.0 \text{ m/s westward}}.$$

44. $m_1 = 0.150 \text{ kg}, \quad m_2 = 70.0 \text{ kg}, \quad v_{1o} = 0, \quad v_{2o} = 0, \quad v_1 = 2.00 \text{ m/s}, \quad v_2 = ?$

$\mathbf{P_o} = \mathbf{P}, \quad \Rightarrow \quad m_1 v_{1o} + m_2 v_{2o} = m_1 v_1 + m_2 v_2.$

$$v_2 = \frac{m_1 v_{1o} + m_2 v_{2o} - m_1 v_1}{m_2} = \frac{0 + 0 - (0.150 \text{ kg})(2.00 \text{ m/s})}{70.0 \text{ kg}} = -4.29 \times 10^{-3} \text{ m/s}.$$

Therefore it takes $\dfrac{5.00 \text{ m}}{4.29 \times 10^{-3} \text{ m/s}} = \boxed{1.17 \times 10^{3} \text{ s} = 19.5 \text{ min}}.$

45.   From momentum conservation $\mathbf{P_o} = \mathbf{P}$: $(0.100 \text{ kg})(250 \text{ m/s}) + (14.9 \text{ kg})(0) = (0.100 \text{ kg} + 14.9 \text{ kg})v,$

we have $v = \boxed{1.67 \text{ m/s}}$ in the original direction of the bullet.

46.　　Apply momentum conservation $P_0 = P$

　　　in x axis:　$(2.0 \text{ kg})(0) = (0.50 \text{ kg})(-2.8 \text{ m/s}) + (1.3 \text{ kg})(0) + (1.2 \text{ kg})v_x$,　☞　$v_x = 1.17 \text{ m/s}$;

　　　in y axis:　$(3.0 \text{ kg})(0) = (0.50 \text{ kg})(0) + (1.3 \text{ kg})(-1.5 \text{ m/s}) + (1.2 \text{ kg})v_y$,　☞　$v_y = 1.63 \text{ m/s}$.

　　　So　$v = \sqrt{(1.17 \text{ m/s})^2 + (1.63 \text{ m/s})^2} = \boxed{2.0 \text{ m/s}}$,　$\theta = \tan^{-1}\left(\dfrac{1.63}{1.17}\right) = \boxed{54° \text{ above } +x \text{ axis}}$.

47.　　Apply momentum conservation $P_0 = P$ in x axis:

　　　$(3.0 \text{ kg})(2.5 \text{ m/s}) = (0.50 \text{ kg})(-2.8 \text{ m/s}) + (1.3 \text{ kg})(0) + (1.2 \text{ kg})v_x$,　☞　$v_x = 7.42 \text{ m/s}$;

　　　so　$v = \sqrt{(7.42 \text{ m/s})^2 + (1.63 \text{ m/s})^2} = \boxed{7.6 \text{ m/s}}$,　$\theta = \tan^{-1}\left(\dfrac{1.63}{7.42}\right) = \boxed{12° \text{ above } +x \text{ axis}}$.

48.　　$m_1 = m_2 = m$ (identical),　$v_1 = v_2 = v$ (coupling).

　　　$P_0 = P$,　☞　$m_1 v_{1o} + m_2 v_{2o} = (m_1 + m_2)v$,　so　$v = \dfrac{m_1 v_{1o} + m_2 v_{2o}}{m_1 + m_2} = \dfrac{v_{1o} + v_{2o}}{2}$.

　　　(a) $v = \dfrac{90 \text{ km/h} + 0}{2} = \boxed{45 \text{ km/h}}$ in the direction of moving car.

　　　(b) $v = \dfrac{120 \text{ km/h} - 90 \text{ km/h}}{2} = \boxed{15 \text{ km/h}}$ in the direction of faster car.

　　　(c) $v = \dfrac{90 \text{ km/h} + 120 \text{ km/h}}{2} = \boxed{105 \text{ km/h}}$ in the same direction as initial motion.

49.　　$m_1 = 1200 \text{ kg}$, $m_2 = 1500 \text{ kg}$,　$v_{1o} = 25 \text{ m/s}$,　$v_1 = v_2 = v$? (coupling)

　　　$P_0 = P$,　☞　$m_1 v_{1o} + m_2 v_{2o} = (m_1 + m_2)v$,　so　$v = \dfrac{m_1 v_{1o} + m_2 v_{2o}}{m_1 + m_2}$.

　　　(a) $v = \dfrac{(1200 \text{ kg})(25 \text{ m/s}) + (0)}{1200 \text{ kg} + 1500 \text{ kg}} = \boxed{11 \text{ m/s to the right}}$.

　　　(b) $v = \dfrac{(1200 \text{ kg})(25 \text{ m/s}) + (1500 \text{ kg})(20 \text{ m/s})}{1200 \text{ kg} + 1500 \text{ kg}} = \boxed{22 \text{ m/s to the right}}$.

　　　(c) $v = \dfrac{(1200 \text{ kg})(25 \text{ m/s}) + (1500 \text{ kg})(-20 \text{ m/s})}{1200 \text{ kg} + 1500 \text{ kg}} = \boxed{0}$ or at rest.

50.　　$m_1 = 0.010 \text{ kg}$,　$m_2 = 3.0 \text{ kg}$,　$v = 3.0 \text{ kg}$,　$v_{1o} = 400 \text{ m/s}$,　$v_{2o} = 0$,　$v_1 = 300 \text{ m/s}$,　$v_2 = ?$

　　　$P_0 = P$,　☞　$m_1 v_{1o} + m_2 v_{2o} = m_1 v_1 + m_2 v_2$.

　　　$v_2 = \dfrac{m_1 v_{1o} + m_2 v_{2o} - m_1 v_1}{m_2} = \dfrac{(0.010 \text{ kg})(400 \text{ m/s}) + 0 - (0.010 \text{ kg})(300 \text{ m/s})}{3.0 \text{ kg}} = \boxed{0.33 \text{ m/s}}$.

51.　　$p_0 = mv_0 = p = m'v$,　☞　$v = \dfrac{m v_0}{m'} = \dfrac{(1600 \text{ kg})(2.5 \text{ m/s})}{1600 \text{ kg} + 3500 \text{ kg}} = \boxed{0.78 \text{ m/s}}$.

52.　90.0 km/h = 25.0 m/s.

First find the horizontal velocity of the "other" segment at top of the trajectory (explosion).

Apply momentum conservation $\mathbf{P_o} = \mathbf{P}$ in the horizontal direction.

$$m(25.0 \text{ m/s}) \cos 60.0° = \frac{m}{2}(0) + \frac{m}{2}v_x, \quad ☞ \quad v_x = 25.0 \text{ m/s}.$$

Now the "other" segment will undergo a horizontal projectile motion with $v_{xo} = 25.0$ m/s from a height of

$$y_{max} = \frac{(v_o \sin\theta)^2}{2g} = \frac{(25.0 \text{ m/s})^2 \sin^2 60.0°}{2(9.80 \text{ m/s}^2)} = 23.916 \text{ m} \quad (\text{from } v_y^2 = v_{yo}^2 - 2gy).$$

The time of flight is $t = \sqrt{-\dfrac{2y}{g}} = \sqrt{-\dfrac{2(-23.916 \text{ m})}{9.80 \text{ m/s}^2}} = 2.209 \text{ s} \quad (\text{from } y = v_o t - \frac{1}{2}gt^2).$

So $x = v_{xo}t = (25.0 \text{ m/s})(2.209 \text{ s}) = 55.23$ m, which is the horizontal distance from explosion to landing.

The horizontal distance from the gun to explosion is $x' = (25.0 \text{ m/s}) \cos 60° (2.209 \text{ s}) = 27.62$ m.

Therefore the horizontal distance from the gun to the landing is $x + x' = \boxed{82.8 \text{ m}}$.

53.　First use energy conservation to find the velocity of the bullet and the bob right after collision from the swing motion. The velocity right after the collision is the same as the velocity at the start of the swing.

So $\frac{1}{2}(m + M)v^2 + (m + M)g(0) = \frac{1}{2}(m + M)(0)^2 + (m + M)g(h), \quad ☞ \quad v = \sqrt{2gh}.$

Now apply momentum conservation $\mathbf{P_o} = \mathbf{P}. \quad mv_o + M(0) = (m + M)v = (m + M)\sqrt{2gh},$

so $v_o = \dfrac{m + M}{m} \sqrt{2gh}.$

54.　(c).

55.　(a).

56.　(c).

57.　$\boxed{\text{Momentum is a vector and kinetic energy is a scalar}}$. For example, two objects of equal mass traveling with the same speed in opposite directions have positive total kinetic energy but zero total momentum. After they collide inelastically, both stop, resulting in zero total kinetic energy and zero total momentum. Therefore kinetic energy is lost and momentum is conserved.

58.　$v_1 = \dfrac{m_1 - m_2}{m_1 + m_2} v_{1o} = \dfrac{4.0 \text{ kg} - 2.0 \text{ kg}}{4.0 \text{ kg} + 2.0 \text{ kg}} (4.0 \text{ m/s}) = \boxed{+1.3 \text{ m/s}}.$

$v_2 = \dfrac{2m_1}{m_1 + m_2} v_{1o} = \dfrac{2(4.0 \text{ kg})}{4.0 \text{ kg} + 2.0 \text{ kg}} (4.0 \text{ m/s}) = \boxed{+5.3 \text{ m/s}}.$

59. $v_1 = \dfrac{m_1 - m_2}{m_1 + m_2} v_{1o} = \dfrac{0.10 \text{ kg} - 5.0 \text{ kg}}{0.10 \text{ kg} + 5.0 \text{ kg}} (0.50 \text{ m/s}) = \boxed{-0.48 \text{ m/s}}$.

$v_2 = \dfrac{2m_1}{m_1 + m_2} v_{1o} = \dfrac{2(0.10 \text{ kg})}{0.10 \text{ kg} + 5.0 \text{ kg}} (0.50 \text{ m/s}) = \boxed{0.020 \text{ m/s}}$.

60. $K_o = \frac{1}{2} m v_o^2$ and $K = \frac{1}{2} m \left(\dfrac{v_o}{2}\right)^2 + \frac{1}{2} m \left(\dfrac{v_o}{2}\right)^2 = \frac{1}{4} m v_o^2$.

So kinetic energy is not conserved. Therefore it can not happen.

However momentum is conserved. $mv_o = m \dfrac{v_o}{2} + m \dfrac{v_o}{2} = mv_o$.

61. $v_p = \dfrac{m_p - m_a}{m_p + m_a} v_{po} = \dfrac{m - 4m}{m + 4m} (3.0 \times 10^6 \text{ m/s}) = \boxed{-1.8 \times 10^6 \text{ m/s}}$.

$v_a = \dfrac{2m_p}{m_p + m_a} v_{ao} = \dfrac{2m}{m + 4m} (3.0 \times 10^6 \text{ m/s}) = \boxed{1.2 \times 10^6 \text{ m/s}}$

62. First find the velocity of the 6.0-kilogram ball right after collision from momentum conservation $\mathbf{P_o} = \mathbf{P}$.

$m_1 = 2.0 \text{ kg}$, $m_2 = 6.0 \text{ kg}$, $v_{1o} = 12 \text{ m/s}$, $v_{2o} = -4.0 \text{ m/s}$ ("toward each other"),

$v_1 = -8.0 \text{ m/s}$ ("recoil").

$(2.0 \text{ kg})(12 \text{ m/s}) + (6.0 \text{ kg})(-4.0 \text{ m/s}) = (2.0 \text{ kg})(-8.0 \text{ m/s}) + (6.0 \text{ kg})v_2$, ☞ $v_2 = 2.67 \text{ m/s}$.

$K_o = \frac{1}{2}(2.0 \text{ kg})(12 \text{ m/s})^2 + \frac{1}{2}(6.0 \text{ kg})(4.0 \text{ m/s})^2 = 192 \text{ J}$;

$K = \frac{1}{2}(2.0 \text{ kg})(8.0 \text{ m/s})^2 + \frac{1}{2}(6.0 \text{ kg})(2.67 \text{ m/s})^2 = 84.5 \text{ J}$.

The kinetic energy lost is $K_o - K = \boxed{1.1 \times 10^2 \text{ J}}$.

63. First find the velocity of the combination (truck and car) right after collision.

$m_1 = 1500 \text{ kg}$, $m_2 = 1200 \text{ kg}$, $v_{1o} = 25 \text{ m/s}$, $v_{2o} = 0 \text{ m/s}$, $v_1 = v_2 = v = ?$

$\mathbf{P_o} = \mathbf{P}$, ☞ $m_1 v_{1o} + m_2 v_{2o} = m_1 v_1 + m_2 v_2 = (m_1 + m_2)v$.

So $v = \dfrac{m_1 v_{1o} + m_2 v_{2o}}{m_1 + m_2} = \dfrac{(1500 \text{ kg})(25 \text{ m/s}) + (0)}{1500 \text{ kg} + 1200 \text{ kg}} = 13.9 \text{ m/s}$.

$K_o = \frac{1}{2}(1500 \text{ kg})(25 \text{ m/s})^2 + \frac{1}{2}(1200 \text{ kg})(0)^2 = 4.69 \times 10^5 \text{ J}$;

$K = \frac{1}{2}(1500 \text{ kg})(13.9 \text{ m/s})^2 + \frac{1}{2}(1200 \text{ kg})(13.9 \text{ m/s})^2 = 2.61 \times 10^5 \text{ J}$.

The kinetic energy lost is $K_o - K = \boxed{2.1 \times 10^5 \text{ J}}$.

64. (a) Apply momentum conservation $\mathbf{P}_o = \mathbf{P}$

in x: $\quad mv + M(0) = (m + M)\,v'_x, \quad$ ☞ $\quad v'_x = \dfrac{mv}{m + M} = \dfrac{(2.0\ \text{kg})(3.0\ \text{m/s})}{(2.0\ \text{kg}) + 4.0\ \text{kg}} = \boxed{1.0\ \text{m/s}}$;

in y: $\quad m(0) + M(V) = (m + M)\,v'_y, \quad$ ☞ $\quad v'_y = \dfrac{MV}{m + M} = \dfrac{(4.0\ \text{kg})(5.0\ \text{m/s})}{(2.0\ \text{kg}) + 4.0\ \text{kg}} = \boxed{3.3\ \text{m/s}}$.

(b) $\theta = \tan^{-1}\left(\dfrac{3.3}{1.0}\right) = \boxed{73°}$.

65. $\quad$ 90.0 km/h = 25.0 m/s, $\quad$ 60.0 km/h = 16.67 m/s.

Using result from Exercise 6.64, we have $\quad v'_x = \dfrac{mv}{m + M}$ and $v'_y = \dfrac{MV}{m + M}$.

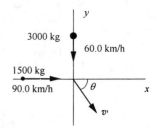

$$v' = \dfrac{\sqrt{m^2 v^2 + M^2 V^2}}{m + M}$$

$$= \dfrac{\sqrt{(1500\ \text{kg})^2 (25.0\ \text{m/s})^2 + (3000\ \text{kg})^2 (16.67\ \text{m/s})^2}}{1500\ \text{kg} + 3000\ \text{kg}}$$

$$= \boxed{13.9\ \text{m/s}}.$$

$$\theta = \tan^{-1}\left[\dfrac{(3000\ \text{kg})(16.67\ \text{m/s})}{(1500\ \text{kg})(25.0\ \text{m/s})}\right] = \boxed{53.1°\ \text{south of east}}.$$

66. The balls have the same mass. Apply momentum conservation $\mathbf{P}_o = \mathbf{P}$.

in x: $\quad m(0.750\ \text{m/s}) + m(0) = m(0.250\ \text{m/s})\cos 37° + m\,v'_x$,

so $\quad v'_x = 0.550\ \text{m/s}$;

in y: $\quad m(0) + m(0) = m(0.250\ \text{m/s})\sin 37° + m\,v'_y$,

so $\quad v'_y = -0.150\ \text{m/s}$.

Therefore $\quad \theta = \tan^{-1}\left(\dfrac{0.150}{0.550}\right) = \boxed{15°}$.

$$v' = \sqrt{(0.550\ \text{m/s})^2 + (0.150\ \text{m/s})^2} = \boxed{0.57\ \text{m/s}}.$$

67. Apply momentum conservation $\mathbf{P}_o = \mathbf{P}$.

in x: $\quad P_{xo} = 0$,

$P_x = (0.25\ \text{kg})(4.0\ \text{m/s}) + (0.20\ \text{kg})(6.0\ \text{m/s})\cos 120° + (0.33\ \text{kg})(2.5\ \text{m/s})\cos 230° = -0.13\ \text{kg·m/s}$,

in y: $\quad P_{yo} = 0$,

$P_y = (0.25\ \text{kg})(0) + (0.20\ \text{kg})(6.0\ \text{m/s})\sin 120° + (0.33\ \text{kg})(2.5\ \text{m/s})\sin 230° = 0.41\ \text{kg·m/s}$.

So $\quad P_o \neq P$. $\quad$ Therefore the answer is $\boxed{\text{no}}$.

Now in x: $0 = (0.25 \text{ kg})(4.0 \text{ m/s}) + (0.20 \text{ kg})(6.0 \text{ m/s}) \cos 120° + p_x,$ ☞ $p_x = -0.40 \text{ kg·m/s}.$

in y: $0 = (0.25 \text{ kg})(0) + (0.20 \text{ kg})(6.0 \text{ m/s}) \sin 120° + p_y,$ ☞ $p_y = -1.04 \text{ kg·m/s}.$

So $p = \sqrt{(0.40 \text{ kg·m/s})^2 + (1.04 \text{ kg·m/s})^2} = \boxed{1.1 \text{ kg·m/s}},$

$\theta = \tan^{-1}\left(\dfrac{1.04}{0.40}\right) = 69° \text{ below } x \text{ axis or } \boxed{291°}.$

68.   Since the cars are identical, $m_1 = m_2 = m$.   From momentum conservation $\mathbf{P}_o = \mathbf{P}$:

$m(v_o) + m(0) = (m + m)v = 2mv,$ ☞ $v = \dfrac{v_o}{2}.$ $K_o = \tfrac{1}{2} m\, v_o^2$ and $K = \tfrac{1}{2}(2m)\left(\dfrac{v_o}{2}\right)^2 = \tfrac{1}{4} m v_o^2.$

So the fraction of kinetic energy lost is $\dfrac{|\Delta K|}{K_o} = \dfrac{K_o - K}{K_o} = 1 - \dfrac{K}{K_o} = 1 - \dfrac{1}{2} = \boxed{50\%}.$

69.   (a) Since $v_1 = \dfrac{m_1 - m_2}{m_1 + m_2} v_{1o}$ and $\dfrac{v_1}{v_{1o}} = -\tfrac{1}{3}$ ("recoils").

we have $-\dfrac{1}{3} = \dfrac{m_1 - m_2}{m_1 + m_2} = \dfrac{m_1/m_2 - 1}{m_1/m_2 + 1},$ or $\dfrac{m_1}{m_2} + 1 = -3\dfrac{m_1}{m_2} + 3,$ so $\dfrac{m_1}{m_2} = \boxed{\tfrac{1}{2}}.$

(b) $v_2 = \dfrac{2m_1}{m_1 + m_2} v_{1o} = \dfrac{2m_1/m_2}{m_1/m_2 + 1} v_{1o} = \dfrac{2 \times \tfrac{1}{2}}{\tfrac{1}{2} + 1} = \boxed{\tfrac{2}{3} v_{1o}}.$

70.   From momentum conservation $\mathbf{P}_o = \mathbf{P}$: $m\, v_o + M(0) = (m + M)v,$ ☞ $v = \dfrac{m\, v_o}{m + M}.$

$K_o = \tfrac{1}{2} m_1\, v_o^2$ and $K = \tfrac{1}{2}(m + M)v^2 = \tfrac{1}{2}(m + M)\left(\dfrac{m_1 v_o}{m + M}\right)^2 = \tfrac{1}{2}\dfrac{(m\, v_o)^2}{m + M}.$

The fraction of kinetic energy lost is

$\dfrac{|\Delta K|}{K_o} = \dfrac{K_o - K}{K_o} = 1 - \dfrac{K}{K_o} = 1 - \dfrac{\tfrac{1}{2}\dfrac{(m\, v_o)^2}{m + M}}{\tfrac{1}{2} m\, v_o^2} = 1 - \dfrac{m}{m + M} = \dfrac{M}{m + M}.$

71.   (a) From the result of Exercise 6.70, $v = \dfrac{m\, v_o}{m + M} = \dfrac{0.010 \text{ kg}}{0.010 \text{ kg} + 0.890 \text{ kg}} v_o = \boxed{\dfrac{v_o}{90}}.$

(b) From energy conservation: $v = \sqrt{2gh} = \sqrt{2(9.80 \text{ m/s}^2)(0.40 \text{ m})} = 2.8 \text{ m/s}.$

So $v_o = 90v = \boxed{2.5 \times 10^2 \text{ m/s}}.$

(c) From the result of Exercise 6.70, the fraction of kinetic energy lost is

$\dfrac{M}{m + M} = \dfrac{0.890 \text{ kg}}{0.010 \text{ kg} + 0.890 \text{ kg}} = \boxed{99\%}.$

72. $m_1 = m_2 = m.$ Apply momentum conservation $\mathbf{P}_o = \mathbf{P}$:

in x: $mv_{1o} + m(0) = mv_1 \cos 45° + mv_{2x}$, so $v_{2x} = -v_1 \cos 45° = -\dfrac{\sqrt{2}}{2} v_1$,

in y: $m(0) + m(0) = mv_1 \sin 45° + mv_{2y}$, so $v_{2y} = -v_1 \sin 45° = -\dfrac{\sqrt{2}}{2} v_1$.

Therefore $v_2 = \sqrt{\left(\dfrac{\sqrt{2}}{2} v_1\right)^2 + \left(\dfrac{\sqrt{2}}{2} v_1\right)^2} = \sqrt{v_1^2(\cos^2 45° + \sin^2 45°)} = \sqrt{v_1^2(1)} = v_1$,

where we used $\sin^2 x + \cos^2 x = 1$.

Since $v_{2x} = v_{2y}$, $\theta = \tan^{-1}(1) = 45°$, the angle between v_1 and v_2 is $45° + 45° = 90°$.

73. (a) From momentum conservation $\mathbf{P}_o = \mathbf{P}$: $m_1 v_{1o} + m_2 v_{2o} = m_1 v_1 + m_2 v_2$,

or $m_1(v_{1o} - v_1) = m_2(v_2 - v_{2o})$.   Eq. (1)

From kinetic energy conservation: $\frac{1}{2} m_1 v_{1o}^2 + \frac{1}{2} m_1 v_{2o}^2 = \frac{1}{2} m_1 v_1^2 + \frac{1}{2} m_1 v_2^2$,

or $m_1(v_{1o}^2 - v_1^2) = m_2(v_2^2 - v_{2o}^2)$,   i.e., $m_1(v_{1o} + v_1)(v_{1o} - v_1) = m_2(v_2 - v_{2o})(v_2 + v_{2o})$.   Eq. (2)

Dividing Eq. (2) by Eq. (1) gives $v_{1o} + v_1 = v_2 + v_{2o}$,   so $v_2 - v_1 = -(v_{2o} - v_{1o})$.

(b) $e = -\dfrac{v_2 - v_1}{v_{2o} - v_{1o}}$.

For elastic collision, $v_2 - v_1 = -(v_{2o} - v_{1o})$ as in part (a),   so $\boxed{e_{\text{elastic}} = 1.0}$.

For completely inelastic collision, $v_1 = v_2$,   so $\boxed{e_{\text{inelastic}} = 0}$.

74. The steel plate is more massive so its velocities before and after the impact are essentially zero.

So $e = -\dfrac{v_2 - v_1}{v_{2o} - v_{1o}} = -\dfrac{v_1}{v_{1o}} = 0.95$,   or $v_1 = -0.95 v_{1o}$.

From energy conservation: $v = \sqrt{2gh}$,   or $h = \dfrac{v^2}{2g}$.

So $\dfrac{h_1}{h_o} = \dfrac{v_1^2}{v_{1o}^2} = (0.95)^2 = 0.90$.   Therefore $\boxed{h_1 = 0.90 h_o}$.

75. This pole will $\boxed{\text{lower the center of mass}}$ of the walker-pole system. The pole will also increase the moment of inertia of the system, and with a torque that rotates around the rope, the angular acceleration is smaller, giving the walker more time to recover.

76. (d).

77. (d).

78. In the center of mass reference frame, there is no net force acting on the rocket-spacecraft system so the momentum of the system is zero. Therefore the $\boxed{\text{CM does not move}}$.

79. (a) $X_{CM} = \dfrac{\Sigma_i \, m_i \, x_i}{M} = \dfrac{(0.10 \text{ kg})(0) + (0.10 \text{ kg})x_2}{0.10 \text{ kg} + 0.10 \text{ kg}} = 0,$ ☞ $x_2 = \boxed{0}.$

$Y_{CM} = \dfrac{(0.10 \text{ kg})(0.45 \text{ m}) + (0.10 \text{ kg})y_2}{0.10 \text{ kg} + 0.10 \text{ kg}} = 0,$ ☞ $y_2 = \boxed{-0.45 \text{ m}}.$

(b) $\boxed{\text{No}}$, only that they are $\boxed{\text{equidistant from CM}}$ due to the equal masses of the particles.

80. Choose the less massive mass as the origin ($x = 0$).

$X_{CM} = \dfrac{\Sigma_i \, m_i \, x_i}{M} = \dfrac{(4.0 \text{ kg})(0) + (7.5 \text{ kg})(1.5 \text{ m})}{4.0 \text{ kg} + 7.5 \text{ kg}} = \boxed{0.98 \text{ m}}$ from the less massive sphere.

81. (a) $X_{CM} = \dfrac{\Sigma_i \, m_i \, x_i}{M} = \dfrac{(6.0 \times 10^{24} \text{ kg})(0) + (6.4 \times 10^{22} \text{ kg})(3.8 \times 10^8 \text{ m})}{6.0 \times 10^{24} \text{ kg} + 7.4 \times 10^{22} \text{ kg}}$

$= \boxed{4.6 \times 10^6 \text{ m from the center of the Earth}}.$

(b) From the surface of the Earth, it is at

$4.6 \times 10^6 \text{ m} - r_e = 4.6 \times 10^6 \text{ m} - 7.37 \times 10^6 \text{ m} = -1.8 \times 10^6 \text{ m},$

i.e., $\boxed{1.8 \times 10^6 \text{ m below the surface of the Earth}}.$

Earth

Moon

r_e

$x = 0$

$3.8 \times 10^8 \text{ m}$

82. $X_{CM} = \dfrac{\Sigma_i \, m_i \, x_i}{M} = \dfrac{(3.0 \text{ kg})(-6.0 \text{ m/s}) + (2.0 \text{ kg})(1.0 \text{ m}) + (4.0 \text{ kg})(3.0 \text{ m})}{3.0 \text{ kg} + 2.0 \text{ kg} + 4.0 \text{ kg}} = -0.44 \text{ m},$

$Y_{CM} = 0.$ So the CM is at $\boxed{(-0.44 \text{ m}, 0)}.$

83. $X_{CM} = \dfrac{\Sigma_i \, m_i \, x_i}{M},$

so $0 = \dfrac{(3.0 \text{ kg})(-6.0 \text{ m/s}) + (2.0 \text{ kg})(1.0 \text{ m}) + (4.0 \text{ kg})(3.0 \text{ m}) + (0.50 \text{ kg})x}{3.0 \text{ kg} + 2.0 \text{ kg} + 4.0 \text{ kg} + 0.50 \text{ kg}},$

therefore $x = 8.0 \text{ m}.$ $y = 0.$ Thus it is at $\boxed{(8.0 \text{ m}, 0)}.$

84. Choose the 4.0-kilogram mass as the origin ($x = 0$). The center of mass of the rod is then at 2.5 m.

$X_{CM} = \dfrac{\Sigma_i \, m_i \, x_i}{M} = \dfrac{(4.0 \text{ kg})(0) + (3.0 \text{ kg})(2.5 \text{ m}) + (6.0 \text{ kg})(5.0 \text{ m})}{4.0 \text{ kg} + 3.0 \text{ kg} + 6.0 \text{ kg}} = \boxed{2.9 \text{ m}},$

from the 4.0-kilogram mass.

85. The CM of both the square sheet and the circle are at the center of the square.

So from symmetry, the CM of the remaining portion is still $\boxed{\text{at center of sheet.}}$.

86. (a) The system is symmetrical about the geometrical center of the system, so the

CM is at the center of the system, or $\boxed{(2.0 \text{ m}, 2.0 \text{ m})}$.

(b) Again it is symmetrical about the center. It is still at $\boxed{(2.0 \text{ m}, 2.0 \text{ m})}$.

(c) $X_{CM} = \dfrac{\Sigma_i \, m_i \, x_i}{M} = \dfrac{(1.0 \text{ kg})(0) + (2.0 \text{ kg})(0) + (3.0 \text{ kg})(4.0 \text{ m}) + (4.0 \text{ kg})(4.0 \text{ m})}{1.0 \text{ kg} + 2.0 \text{ kg} + 3.0 \text{ kg} + 4.0 \text{ kg}} = 2.8 \text{ m},$

$Y_{CM} = \dfrac{(1.0 \text{ kg})(0) + (2.0 \text{ kg})(4.0 \text{ m}) + (3.0 \text{ kg})(4.0 \text{ m}) + (4.0 \text{ kg})(0)}{1.0 \text{ kg} + 2.0 \text{ kg} + 3.0 \text{ kg} + 4.0 \text{ kg}} = 2.0 \text{ m}.$

So the CM is at $\boxed{(2.8 \text{ m}, 2.0 \text{ m})}$.

87. $X_{CM1} = \dfrac{\Sigma_i \, m_i \, x_i}{M} = \dfrac{m_1 \, x_1 + m_2 \, x_2 + m_3 \, x_3}{m_1 + m_2 + m_3}$ and $X_{CM2} = \dfrac{m_4 \, x_4 + m_5 \, x_5}{m_4 + m_5}$.

$X_{CM} = \dfrac{m_1 \, x_1 + m_2 \, x_2 + m_3 \, x_3 + m_4 \, x_4 + m_5 \, x_5}{m_1 + m_2 + m_3 + m_4 + m_5}$. So generally $X_{CM} \neq X_{CM1} + X_{CM2}$.

However if $m_1 = m_2 = m_3 = m_4 = m_5$, then $X_{CM} = X_{CM1} + X_{CM2}$.

88. Due to the lack of external force, the CM is stationary and is at where they meet.

$X_{CM} = \dfrac{\Sigma_i \, m_i \, x_i}{M} = \dfrac{(3000 \text{ kg})(0) + (100 \text{ kg})(5.0 \text{ m})}{3000 \text{ kg} + 100 \text{ kg}}$

$= \boxed{0.16 \text{ m from capsule's original position}}$.

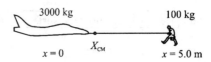

89. (a) Due to the lack of external force, the CM is stationary at where they meet.

$X_{CM} = \dfrac{\Sigma_i \, m_i \, x_i}{M} = \dfrac{(65 \text{ kg})(0) + (45 \text{ kg})(8.0 \text{ m})}{65 \text{ kg} + 45 \text{ kg}} = 3.3 \text{ m}.$

So $\boxed{\text{the 65 kg travels 3.3 m and the 45 kg travels 4.7 m}}$.

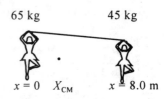

(b) Still there is no external force; they travel the $\boxed{\text{same distances}}$ as in part (a).

90. $M = 3(0.25 \text{ kg}) = 0.75 \text{ kg}$. $\mathbf{F}_{net} = -(3.0 \text{ N}) \, \hat{\mathbf{y}} + (5.0 \text{ N}) \, \hat{\mathbf{y}} + (4.0 \text{ N}) \, \hat{\mathbf{x}} = (4.0 \text{ N}) \, \hat{\mathbf{x}} + (2.0 \text{ N}) \, \hat{\mathbf{y}},$

so $\mathbf{A}_{CM} = \dfrac{\mathbf{F}_{net}}{M} = \dfrac{(4.0 \text{ N}) \, \hat{\mathbf{x}} + (2.0 \text{ N}) \, \hat{\mathbf{y}}}{0.75 \text{ kg}} = \boxed{(5.3 \text{ m/s}^2) \, \hat{\mathbf{x}} + (2.7 \text{ m/s}^2) \, \hat{\mathbf{y}}}$.

Or $A = \sqrt{(5.3 \text{ m/s})^2 + (2.7 \text{ m/s})^2} = \boxed{5.9 \text{ m/s}}$, $\theta = \tan^{-1}\left(\dfrac{2.7}{5.3}\right) = \boxed{27° \text{ above } +x \text{ axis}}$.

91. (a) No, only if masses are the same.

    (b) In the same direction.

92. First calculate the velocity of both objects right after the collision from momentum conservation.

    $(1.0 \text{ kg})(10 \text{ m/s}) + (2.0 \text{ kg})(0) = (1.0 \text{ kg} + 2.0 \text{ kg})v,$ ☞ $v = 3.33 \text{ m/s}.$

    From the conservation of energy, $\frac{1}{2} m(3.33 \text{ m/s})^2 = m(9.80 \text{ m/s}^2)h,$ ☞ $h = 0.566 \text{ m}.$

    So $x = \dfrac{0.566 \text{ m}}{\sin 37°} = \boxed{0.94 \text{ m}}.$

93. First $m_Q = 3.0 \, m_P = 3.0 \, m,$ $m_K = 4.0 \, m_P = 4.0 \, m,$ where $m_P = m.$

    The coordinates of the 6 pieces are: BP: $(0.5d, 0.5d)$, BK: $(3.5d, 0.5d)$, BQ: $(7.5d, 2.5d)$,

    WP: $(0.5d, 4.5d)$, WK: $(3.5d, 7.5d)$, WQ: $(5.5d, 5.5d)$.

    (a) $X_{CM} = \dfrac{\Sigma_i m_i x_i}{M} = \dfrac{m(0.5d) + 4.0m(3.5d) + 3.0 \, m(7.5d)}{m + 4.0m + 3.0m} = 4.6d,$

    $Y_{CM} = \dfrac{m(0.5d) + 4.0m(0.5d) + 3.0 \, m(2.5d)}{m + 4.0m + 3.0m} = 1.3d.$ So the CM of the black pieces is at $\boxed{(4.6d, 1.3d)}.$

    (b) $X_{CM} = \dfrac{m(0.5d) + 4.0m(3.5d) + 3.0 \, m(5.5d)}{m + 4.0m + 3.0m} = 3.9d,$

    $Y_{CM} = \dfrac{m(4.5d) + 4.0m(7.5d) + 3.0 \, m(5.5d)}{m + 4.0m + 3.0m} = 6.4d.$

    So the CM of the white pieces is at $\boxed{(3.9d, 6.4d)}.$

    (c) $X_{CM} = \dfrac{m(0.5d) + 4.0m(3.5d) + 3.0 \, m(7.5d) + m(0.5d) + 4.0m(3.5d) + 3.0 \, m(5.5d)}{m + 4.0m + 3.0m + m + 4.0m + 3.0m} = 4.3d,$

    $Y_{CM} = \dfrac{m(0.5d) + 4.0m(0.5d) + 3.0 \, m(2.5d) + m(4.5d) + 4.0m(7.5d) + 3.0 \, m(5.5d)}{m + 4.0m + 3.0m + m + 4.0m + 3.0m} = 3.8d.$

    So the CM of all pieces is at $\boxed{(4.3d, 3.8d)}.$

94. $\boxed{\text{Yes}}.$ The black pieces and the white pieces each have a mass of $m + 4.0m + 3.0m = 8.0m.$

    So $X_{CM} = \dfrac{8.0m(4.63d) + 8.0m(3.88d)}{8.0m + 8.0m} = 4.3d,$

    $Y_{CM} = \dfrac{8.0m(1.25d) + 8.0m(6.38d)}{8.0m + 8.0m} = 3.8d,$ the same as in part (c) of Exercise 6.93.

95. (a) $p_x = p_y = (0.50 \text{ kg})(3.3 \text{ m/s}) = 1.65 \text{ kg·m/s}.$

    $p = \sqrt{(1.65 \text{ kg·m/s})^2 + (1.65 \text{ kg·m/s})^2} = \boxed{2.3 \text{ kg·m/s}},$ $\theta = \tan^{-1}\left(\dfrac{1.65}{1.65}\right) = \boxed{45° \text{ below the } -x \text{ axis}}.$

    (b) $\boxed{\text{Not necessarily}}$, a collision does not have to occur; momentum would be the same.

96.   From momentum conservation $P_0 = P$ (note $m_1 = m_2 = m$):

$m_1 v_{1o} + m_2 v_{2o} = m_1 v_1 + m_2 v_2$,   so $v_1 + v_2 = v_{1o} + v_{2o}$,   Eq. (1)

also from the result of Exercise 6.73(a) $v_2 - v_1 = -(v_{2o} - v_{1o})$.   Eq. (2)

Eq. (1) + Eq. (2) gives $2v_2 = 2v_{1o}$,   so $v_2 = v_{1o} = 2.0$ m/s

and $v_1 = v_{1o} + v_{2o} - v_2 = 2.0$ m/s $+ (-2.0$ m/s$) - 2.0$ m/s $= -2.0$ m/s,

where $v_{2o} = -2.0$ m/s is because the balls are "approaching each other."

Therefore the speeds are $\boxed{v_1 = v_2 = 2.0 \text{ m/s}}$.

97.   (a) 90 km/h = 25 m/s. $p_0 = mv = (2400 \text{ kg})(25 \text{ m/s}) = \boxed{6.0 \times 10^4 \text{ kg·m/s}}$.

(b) $\bar{F} \Delta t = \Delta p = 0 - p_0$,   ☞ $\bar{F} = -\dfrac{p_0}{\Delta t} = -\dfrac{6.0 \times 10^4 \text{ kg·m/s}}{8.0 \text{ s}} = \boxed{-7.5 \times 10^3 \text{ N}}$.

98.   (a) Apply momentum conservation $\mathbf{P_0} = \mathbf{P}$

in x: $\dfrac{7500 \text{ N}}{g}(60 \text{ km/h}) + \dfrac{15\,000 \text{ N}}{g}(0)$

$= \dfrac{7500 \text{ N}}{g} v_x + \dfrac{15\,000 \text{ N}}{g} v_x$,

so $v_x = 20$ km/h.

in y: $\dfrac{7500 \text{ N}}{g}(0) + \dfrac{15\,000 \text{ N}}{g}(45 \text{ km/h})$

$= \dfrac{7500 \text{ N}}{g} v_y + \dfrac{15\,000 \text{ N}}{g} v_y$,   so $v_y = 30$ km/h.

Therefore $v = \sqrt{(20 \text{ km/h})^2 + (30 \text{ km/h})^2} = \boxed{36 \text{ km/h}}$, $\theta = \tan^{-1}\left(\dfrac{30}{20}\right) = \boxed{56° \text{ north of east}}$.

(b) The percentage of kinetic energy lost is

$\dfrac{|\Delta K|}{K_0} = \dfrac{K_0 - K}{K_0} = 1 - \dfrac{K}{K_0} \propto 1 - \dfrac{\frac{1}{2}(7500 + 15\,000)(36)^2}{\frac{1}{2}(7500)(60)^2 + \frac{1}{2}(15\,000)(45)^2} = 0.51 = \boxed{51\%}$. (Note $\propto$ sign.)

99.   (a) The stunt man has zero horizontal velocity before he jumps onto the sled.

Apply momentum conservation $P_0 = P$ in the horizontal direction.

$(75 \text{ kg})(0) + (50 \text{ kg})(10 \text{ m/s}) = (75 \text{ kg} + 50 \text{ kg})v = (125 \text{ kg})v$,   ☞ $v = \boxed{4.0 \text{ m/s}}$.

(b) The stunt man's momentum is still conserved, so he continues to move with a speed of $\boxed{4.0 \text{ m/s}}$.

100. (a) $\bar{F}\Delta t = mv - mv_0 = -mv_0 = 0 - (0.25 \text{ kg})(14 \text{ m/s}) = -\boxed{3.5 \text{ N·s}}$. $\boxed{\text{No}}$, this is not an elastic collision.

(b) $\bar{F} = \dfrac{-3.5 \text{ N·s}}{0.10 \text{ s}} = -\boxed{35 \text{ N}}$.

101. (a) The blocks stick together after collision for a completely inelastic collision.

From momentum conservation $\mathbf{P}_0 = \mathbf{P}$: $\quad m_1 v_{10} + m_2 v_{20} = m_1 v_1 + m_2 v_2$,

so $\quad (2.5 \text{ kg})(6.0 \text{ m/s}) + (6.5 \text{ kg})(0) = (2.5 \text{ kg} + 6.5 \text{ kg})v$, ☞ $v = \boxed{1.7 \text{ m/s}}$.

(b) $K_0 = \frac{1}{2}mv^2 = \frac{1}{2}(2.5 \text{ kg})(6.0 \text{ m/s})^2 + 0 = 45 \text{ J}$, $\quad K = \frac{1}{2}(2.5 \text{ kg} + 6.5 \text{ kg})(1.67 \text{ m/s})^2 = 12.6 \text{ J}$.

So the mechanical energy lost is $45 \text{ J} - 12.6 \text{ J} = \boxed{32 \text{ J}}$.

102. First find the recoil velocity of the astronaut from momentum conservation $\mathbf{P}_0 = \mathbf{P}$.

$m_1 v_{10} + m_2 v_{20} = m_1 v_1 + m_2 v_2$, ☞ $(0.50 \text{ kg})(0) + (90 \text{ kg})(0) = (0.50 \text{ kg})(4.0 \text{ m/s}) + (90 \text{ kg})v$,

so $\quad v = -0.0222 \text{ m/s}$. Therefore it takes him $\dfrac{6.0 \text{ m}}{0.0222 \text{ m/s}} = \boxed{2.7 \times 10^2 \text{ s} = 4.5 \text{ min}}$.

103. (a) $v_1 = \dfrac{m_1 - m_2}{m_1 + m_2}v_{10} = \dfrac{m - 12m}{m + 12m}v_{10} = \frac{11}{13}v_{10}$.

So the fraction of kinetic energy lost is

$\dfrac{|\Delta K|}{K_0} = \dfrac{K_0 - K}{K_0} = 1 - \dfrac{K}{K_0} = 1 - \dfrac{\frac{1}{2}m\left(\frac{11}{13}\right)^2 v_{10}^2}{\frac{1}{2}mv_{10}^2} = 0.28 = \boxed{28\%}$.

(b) $v_1 = \frac{11}{13}(1.5 \times 10^7 \text{ m/s}) = \boxed{1.3 \times 10^7 \text{ m/s}}$.

104. First find the velocity of the athlete right after leaving from energy conservation.

$v_0 = \sqrt{2gh} = \sqrt{2(9.80 \text{ m/s}^2)(2.25 \text{ m})} = 6.64 \text{ m/s}$.

Now from momentum conservation $\mathbf{P}_0 = \mathbf{P}$: $\quad m_1 v_{10} + m_2 v_{20} = m_1 v_1 + m_2 v_2$,

$(70 \text{ kg})(0) + (6.0 \times 10^{24} \text{ kg})(0) = (70 \text{ kg})(6.64 \text{ m/s}) + (6.0 \times 10^{24} \text{ kg})v$, ☞ $v = -\boxed{7.7 \times 10^{-23} \text{ m/s}}$.

105. If the triangle is suspended at one corner, the CM will be on a line perpendicular to the base and through the corner. If the triangle is suspended at a second corner, the CM will be where the two lines cross (see diagram). From symmetry $\quad Y_{CM} = 15 \text{ cm}$, and $\quad X_{CM} = (15 \text{ cm})\tan 30° = 8.7 \text{ cm}$.

Thus the CM is at $\boxed{(8.7 \text{ cm}, 15 \text{ cm})}$.

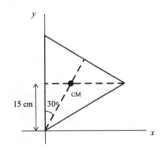

CHAPTER 7

1. (c).

2. (c).

3. $r = \sqrt{(1.5\text{ m})^2 + (2.0\text{ m})^2} = \boxed{2.5\text{ m}}, \quad \theta = \tan^{-1}\left(\dfrac{2.0}{1.5}\right) = \boxed{53°}.$

4. $r^2 = x^2 + y^2$, so the equation of a circle is $\boxed{r = a}$.

5. (a) $(15°) \times \dfrac{\pi\text{ rad}}{180°} = \boxed{0.26\text{ rad}}.$ (b) $(45°) \times \dfrac{\pi\text{ rad}}{180°} = \boxed{0.79\text{ rad}}.$

   (c) $(90°) \times \dfrac{\pi\text{ rad}}{180°} = \boxed{1.6\text{ rad}}.$ (d) $(120°) \times \dfrac{\pi\text{ rad}}{180°} = \boxed{2.1\text{ rad}}.$

6. (a) $(\pi/6\text{ rad}) \times \dfrac{180°}{\pi\text{ rad}} = \boxed{30°}.$ (b) $(5\pi/12\text{ rad}) \times \dfrac{180°}{\pi\text{ rad}} = \boxed{75°}.$

   (c) $(3\pi/4\text{ rad}) \times \dfrac{180°}{\pi\text{ rad}} = \boxed{135°}.$ (d) $(\pi\text{ rad}) \times \dfrac{180°}{\pi\text{ rad}} = \boxed{180°}.$

7. $s = r\theta = (6.0\text{ cm})(\pi/4\text{ rad}) = \boxed{4.7\text{ cm}}.$

8. $s = r\theta, \quad \text{☞} \quad r = \dfrac{s}{\theta} = \dfrac{5.0\text{ m}}{2.0°(\pi\text{ rad}/180°)} = \boxed{1.4 \times 10^2\text{ m}}.$

9. (a) $\theta = \dfrac{s}{r} = \dfrac{1.00 \times 10^3\text{ m}}{0.250 \times 10^3\text{ m}} = \boxed{4.00\text{ rad}}.$

   (b) $(4.00\text{ rad}) \times \dfrac{180°}{\pi\text{ rad}} = \boxed{229°}.$

10. In 3 months, the Earth travels $\dfrac{3}{12} = \dfrac{1}{4}$ of a circle or $\dfrac{1}{4} \times (2\pi\text{ rad}) = \dfrac{\pi}{2}\text{ rad}.$

    So $s = r\theta = (1.5 \times 10^8\text{ km}) \times \dfrac{\pi\text{ rad}}{2} = \boxed{2.4 \times 10^8\text{ km}}.$

11. (a) For a full circle $\dfrac{2\pi r}{2\pi \text{ rad}} = \dfrac{2\pi r}{360°}$, so 2π rad $= 360°$,

or $\dfrac{2\pi \text{ rad}}{2\pi} = \dfrac{360°}{2\pi}$, i.e., $\boxed{1 \text{ rad} = 57.3°}$.

(b) As in part (a), $\boxed{2\pi \text{ rad} = 360°}$.

12. In 30 min, the hour hand travels $\pi/12 =$ rad, the minute hand π rad, and the second hand $30(2\pi) = 60\pi$ rad.

Hour hand: $s = r\theta = (0.25 \text{ m})(\pi/12 \text{ rad}) = \boxed{0.065 \text{ m}}$.

Minute hand: $s = (0.30 \text{ m})(\pi \text{ rad}) = \boxed{0.94 \text{ m}}$.

Second hand: $s = (0.35 \text{ m})(60\pi \text{ rad}) = \boxed{66 \text{ m}}$.

13. $\theta = \dfrac{s}{r} = \dfrac{(3.00 \text{ mi})(1600 \text{ m/mi})}{0.450 \times 10^3 \text{ m}} = \boxed{10.7 \text{ rad}}$.

14. The circumference is $c = \pi d = \pi(12 \text{ in.})(00254 \text{ m/1 in.}) = 0.958 \text{ m}$.

So the arc length for each piece is $s = \dfrac{0958 \text{ m}}{5} = \boxed{0.19 \text{ m}}$.

Or the angular width of each piece is $\theta = \dfrac{360°}{5} = \boxed{72°}$.

15. (a) $\theta = \dfrac{s}{r} = \dfrac{3500 \text{ km}}{3.8 \times 10^5 \text{ km}} = \boxed{9.2 \times 10^{-3} \text{ rad} = 0.53°}$.

(b) $\theta = \dfrac{2(6.4 \times 10^3 \text{ km})}{3.8 \times 10^5 \text{ km}} = \boxed{3.4 \times 10^{-2} \text{ rad} = 1.9°}$.

16. $s = r\theta = (6.4 \times 10^3 \text{ km})(119° - 84°) \times \dfrac{\pi \text{ rad}}{180°} = \boxed{3.9 \times 10^3 \text{ km}}$.

17. Since the circumference $c = 2\pi r = (6.28 \text{ rad})r$, the answer is $\boxed{\text{no}}$.

So we can cut $\boxed{6 \text{ such pieces and one 0.28 rad piece}}$.

18. (a) The number of turns of wire which can be wound on the spool is

$\dfrac{24 \text{ cm}}{0.75 \text{ cm}} = 32$ turns. So $\theta = (2\pi \text{ rad/turn})(32 \text{ turns}) = \boxed{2.0 \times 10^2 \text{ rad}}$.

(b) The radius at the center of the wire is $R = 0.30 \text{ m} + 0.0075 \text{ m}/2 = .30375 \text{ m}$.

$s = R\theta = (0.30375 \text{ m})(2.0 \times 10^2 \text{ rad}) = \boxed{61 \text{ m}}$.

19.   (b).

20.   (d).

21. $\boxed{\text{Yes}}$, they all sweep through the same angle. $\boxed{\text{No}}$, they do not have the same tangential speed as the distances to the center of the wheel are different.

22.   Viewing from opposite sides would give different circular senses, i.e., make clockwise counterclockwise and vice versa.

23.   The $\boxed{\text{point farthest from the center}}$ has the greatest tangential speed and $\boxed{\text{the point closest to the center}}$ has the smallest tangential speed, because the tangential speed is directly proportional to the radius.

24. $30 \text{ rpm} = (30 \text{ rev/min}) \times \dfrac{2\pi \text{ rad}}{1 \text{ rev}} \times \dfrac{1 \text{ min}}{60 \text{ s}} = \boxed{3.1 \text{ rad/s}}$.

25. $f = \dfrac{1}{T} = \dfrac{1}{(10 \text{ h})/(24 \text{ h/d})} = \boxed{2.4 \text{ rev/d}}$.

26. $\omega = \dfrac{\Delta \theta}{\Delta t} = \dfrac{2.5(2\pi \text{ rad})}{(3.0 \text{ min})(60 \text{ s/min})} = \boxed{0.087 \text{ rad/s}}$.

27. $\omega = \dfrac{\Delta \theta}{\Delta t}, \quad \mathscr{F} \quad \Delta t = \dfrac{\Delta \theta}{\omega} = \dfrac{2\pi \text{ rad}}{3.5 \text{ rad/s}} = \boxed{1.8 \text{ s}}$.

28.   (a) $f = 12\,000 \text{ rev/min}$, so $T = \dfrac{1}{f} = \dfrac{1}{12\,000 \text{ rev/min}} = 8.33 \times 10^{-5} \text{ min} = 5.0 \times 10^{-3} \text{ s} = \boxed{5.0 \text{ ms}}$.

        (b) $T = \dfrac{1}{10\,000 \text{ rev/min}} = 1.0 \times 10^{-4} \text{ min} = \boxed{6.0 \text{ ms}}$.

29. $\omega_A = \dfrac{\Delta \theta}{\Delta t} = \dfrac{(160°)(\pi \text{ rad}/180°)}{2.00 \text{ s}} = 1.40 \text{ rad/s}, \quad \omega_B = \dfrac{4\pi \text{ rad}}{8.00 \text{ s}} = 1.57 \text{ rad/s}$.

        So $\boxed{\text{B is faster}}$.

30. $\omega = \dfrac{v_t}{r} = \dfrac{3.0 \text{ m/s}}{0.20 \text{ m}} = 15 \text{ rad/s}$.

        $\omega = \dfrac{\Delta \theta}{\Delta t}, \quad \mathscr{F} \quad \Delta t = \dfrac{\Delta \theta}{\omega} = \dfrac{2\pi \text{ rad}}{15 \text{ rad/s}} = \boxed{0.42 \text{ s}}$.

31.   (a) $\omega = \dfrac{\Delta\theta}{\Delta t} = \dfrac{(24\ \text{rev})(2\pi\ \text{rad/rev})}{(3.0\ \text{min})(60\ \text{s/min})} = \boxed{0.84\ \text{rad/s}}$.

      (b) $v = r\,\omega$, $v_4 = (4.0\ \text{m})(0.838\ \text{rad/s}) = \boxed{3.4\ \text{m/s}}$ and $v_5 = (5.0\ \text{m})(0.838\ \text{rad/s}) = \boxed{4.2\ \text{m/s}}$.

32.   (a) $\omega = \dfrac{\Delta\theta}{\Delta t} = \dfrac{(0.5\ \text{rev})(2\pi\ \text{rad/rev})}{(1.5\ \text{min})(60\ \text{s/min})} = \boxed{3.5 \times 10^{-2}\ \text{rad/s}}$.

      (b) $v_t = r\omega = (500\ \text{m})(3.49 \times 10^{-2}\ \text{rad/s}) = \boxed{17\ \text{m/s}}$.

33.   (a) The Earth rotate once a day. $\omega = \dfrac{\Delta\theta}{\Delta t} = \dfrac{2\pi\ \text{rad}}{(24)(3600\ \text{s})} = \boxed{7.27 \times 10^{-5}\ \text{rad/s}}$.

      (b) The Earth revolve the Sun once a year. $\omega = \dfrac{2\pi\ \text{rad}}{(365)(24)(3600\ \text{s})} = \boxed{1.99 \times 10^{-7}\ \text{rad/s}}$.

34. $f = 500\ \text{rpm}$, $T = \dfrac{1}{f} = \dfrac{1}{500\ \text{rpm}} = 2.00 \times 10^{-3}\ \text{min} = \boxed{0.120\ \text{s}}$.

35.   (a) $v = r\omega$, ☞ $\omega = \dfrac{v}{r} = \dfrac{15\ \text{m/s}}{(120\ \text{m})/2} = 0.25\ \text{rad/s}$.

      $\theta = \omega\Delta t = (0.25\ \text{rad/s})(4.00\ \text{min})(60\ \text{s/min}) = \boxed{60\ \text{rad}}$.

      (b) $s = r\theta = \dfrac{120\ \text{m}}{2} \times (60\ \text{rad}) = \boxed{3.6 \times 10^{3}\ \text{m}}$.

36.   (b).

37.   (d).

38.   Centripetal force is proportional to the square of the speed. When there is insufficient centripetal force (provided by friction and adhesive forces), the mud cannot maintain the circular path and it flies off along a tangent.

39.   There is insufficient centripetal force (provided by friction and adhesive forces) on the water drops so the water drops fly out along a tangent and the clothes get dry.

40.   The floats of the little mass will move $\boxed{\text{in direction of acceleration, inward}}$. It works the same way as the accelerometer in Figure 4.26. $\boxed{\text{No}}$, it does not make a difference since the centripetal acceleration is always inward.

41. The inertia of your body has a tendency to keep moving forward along a straight line (Newton's first law) and the car makes a turn by the centripetal force between the tires and the road. So we feel as if we were being "thrown outward."

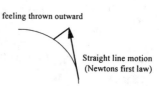

42. Centripetal force is required for a car to maintain its circular path. When a car is on a banked turn, the horizontal component of the normal force on the car is pointing toward the center of the circular path. This component will enable the car to negotiate the turn even when there is no friction.

43. $a_c = r\omega^2$, ☞ $\omega = \sqrt{\dfrac{a_c}{r}} = \sqrt{\dfrac{9.80 \text{ m/s}^2}{(2.5 \text{ mi})(1609 \text{ m/mi})}} = \boxed{0.049 \text{ rad/s or about 680 rev/day}}$.

44. 120 km/h = 33.33 m/s. $a_c = \dfrac{v^2}{r} = \dfrac{(33.33 \text{ m/s})^2}{(1.00 \times 10^3 \text{ m})} = \boxed{1.11 \text{ m/s}^2}$.

45. $a_c = \dfrac{v^2}{r}$, ☞ $v = \sqrt{a_c r} = \sqrt{(1.2 \text{ m/s}^2)(1.5 \text{ m})} = \boxed{1.3 \text{ m/s}}$.

46. $a_c = r\omega^2 = (3.80 \times 10^8 \text{ m})\left[\dfrac{2\pi \text{ rad}}{(29.5 \text{ d})(86400 \text{ s/d})}\right]^2 = \boxed{2.31 \times 10^{-3} \text{ m/s}^2}$.

47. 83.0 km/h = 23.06 m/s, $a_c = \dfrac{v^2}{r} = \dfrac{(23.06 \text{ m/s})^2}{0.400 \times 10^3 \text{ m}} = 1.33 \text{ m/s}^2 > 1.25 \text{ m/s}^2$. $\boxed{\text{No}}$.

48. (a) $v = \dfrac{d}{t} = \dfrac{2\pi r}{t} = \dfrac{2\pi(1.50 \text{ m})}{1.20 \text{ s}} = \boxed{7.85 \text{ m/s}}$.

    (b) $F_c = ma_c = m\dfrac{v^2}{r} = \dfrac{(0.250 \text{ kg})(7.85 \text{ m/s})^2}{1.50 \text{ m}} = \boxed{10.3 \text{ N}}$.

    (c) $\boxed{\text{No}}$, the string cannot be exactly horizontal. There must be something upward (a component of the tension) to balance the downward gravitational force.

49. $\theta = \tan^{-1}\left(\dfrac{mg}{F_c}\right) = \tan^{-1}\left[\dfrac{(0.250 \text{ kg})(9.80 \text{ m/s}^2)}{10.3 \text{ N}}\right] = = \boxed{13.4°}$.

50. To keep the water from coming out of the bucket, we have to match the gravitational force to centripetal force. $mg = F_c = m\dfrac{v^2}{r}$, ☞ $v = \sqrt{gr} = \sqrt{(9.80 \text{ m/s}^2)(1.0 \text{ m})} = \boxed{3.1 \text{ m/s}}$.

51. Static friction force provides centripetal force.

$$f_s = \mu_s N = \mu_s mg = F_c = m\frac{v^2}{r}, \quad \text{☞} \quad v = \sqrt{\mu_s gr} = \sqrt{0.50(9.80 \text{ m/s}^2)(20 \text{ m})} = \boxed{9.9 \text{ m/s}}.$$

52. (a) 700 km/h = 194 m/s. At the bottom, the centripetal force is provided by
the difference $N - mg$. So $F_c = N - mg = m\frac{v^2}{r}$,

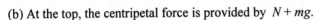

$$N = mg + m\frac{v^2}{r} = mg + m\frac{(194 \text{ m/s})^2}{2.0 \times 10^3 \text{ m}} = mg + m(18.8 \text{ m/s}^2)$$

$$= mg + 1.9mg = \boxed{2.9mg}.$$

(b) At the top, the centripetal force is provided by $N + mg$.

$$N = m\frac{v^2}{r} - mg = m\frac{(194 \text{ m/s})^2}{2.0 \times 10^3 \text{ m}} - mg = m(18.8 \text{ m/s}^2) - mg = 1.93mg - mg = \boxed{0.93mg}.$$

53. (a) A normal force by the loop must act on the block to provide extra centripetal force. Minimum speed corresponds to a minimum normal force of zero so the only force on the block is gravity, which is the sole source of centripetal force.

So $F_c = mg = m\frac{v^2}{r}$, ☞ $v = \boxed{\sqrt{rg}}$.

(b) From energy conservation: $mgh + \frac{1}{2}m(0)^2 = +mg(2r) + \frac{1}{2}mv^2$,

so $h = 2r + \frac{1}{2}\frac{rg}{g} = \boxed{(5/2)r}$.

54. To clear the gully the truck must travel a minimum horizontal distance of 10.0 m + 4.25 m = 14.25 m. First use kinematics to calculate the velocity of the truck which is a horizontal projectile.

The time of flight is $t = \sqrt{-\frac{2y}{g}} = \sqrt{-\frac{2(-2.96 \text{ m})}{9.80 \text{ m/s}^2}} = 0.777 \text{ s}$ (from $y = v_0 t - \frac{1}{2}gt^2$).

So $v_x = \frac{14.25 \text{ m}}{0.777 \text{ s}} = 18.3 \text{ m/s}$. Therefore $a_c = \frac{v^2}{r} = \frac{(18.3 \text{ m/s})^2}{333 \text{ m}} = \boxed{1.01 \text{ m/s}^2}$.

55. (a) In the vertical direction: $N\cos\theta - mg = 0$, ☞ $N = \frac{mg}{\cos\theta}$.

In the horizontal direction: $F_c = N\sin\theta = \frac{mg}{\cos\theta}\sin\theta = mg\tan\theta = m\frac{v^2}{r}$,

so $\tan\theta = \frac{v^2}{gr}$.

(b) Since mass is not in the result in part (a), the angle is $\boxed{\text{independent of mass}}$.

(c) If there is friction, it will point along the inclined plane,

so the contribution from friction to centripetal force is $f_s \cos\theta = (\mu_s N)\cos\theta = \mu_s \dfrac{mg}{\cos\theta} = \mu_s\, mg$.

Therefore $\quad mg\tan\theta + \mu_s\, mg = m\dfrac{v^2}{r}$, $\quad \textreferencemark \quad \boxed{\tan\theta = \dfrac{v^2}{gr} - \mu_s}$.

As expected, the angle does not need to be as big as in part (a) when there is friction.

56. The static friction force between you and the wall provides the upward force to balance your weight. The normal force on you by the wall provides centripetal force.

$N = F_c = mr\omega^2$.   So $f_s = \mu_s N = \mu_s\, mr\omega^2 = mg$,

Therefore $\quad \omega = \sqrt{\dfrac{g}{\mu_s\, r}} = \sqrt{\dfrac{9.80 \text{ m/s}^2}{0.30(2.5 \text{ m})}} = \boxed{3.6 \text{ rad/s}}$.

57. (d).

58. Yes, when a car is $\boxed{\text{changing its speed on a curve}}$.

59. $\boxed{\text{No}}$, this is not possible. Any car in circular motion always has centripetal acceleration.

60. 700 rpm = 73.3 rad/s,   3000 rpm = 314 rad/s.

$\alpha = \dfrac{\Delta\omega}{\Delta t} = \dfrac{314 \text{ rad/s} - 73.3 \text{ rad/s}}{3.0 \text{ s}} = \boxed{80 \text{ rad/s}^2}$.

61. Given: $\omega_0 = 0$, $\omega = 2.5$ rpm $= 0.262$ rad/s, $\theta = 5$ rev $= 10\pi$ rad.   Find: α.

$\omega^2 = \omega_0^2 + 2\alpha\theta$, $\quad \textreferencemark \quad \alpha = \dfrac{\omega^2 - \omega_0^2}{2\theta} = \dfrac{(0.262 \text{ rad/s})^2 - 0}{2(10\pi \text{ rad})} = \boxed{1.1 \times 10^{-3} \text{ rad/s}^2}$.

62. (a) Given: $\omega_0 = 0$, $\omega = 33\text{-}\frac{1}{3}$ rpm $= 3.49$ rad/s, $t = 2.45$ s.   Find: θ.

$\theta = \dfrac{\omega + \omega_0}{2}\, t = \dfrac{0 + 3.49 \text{ rad/s}}{2} \times (2.45 \text{ s}) = \boxed{4.28 \text{ rad}}$.

(b) $s = r\theta = (6.0 \text{ in})(4.28 \text{ rad}) = 25.7$ in $= \boxed{2.14 \text{ ft}}$.

63. Given: $\omega_0 = 60$ rpm $= 6.28$ rad/s, $\omega = 0$, $t = 15$ s.   Find: θ.

$\theta = \dfrac{\omega + \omega_0}{2}\, t = \dfrac{6.28 \text{ rad/s} + 0}{2} \times (15 \text{ s}) = 47.1$ rad $= \boxed{7.5 \text{ rev}}$.

64.   (a) Given: $\omega_0 = 0$, $\omega = \dfrac{v}{r} = \dfrac{2.20 \text{ m/s}}{17.5 \text{ m}} = 0.126 \text{ rad/s}$, $t = 15.0 \text{ s}$. Find: α.

$\alpha = \dfrac{\omega - \omega_0}{t} = \dfrac{0.126 \text{ rad/s} - 0}{15.0 \text{ s}} = \boxed{8.40 \times 10^{-3} \text{ rad/s}^2}$.

(b) After reaching the constant operating speed, $\alpha = 0$ and so $a_t = r\alpha = \boxed{0}$.

65.   (a) Given: $\omega_0 = 250 \text{ rpm} = 26.18 \text{ rad/s}$, $\omega = 350 \text{ rpm} = 36.65 \text{ rad/s}$, $t = 5.75 \text{ s}$. Find: α.

$\alpha = \dfrac{\omega - \omega_0}{t} = \dfrac{36.65 \text{ rad/s} - 26.18 \text{ rad/s}}{5.75 \text{ s}} = \boxed{1.82 \text{ rad/s}^2}$.

(b) $\theta = \dfrac{\omega + \omega_0}{2} t = \dfrac{26.18 \text{ rad/s} + 36.65 \text{ rad/s}}{2} \times (5.75 \text{ s}) = 181 \text{ rad} = \boxed{28.7 \text{ rev}}$.

66.   Given: $\omega_0 = 4500 \text{ rpm} = 471 \text{ rad/s}$, $\omega = 0$, $t = 5.0 \text{ s}$. Find: θ.

$\theta = \dfrac{\omega + \omega_0}{2} t = \dfrac{471 \text{ rad/s} + 0}{2} \times (5.0 \text{ s}) = 1.18 \times 10^3 \text{ rad} = \boxed{1.9 \times 10^2 \text{ rev}}$.

67.   (a) Given: $\omega_0 = 0$, $\alpha = 4.5 \times 10^{-3} \text{ rad/s}^2$, $\theta = 1 \text{ rev} = 2\pi \text{ rad}$. Find: t.

$\theta = \omega_0 t + \tfrac{1}{2}\alpha t^2 = 0 + \tfrac{1}{2}\alpha t^2$, ☞ $t = \sqrt{\dfrac{2\theta}{\alpha}} = \sqrt{\dfrac{2(2\pi \text{ rad})}{4.5 \times 10^{-3} \text{ rad/s}^2}} = \boxed{53 \text{ s}}$.

(b) After half a lap, $\omega^2 = \omega_0^2 + 2\alpha\theta = 0 + 2(4.5 \times 10^{-3} \text{ rad/s}^2)(\pi \text{ rad}) = 0.0283 \text{ rad}^2/\text{s}^2$,

so $\omega = 0.168 \text{ rad/s}$.

The centripetal acceleration is $a_c = r\omega^2 = (0.30 \times 10^3 \text{ m})(0.168 \text{ rad/s})^2 = 8.5 \text{ m/s}^2$,

the tangential acceleration is $a_t = r\alpha = (0.30 \times 10^3 \text{ m})(4.5 \times 10^{-3} \text{ rad/s}^2) = 1.4 \text{ m/s}^2$.

So the total acceleration is $\mathbf{a} = \boxed{(8.5 \text{ m/s}^2)\,\hat{\mathbf{r}} + (1.4 \text{ m/s}^2)\,\hat{\mathbf{t}}}$.

68.   (a) The static friction is not sufficient to provide the centripetal force needed for circular motion.

(b) $\omega = \omega_0 + \alpha t = 0 + (1.42 \text{ rad/s}^2)(2.25 \text{ s}) = 3.195 \text{ rad/s}$.

$F_c = f_s = \mu_s N = \mu_s mg = mr\omega^2$, ☞ $\mu_s = \dfrac{r\omega^2}{g} = \dfrac{(0.10 \text{ m})(3.195 \text{ rad/s})^2}{9.80 \text{ m/s}^2} = \boxed{0.10}$.

69.   (b).

70.   (d).

71. $\boxed{\text{No}}$. Gravity acts on the astronauts and the spacecraft, providing the necessary centripetal force for the orbit, so g is not zero and there is weight by definition ($w = mg$). The "floating" occurs because the spacecraft and astronauts are "falling" ("accelerating" toward Earth at the same rate).

72. When the cup is held, water runs out the holes. However if the cup is let go, $\boxed{\text{water will not run}}$ since both the cup and the water are in free fall.

73. $\boxed{\text{Yes}}$, if we also know the radius of the Earth. The acceleration due to gravity near the surface of the Earth can be written as $a_g = \dfrac{GM_E}{R_E^2}$. By simply measuring a_g, you can determine $M_E = \dfrac{a_g R_E^2}{G}$.

74. (a) $\boxed{\text{No}}$. Although the scale is calibrated in kilograms, it is still measuring gravitational force. Due to the different gravitational accelerations on the Earth and Moon, it will not read correctly.

(b) Due to its rotation, the Earth bulges at the equator. So it will read $\boxed{\text{less}}$ on the equator because the gravitational force depends on $1/r^2$.

75. $g = \dfrac{GM_E}{R_E^2} = \dfrac{(6.67 \times 10^{-11}\ \text{N·m}^2/\text{kg}^2)(5.98 \times 10^{24}\ \text{kg})}{(6.38 \times 10^6\ \text{m})^2} = \boxed{9.80\ \text{m/s}^2}$.

76. $F = \dfrac{GM_E M_M}{r_{E\text{-}M}^2} = \dfrac{(6.67 \times 10^{-11}\ \text{N·m}^2/\text{kg}^2)(5.98 \times 10^{24}\ \text{kg})(7.4 \times 10^{22}\ \text{kg})}{(3.8 \times 10^8\ \text{m})^2} = \boxed{2.0 \times 10^{20}\ \text{N}}$.

77. (a) $F_E = \dfrac{GM_E M_M}{r_{E\text{-}M}^2} = \dfrac{(6.67 \times 10^{-11}\ \text{N·m}^2/\text{kg}^2)(5.98 \times 10^{24}\ \text{kg})(7.4 \times 10^{22}\ \text{kg})}{(3.8 \times 10^8\ \text{m})^2} = 2.0 \times 10^{20}\ \text{N},$

$F_S = \dfrac{(6.67 \times 10^{-11}\ \text{N·m}^2/\text{kg}^2)(2.0 \times 10^{30}\ \text{kg})(7.4 \times 10^{22}\ \text{kg})}{(1.5 \times 10^{11}\ \text{m} - 3.8 \times 10^8\ \text{m})^2} = 4.4 \times 10^{20}\ \text{N}.$

So $F_M = F_S - F_E = 4.4 \times 10^{20}\ \text{N} - 2.0 \times 10^{20}\ \text{N} = \boxed{2.4 \times 10^{20}\ \text{N toward the Sun}}$.

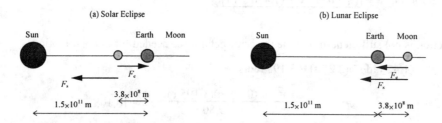

(b) $F_E = \dfrac{(6.67 \times 10^{-11}\ \text{N·m}^2/\text{kg}^2)(5.98 \times 10^{24}\ \text{kg})(7.4 \times 10^{22}\ \text{kg})}{(3.8 \times 10^8\ \text{m})^2} = 2.0 \times 10^{20}\ \text{N},$

$F_S = \dfrac{(6.67 \times 10^{-11}\ \text{N·m}^2/\text{kg}^2)(2.0 \times 10^{30}\ \text{kg})(7.4 \times 10^{22}\ \text{kg})}{(1.5 \times 10^{11}\ \text{m} + 3.8 \times 10^8\ \text{m})^2} = 4.4 \times 10^{20}\ \text{N}.$

So $F_M = F_S + F_E = 4.4 \times 10^{20}\ \text{N} + 2.0 \times 10^{20}\ \text{N} = \boxed{6.4 \times 10^{20}\ \text{N toward the Sun}}$.

78. $F = \dfrac{Gm_1 m_2}{r^2} \propto \dfrac{1}{r^2}$,   ☞ $\dfrac{F_2}{F_1} = \dfrac{r_1^{\,2}}{r_2^{\,2}} = \dfrac{1^2}{3^2} = \dfrac{1}{9}$.

So $F_2 = \dfrac{F_1}{9} = \dfrac{0.90\ \text{N}}{9} = \boxed{0.10\ \text{N}}$.

79. $F_1 = F_3 = \dfrac{Gm^2}{d^2} = \dfrac{(6.67 \times 10^{-11}\ \text{N·m}^2/\text{kg}^2)(2.5\ \text{kg})^2}{(1.0\ \text{m})^2} = 4.17 \times 10^{-10}\ \text{N}$,

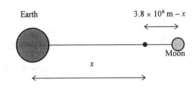

The diagonal distance is $\sqrt{(1.0\ \text{m})^2 + (1.0\ \text{m})^2} = \sqrt{2}\ \text{m}$,

so $F_3 = \dfrac{(6.67 \times 10^{-11}\ \text{N·m}^2/\text{kg}^2)(2.5\ \text{kg})^2}{(\sqrt{2}\ \text{m})^2} = 2.08 \times 10^{-10}\ \text{N}$.

From symmetry the net force is

$F = \sqrt{(4.17 \times 10^{-10}\ \text{N})^2 + (4.17 \times 10^{-10}\ \text{m})^2} + 2.08 \times 10^{-10}\ \text{N} = \boxed{8.0 \times 10^{-10}\ \text{N, toward opposite corner}}$.

80. $a_\text{g} = \dfrac{GM_\text{E}}{(R_\text{E} + h)^2} = \dfrac{(6.67 \times 10^{-11}\ \text{N·m}^2/\text{kg}^2)(5.98 \times 10^{24}\ \text{kg})}{(6.38 \times 10^6\ \text{m} + 8.80 \times 10^3\ \text{m})^2} = \boxed{9.77\ \text{m/s}^2}$.

81.   The 10% weight reduction is caused by a 10% reduction in gravitational acceleration.

From $a_\text{g} = \dfrac{GM_\text{E}}{(R_\text{E} + h)^2}$.

$h = \sqrt{\dfrac{GM_\text{E}}{a_\text{g}}} - R_\text{E} = \sqrt{\dfrac{(6.67 \times 10^{-11}\ \text{N·m}^2/\text{kg}^2)(5.98 \times 10^{24}\ \text{kg})}{0.90(9.80\ \text{m/s}^2)}} - 6.38 \times 10^6\ \text{m} = \boxed{3.4 \times 10^5\ \text{m}}$.

82.   When the Earth's gravitational force equals the lunar gravitational force,

$F_\text{E} = \dfrac{GM_\text{E}m}{x^2} = F_\text{M} = \dfrac{GM_\text{M}m}{(3.8 \times 10^8\ \text{m} - x)^2}$.

Taking the square root on both sides gives

$\dfrac{\sqrt{M_\text{E}}}{x} = \dfrac{\sqrt{M_\text{M}}}{3.8 \times 10^8\ \text{m} - x}$,

or $\sqrt{7.4 \times 10^{22}\ \text{kg}}\ x = \sqrt{5.98 \times 10^{24}\ \text{kg}}\ (3.8 \times 10^8\ \text{m} - x)$.

Solving, $x = \boxed{3.4 \times 10^8\ \text{m from Earth}}$.

$\boxed{\text{No}}$, there are still other gravitational forces from the other planets and the Sun.

83. $F = \dfrac{Gm_1 m_2}{r^2}$,   ☞ $\dfrac{F_{\text{E-S}}}{F_{\text{E-M}}} = \dfrac{\dfrac{M_\text{S}}{r_{\text{E-S}}^2}}{\dfrac{M_\text{M}}{r_{\text{E-M}}^2}} = \dfrac{M_\text{S}\, r_{\text{E-M}}^2}{M_\text{m}\, r_{\text{E-S}}^2} = \dfrac{(2.0 \times 10^{30}\ \text{kg})(3.8 \times 10^8\ \text{m})^2}{(7.4 \times 10^{22}\ \text{kg})(1.5 \times 10^{11}\ \text{m})^2} = 1.7 \times 10^2$.

So the gravitational force $\boxed{\text{by the Sun is greater by } 1.7 \times 10^2 \text{ times}}$.

84. Assume the thickness of the layer is d. So the mass is $M = \rho V = \rho \frac{4\pi}{3}(R_E + d)^3$.

Also $a_g = \frac{GM}{(R_E + d)^2} = \frac{4\pi}{3} \times G\rho(R_E + d)$, so

$d = \frac{3a_g}{4\pi G\rho} - R_E = \frac{3(10.0 \text{ m/s}^2)}{4\pi(6.67 \times 10^{-11} \text{ N·m}^2/\text{kg}^2)(5.52 \times 10^3 \text{ kg/m}^3)} - 6.38 \times 10^6 \text{ m} = 1.04 \times 10^5 \text{ m}$

$= \boxed{104 \text{ km}}$.

85. (a) $U_{\text{tot}} = -\frac{Gm_1m_2}{r_{12}} - \frac{Gm_1m_3}{r_{13}} - \frac{Gm_2m_3}{r_{23}}$

$= -(6.67 \times 10^{-11} \text{ N·m}^2/\text{kg}^2)\left[\frac{(1.0 \text{ kg})^2}{0.80 \text{ m}} + \frac{(1.0 \text{ kg})^2}{0.80 \text{ m}} + \frac{(1.0 \text{ kg})^2}{0.80 \text{ m}}\right] = \boxed{-2.5 \times 10^{-10} \text{ J}}$.

(b) From symmetry, the force at the center is zero. So the force per unit mass is also $\boxed{0}$.

86. (c).

87. (c), according to Kepler's second law.

88. (a) $\boxed{0}$ because the direction of the force and the displacement (velocity) are perpendicular ($W = F\,d \cos\theta$).

(b) $\boxed{\text{No}}$. When the person comes down, it is still a free fall.

89. (a) $\boxed{\text{To get more velocity relative to space}}$ because the Earth rotates toward the east. Also, the launch is over the ocean for safety.

(b) The $\boxed{\text{tangential speed of the Earth is higher in Florida}}$ because Florida is closer to the equator than California, and hence a greater distance from the axis of rotation. Also, California launches are polar (not eastward) for safety.

90. (a) From energy conservation: $K + U = $ constant,

$\frac{1}{2}mv^2 - \frac{G M_E m}{R_E^2} = \frac{1}{2}m(0)^2 - \frac{GM_E m}{(R_E + h)^2}$, so

$\frac{1}{2}v^2 = \frac{(6.67 \times 10^{-11} \text{ N·m}^2/\text{kg}^2)(6.0 \times 10^{24} \text{ kg})}{6.4 \times 10^6 \text{ m}} - \frac{(6.67 \times 10^{-11} \text{ N·m}^2/\text{kg}^2)(6.0 \times 10^{24} \text{ kg})}{6.4 \times 10^6 \text{ m} + 800 \times 10^3 \text{ m}}$

$= 6.965 \times 10^6 \text{ m}^2/\text{s}^2$, therefore $v = \boxed{3.7 \times 10^3 \text{ m/s}}$.

(b) The percentage is $\frac{3.7 \times 10^3 \text{ m/s}}{11 \times 10^3 \text{ m/s}} = \boxed{34\%}$.

91.   (a) $K = \dfrac{4\pi^2}{GM_S} = \dfrac{4\pi^2}{(6.67 \times 10^{-11} \text{ N·m}^2/\text{kg}^2)(2.0 \times 10^{30} \text{ kg})} = \boxed{3.0 \times 10^{-19} \text{ s}^2/\text{m}^3}$.

(b) It is the $\boxed{\text{same}}$ since K is independent on the mass of the planet.

92.   For the Earth orbiting the Sun, $K = \dfrac{4\pi^2}{GM_S}$.

Replace the mass of the Sun with the mass of the Earth for satellites orbiting the Earth.

$K = \dfrac{4\pi^2}{GM_E} = \dfrac{4\pi^2}{(6.67 \times 10^{-11} \text{ N·m}^2/\text{kg}^2)(5.98 \times 10^{24} \text{ kg})} = 9.90 \times 10^{-14} \text{ s}^2/\text{m}.$

$T = 1 \text{ day} = 24(3600 \text{ s}) = 86\,400 \text{ s}$ (synchronous satellite).   From $T^2 = Kr^3 = K(R_E + h)^3$,

we have $h = \sqrt[3]{\dfrac{T^2}{K}} - R_E = \sqrt[3]{\dfrac{(86\,400 \text{ s})^2}{9.90 \times 10^{-14} \text{ s}^2/\text{m}}} - 6.38 \times 10^6 \text{ m} = \boxed{3.6 \times 10^7 \text{ m}}$.

93.   For the Earth orbiting the Sun, $K = \dfrac{4\pi^2}{GM_S}$.

Replace the mass of the sun with the mass of Venus for satellites orbiting Venus.

$K = \dfrac{4\pi^2}{GM_V} = \dfrac{4\pi^2}{(6.67 \times 10^{-11} \text{ N·m}^2/\text{kg}^2)[(0.8150)(5.98 \times 10^{24} \text{ kg})]} = 1.21 \times 10^{-13} \text{ s}^2/\text{m}.$

$T = 1 \text{ day} = 243(24)(3600 \text{ s}) = 2.10 \times 10^7 \text{ s}$ (synchronous satellite).

From $T^2 = Kr^3 = K(R_V + h)^3$,   we have

$h = \sqrt[3]{\dfrac{T^2}{K}} - R_V = \sqrt[3]{\dfrac{(2.10 \times 10^7 \text{ s})^2}{1.21 \times 10^{-13} \text{ s}^2/\text{m}}} - 6.05 \times 10^6 \text{ m} = \boxed{1.53 \times 10^9 \text{ m}}$.

94. $T = 5.0 \text{ y} = (5.0)(365)(24)(3600 \text{ s}) = 1.58 \times 10^8 \text{ s}.$ From $T^2 = Kr^3$,

we have $r = \sqrt[3]{\dfrac{T^2}{K}} = \sqrt[3]{\dfrac{(1.58 \times 10^8 \text{ s})^2}{3.0 \times 10^{-19} \text{ s}^2/\text{m}}} = \boxed{4.4 \times 10^{11} \text{ m}}$.

95.   The angular velocity of the Sun's setting is the same as the angular velocity of the Earth's rotation.

$\omega = \dfrac{\Delta\theta}{\Delta t} = \dfrac{2\pi \text{ rad}}{24(3600 \text{ s})} = 7.27 \times 10^{-5} \text{ rad/s.}$ $\Delta t = \dfrac{\Delta\theta}{\omega} = \dfrac{(0.50°)(\pi \text{ rad}/180°)}{7.27 \times 10^{-5} \text{ rad/s}} = 120 \text{ s} = \boxed{2.0 \text{ min}}$.

96.   The Moon's gravitational attraction on the near side is greater on the water than on the Earth and produces one bulge for one tide; the attraction is greater on the Earth than on the water on the far side and so the Earth moves toward the Moon and leaves the water behind for another bulge.

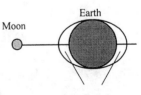

Earth

Moon

Water Bulge

97. The centripetal force is provided by the combination of

$T - mg\cos\theta = m\dfrac{v^2}{r}$, where $\cos\theta = \dfrac{h}{l}$ and v could be found from energy

conservation. When the girl is h below the original position,

we have $\quad \frac{1}{2}m(0)^2 + mgh = \frac{1}{2}mv^2 + mg(0)$, so $v^2 = 2gh$.

Therefore $\quad T = mg\cos\theta + m\dfrac{v^2}{r} = \dfrac{mgh}{l} + \dfrac{m(2gh)}{l} = \dfrac{3mgh}{l}$.

(a) $h = 0$, $\qquad\qquad\qquad\qquad$ so $\qquad T = \boxed{0}$.

(b) $h = 12\ m - 5.0\ m = 7.0\ m$, $\quad$ so $\qquad T = \dfrac{3(60\ \text{kg})(9.80\ \text{m/s}^2)(7.0\ \text{m})}{10\ \text{m}} = \boxed{1.2 \times 10^3\ \text{N}}$.

(c) $h = 12\ m - 2.0\ m = 10\ m$, $\quad$ so $\qquad T = \dfrac{3(60\ \text{kg})(9.80\ \text{m/s}^2)(10\ \text{m})}{10\ \text{m}} = \boxed{1.8 \times 10^3\ \text{N}}$.

98. (a) Use the diagram and the results in Exercise 7.97.

In the tangential direction (perpendicular to the rope): $\quad F_{\text{net}} = -mg\sin\theta = ma$,

so $\quad a = g\sin\theta = (9.80\ \text{m/s}^2)\sin 30° = \boxed{4.9\ \text{m/s}^2}$.

(b) $a_{\text{c}} = \dfrac{v^2}{r} = \dfrac{(8.5\ \text{m/s})^2}{10\ \text{m}} = 7.23\ \text{m/s}^2$. So the magnitude of the vector sum of the tangential and centripetal

accelerations is $\quad a = \sqrt{(4.9\ \text{m/s}^2)^2 + (7.23\ \text{m/s}^2)^2} = \boxed{8.7\ \text{m/s}^2}$.

(c) Assume she starts at h' above the pond surface (with zero velocity).

When $\theta = 30°$, $h = (10\ \text{m})\cos 30° = 8.66\ \text{m}$ or she is $12\ \text{m} - 8.66\ \text{m} = 3.34\ \text{m}$ above the pond surface.

From energy conservation: $\quad \frac{1}{2}m(8.5\ \text{m/s})^2 + mg(3.34\ \text{m}) = \frac{1}{2}m(0)^2 + mgh'$,

so $\quad h' = \dfrac{(8.5\ \text{m/s})^2}{2(9.80\ \text{m/s}^2)} + 3.34\ \text{m} = \boxed{7.0\ \text{m}}$.

99. (a) $\omega = (5.00 \times 10^6\ \text{rpm}) \times \dfrac{2\pi\ \text{rad/rev}}{60\ \text{s/min}} = 5.24 \times 10^5\ \text{rad/s}$.

$a_{\text{c}} = r\omega^2 = (0.0400\ \text{m})(5.24 \times 10^5\ \text{rad/s})^2 = \boxed{1.10 \times 10^{10}\ \text{m/s}^2}$.

(b) $\dfrac{1.1 \times 10^8\ \text{m/s}^2}{g} = \dfrac{1.1 \times 10^{10}\ \text{m/s}^2}{9.80\ \text{m/s}^2} = \boxed{1.12 \times 10^9\ g}$.

100. $s = r\theta = (0.45\ \text{m})(3\ \text{rev})(2\pi\ \text{rad/rev}) = \boxed{8.5\ \text{m}}$.

101. $K + U = 0$, $\quad \Rightarrow \quad \frac{1}{2}mv_{\text{E}}^2 - \dfrac{GM_{\text{E}}m}{R_{\text{E}} + h} = 0$.

So $\quad v_{\text{E}} = \sqrt{\dfrac{2GM_{\text{E}}}{R_{\text{E}} + h}} = \sqrt{\dfrac{2(6.67 \times 10^{-11}\ \text{N·m}^2/\text{kg}^2)(5.98 \times 10^{24}\ \text{kg})}{6.38 \times 10^6\ \text{m} + 750 \times 10^3\ \text{m}}} = \boxed{1.1 \times 10^4\ \text{m/s}}$.

102. $m = \dfrac{w}{g} = \dfrac{735 \text{ N}}{9.80 \text{ m/s}^2} = 75 \text{ kg.}$

        $F = \dfrac{GM_E m}{(R_E + h)^2} = \dfrac{(6.67 \times 10^{-11} \text{ N·m}^2/\text{kg}^2)(5.98 \times 10^{24} \text{ kg})(75 \text{ kg})}{(6.38 \times 10^6 \text{ m} + 450 \times 10^3 \text{ m})^2} = \boxed{641 \text{ N}}.$

103. $T^2 = Kr^3.$ For the Earth, $T = 1$ year   and $r = 1$ AU.

        So $(1 \text{ y})^2 = K(1 \text{ AU})^3,$ ☞ $K = \boxed{1 \text{ y}^2/\text{AU}^3}.$

104.   (a) $a_t = g \sin\theta = (9.80 \text{ m/s}^2) \sin 15° = \boxed{2.5 \text{ m/s}^2}.$ $a_c = \dfrac{v^2}{r} = \dfrac{(2.7 \text{ m/s})^2}{0.75 \text{ m}} = \boxed{9.7 \text{ m/s}^2}.$

       (b) $\boxed{\text{At the lowest point of the swing}}$ since v is maximum there. $a_t = \boxed{0}$ since $\theta = 0.$

CHAPTER 8

ROTATIONAL MOTION AND EQUILIBRIUM

1. (a).

2. (b).

3. $\boxed{\text{Yes}}$. Rolling motion is a good example.

4. If v is less than $R\omega$, the object slips, yes, it is possible for v to be greater than $R\omega$ when the object slides.

5. (b).

6. $s = r\theta = (0.065 \text{ m})(4 \text{ rev})(2\pi \text{ rad/rev}) = \boxed{1.6 \text{ m}}$.

7. $s = r\theta$, ☞ $r = \dfrac{s}{\theta} = \dfrac{3.2 \text{ m}}{5(2\pi \text{ rad})} = \boxed{0.10 \text{ m}}$.

8. At the 9-o'clock position, the velocity is straight upward. So it is a "free-fall" with an initial upward velocity. It will rise, reach a maximum height, and then fall back down.

9. (a) $v_{CM} = r\omega = (0.25 \text{ m})(2.0 \text{ rad/s}) = \boxed{0.50 \text{ m/s}}$.

    (b) The disk rotates about a point which makes a contact with the surface. The distance from the top of the disk to that point is $2r$. So $v = 2(0.25 \text{ m})(2.0 \text{ rad/s}) = \boxed{1.0 \text{ m/s}}$.

10. $v_{CM} = r\omega$, ☞ $\omega = \dfrac{v_{CM}}{r} = \dfrac{0.25 \text{ m/s}}{0.15 \text{ m}} = \boxed{1.7 \text{ rad/s}}$.

11. $s = 0.71 \text{ m}$. $r\theta = (0.15 \text{ m})(270°)(\pi \text{ rad}/180°) = 0.71 \text{ m}$. So $s = r\theta$, $\boxed{\text{yes}}$, it rolls without slipping.

12. Dividing $s = r\theta$ (the condition of without slipping) by a time interval t gives

    $\dfrac{s}{t} = r\dfrac{\theta}{t}$, or $v = r\omega$.

    Dividing $v = r\omega$ by a time interval t again yields

    $\dfrac{v}{t} = r\dfrac{\omega}{t}$, or $a = r\alpha$.

13. $\alpha = \dfrac{a_t}{r} = \dfrac{0.018 \text{ m/s}^2}{0.10 \text{ m}} = 0.18 \text{ rad/s}^2.$ $\omega^2 = \omega_o^2 + 2\alpha\theta,$

so $\theta = \dfrac{\omega^2 - \omega_o^2}{2\alpha} = \dfrac{(1.25 \text{ rad/s})^2 - (0.50 \text{ rad/s})^2}{2(0.18 \text{ rad/s}^2)} = 36.5 \text{ rad} = \boxed{0.58 \text{ rotations}}.$

14. (b).

15. (a).

16. In all three cases, the centers of gravity must be directly below the base of support. The torque is zero because the force of the CG is through the axis of rotation.

17. $\boxed{\text{Yes}}$, the toy clown is in stable equilibrium. Its center of gravity is directly below the tightrope. If the clown leans to one side, his own weight will restore its equilibrium position. If the weights are removed, the clown will be in an unstable equilibrium and he will fall.

18. When the force is applied perpendicular to the length of the wrench, minimum force is required and the lever arm equals the length of the wrench. At $\theta = 90°$, $r_\perp = 0.15$ m.

$\tau = Fr_\perp,$ ☞ $F = \dfrac{\tau}{r_\perp} = \dfrac{25 \text{ m·N}}{0.15 \text{ m}} = \boxed{1.7 \times 10^2 \text{ N}}.$

19. In this case, $r_\perp = (0.15 \text{ m}) \sin 30°.$

$F = \dfrac{\tau}{r_\perp} = \dfrac{25 \text{ m·N}}{(0.15 \text{ m}) \sin 30°} = \boxed{3.3 \times 10^2 \text{ N}}.$

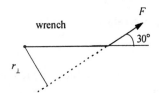

20. Use the numbers from Example 8.2.

$\tau = Fr_\perp,$ ☞ $F = \dfrac{\tau}{r_\perp} = \dfrac{18 \text{ m·N}}{(0.040 \text{ m}) \cos 37°} = \boxed{5.6 \times 10^2 \text{ N}}.$

21. 6 stable (faces) and 20 unstable (12 edges and 8 corners).

22. $\tau = r_\perp F = r_\perp mg = (0.20 \text{ m})(55 \text{ kg})(9.80 \text{ m/s}^2) = \boxed{1.1 \times 10^2 \text{ m·N}}.$

23. $\Sigma\tau = 0,$ ☞ $m_1 g(2.0 \text{ m}) - m_2 g x = 0,$

so $x = \dfrac{m_1}{m_2}(2.0 \text{ m}) = \dfrac{35 \text{ kg}}{30 \text{ kg}}(2.0 \text{ m}) = \boxed{2.3 \text{ m}}.$

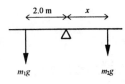

24. (a) $\Sigma\tau = 0$, ☞ $(0.100\text{ kg})g(0.500\text{ m} - 0.250\text{ m}) - (0.0750\text{ kg})g(x - 0.500\text{ m}) = 0$,

so $x = 0.833\text{ m} = \boxed{83.3\text{ cm}}$.

(b) $(0.100\text{ kg})g(0.500\text{ m} - 0.250\text{ m}) - m(0.900\text{ m} - 0.500\text{ m}) = 0$,

so $m = 0.0625\text{ kg} = \boxed{62.5\text{ g}}$.

25. $R = Mg = (0.025\text{ kg} + 0.075\text{ kg} + 0.100\text{ kg})g = (0.200\text{ kg})g$.

The net torque about an axis through the zero end is

$\Sigma\tau = (0.025\text{ kg})g(0) - (0.075\text{ kg})g(0.20\text{ m}) + (0.200\text{ kg})g(0.50\text{ m}) - (0.100\text{ kg})g(0.85\text{ m}) \approx 0$.

(within significant figures.)

26. $\theta = \tan^{-1}\left(\dfrac{0.010}{15}\right) = 0.0382°$.

$\Sigma F_y = 2T\sin\theta - mg = 0$.

So $T = \dfrac{mg}{2\sin\theta} = \dfrac{(0.25\text{ kg})(9.80\text{ m/s}^2)}{2\sin 0.0382°} = \boxed{1.8 \times 10^3\text{ N} > 400\text{ lb}}$.

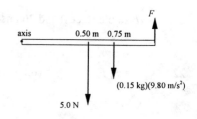

27. Choose the joint (where F_j is) as the axis of rotation.

$\Sigma\tau = F_m(0.18\text{ m})\sin 15° - (3.0\text{ kg})(9.80\text{ m/s}^2)(0.26\text{ m}) = 0$, ☞ $F_m = \boxed{1.6 \times 10^2\text{ N}}$.

28. (a) The tension in the rope attached to m_1 is $T = (4.50\text{ kg})(9.80\text{ m/s}^2) = 44.1\text{ N}$ and there are two such tensions pulling the leg horizontally.

So the reaction force is $R = 2T = \boxed{88.2\text{ N}}$.

(b) $\Sigma F_y = 0$, ☞ $(m_1 + m_2)g - Mg = 0$, so $m_2 = M - m_1 = 15.0\text{ kg} - 4.50\text{ kg} = \boxed{10.5\text{ kg}}$.

29. $\Sigma\tau = -(5.0\text{ N})(0.50\text{ m}) - (0.15\text{ kg})(9.80\text{ m/s}^2)(0.75\text{ m}) + F(1.0\text{ m}) = 0$,

so $F = \boxed{3.6\text{ N}}$.

30. Repeat the calculation of Example 8.5.

$N = \dfrac{(15\text{ kg})(9.8\text{ m/s}^2)(1.0\text{ m}) + (65\text{ kg})(9.8\text{ m/s}^2)(1.6\text{ m})}{5.6\text{ m}} = 2.1 \times 10^4 {=}2\text{ N}$.

So $f_s = N = \boxed{2.1 \times 10^2\text{ N}}$.

31.   Choose where the string is as the axis and work from the bottom up. Apply $\Sigma\tau$ to the

bees: $\qquad\qquad\qquad\qquad m_1\, g(40 \text{ cm}) - m_2\, g(20 \text{ cm}) = 0, \qquad \text{☞} \qquad m_2 = 2\, m_1 = \boxed{0.20 \text{ kg}}.$

bees–1st bird combination: $(m_1 + m_2)g(25 \text{ cm}) - m_3\, g(15 \text{ cm}), \qquad \text{☞} \qquad m_3 = \dfrac{5}{3}\,(m_1 + m_2) = \boxed{0.50 \text{ kg}}.$

bees and 1st bird–2nd bird combination: $\quad m_4\, g(30 \text{ cm}) - (m_1 + m_2 + m_3)g(15 \text{ cm}) = 0,$

so $\quad m_4 = \tfrac{1}{2}(m_1 + m_2 + m_3) = \boxed{0.40 \text{ kg}}.$

32.   (a) The center of gravity (CG) of the first book is at the center. So for the last book not to fall, its CG can
not displace more than 12.5 cm relative to the CG of the first book (within the base). The CG of each
successive book on the top is moved 1.5 cm relative to that of the one below. Therefore the number of

books which can be on top of the first one is $\dfrac{12.5 \text{ cm}}{1.5 \text{ cm}} = 8.33.$

Thus we can stack a total of $1 + 8 = \boxed{9}$ books, including the first one.

(b) The total height is $9(5.0) \text{ cm} = 45 \text{ cm}.$

So the CM is at $\dfrac{45 \text{ cm}}{2} = \boxed{22.5 \text{ cm}}.$

33. $\boxed{\text{Yes}}$. The center of gravity of every stick is at or to the left of the edge of the table.

34.   The height of the center of gravity at stable equilibrium is

$d = \dfrac{0.500 \text{ m}}{2} = 0.250 \text{ m}.$

The minimum height of the center of gravity at unstable

equilibrium is half the diagonal distance

$d' = \sqrt{2}\;\dfrac{0.500 \text{ m}}{2} = 0.3536 \text{ m}.$

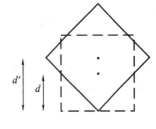

So the minimum distance that CG has to be raised is $0.3536 \text{ m} - 0.250 \text{ m} = 0.1036 \text{ m}.$

Therefore the work done against gravity is $W = (10.0 \text{ kg})(9.80 \text{ m/s}^2)(0.1036 \text{ m}) = \boxed{10.2 \text{ J}}.$

35.   When it is about to tip over the left support, the force on the right support is zero.

Choose the left support as the axis of rotation.

Using $\Sigma\tau = 0,$ $(70 \text{ kg})g\, x - (15 \text{ kg})g(1.25 \text{ m}) = 0,$ so $x = 0.27 \text{ m}.$

So it is $1.5 \text{ m} - 0.27 \text{ m} = \boxed{1.2 \text{ m}}$ from left end of board

36.   Choose the left end as the axis. $\Sigma\tau = 0$,

$$T_2(0) - (70 \text{ kg})(9.80 \text{ m/s}^2)(1.5 \text{ m}) - (15 \text{ kg})(9.80 \text{ m/s}^2)(2.75 \text{ m}) + T_1(5.5 \text{ m}) = 0,$$

so $T_1 = \boxed{2.6 \times 10^2 \text{ N}}$.

$\Sigma F_y = 0$,   ☞ $T_1 + T_2 = (70 \text{ kg} + 15 \text{ kg})(9.80 \text{ m/s}^2)$,

so $T_2 = 833 \text{ N} - 261 \text{ N} = \boxed{5.7 \times 10^2 \text{ N}}$.

T_2 can also be found by choosing the right end as the axis.

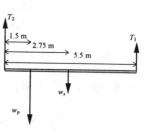

37.   (a) Assume the distance from the center of gravity (CG) to the point where the wheel touches the ground is *d*. Choose CG as the axis. $\Sigma\tau = 0$,

$f_s d \cos\theta - Nd \sin\theta = 0$,   ☞ $f_s d \cos\theta = Nd \sin\theta$,   or $\tan\theta = f_s/N$.

(b) $f_s = \mu_s N = N \tan\theta$,   ☞ $\mu_s = \tan\theta = \tan 11° = \boxed{0.19}$.

(c) $\Sigma F_y = N - mg = 0$,   ☞ $N = mg$.

$$f_s = \mu_s N = \mu_s mg = F_c = m\frac{v^2}{r}, \quad ☞ \quad v = \sqrt{\mu_s gr} = \sqrt{0.19(9.80 \text{ m/s}^2)(6.5 \text{ m})} = \boxed{3.5 \text{ m/s}}.$$

38.   (d).

39.   (a).

40.   (a) $\boxed{\text{Yes}}$. Moment of inertia has a minimum value at the center of mass.

        (b) $\boxed{\text{No}}$. Mass would have to be negative.

41.   The moment of inertia depends on how mass is distributed about an axis. Physically, this means that, under a constant torque, the angular acceleration depends on the location of the axis of rotation.

42.   The hard-boiled egg is a rigid body, while the raw egg is not.

43.   This is the rotational analog of "pulling the table cloth" in Exercise 4.9. It takes a certain amount of torque to accelerate the paper tower and the paper can only exert a certain amount of force, and therefore torque. When the paper is pulled quickly (a large force is required to accelerate the roll), the force the paper can provide is not great enough to accelerate the paper roll. However, if the paper is pulled slowly, the paper is strong enough to accelerate the roll because the force required is smaller. The amount of paper on the roll affects the results. The more paper the roll has, the greater the moment of inertia, the greater the force required to accelerate the roll, and therefore the easier to tear.

44.   (a) The meterstick has a higher center of mass; larger moment of inertia and smaller angular acceleration.

(b) Softball wins, volleyball and basketball tie, because the softball (a sphere) has a smaller moment of inertia and so a larger angular acceleration.

45.   (a) $I = \Sigma(mr^2) = (2.00\ \text{kg})(1.50\ \text{m})^2 + (3.00\ \text{kg})(1.50\ \text{m})^2 + (1.00\ \text{kg})(1.50\ \text{m})^2 + (4.00\ \text{kg})(1.50\ \text{m})^2$

$= \boxed{22.5\ \text{kg·m}^2}$.

(b) $I = (2.00\ \text{kg})(2.50\ \text{m})^2 + (3.00\ \text{kg})(2.50\ \text{m})^2 + (1.00\ \text{kg})(2.50\ \text{m})^2 + (4.00\ \text{kg})(2.50\ \text{m})^2 = \boxed{62.5\ \text{kg·m}^2}$.

(c) $r^2 = (1.50\ \text{m})^2 + (2.50\ \text{m})^2 = 8.50\ \text{m}^2$.

$I = (2.00\ \text{kg})(8.50\ \text{m}^2) + (3.00\ \text{kg})(8.50\ \text{m}^2) + (1.00\ \text{kg})(8.50\ \text{m}^2) + (4.00\ \text{kg})(8.50\ \text{m}^2) = \boxed{85.0\ \text{kg·m}^2}$.

46. $I = \tfrac{1}{2}mr^2 = \tfrac{1}{2}(0.15\ \text{kg})(0.075\ \text{m})^2 = 4.219 \times 10^{-4}\ \text{kg·m}^2$.

$\tau = I\alpha$,   ☞ $\alpha = \dfrac{\tau}{I} = \dfrac{6.4\ \text{m·N}}{4.219 \times 10^{-4}\ \text{kg·m}^2} = \boxed{3.4 \times 10^4\ \text{rad/s}^2}$.

47.   For a solid ball, $I = \tfrac{2}{5}MR^2 = \tfrac{2}{5}(20\ \text{kg})(0.20\ \text{m})^2 = 0.32\ \text{kg·m}^2$.

$\tau = I\alpha = (0.32\ \text{kg·m}^2)(2.0\ \text{rad/s}^2) = \boxed{0.64\ \text{m·N}}$.

48.   (a) $I = \Sigma(mr^2) = (2.0\ \text{kg})(0.30\ \text{m})^2 + (4.0\ \text{kg})(0.75\ \text{m})^2 = \boxed{2.4\ \text{kg·m}^2}$.

(b) $X_{CM} = \dfrac{\Sigma_i(m_i x_i)}{M} = \dfrac{(2.0\ \text{kg})(0.30\ \text{m}) + (4.0\ \text{kg})(0.75\ \text{m})}{2.0\ \text{kg} + 4.0\ \text{kg}} = 0.60\ \text{m}$.

So $I = (2.0\ \text{kg})(0.60\ \text{m} - 0.30\ \text{m})^2 + (4.0\ \text{kg})(0.75\ \text{m} - 0.60\ \text{m})^2 = \boxed{0.27\ \text{kg·m}^2}$.

(c) $I = I_{CM} + Md^2 = 0.27\ \text{kg·m}^2 + (6.0\ \text{kg})(0.60\ \text{m})^2 = \boxed{2.4\ \text{kg·m}^2}$.

49.   (a) $I = \Sigma(mr^2) = (3.0\ \text{kg})(1.0\ \text{m})^2 + (5.0\ \text{kg})(1.0\ \text{m})^2 = \boxed{8.0\ \text{kg·m}^2}$.

(b) $X_{CM} = \dfrac{\Sigma_i(m_i x_i)}{M} = \dfrac{(3.0\ \text{kg})(0) + (5.0\ \text{kg})(2.0\ \text{m})}{3.0\ \text{kg} + 5.0\ \text{kg}} = 1.25\ \text{m}$ from the 3.0-kilogram mass.

$I = (3.0\ \text{kg})(1.25\ \text{m})^2 + (5.0\ \text{kg})(0.75\ \text{m})^2 = \boxed{7.5\ \text{kg·m}^2}$.

(c) $\boxed{\text{Yes}}$, according to the parallel axis theorem $(I = I_{CM} + Md^2)$, since md^2 can never be negative.

50.   First calculate the angular acceleration from kinematics.

$\alpha = \dfrac{\Delta\omega}{\Delta t} = \dfrac{2.0\ \text{rad/s} - 0}{12\ \text{s}} = 0.167\ \text{rad/s}^2$.

So $\tau = I\alpha = \tfrac{1}{2}mr^2\alpha = \tfrac{1}{2}(2000\ \text{kg})(30\ \text{m})^2\ (0.167\ \text{rad/s}^2) = \boxed{1.5 \times 10^5\ \text{m·N}}$.

51. First find the angular acceleration from dynamics.

$I_{CM} = \frac{2}{5} MR^2.$ $I = I_{CM} + Md^2 = \frac{2}{5} MR^2 + MR^2 = \frac{7}{5} MR^2.$

$\alpha = \frac{\tau}{I} = \frac{\tau}{\frac{7}{5} MR^2} = \frac{10 \text{ m·N}}{\frac{7}{5}(15 \text{ kg})(0.15 \text{ m})^2} = 21.2 \text{ rad/s}^2.$

So $\omega^2 = \omega_o^2 + 2\alpha\theta,$ ☞ $\theta = \frac{\omega^2 - \omega_o^2}{2\alpha} = \frac{(7.5 \text{ rad/s})^2 - (3.0 \text{ rad/s})^2}{2(21.2 \text{ rad/s}^2)} = \boxed{1.1 \text{ rad}}.$

52. First find the angular acceleration from kinematics.

$\omega^2 = \omega_o^2 + 2\alpha\theta,$ ☞ $a = \frac{\omega^2 - \omega_o^2}{2\theta} = \frac{(3.0 \text{ rad/s})^2 - (0)^2}{2(2.0)(2\pi \text{ rad})}) = 0.358 \text{ rad/s}^2.$

$I = \frac{1}{2} MR^2 = \frac{1}{2}(10 \text{ kg})(0.50 \text{ m})^2 = 1.25 \text{ kg·m}^2.$

$\tau = I\alpha = (1.25 \text{ kg·m}^2)(0.358 \text{ rad/s}^2) = \boxed{0.45 \text{ m·N}}.$

53. $I_{CM} = \frac{2}{5} MR^2.$ $I = I_{CM} + Md^2 = \frac{2}{5} MR^2 + MR^2 = \frac{7}{5} MR^2.$

So $\frac{I}{I_{CM}} = \frac{\frac{7}{5}}{\frac{2}{5}} = 3.5,$ or $\boxed{3.5 \text{ times}}.$

54. (a) $I = I_{CM} + Md^2 = \frac{1}{2} MR^2 + M\left(\frac{2}{3} R\right)^2 = \frac{17}{18} MR^2.$

$\tau = I\alpha = \frac{17}{18}(0.25 \text{ kg})(0.060 \text{ m})^2(2.0 \text{ rad/s}^2) = \boxed{1.7 \times 10^{-3} \text{ m·N}}.$

(b) The difference in moment of inertia is $\Delta I = I - I_{CM} = M\left(\frac{2}{3} R\right)^2 = \frac{4}{9} MR^2.$

So the corresponding difference in torque is $\Delta\tau = \frac{4}{9}(0.25 \text{ kg})(0.060 \text{ m})^2(2.0 \text{ rad/s}^2) = \boxed{8.0 \times 10^{-4} \text{ m·N}}.$

55. Apply Newton's second law and note $a = r\alpha.$

m_2: $m_2 g - T_2 = m_2 a,$ Eq. (1)

pulley: $T_2 R - T_1 R - \tau_f = I\alpha = \frac{1}{2} MR^2 \alpha = \frac{1}{2} MRa,$

        or $T_2 - T_1 - \frac{\tau_f}{R} = \frac{1}{2} Ma,$ Eq. (2)

m_1: $T_1 - m_1 g = m_1 a.$ Eq. (3)

Eq. (1) + Eq. (2) + Eq. (3) gives $(m_2 - m_1)g - \frac{\tau_f}{R} = (m_1 + m_2 + 0.5M)a,$

so $a = \frac{(m_2 - m_1)g - \frac{\tau_f}{R}}{m_1 + m_2 + 0.5M} = \frac{(0.80 \text{ kg} - 0.40 \text{ kg})(9.80 \text{ m/s}^2) - \frac{0.35 \text{ m·N}}{0.15 \text{ m}}}{0.40 \text{ kg} + 0.80 \text{ kg} + 0.5(0.20 \text{ kg})} = \boxed{1.2 \text{ m/s}^2}.$

56. (a) Apply Newton's second law and note $a = r\alpha$.

m_2: $\qquad\qquad T_2 - m_2 g = m_2 a,$ $\qquad\qquad\qquad\qquad\qquad\qquad$ Eq. (1)

pulley: $\qquad\quad T_1 R - T_2 R = I\alpha = \frac{1}{2}MR^2\alpha = \frac{1}{2}MRa,$

or $\qquad\qquad\quad T_1 - T_2 = 0.5Ma,$ $\qquad\qquad\qquad\qquad\qquad\qquad$ Eq. (2)

m_1: $\qquad\qquad m_1 g \sin\theta - T_1 = m_1 a,$ $\qquad\qquad\qquad\qquad\qquad$ Eq. (3)

Eq. (1) + Eq. (2) + Eq. (3) gives $\quad m_1 g \sin\theta - m_2 g = (m_1 + m_2 + 0.5M)a,$

so $\quad a = \dfrac{(m_1 \sin\theta - m_2)g}{m_1 + m_2 + 0.5M} = \dfrac{[(8.0\text{ kg}) \sin 30° - (3.0\text{ kg})](9.80\text{ m/s}^2)}{8.0\text{ kg} + 3.0\text{ kg} + 0.5(0.10\text{ kg})} = \boxed{0.89\text{ m/s}^2}.$

(b) pulley: $\quad T_1 R - T_2 R - \tau_f = I\alpha = \frac{1}{2}MR^2\alpha = \frac{1}{2}MRa,$

or $\quad T_1 - T_2 - \dfrac{\tau_f}{R} = 0.5Ma.$ $\qquad\qquad\qquad\qquad\qquad\qquad$ Eq. (2)

So $\quad a = \dfrac{(m_1 \sin\theta - m_2)g - \dfrac{\tau_f}{R}}{m_1 + m_2 + 0.5M} = \dfrac{[(8.0\text{ kg}) \sin 30° - (3.0\text{ kg})](9.80\text{ m/s}^2) - \dfrac{0.050\text{ m·N}}{0.10\text{ m}}}{8.0\text{ kg} + 3.0\text{ kg} + 0.5(0.10\text{ kg})}$

$\qquad = \boxed{0.84\text{ m/s}^2}.$

The tensions are different because of the frictional torque.

57. $\quad \tau = RF = I\alpha = \frac{1}{2}MR^2\alpha,$ ☞ $\quad F = \frac{1}{2}MR\alpha = \frac{1}{2}(2.0\text{ kg})(0.50\text{ m})(4.8\text{ rad/s}^2) = \boxed{2.4\text{ N}}.$

58. First find the angular acceleration from dynamics.

The moment of inertia for a disk-shaped wheel $I = \frac{1}{2}MR^2$.

$\tau = RF = I\alpha = \frac{1}{2}MR^2\alpha,$ ☞ $\quad \alpha = \dfrac{2F}{MR} = \dfrac{2(150\text{ N})}{(0.30\text{ kg})(0.090\text{ m})} = 1.11 \times 10^4\text{ rad/s}^2.$

So $\quad \omega^2 = \omega_o^2 + 2\alpha\theta = 0 + 2(1.11 \times 10^4\text{ rad/s}^2)(2\pi\text{ rad}) = 1.39 \times 10^5\text{ rad}^2/\text{s}^2,$ ☞ $\quad \omega = \boxed{3.7 \times 10^2\text{ rad/s}}.$

59. (a) The moment of inertia of a meterstick about its end is $I = \frac{1}{3}ML^2$. The torque is generated by the weight of the stick through its center of mass.

$\tau = RF = \frac{1}{2}LMg = I\alpha = \frac{1}{3}ML^2\alpha,$ ☞ $\quad \alpha = \dfrac{3g}{2L}.$ So $\quad a = r\alpha = L\dfrac{3g}{2L} = \boxed{1.5g}.$

(b) $a = g = r\dfrac{3g}{2L},$ ☞ $\quad r = \dfrac{2L}{3} = 0.67\text{ m} = \boxed{\text{67-cm position}}.$

60. If the finger is pulled away, all the pennies will fall freely under gravity and have acceleration equal to g. From the calculation in Exercise 8.59, the acceleration above the 67 cm position is greater than g. So the last four pennies at 70, 80, 90, and the 100 cm positions will not fall as fast as the meterstick.

61. Apply Newton's second law and note $a = r\alpha$.

For the CM: $\qquad\qquad \Sigma F = Mg - 2T = Ma$, $\qquad\qquad\qquad\qquad\qquad$ Eq. (1)

For rotation about CM: $\quad \Sigma \tau = 2TR = I\alpha = \frac{1}{2}MR^2\alpha = \frac{1}{2}MRa$,

or $\qquad\qquad\qquad\qquad 2T = 0.5Ma$, $\qquad\qquad\qquad\qquad\qquad\qquad$ Eq. (2)

Eq. (1) + Eq. (2) gives $\quad Mg = 1.5Ma$, $\quad$ so $\quad a = \dfrac{g}{1.5} = \dfrac{9.80 \text{ m/s}^2}{1.5} = \boxed{6.5 \text{ m/s}^2}$.

62. The hoop rotates about an instantaneous axis of rotation through

the point of contact (point O).

The moment of inertia about this axis is

$I = I_{CM} + Md^2 = MR^2 + MR^2 = 2MR^2$.

The torque by gravity is $\quad \tau = MgR\sin\theta$.

So $\quad a = R\alpha = R\dfrac{\tau}{I} = R\dfrac{MgR\sin\theta}{2MR^2} = \dfrac{g\sin\theta}{2}$

$\qquad = \dfrac{(9.80 \text{ m/s}^2)\sin 15°}{2} = \boxed{1.3 \text{ m/s}^2}$.

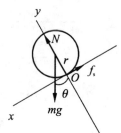

63. From Example 8.11, $\quad f_s = \frac{2}{5}Ma$, $\quad$ and $\quad a = \frac{5}{7}g\sin\theta$, $\quad$ so $\quad f_s = \frac{2}{7}Mg\sin\theta$.

Also $\quad \mu_s = \dfrac{f_s}{N} = \dfrac{\frac{2}{72}Mg\sin\theta}{Mg\cos\theta} = \dfrac{2}{7}\tan\theta$.

Therefore $\quad \theta = \boxed{\tan^{-1}\dfrac{7\mu_s}{2}}$.

64. (b).

65. (c).

66. $W = \tau\theta = \tau\dfrac{s}{r} = (12 \text{ m·N})\dfrac{15 \text{ m}}{0.40 \text{ m}} = \boxed{4.5 \times 10^2 \text{ J}}$.

67. (a) $W = \tau\theta = rF\theta = (0.90 \text{ m})(15 \text{ N})(120°)(\pi \text{ rad}/180°) = \boxed{28 \text{ J}}$.

(b) $P = \dfrac{W}{\Delta t} = \dfrac{28 \text{ J}}{2.0 \text{ s}} = \boxed{14 \text{ W}}$.

68. From the work energy theorem:

$W = \tau\theta = \frac{1}{2}I\omega^2 - \frac{1}{2}I\omega_o^2 = \frac{1}{2}I\omega^2 - \frac{1}{2}I(0)^2 = \frac{1}{2}I\omega^2 = \frac{1}{2}(\frac{1}{2}MR^2)\omega^2 = \frac{1}{4}MR^2\omega^2$.

So $\quad \omega = \sqrt{\dfrac{4\tau\theta}{MR^2}} = \sqrt{\dfrac{4(10 \text{ m·N})(2.0)(2\pi \text{ rad})}{(10 \text{ kg})(0.20 \text{ m})^2}} = \boxed{35 \text{ rad/s}}$.

69. From the work energy theorem:

$$W = \tau\theta = \tfrac{1}{2}I\omega^2 - \tfrac{1}{2}I\omega_0^{~2} = \tfrac{1}{2}I\omega^2 - \tfrac{1}{2}I(0)^2 = \tfrac{1}{2}I\omega^2 = \tfrac{1}{2}(\tfrac{1}{2}MR^2)\omega^2 = \tfrac{1}{4}MR^2\omega^2.$$

So $\quad \tau = \dfrac{MR^2\omega^2}{4\theta} = \dfrac{(2.5\text{ kg})(0.15\text{ m})^2(25\text{ rad/s})^2}{4(3.0)(2\pi\text{ rad})} = \boxed{0.47\text{ m·N}}$.

70. From energy conservation: $\quad \tfrac{1}{2}m(0)^2 + \tfrac{1}{2}I(0)^2 + mgh = \tfrac{1}{2}mv^2 + \tfrac{1}{2}I\omega^2 + mg(0)$.

Since $v = R\omega \quad$ and $\quad I = \tfrac{1}{2}MR^2$,

we have $\quad mgh = \tfrac{1}{2}mv^2 + \tfrac{1}{2}\tfrac{1}{2}MR^2\,\dfrac{v^2}{R^2} = \tfrac{1}{2}mv^2 + \tfrac{1}{4}Mv^2$.

So $\quad v = \sqrt{\dfrac{4mgh}{2m + M}} = \sqrt{\dfrac{4(1.0\text{ kg})(9.80\text{ m/s}^2)(2.0\text{ m})}{2(1.0\text{ kg}) + 0.30\text{ kg}}} = \boxed{5.8\text{ m/s}}$.

71. Apply energy conservation and note $v = r\omega$. $\quad \tfrac{1}{2}Mv^2 + \tfrac{1}{2}I\omega^2 + Mg(0) = \tfrac{1}{2}M(0)^2 + \tfrac{1}{2}I(0)^2 + Mgh$,

or $\quad \tfrac{1}{2}MR^2\omega^2 + \tfrac{1}{2}\tfrac{2}{5}MR^2\omega^2 = Mgh$,

so $\quad h = \dfrac{7}{10g}r^2\omega^2 = \dfrac{7}{10(9.80\text{ m/s}^2)}(0.15\text{ m})^2(10\text{ rad/s})^2 = \boxed{0.16\text{ m}}$.

72. The CM lowers by an amount of $h = 0.50$ m.

From energy conservation: $\quad \tfrac{1}{2}I(0)^2 + mgh = \tfrac{1}{2}I\omega^2 + mg(0)$,

so $\quad \omega = \sqrt{\dfrac{2mgh}{I}} = \sqrt{\dfrac{2mgh}{\tfrac{1}{3}m L^2}} = \sqrt{\dfrac{6gh}{L^2}} = \dfrac{6(9.80\text{ m/s}^2)(0.50\text{ m})}{(1.0\text{ m})^2} = \boxed{5.4\text{ rad/s}}$.

73. The cylinder has more moment of inertia ($\tfrac{1}{2}MR^2$ versus $\tfrac{2}{5}MR^2$ for the ball).

So the cylinder has more kinetic energy and will go higher.

The total kinetic energy of the cylinder is $\quad K_c = \tfrac{1}{2}Mv^2 + \tfrac{1}{2}I\omega^2 = \tfrac{1}{2}Mv^2 + \tfrac{1}{2}(\tfrac{1}{2}MR^2)\dfrac{v^2}{R^2} = \tfrac{3}{4}Mv^2$,

The total kinetic energy of the sphere is $\quad K_s = \tfrac{1}{2}Mv^2 + \tfrac{1}{2}(\tfrac{2}{5}MR^2)\dfrac{v^2}{R^2} = \tfrac{7}{10}Mv^2$.

So from energy conservation, $K + 0 = 0 + Mgh$, we have

$$\dfrac{h_c - h_s}{h_s} = \dfrac{Mgh_c - Mgh_s}{Mgh_s} = \dfrac{K_c - K_s}{K_s} = \dfrac{3/4 - 7/10}{7/10} = 7\%$$

Thus $\boxed{\text{cylinder goes higher by 7.1\%}}$.

74. Apply energy conservation and note $v = r\omega$. $\quad \tfrac{1}{2}M(0)^2 + \tfrac{1}{2}I(0)^2 + Mgh = \tfrac{1}{2}Mv^2 + \tfrac{1}{2}I\omega^2 + Mg(0)$.

or $\quad \tfrac{1}{2}Mv^2 + \tfrac{1}{2}Mv^2 = Mv^2 = Mgh$, ☞ $v = \sqrt{gh} = \sqrt{(9.80\text{ m/s}^2)(1.2\text{ m})} = \boxed{3.4\text{ m/s}}$.

75.   (a) 7500 rpm = 785.4 rad/s.   From the work-energy theorem:

$$W = \tfrac{1}{2}I\omega^2 - \tfrac{1}{2}I\omega_0^2 = \tfrac{1}{2}I(0)^2 - \tfrac{1}{2}I\omega_0^2 = \tfrac{1}{2}(4.25 \times 10^2 \text{ kg·m}^2)(785.4 \text{ rad/s})^2 = -\boxed{1.31 \times 10^8 \text{ J}}.$$

   (b) $P = \dfrac{W}{t} = \dfrac{1.31 \times 10^8 \text{ J}}{1.5(60 \text{ s})} = \boxed{1.46 \times 10^6 \text{ W}}.$

76. $K = \tfrac{1}{2}mv^2 + \tfrac{1}{2}I\omega^2 = \tfrac{1}{2}mv^2 + \tfrac{1}{2}I\dfrac{v^2}{R^2}.$ So $K_h = \tfrac{1}{2}mv_h^2 + \tfrac{1}{2}(mR^2)\dfrac{v_h^2}{R^2} = mv_h^2,$

   $K_c = \tfrac{1}{2}mv_c^2 + \tfrac{1}{2}(\tfrac{1}{2}mR^2)\dfrac{v_c^2}{R^2} = \tfrac{3}{4}mv_c^2,$ and $K_s = \tfrac{1}{2}mv_s^2 + \tfrac{1}{2}(\tfrac{2}{5}mR^2)\dfrac{v_s^2}{R^2} = \tfrac{7}{10}mv_s^2.$

Since they are all released from the same height, the K's are the same. That means the v is the greatest for the sphere and smallest for the hoop. Therefore the sphere gets to the bottom first and the hoop last.

$$v_s = \sqrt{\frac{10K}{7m}}, \qquad v_c = \sqrt{\frac{4K}{3m}}, \quad \text{and} \quad v_h = \sqrt{\frac{K}{m}}.$$

77.   (a) $K_{tot} = \tfrac{1}{2}Mv^2 + \tfrac{1}{2}I\omega^2 = \tfrac{1}{2}Mv^2 + \tfrac{1}{2}I\dfrac{v^2}{R^2} = \tfrac{1}{2}Mv^2 + \tfrac{1}{2}(\tfrac{2}{5}MR^2)\dfrac{v^2}{R^2} = \tfrac{7}{10}Mv^2,$

   so $\dfrac{K_{rot}}{K_{tot}} = \dfrac{1/5}{7/10} = \boxed{29\%}.$

   (b) $K_{tot} = \tfrac{1}{2}mv^2 + \tfrac{1}{2}(\tfrac{2}{3}MR^2)\dfrac{v^2}{R^2} = \tfrac{5}{6}Mv^2,$ os $\dfrac{K_{rot}}{K_{tot}} = \dfrac{1/3}{5/6} = \boxed{40\%}.$

   (c) $K_{tot} = \tfrac{1}{2}Mv^2 + \tfrac{1}{2}MR^2\dfrac{v^2}{R^2} = Mv^2,$ so $\dfrac{K_{rot}}{K_{tot}} = \tfrac{1}{2} = \boxed{50\%}.$

78. $\omega = 33\tfrac{1}{3}$ rpm = 3.49 rad/s. From the work-energy theorem:

$$W = \tfrac{1}{2}I\omega^2 - \tfrac{1}{2}I\omega_0^2 = \tfrac{1}{2}I\omega^2 - \tfrac{1}{2}I(0)^2 = \tfrac{1}{2}I\omega^2 = \tfrac{1}{2}(\tfrac{1}{2}MR^2)\omega^2 = \tfrac{1}{4}(0.05 \text{ kg})(0.15 \text{ m})^2 (3.49 \text{ rad/s})^2 = \boxed{3.4 \times 10^{-3} \text{ J}}.$$

This work is supplied by the motor.

79.   (a) The centripetal force is provided solely by gravity at the minimum speed. In this case the centripetal force at the top of the track is just equal to the weight of the ball.

$$Mg = F_c = M\frac{v^2}{R}, \qquad ☞ \qquad v = \boxed{\sqrt{gR}}.$$

   (b) From energy conservation:

$$\tfrac{1}{2}M(0)^2 + \tfrac{1}{2}I(0)^2 + Mgh = \tfrac{1}{2}Mv^2 + \tfrac{1}{2}I\omega^2 + Mg(2R) = \tfrac{1}{2}Mv^2 + \tfrac{1}{2}(\tfrac{2}{5}MR^2)\frac{v^2}{R^2} + Mg(2R)$$

$$= \tfrac{7}{10}MgR + 2MgR = \tfrac{27}{10}MgR, \quad \text{so} \quad h = \boxed{2.7R}.$$

   (c) Since all the gravity is "used up" as centripetal force, the rider feels $\boxed{\text{weightless}}$.

80.   (c).

81.   Walking toward the center decreases the moment of inertia and so increases the rotational speed.

82.   The polar ice caps (with almost zero moment of inertia) will go to the ocean and increase the moment of inertia of the Earth. This results in a slower rotational speed or a $\boxed{\text{longer day}}$.

83.   The arms and legs are put onto these positions to decrease the moment of inertia. This decrease in moment of inertia increases the rotational speed.

84.   In each case, the change in the wheel's angular momentum vector is compensated by the rotation of the person to conserve the total angular momentum so the vertical angular momentum remains constant.

85.   The cat manipulates its body to change the moment of inertia to rotate or flip over. It is done by twisting one way with part of the body and then the desired part (the feet) may be rotated the other way.

86. $L = I\omega = MR^2\omega = (2.0 \times 10^{-3}\text{ kg})(0.15\text{ m})^2(5\pi\text{ rad/s}) = \boxed{7.1 \times 10^{-4}\text{ kg·m/s toward you}}$.

87. $L = I\omega,$ ☞ $\omega = \dfrac{L}{I} = \dfrac{L}{\frac{1}{2}MR^2} = \dfrac{0.45\text{ kg·m}^2/\text{s}}{\frac{1}{2}(10\text{ kg})(0.25\text{ m})^2} = \boxed{1.4\text{ rad/s}}$.

88.   Orbital: The Earth can be considered as a particle to the sun.

$\omega_o = \dfrac{2\pi\text{ rad}}{(365)(24)(3600\text{ s})} = 1.99 \times 10^{-7}\text{ rad/s},$ and $I_o = MR^2,$

so $L_o = I_o\,\omega_o = (6.0 \times 10^{24}\text{ kg})(1.5 \times 10^{11}\text{ m})^2(1.99 \times 10^{-7}\text{ rad/s}) = 2.69 \times 10^{40}\text{ kg·m}^2/\text{s}.$

Spin: The Earth has to be considered as a sphere.

$\omega_s = \dfrac{2\pi\text{ rad}}{(24)(3600\text{ s})} = 7.27 \times 10^{-5}\text{ rad/s},$ and $I_s = \frac{2}{5}Mr^2,$

so $L_s = \frac{2}{5}(6.0 \times 10^{24}\text{ kg})(6.4 \times 10^{6}\text{ m})^2\,(7.27 \times 10^{-5}\text{ rad/s}) = 7.15 \times 10^{33}\text{ kg·m}^2/\text{s}.$

Therefore $\dfrac{L_o}{L_s} = \dfrac{2.69 \times 10^{40}}{7.15 \times 10^{33}} = \boxed{3.8 \times 10^{6}}$.

They are not in the same direction because the Earth's axis is tilted.

89.   Similar to Exercise 8.88. $\omega_{rev} = \omega_{rot} = \dfrac{2\pi\text{ rad}}{(29.5)(24)(3600\text{ s})} = 2.66 \times 10^{-6}\text{ rad/s}.$

$L_{rev} = mR^2\omega_{rev} = (7.4 \times 10^{22}\text{ kg})(3.8 \times 10^{8}\text{ m})^2(2.66 \times 10^{-6}\text{ rad/s}) = \boxed{2.8 \times 10^{34}\text{ kg·m}^2/\text{s}}$.

$L_{rot} = \frac{2}{5}mr^2\omega_{rot} = \frac{2}{5}(7.4 \times 10^{22}\text{ kg})(1.75 \times 10^{6}\text{ m})^2(2.66 \times 10^{-6}\text{ rad/s}) = \boxed{2.4 \times 10^{29}\text{ kg·m}^2/\text{s}}$.

90.   After the coupling, both disks have the same angular speed. From angular momentum conservation:

$I_1 \omega_{1o} + I_2 \omega_{2o} = I_1 \omega_1 + I_2 \omega_2$,   ☞ $I_1(800 \text{ rpm}) + 0 = I_1 \omega + 3I_1 \omega = 4I_1 \omega$.

So $\omega = \boxed{200 \text{ rpm}}$.

91.   Since $V = \frac{4\pi}{3} R^3$, $R \propto \sqrt[3]{V}$.   So $\frac{R}{R_o} = \sqrt[3]{6} = 1.82$.

From angular momentum conservation: $I\omega = I_o \omega_o$,

$\frac{2}{5} MR^2 \frac{2\pi \text{ rad}}{T} = \frac{2}{5} MR_o^2 \frac{2\pi \text{ rad}}{T_o}$,   ☞ $\frac{T}{T_o} = \frac{R^2}{R_o^2} = (1.82)^2 = \boxed{3.3 \text{ times}}$.

92.   From angular momentum conservation: $I\omega = I_o \omega_o$,

$\omega = \frac{I_o \omega_o}{I} = \frac{(100 \text{ kg·m}^2)(2.0 \text{ rps})}{75 \text{ kg·m}^2} = \boxed{2.7 \text{ rps}}$.

93.   (a) From angular momentum conservation: $I\omega = I_o \omega_o$,

so $\omega = \frac{I_o}{I} \omega_o = \frac{1}{1 - 0.075}(4.0 \text{ rad/s}) = \boxed{4.3 \text{ rad/s}}$.

(b) $\frac{K}{K_o} = \frac{\frac{1}{2} I \omega^2}{\frac{1}{2} I_o \omega_o^2} = \frac{(0.925)(4.32 \text{ rad/s})^2}{(1)(4.0 \text{ rad/s})^2} = \boxed{1.1 \text{ times}}$.

(c) The extra kinetic energy comes from the $\boxed{\text{work done by the skater}}$ in tucking her arms.

94.   From angular momentum conservation: $I_o \omega_o = I\omega$,

or $Mb^2 \frac{v_o}{b} = Md^2 \frac{v}{d}$.   So $d = \boxed{b(v_o/v)}$.

95.   (a) From angular momentum conservation, the lazy Susan will $\boxed{\text{rotate in opposite direction}}$.

(b) The initial total angular momentum (before the kitten walks) is zero.

$L = L_o$,   ☞ $mR^2 \omega_k + \frac{1}{2} M_1 R^2 \omega_1 = m_k R^2 \frac{v_k}{R} + \frac{1}{2} M_1 R^2 \omega_1 = 0 + 0$,

so $\omega_1 = -\frac{2m_k v_k}{M_1 R} = -\frac{2(0.50 \text{ kg})(0.25 \text{ m/s})}{(1.5 \text{ kg})(0.30 \text{ m})} = -0.56 \text{ rad/s}$.

Therefore the lazy Susan rotates at $\boxed{0.56 \text{ rad/s}}$.

(c) The kitten will not be above the same point due to the rotation of the lazy Susan.

The relative angular velocity of the kitten relative to the ground is

$$\frac{0.25 \text{ m/s}}{0.30 \text{ m}} + (-0.556 \text{ rad/s}) = 0.277 \text{ rad/s}.$$

It takes $\dfrac{2\pi \text{ rad}}{(0.25 \text{ m/s})/(0.30 \text{ m})} = 7.54$ s for the kitten to go around. During that time the angular distance from where the kitten was to where the kitten is (relative to the ground) is

$\theta = (0.277 \text{ rad/s})(7.54 \text{ s}) = \boxed{2.1 \text{ rad}}$. (If we all run eastward the Earth would have to rotate slower in the eastward direction due to angular momentum conservation. This results in a longer day.)

96.   Chose the right support as axis of rotation.

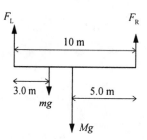

$\Delta\tau = Mg(5.0 \text{ m}) + mg(7.0 \text{ m}) - F_L(10 \text{ m}) = 0,$ so

$(10\,000 \text{ kg})(9.80 \text{ m/s}^2)(5.0 \text{ m}) + (2000 \text{ kg})(9.80 \text{ m/s}^2)(7.0 \text{ m}) = F_L(10 \text{ m})$

$F_L = 6.27 \times 10^4 \text{ N} = \boxed{6.3 \times 10^4 \text{ N}}.$

$\Sigma F_y = F_L + F_R - mg - Mg = 0,$ ☞ $F_R = (m + M)g - F_L$

$\qquad = (10\,000 \text{ kg} + 2000 \text{ kg})(9.80 \text{ m/s}^2) - 6.27 \times 10^4 \text{ N} = \boxed{5.5 \times 10^4 \text{ N}}.$

97. $\tau = k\theta,$ ☞ $k = \dfrac{\tau}{\theta}.$ Since $U = \frac{1}{2}k\theta^2$ (analog of $U = \frac{1}{2}kx^2$),

$U = \frac{1}{2}\dfrac{\tau}{\theta}\,\theta^2 = \frac{1}{2}\tau\theta = \frac{1}{2}(100 \text{ m·N})(60°)\dfrac{\pi \text{ rad}}{180°} = \boxed{52.4 \text{ J}}.$

98.   Both rotate about an instantaneous axis though the contact point.

From the parallel-axis theorem: $I_h = I_{CM} + Md^2 = MR^2 + MR^2 = 2MR^2,$

$\qquad\qquad\qquad\qquad\qquad\qquad I_c = \frac{1}{2}M(R_1^2 + R_2^2) + MR_2^2 = \frac{1}{2}M(R_1^2 + 2R_2^2).$

From Newton's second law: $Mg(R \sin\theta) = I\alpha = I\dfrac{a}{R},$

so for the hoop: $Mgr \sin\theta = 2MR^2\dfrac{a_h}{R},$ ☞ $a_h = \dfrac{g \sin\theta}{2},$

for the annular cylinder: $MgR_2 \sin\theta = \frac{1}{2}M(R_1^2 + 2R_2^2)\dfrac{a_c}{R_2},$

or $a_c = \dfrac{2g \sin\theta}{R_1^2/R_2^2 + 2} = \dfrac{g \sin\theta}{R_1^2/2R_2^2 + 1}.$

Since $R_2 > R_1,$ $R_1^2/2R_2^2 < 1,$ or $R_1^2/2R_2^2 + 1 < 2,$ so $a_c > a_h.$

Therefore the hoop rolls (accelerates) more slowly.

99.   (a) For the mass: $\Sigma F = mg - T = ma$ Eq. (1)

For the pulley: $\Sigma \tau = rT = I\alpha = \frac{1}{2}Mr^2\dfrac{a}{r} = \frac{1}{2}Mra$,   or $T = \frac{1}{2}Ma$ Eq. (2)

Solving for $a = \dfrac{mg}{m + \frac{1}{2}M} = \dfrac{(5.0\ \text{kg})(9.80\ \text{m/s}^2)}{5.0\ \text{kg} + \frac{1}{2}(10\ \text{kg})} = \boxed{4.9\ \text{m/s}^2}$.

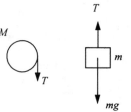

(b) $\alpha = \dfrac{a}{r} = \dfrac{4.9\ \text{m/s}^2}{0.50\ \text{m}} = \boxed{9.8\ \text{rad/s}^2}$.

100.   (a) $\omega = \dfrac{v}{R} = \dfrac{1.5\ \text{m/s}}{0.40\ \text{m}} = \boxed{3.8\ \text{rad/s}}$.

(b) $L = I\omega = MR^2\omega = (2.0\ \text{kg})(0.40\ \text{m})^2(3.75\ \text{rad/s}) = \boxed{1.2\ \text{kg·m}^2/\text{s}}$.

101.   Since the angular velocity is constant, the net torque acting on the piece is $\boxed{0}$.

102.   Choose the center of gravity as the axis of rotation.

$\Sigma \tau = (25\ \text{kg})gx - (30\ \text{kg})g(1.6\ \text{m} - x) = 0$,   or $25\,x - 48 + 30\,x = 0$.

Solving, $x = \boxed{0.87\ \text{m from feet}}$.

$\boxed{\text{No}}$, the mass of the human body is not uniformly distributed.

103.   (a) The first brick is not displaced.

So for each brick, the maximum displacement is $\dfrac{20\ \text{cm}}{8} = \boxed{2.5\ \text{cm}}$.

(b) The height of the center of mass is $\dfrac{9(8.0\ \text{cm})}{2} = \boxed{36\ \text{cm}}$.

104.   (a) $I = Mk = \frac{2}{5}MR^2$,   ☞ $k = \boxed{\sqrt{\frac{2}{5}}R}$.

(b) $I = Mk = \frac{1}{2}MR^2$,   ☞ $k = \boxed{\sqrt{\frac{1}{2}}R}$.

(c) $I = Mk = MR^2$,   ☞ $k = \boxed{R}$.

105.   After the child jumps onto the rim the angular speed of the child and the disk are the same. From angular

momentum conservation: $\frac{1}{2}(100\ \text{kg})(2.0\ \text{m})^2(2.0\ \text{rad/s}) + 0 = \frac{1}{2}(100\ \text{kg})(2.0\ \text{m})^2\omega + (25\ \text{kg})(2.0\ \text{m})^2\omega$.

Solving for $\omega = \boxed{1.3\ \text{rad/s}}$.

106. $\Sigma F_x = -T_1 \cos 45° + T_2 \cos 30° = 0$,   or $-\sqrt{2}\,T_1 + \sqrt{3}\,T_2 = 0$ Eq. (1)

$\Sigma F_y = T_1 \sin 45° - T_2 \sin 30° - mg = 0$,   or $\sqrt{2}\,T_1 - T_2 - 2mg = 0$.   Eq. (2)

Eq. (1) + Eq. (2) gives $(\sqrt{3} - 1)T_2 = 2mg$,

so $T_2 = \dfrac{2(1.5 \text{ kg})(9.80 \text{ m/s}^2)}{\sqrt{3} - 1} = \boxed{40 \text{ N}}$ and $T_1 = \sqrt{\dfrac{3}{2}}\,T_2 = \boxed{49 \text{ N}}$.

107. $\Sigma F_y = T_1 \sin 45° - mg = 0$,   ☞ $T_1 = \dfrac{mg}{\sin 45°} = \dfrac{(1.5 \text{ kg})(9.80 \text{ m/s}^2)}{\sin 45°} = 21 \text{ N}$,

$\Sigma F_x = -T_1 \cos 45° + T_2 = 0$, $T_2 = T_1 \cos 45° = 15 \text{ N}$.   So the tensions are $\boxed{21 \text{ N and } 15 \text{ N}}$.

108. On the verge of the unstable equilibrium, the weight goes through the lower corner of the trailer.

So $\tan\theta = \dfrac{L/2}{h} = \dfrac{3.66 \text{ m}}{2(3.58 \text{ m})} = 0.511$,

therefore $\theta = \boxed{27°}$.

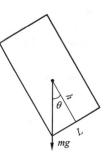

109. Since $I \propto r^2$, the moment of inertia is more when the axis is on the $\boxed{\text{smaller side}}$.

Let $a = 40$ cm and $b = 30$ cm.

From the parallel-axis theorem: $I = I_{CM} + Md^2$,

the moment of inertia for an axis on the smaller side is

$I_s = \frac{1}{12}M(a^2 + b^2) + M(a/2)^2 = \frac{1}{12}M(3a^2 + b^2)$,

the moment of inertia for an axis on the larger axis is

$I_l = \frac{1}{12}M(a^2 + b^2) + M(b/2)^2 = \frac{1}{12}M(a^2 + 3b^2)$.

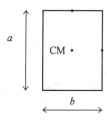

So $\dfrac{I_s}{I_l} = \dfrac{3a^2 + b^2}{a^2 + 3b^2} = \dfrac{3(40)^2 + (30)^2}{(40)^2 + 3(30)^2} = \boxed{1.3 \text{ times}}$.

CHAPTER 9

1.   (c).

2.   (a).

3.   It will have less strain for a given stress or greater stress for a given strain.

4.   Scissors exert large shear forces on materials. So $\boxed{\text{yes}}$, this name is in physical sense.

5. $\dfrac{F}{A} = Y\dfrac{\Delta L}{L_o}$, ☞ $F = YA\dfrac{\Delta L}{L_o} = \dfrac{YA}{L_o}\Delta L$. Compare with $F = k\Delta x$,

   we have $k = \dfrac{YA}{L_o}$.   So the units are $\dfrac{\text{N/m}^2 \cdot \text{m}^2}{\text{m}} = \boxed{\text{N/m}}$.

6. $\text{Stress} = \dfrac{F}{A} = \dfrac{mg}{\pi r^2} = \dfrac{(50\ \text{kg})(9.80\ \text{m/s}^2)}{\pi(1.0 \times 10^{-2}\ \text{m})^2} = \boxed{1.6 \times 10^6\ \text{N/m}^2}$.

7. $\text{Stain} = \dfrac{\Delta L}{L_o} = \dfrac{0.10\ \text{m}}{5.0\ \text{m}} = \boxed{0.020}$.

8.   (a) The compression stress $= \dfrac{F}{A} = \dfrac{(250\ \text{N})\sin 37°}{(0.040\ \text{m})(0.040\ \text{m})} = \boxed{9.4 \times 10^4\ \text{N/m}^2}$.

   (b) The shear stress $= \dfrac{(250\ \text{N})\cos 37°}{(0.040\ \text{m})(0.040\ \text{m})} = \boxed{1.2 \times 10^5\ \text{N/m}^2}$.

9. $\text{Stress} = \dfrac{F}{A} = \dfrac{mg}{\pi r^2} = \dfrac{(6.0\ \text{kg})(9.80\ \text{m/s}^2)}{\pi(0.50 \times 10^{-3}\ \text{m})^2} = 7.49 \times 10^7\ \text{N/m}^2$,

   $\text{strain} = \dfrac{\Delta L}{L_o} = \dfrac{1.4 \times 10^{-3}\ \text{m}}{2.0\ \text{m}} = 7.0 \times 10^{-4}$.

   So $Y = \dfrac{\text{stress}}{\text{strain}} = \dfrac{7.49 \times 10^7\ \text{N/m}^2}{7.0 \times 10^{-4}} = \boxed{1.1 \times 10^{11}\ \text{N/m}^2}$.

10.   From $Y = \dfrac{F/A}{\Delta L/L_o} = \dfrac{FL_o}{A\Delta L}$,

   $\Delta L = \dfrac{FL_o}{YA} = \dfrac{(5.0\ \text{kg})(9.80\ \text{m/s}^2)(2.0\ \text{m})}{(7.0 \times 10^{10}\ \text{N/m}^2)(\pi)(1.0 \times 10^{-3}\ \text{m})^2} = 4.5 \times 10^{-4}\ \text{m} = \boxed{0.45\ \text{mm}}$.

11. From $\quad Y = \dfrac{F/A}{\Delta L/L_0} = \dfrac{FL_0}{A\Delta L}$,

$$F = \frac{YA\Delta L}{L_0} = \frac{(11 \times 10^{10} \text{ N/m}^2)(\pi)(1.5 \times 10^{-3} \text{ m})^2(0.3 \times 10^{-3} \text{ m})}{5.0 \text{ m}} = \boxed{47 \text{ N}}.$$

12. From $\quad Y = \dfrac{F/A}{\Delta L/L_0} = \dfrac{FL_0}{A\Delta L}$,

$$F = \frac{YA\Delta L}{L_0} = \frac{(20 \times 10^{10} \text{ N/m}^2)(\pi)(2.5 \times 10^{-3} \text{ m})^2(3.0 \times 10^{-3} \text{ m})}{8.0 \text{ m}} \quad \boxed{1.9 \times 10^5 \text{ N}}.$$

This is about 43 tons. So yes, it is a good reason to leave a a gap to eliminate this stress.

13. From $\quad Y = \dfrac{F/A}{\Delta L/L_0} = \dfrac{FL_0}{A\Delta L}$,

$$\Delta L = \frac{FL_0}{YA} = \frac{(12.0 \times 10^3 \text{ kg})(9.80 \text{ m/s}^2)(2.00 \text{ m})}{(20 \times 10^{10} \text{ N/m}^2)(0.200 \text{ m})(0.150 \text{ m})} = = \boxed{3.92 \times 10^{-5} \text{ m}}.$$

14. Since the compression strain $= \dfrac{\Delta L}{L_0} = -\dfrac{\text{stress}}{Y}$, the stresses are the same for both and brass has a smaller

Young's modulus. Brass will have a greater strain $\dfrac{\Delta L}{L_0}$ and so it will be compressed more. Therefore the

brass will be shorter than the copper and thus it will bend $\boxed{\text{toward brass}}$.

15. Shear strain: $\quad \phi = \dfrac{\text{shear stress}}{S} = \dfrac{F/A}{S} = \dfrac{F}{SA} = \dfrac{500 \text{ N}}{(2.5 \times 10^{10} \text{ N/m}^2)(0.10 \text{ m})^2} = 2.0 \times 10^{-6} = \dfrac{x}{h}.$

So $\quad x = (2.0 \times 10^{-6})(0.10 \text{ m}) = \boxed{2.0 \times 10^{-7} \text{ m}}.$

16. Shear strain $\quad \phi = \dfrac{\text{shear stress}}{S}, \quad \text{☞} \quad \dfrac{\phi_{\text{Al}}}{\phi_{\text{Cu}}} = \dfrac{S_{\text{Cu}}}{S_{\text{Al}}} = \dfrac{3.8 \times 10^{10} \text{ N/m}^2}{2.5 \times 10^{10} \text{ N/m}^2} = 1.52.$

$\boxed{\text{Aluminum by 1.5 times}}.$

17. $S = \dfrac{\text{stress}}{\text{strain}} = \dfrac{F/A}{x/h} = \dfrac{Fh}{Ax} = \dfrac{(0.40 \text{ N})(0.040 \text{ m})}{(0.10 \text{ m})(0.080 \text{ m})(0.30 \times 10^{-3} \text{ m})} = \boxed{6.7 \times 10^3 \text{ N/m}^2}.$

18. To completely shear off the rivets, $x = 0.20$ cm. $\quad S = \dfrac{\text{stress}}{\text{strain}} = \dfrac{F/A}{x/h} = \dfrac{F\,h}{A\,x},$

so $\quad F = \dfrac{SAx}{h} = \dfrac{(8.2 \times 10^{10} \text{ N/m}^2)(\pi)(0.10 \times 10^{-2} \text{ m})^2(0.20 \times 10^{-2} \text{ m})}{1.0 \times 10^{-2} \text{ m}} = 5.15 \times 10^4 \text{ N}.$

Since there are two rivets, the force required is $2(5.15 \times 10^4 \text{ N}) = \boxed{1.0 \times 10^5 \text{ N}}.$

19. (a) Since $B = -\dfrac{\Delta p}{\Delta V/V_o}$, the smaller the B, the greater the compressibility. So it is $\boxed{\text{ethyl alcohol}}$.

(b) $\dfrac{\Delta p_w}{\Delta p_e} = \dfrac{B_w}{B_e} = \dfrac{2.2 \times 10^9 \text{ N/m}^2}{1.0 \times 10^9 \text{ N/m}^2} = \boxed{2.2 \text{ times}}$.

20. $\dfrac{\Delta V}{V_o} = -\dfrac{\Delta p}{B} = -\dfrac{1.2 \times 10^7 \text{ N/m}^2}{7.5 \times 10^{10} \text{ N/m}^2} = 1.6 \times 10^{-4}$.

So $V = V_o + \Delta V = (1 - 1.6 \times 10^{-4})(0.060 \text{ m})^3 = 2.16 \times 10^{-4} \text{ m}^3$.

$\Delta L = L - L_o = \sqrt[3]{V} - L_o = \sqrt[3]{V_o + \Delta V} - L_o = \sqrt[3]{(1 - 1.6 \times 10^{-4})(0.060 \text{ m})^3} - 0.060 \text{ m}$

$= -\boxed{3.2 \times 10^{-6} \text{ m}}$.

21. First find the tensions on the cables. The system is symmetrical. So in the vertical direction:

$2T \sin 15° = mg,$ ☞ $T = \dfrac{(45 \text{ kg})(9.80 \text{ m/s}^2)}{2 \sin 15°} = 852 \text{ N}.$

$\dfrac{\Delta L}{L_o} = \dfrac{\text{stress}}{Y} = \dfrac{T/A}{Y} = \dfrac{T}{YA} = \dfrac{852 \text{ N}}{(20 \times 10^{10} \text{ N/m}^2)(\pi)(0.50 \times 10^{-2} \text{ m})^2} = \boxed{5.4 \times 10^{-5}}$.

22. The pressure is small on any one nail due to the large number of nails (large area).

23. (c).

24. The pressure is determined by depth only so there is $\boxed{\text{no effect}}$. If the depth is the same, the pressure is the same.

25. When the bowl is full, the atmospheric pressure on the water does not allow any water out of the bottle. When the water level in the bowl decreases below the neck of the bottle, air bubbles in and water flows out until the pressures are equalized again. No, the height does not depend on the surface area.

26. (a) The pressure inside the can is equal to the atmospheric pressure outside. When the liquid is poured from an unvented can, a partial vacuum develops inside and the pressure difference causes the pouring to be difficult. By opening the vent, you are allowing air to go into the can and the pressures are equalized so the liquid can be easily poured.

(b) When you squeeze a medicine dropper before inserting it into a liquid, you are forcing the air out and reducing the pressure inside the dropper. When you release the top with the dropper in a liquid, the liquid rises in the dropper due to atmospheric pressure.

(c) To inhale, the lungs physically expand, the internal pressure decreases, and air flows into the lungs. To exhale, the lungs contract, the internal pressure increases, and air is forced out.

27.   Bicycle tires have a much smaller contact area with the ground so they need a higher pressure to balance the weight of the bicycle and the rider.

28.   Yes. The pressure taken from the calf is higher than that taken from the arm because of a height pressure difference.

29. $p_a = \rho g h$, ☞ $h = \dfrac{1.01 \times 10^5 \text{ Pa}}{(1000 \text{ kg/m}^3)(9.80 \text{ m/s}^2)} = \boxed{10 \text{ m}}$. $\boxed{\text{No}}$, this is not practical.

30.   (a) $p_w = \rho g h = (1000 \text{ kg/m}^3)(9.80 \text{ m/s}^2)(15 \text{ m}) = \boxed{1.5 \times 10^5 \text{ Pa}}$.

        (b) $p = p_o + p_w = 1.01 \times 10^5 \text{ Pa} + 1.5 \times 10^5 \text{ Pa} = \boxed{2.5 \times 10^5 \text{ Pa}}$.

31.   The pressure by the water is equal to the pressure by the gasoline.

        $\rho_w g h_w = \rho_g g h_g$, ☞ $h_g = \dfrac{\rho_w h_w}{\rho_g} = \dfrac{(1000 \text{ kg/m}^3)(15 \text{ cm})}{680 \text{ kg/m}^3} = \boxed{22 \text{ cm}}$.

32. $p = \dfrac{F}{A} = \dfrac{mg}{A} = \dfrac{(75 \text{ kg})(9.80 \text{ m/s}^2)}{125 \times 10^{-4} \text{ m}^2} = \boxed{5.9 \times 10^4 \text{ Pa}}$.

33. $p = \dfrac{F}{2A}$, where A is the contact area of each tire.

        So $A = \dfrac{F}{p} = \dfrac{mg}{2p} = \dfrac{(90 \text{ kg})(9.80 \text{ m/s}^2)}{2(690 \times 10^3 \text{ Pa})} = \boxed{6.39 \times 10^{-4} \text{ m}^2}$.

34.   The pressure is exerted by the normal force $N = mg \cos\theta$.

        $p = \dfrac{F}{A} = \dfrac{mg \cos\theta}{A} = \dfrac{(90 \text{ kg})(9.80 \text{ m/s}^2) \cos 15°}{0.40 \text{ m}^2} = \boxed{2.1 \times 10^3 \text{ Pa}}$.

35.   Since there is a partial vacuum, the net force exerted by the atmospheric pressure on the outside crushes the can. The total surface area of the can is calculated from all six sides.

        $F = PA = (1.01 \times 10^5 \text{ Pa})(2)[(0.24 \text{ m})(0.16 \text{ m}) + (0.24 \text{ m})(0.10 \text{ m}) + (0.16 \text{ m})(0.10 \text{ m})]$

        $= \boxed{1.6 \times 10^4 \text{ N} = 3600 \text{ lb}}$.

36. $\Delta p = \rho g h = (1.29 \text{ kg/m}^3)(9.80 \text{ m/s}^2)(35 \text{ m}) = 442 \text{ Pa}$.

        So the fractional decrease is $\dfrac{\Delta p}{p_a} = \dfrac{442 \text{ Pa}}{1.013 \times 10^5 \text{ Pa}} = 4.37 \times 10^{-3} = \boxed{0.44\%}$.

37. $p = p_a - \rho g h = 1.013 \times 10^5 \text{ Pa} - (1.29 \text{ kg/m}^3)(9.80 \text{ m/s}^2)(29\,028 \text{ ft}) \times \dfrac{1 \text{ m}}{3.28 \text{ ft}} = -1.1 \times 10^4 \text{ Pa.}$

Obviously, pressure cannot be negative, so this calculation shows that the air density is not a constant but decreases rapidly with altitude.

38. (a) $w = mg = \rho V g = (1000 \text{ kg/m}^3)(5.0 \times 10^{-5} \text{ m}^2)(12 \text{ m})(9.80 \text{ m/s}^2) = \boxed{5.9 \text{ N}}.$

   (b) $p_w = \rho g h = (1000 \text{ kg/m}^3)(9.80 \text{ m/s}^2)(12 \text{ m}) = \boxed{1.2 \times 10^5 \text{ Pa}}.$

   (c) $F = PA = (1.2 \times 10^5 \text{ Pa})(0.20 \text{ m}^2) = \boxed{2.4 \times 10^4 \text{ N}}.$

39. $p = p_a + \rho_1 g h_1 + \rho_2 g h_2$

   $= 1.013 \times 10^5 \text{ Pa} + (0.75 \times 10^3 \text{ kg/m}^3)(9.80 \text{ m/s}^2)(0.040 \text{ m}) + (1000 \text{ kg/m}^3)(9.80 \text{ m/s}^2)(0.55 \text{ m})$

   $= \boxed{1.07 \times 10^5 \text{ Pa}}.$

40. $p = p_a + \rho g h = 1.013 \times 10^5 \text{ Pa} + (1000 \text{ kg/m}^3)(9.80 \text{ m/s}^2)(0.80 \text{ m}) = \boxed{1.09 \times 10^5 \text{ Pa}}.$

41. (a) $p = p_a + \rho g h = 1.013 \times 10^5 \text{ Pa} + (1.03 \times 10^3 \text{ kg/m}^3)(9.80 \text{ m/s}^2)(35\,000 \text{ ft}) \times \dfrac{1 \text{ m}}{3.28 \text{ ft}} = \boxed{1.1 \times 10^8 \text{ Pa}}.$

   (b) $p = \dfrac{F}{A},$ ☞ $F = p\,A = (1.08 \times 10^8 \text{ Pa})(\pi)(0.075 \text{ m})^2 = \boxed{1.9 \times 10^6 \text{ N}}.$

42. (a) From Pascal's principle, $p_{\text{input}} = p_{\text{output}} = \dfrac{F_{\text{output}}}{A_{\text{output}}} = \dfrac{1.5 \times 10^6 \text{ N}}{0.20 \text{ m}^2} = \boxed{7.5 \times 10^6 \text{ Pa}}.$

   (b) $F_{\text{input}} = P_{\text{input}} A_{\text{input}} = (7.5 \times 10^6 \text{ Pa})(\pi)(0.025 \text{ m})^2 = \boxed{1.5 \times 10^4 \text{ N}}.$

43. From Pascal's principle, $p_{\text{input}} = p_{\text{output}},$ ☞ $\dfrac{F_{\text{input}}}{A_{\text{input}}} = \dfrac{F_{\text{output}}}{A_{\text{output}}}.$

   So $F_{\text{input}} = \dfrac{A_{\text{input}}}{A_{\text{output}}} F_{\text{output}} = \dfrac{4.00 \text{ cm}^2}{250 \text{ cm}^2} \times (3000 \text{ kg})(9.80 \text{ m/s}^2) = \boxed{470 \text{ N}}.$

44. $p_{\text{input}} = \dfrac{F_{\text{input}}}{A_{\text{input}}} = \dfrac{470 \text{ N}}{4.00 \times 10^{-4} \text{ m}^2} = \boxed{1.2 \times 10^6 \text{ Pa}}.$

45. The force on the platform must be equal to the weight of the water. So the pressure increase is

   $\Delta p = \dfrac{F}{A} = \dfrac{mg}{A} = \dfrac{(0.25 \times 10^{-3} \text{ kg})(9.80 \text{ m/s}^2)}{p(0.55 \times 10^{-2} \text{ m})^2} = 25.78 \text{ Pa.}$

   So the change in height is $\Delta h = \dfrac{\Delta p}{\rho g} = \dfrac{25.78 \text{ Pa}}{(1000 \text{ kg/m}^3)(9.80 \text{ m/s}^2)} = 2.63 \times 10^{-3} \text{ m} = \boxed{2.6 \text{ mm}}.$

46. (c).

47. (a).

48. (a) A life jacket must have lower density than water, such that the average density of a person and a jacket is less than the density of water.

(b) Salt water has a higher density so it can exert higher buoyant force.

49. There is no change. As the ice melts, the volume of the newly converted water decreases; however, the ice which was initially above the water surface is now under the water. This compensated for the decrease in volume. It does not matter whether the ice is hollow or not. Both can be proved mathematically.

50. The water in New Orleans is partly fresh or less salty. Sea water has a higher density and therefore more buoyancy than harbor water so when the ship is in seawater, the Plimsoll mark will be above the water level.

51. It has to displace an amount of water equal to its weight or mass (if gravity is a constant).

So it is $\boxed{10\,000 \text{ metric tons}}$.

52. $F_b = \rho V g = (1000 \text{ kg/m}^3)(0.085 \text{ m})^3(9.80 \text{ m/s}^2) = 6.02 \text{ N}$,

and $W = mg = (0.65 \text{ kg})(9.80 \text{ m/s}^2) = 6.37 \text{ N}$. Since $W > F_b$, $\boxed{\text{no}}$, the object sinks.

53. (a) He did it by $\boxed{\text{water displacement}}$.

(b) $\rho = \dfrac{m}{V} = \dfrac{0.750 \text{ kg}}{3.980 \times 10^{-5} \text{ m}^3} = 18.8 \times 10^3 \text{ kg/m}^3 < \rho_g = 19.3 \times 10^3 \text{ kg/m}^3$. $\boxed{\text{No}}$.

54. When floating, $w = F_b = \rho_f g V$. $m = \dfrac{w}{g} = \rho_f V = (1000 \text{ kg/m}^3)(4.5 \text{ m})(2.0 \text{ m})(0.29 \text{ m}) = \boxed{2.6 \times 10^3 \text{ kg}}$.

55. $F_b = \rho_f g V = (1000 \text{ kg/m}^3)(9.80 \text{ m/s}^2)(0.15 \text{ m})^3 = \boxed{33 \text{ N}}$. If it cube is made of steel, the answer is the $\boxed{\text{same}}$ as buoyant force depends only on the weight of fluid displaced.

56. First find the volume of the crown with buoyancy.

$F_b = 8.0 \text{ N} - 4.0 \text{ N} = 4.0 \text{ N} = \rho_f g V$,

so $V = \dfrac{F_b}{\rho_f g} = \dfrac{4.0 \text{ N}}{(1000 \text{ kg /m}^3)(9.80 \text{ m/s}^2)} = 4.08 \times 10^{-4} \text{ m}^3$.

$\rho = \dfrac{m}{V} = \dfrac{w/g}{V} = \dfrac{8.0 \text{ N}}{(9.80 \text{ m/s}^2)(4.08 \times 10^{-4} \text{ m}^3)} = \boxed{2.0 \times 10^3 \text{ kg/m}^3}$.

57. First find the volume of the crown with buoyancy. $F_b = (0.80 \text{ kg})(9.80 \text{ m/s}^2) - 7.30 \text{ N} = 0.54 \text{ N}$.

   Since $F_b = \rho_f g V$, $V = \dfrac{F_b}{\rho_f g} = \dfrac{0.54 \text{ N}}{(1000 \text{ kg/m}^3)(9.80 \text{ m/s}^2)} = 5.51 \times 10^{-5} \text{ m}^3$.

   So the density is $\rho = \dfrac{m}{V} = \dfrac{0.80 \text{ kg}}{5.51 \times 10^{-5} \text{ m}^3} = 14.5 \times 10^3 \text{ kg/m}^3 < \rho_g = 19.3 \times 10^3 \text{ kg/m}^3$. $\boxed{\text{No}}$.

58. The buoyant force is $F_b = 0.882 \text{ N} - 0.735 \text{ N} = 0.147 \text{ N}$.

   $F_b = \rho_f g V$,   ☞ $V = \dfrac{F_b}{\rho_f g} = \dfrac{0.147 \text{ N}}{(1000 \text{ kg/m}^3)(9.80 \text{ m/s}^2)} = \boxed{1.50 \times 10^{-5} \text{ m}^3}$.

   $\rho = \dfrac{m}{V} = \dfrac{w/g}{V} = \dfrac{0.882 \text{ N}}{(1.50 \times 10^{-5} \text{ m}^3)(9.80 \text{ m/s}^2)} = \boxed{6.00 \times 10^3 \text{ kg/m}^3}$.

59. For the boat to float, $w = mg = F_b = \rho_f g V = \rho_f g L W H$.

   So $H = \dfrac{m}{\rho_f L W} = \dfrac{2000 \text{ kg}}{(1000 \text{ kg/m}^3)(4.0 \text{ m})(1.5 \text{ m})} = \boxed{0.33 \text{ m}}$.

60. For the open cube to float, $w = mg = F_b = \rho_f g V_f = \rho_f g L^3$, where V_f is the volume of the open cube.

   So $L = \sqrt[3]{\dfrac{m}{\rho_f}} = \sqrt[3]{\dfrac{\rho V}{\rho_f}} = \sqrt[3]{\dfrac{(7.8 \times 10^3 \text{ kg/m}^3)(1.0 \text{ m})^3}{1000 \text{ kg/m}^3}} = \boxed{2.0 \text{ m}}$,

   where V is the volume of the solid cube.

61. For the airship to float, the total weight (weight of the airship plus the weight of helium) must equal to the buoyant force.

   $w = m_{ship} g + m_{helium} g = m_{ship} g + \rho_{helium} g V = m_{ship} g + \rho_{helim} g(\pi r^2 L) = F_b = \rho_f g V = \rho_f g \pi r^2 L$.

   So the diameter is

   $d = 2r = 2\sqrt{\dfrac{m_{ship}}{\pi L (\rho_f - \rho_{helim})}} = 2\sqrt{\dfrac{30.0 \times 10^3 \text{ kg}}{\pi(110 \text{ m})(1.29 \text{ kg/m}^3 - 0.18 \text{ kg/m}^3)}} = \boxed{17.7 \text{ m}}$.

62. (a) For the girl to float, $w = mg = F_b = \rho_f g V_f = \rho_f g (0.90 V)$.

   So $\rho_m = \dfrac{m}{V} = (0.97)\rho_f = (0.97)(1000 \text{ kg/m}^3) = \boxed{9.7 \times 10^2 \text{ kg/m}^3}$.

   (b) $\rho_w = \dfrac{w}{V} = \rho_m g = (970 \text{ kg/m}^3)(9.80 \text{ m/s}^2) = \boxed{9.5 \times 10^3 \text{ N/m}^3}$.

63. First find the volume from buoyancy. $F_b = 9.8 \text{ N} - 9.1 \text{ N} = 0.7 \text{ N}$.

   $F_b = \rho_f g V$,   ☞ $V = \dfrac{F_b}{\rho_f g} = \dfrac{0.7 \text{ N}}{(1000 \text{ kg/m}^3)(9.80 \text{ m/s}^2)} = 7.0 \times 10^{-5} \text{ m}^3$.

   So $\rho = \dfrac{m}{V} = \dfrac{w/g}{V} = \dfrac{9.8 \text{ N}}{(7.0 \times 10^{-5} \text{ m}^3)(9.80 \text{ m/s}^2)} = 14.3 \times 10^3 \text{ kg/m}^3 < \rho_g = 19.3 \times 10^3 \text{ kg/m}^3$. $\boxed{\text{No}}$.

64.   There are many more capillaries than arteries. The total area of the capillaries is greater than that of the arteries. So if A increases, v decreases.

65.   (a).

66.   (c).

67.   The falling water causes a downward air flow inside the curtain. This in turn decreases the pressure in side according to Bernoulli's principle. The pressure difference moves the curtain inward.

68.   The concave bottom makes the air travel faster under the car. This increases in speed will reduce the pressure under the car. The pressure difference forces the car more on the ground to provide a greater normal force and friction for traction.

69.   (a) The air flow above the paper decreases the pressure there. This creates a pressure difference, and a lift force results.

        (b) The egg is kept aloft by the pressure of the air coming out of the end of the tube. As the eggs moves to one side, there is a change in the flow speed around the egg that creates an inward pressure that makes the egg move back to midstream.

70. $A_1 v_1 = A_2 v_2,$ ☞ $v_2 = \dfrac{A_1}{A_2} v_1 = \dfrac{\pi(0.20 \text{ m})^2}{\pi(0.35 \text{ m})^2} \times (3.0 \text{ m/s}) = \boxed{0.98 \text{ m/s}}.$

71. $A_1 v_1 = A_2 v_2,$ ☞ $\dfrac{v_2}{v_1} = \dfrac{A_2}{A_1} = \dfrac{\pi(1)^2}{\pi(0.5)^2} = \boxed{4}.$

72.   From Bernoulli's principle, $p_1 + \frac{1}{2}\rho v_1^2 + \rho g y_1 = p_2 + \frac{1}{2}\rho v_2^2 + \rho g y_2.$

        If $v_1 = v_2 = 0,$ we have $\Delta p = p_1 - p_2 = \rho g(y_2 - y_1).$

73.   (a) The flow rate is $Q = Av = \pi(0.5 \text{ cm})^2(4.5 \text{ cm/s}) = \boxed{3.5 \text{ cm}^3/\text{s}}.$

        (b) The speed in the capillaries is $v = \dfrac{Q}{A} = \dfrac{3.53 \text{ cm}^3/\text{s}}{2500 \text{ cm}^2} = 1.41 \times 10^{-3} \text{ cm/s.}$

        So the percentage is $\dfrac{1.41 \times 10^{-3} \text{ cm/s}}{4.5 \text{ cm/s}} = 3.1 \times 10^{-4} = \boxed{0.031\%}.$

        (c) It is a physiological need. The slow speed is needed to give time for the exchange of substances such as oxygen between the blood and the tissues.

74. (a) The flow rate is $Q = Av = \dfrac{V}{t} = \dfrac{(3.0\ \text{m})(4.5\ \text{m})(6.0\ \text{m})}{(12\ \text{min})(60\ \text{s/min})} = \boxed{0.11\ \text{m}^3/\text{s}}$.

(b) $v = \dfrac{Q}{A} = \dfrac{0.11\ \text{m}^3/\text{s}}{\pi(0.15\ \text{m})^2} = \boxed{1.6\ \text{m/s}}$.

75. (a) Use Bernoulli's principle, $p_1 + \tfrac{1}{2}\rho v_1^2 + \rho g y_1 = p_2 + \tfrac{1}{2}\rho v_2^2 + \rho g y_2$.

Here $p_1 = p_2 = p_a$,   and $v_1 \approx 0$ (at the top of the water surface),

so $v_2 = \sqrt{2g\Delta y}$.

For the 40-cm high (upper) hole, $v_u = \sqrt{2(9.80\ \text{m/s}^2)(0.05\ \text{m})} = \boxed{0.99\ \text{m/s}}$;

for the 30-cm high (middle) hole, $v_m = \sqrt{2(9.80\ \text{m/s}^2)(0.15\ \text{m})} = \boxed{1.7\ \text{m/s}}$;

for the 20-cm high (bottom) hole, $v_b = \sqrt{2(9.80\ \text{m/s}^2)(0.25\ \text{m})} = \boxed{2.2\ \text{m/s}}$;

for the 10-cm high (bottom) hole, $v_b = \sqrt{2(9.80\ \text{m/s}^2)(0.35\ \text{m})} = \boxed{2.6\ \text{m/s}}$.

(b) They are all horizontal projectile motions. First find the time of flight from the vertical motion.

$y = \tfrac{1}{2}gt^2$,   ☞ $t = \sqrt{\dfrac{2y}{g}}$.

So the range is $x = v_x t = v_x \sqrt{\dfrac{2y}{g}}$.

Therefore $x_1 = (0.99\ \text{m/s})\sqrt{\dfrac{2(0.40\ \text{m})}{9.80\ \text{m/s}^2}} = 0.28\ \text{m}$;

$x_2 = (1.7\ \text{m/s})\sqrt{\dfrac{2(0.30\ \text{m})}{9.80\ \text{m/s}^2}} = 0.42\ \text{m}$;

$x_3 = (2.2\ \text{m/s})\sqrt{\dfrac{2(0.20\ \text{m})}{9.80\ \text{m/s}^2}} = 0.44\ \text{m}$;

$x_4 = (2.6\ \text{m/s})\sqrt{\dfrac{2(0.10\ \text{m})}{9.80\ \text{m/s}^2}} = 0.37\ \text{m}$.

So the $\boxed{\text{20-centimeter hole}}$ has the greatest range.

76. From the equation of continuity, $A_1 v_1 = A_2 v_2$.

$v_2 = \dfrac{A_1 v_1}{A_2} = \dfrac{\pi(0.030\ \text{m})^2(0.45\ \text{m/s})}{\pi(0.010\ \text{m})^2} = 4.05\ \text{m/s}$.

From Bernoulli's principle, $p_1 + \tfrac{1}{2}\rho v_1^2 + \rho g y_1 = p_2 + \tfrac{1}{2}\rho v_2^2 + \rho g y_2$.

$p_2 = p_1 + \tfrac{1}{2}\rho(v_1^2 - v_2^2) + \rho g(y_1 - y_2) = (400\ \text{torr}) \times \dfrac{1.013 \times 10^5\ \text{Pa}}{760\ \text{torr}}$

$+ \tfrac{1}{2}(1000\ \text{kg/m}^3)[(0.45\ \text{m/s})^2 - (4.05\ \text{m/s})^2] + (1000\ \text{kg/m}^3)(9.80\ \text{m/s}^2)(0 - 4.0\ \text{m}) = \boxed{5.7 \times 10^3\ \text{Pa}}$.

77. $Q = A_1 v_1$, ☞ $v_1 = \dfrac{Q}{A_1} = \dfrac{(25 \text{ L/min})(10^{-3} \text{ m}^3/\text{L})(1 \text{ min/60 s})}{\pi(0.035 \text{ m})^2} = 0.108 \text{ m/s}$.

From the equation of continuity, $A_1 v_1 = A_2 v_2$.

$v_2 = \dfrac{A_1 v_1}{A_2} = \dfrac{\pi(0.035 \text{ m})^2(0.108 \text{ m/s})}{(30 \text{ cm}^2)(10^{-4} \text{ m}^2/\text{cm}^2)} = 0.139 \text{ m/s}$.

From Bernoulli's principle, $p_1 + \tfrac{1}{2}\rho v_1^2 + \rho g y_1 = p_2 + \tfrac{1}{2}\rho v_2^2 + \rho g y_2$. Here $y_1 = y_2$.

$p_2 = p_1 + \tfrac{1}{2}\rho(v_1^2 - v_2^2) = 6.0 \text{ Pa} + + \tfrac{1}{2}(1000 \text{ kg/m}^3)[(0.108 \text{ m/s})^2 - (0.139 \text{ m/s})^2] = \boxed{2.2 \text{ Pa}}$.

78. From the equation of continuity, $A_1 v_1 = A_2 v_2$, ☞ $v_2 = \dfrac{A_1 v_1}{A_2}$.

From Bernoulli's principle, $p_1 + \tfrac{1}{2}\rho v_1^2 + \rho g y_1 = p_2 + \tfrac{1}{2}\rho v_2^2 + \rho g y_2$.

Here $\Delta p = p_1 - p_2 = \rho g h$ and $y_1 = y_2$.

So $\rho g h + \tfrac{1}{2}\rho v_1^2 = \tfrac{1}{2}\rho v_2^2 = \tfrac{1}{2}\rho \dfrac{A_1^2 v_1^2}{A_2^2}$, or $\tfrac{1}{2}\rho(A_1^2/A_2^2 - 1)v_1^2 = \rho g h$.

Therefore $v_1 = \sqrt{\dfrac{2gh}{A_1^2/A_2^2 - 1}}$.

79. (b).

80. (c).

81. (a).

82. (c).

83. $Q = \dfrac{\pi r^4 \Delta p}{8 \eta L}$, so

$\Delta p = \dfrac{8 \eta L Q}{\pi r^4} = \dfrac{8(1.00 \times 10^{-3} \text{ Pl})(6.0 \text{ m})(40 \text{ L/min})(10^{-3} \text{ m}^3/\text{L})(1 \text{ min/60 s})}{\pi (0.015 \text{ m})^4} = \boxed{2.0 \times 10^2 \text{ Pa}}$.

84. The pressure difference between the bag and the needle is

$\Delta p = \rho g h = (1.05 \times 10^3 \text{ kg/m}^3)(9.80 \text{ m/s}^2)(0.85 \text{ m}) = 8.75 \times 10^3 \text{ Pa}$.

The flow rate $Q = \dfrac{\pi r^4 \Delta p}{8 \eta L} = \dfrac{\pi(0.5 \times 10^{-3} \text{ m})^4(8.75 \times 10^3 \text{ Pa})}{8(1.7 \times 10^{-3} \text{ Pl})(0.050 \text{ m})} = 2.53 \times 10^{-6} \text{ m}^3/\text{s}$.

So the time is $t = \dfrac{V}{Q} = \dfrac{(500 \text{ cm}^3)(10^{-6} \text{ m}^3/\text{cm}^3)}{2.53 \times 10^{-6} \text{ m}^3/\text{s}} = \boxed{2.0 \times 10^2 \text{ s}}$.

85. $Y = \dfrac{F/A}{\Delta L/L_o}$,   ☞ $\dfrac{(\Delta L/L_o)_{Al}}{(\Delta L/L_o)_{Cu}} = \dfrac{Y_{Cu}}{Y_{Al}} = \dfrac{11 \times 10^{10} \text{ N/m}^2}{7.0 \times 10^{10} \text{ N/m}^2} = 1.57$.

So $(\Delta L/L_o)_{Al} = \dfrac{L - L_o}{L_o}{}_{Al} = 1.57 \, (\Delta L/L_o)_{Cu} = (1.57)\dfrac{0.02 \text{ cm}}{100.00 \text{ cm}} = 3.14 \times 10^{-4}$.

Therefore, $L_o = \dfrac{L}{1 + 3.14 \times 10^{-4}} = \dfrac{100.02 \text{ cm}}{1 + 3.14 \times 10^{-4}} = \boxed{99.99 \text{ cm}}$.

86.   The tension in the scale (scale reading) is the difference between the weight and buoyant force.

$T = w - F_b = mg - F_b = \rho V g - \rho_f V g = (\rho - \rho_f) V g$

$= (7800 \text{ kg/m}^3 - 1000 \text{ kg/m}^3)(0.25 \text{ m})^3(9.80 \text{ m/s}^2) = \boxed{1.0 \times 10^3 \text{ N}}$.

87.   (a) $w = mg = F_b = \rho_f V g$,   ☞ $V = \dfrac{m}{\rho_f} = \dfrac{\rho V}{\rho_f} = \dfrac{(700 \text{ kg/m}^3)(0.30 \text{ m})^3}{1000 \text{ kg/m}^3} = 0.0189 \text{ m}^3$.

So the distance from the top of the wood to the water surface is

$0.30 \text{ m} - \dfrac{0.0189 \text{ m}^3}{(0.30 \text{ m})(0.30 \text{ m})} = \boxed{0.09 \text{ m}}$.

(b) The 0.09 m above the water surface can support the mass on top of the wood.

The mass is $\dfrac{(1000 \text{ kg/m}^3)(0.30 \text{ m})^2(0.09 \text{ m})g}{g} = \boxed{8.1 \text{ kg}}$.

88. $p = \dfrac{F}{A} = \dfrac{mg}{A} = \dfrac{(60 \text{ kg})(9.80 \text{ m/s}^2)}{(0.015 \text{ m})^2} = 2.6 \times 10^6 \text{ Pa} = \boxed{2.6 \times 10^6 \text{ Pa} = 3.8 \times 10^2 \text{ lb/in}^2 = 26 \text{ atm}}$.

Here we used 1 atm = 1.013×10^5 Pa = 14.7 lb/in^2.

89. $F = pA = (1.013 \times 10^5 \text{ Pa})(1.30 \text{ m}^2) = \boxed{1.32 \times 10^5 \text{ N} = 2.96 \times 10^4 \text{ lb}}$.

90. $p = \rho g h = (1000 \text{ kg/m}^3)(9.80 \text{ m/s}^2)(12 \text{ m}) = 1.18 \times 10^5 \text{ Pa}$.

$F = pA = (1.18 \times 10^5 \text{ Pa})(\pi)(0.090 \text{ m})^2 = \boxed{3.0 \times 10^3 \text{ N}}$.

91. $p_o = \rho_o g h_o = \rho_m g h_m$,   ☞ $\rho_o = \dfrac{\rho_m h_m}{h_o} = \dfrac{(13.6 \times 10^3 \text{ kg/m}^3)(5.0 \text{ cm})}{80 \text{ cm}} = \boxed{8.5 \times 10^2 \text{ kg/m}^3}$.

92. $p_a = \rho g h$,   ☞ $h = \dfrac{p_a}{\rho g} = \dfrac{1.013 \times 10^5 \text{ Pa}}{(1.29 \text{ kg/m}^3)(9.80 \text{ m/s}^2)} = \boxed{8.0 \times 10^3 \text{ m}}$.

This tells us that the atmosphere extends much higher and is less dense.

93.   First calculate the velocity of the water when it comes out of the spout. Use the result from Exercise 9.75.

$v = \sqrt{2g\Delta y} = \sqrt{2gh} = \sqrt{2(9.80 \text{ m/s}^2)(0.45 \text{ m})} = 2.97$ m/s, which is the initial velocity for the rise.

From kinematics, the maximum height is $\dfrac{v^2}{2g} = \dfrac{(2.97 \text{ m/s})^2}{2(9.80 \text{ m/s}^2)} = \boxed{0.45 \text{ m}}$.

94. $\dfrac{\Delta L}{L_o} = \dfrac{F/A}{Y} = \dfrac{10{,}000 \text{ N}}{(24 \text{ cm}^2)(10^{-4} \text{ m}^2/\text{cm}^2)(20 \times 10^{10} \text{ N/m}^2)} = 2.08 \times 10^{-5} = \boxed{2.1 \times 10^{-3}\%}$.

95.   From the result of Exercise 9.75, $v = \sqrt{2g\Delta y} = \sqrt{2(9.80 \text{ m/s}^2)(0.25 \text{ m})} = \boxed{2.2 \text{ m/s}}$.

96.   Specific gravity $= \dfrac{w}{w_w} = \dfrac{mg}{m_w g} = \dfrac{m}{m_w} = \dfrac{\rho V}{\rho_w V} = \dfrac{\rho}{\rho_w}$.

97.   (a) $Q = A v$, ☞ $v_s = \dfrac{66 \text{ cm}^3/\text{s}}{6.0 \text{ cm}^2} = \boxed{11 \text{ cm/s}}$; $v_n = \dfrac{66 \text{ cm}^3/\text{s}}{1.0 \text{ cm}^2} = \boxed{66 \text{ cm/s}}$.

(b) $p_1 + \frac{1}{2}\rho v_1^2 + \rho g y_1 = p_2 + \frac{1}{2}\rho v_2^2 + \rho g y_2$.   So

$\Delta p = p_1 - p_2 = \frac{1}{2}\rho(v_2^2 - v_1^2) + \rho g(y_2 - y_1)$

$= \frac{1}{2}(1000 \text{ kg/m}^3)[(0.66 \text{ m/s})^2 - (0.11 \text{ m/s})^2] + (1000 \text{ kg/m}^3)(9.80 \text{ m/s}^2)(0.10 \text{ m}) = \boxed{1.2 \times 10^3 \text{ Pa}}$.

98.   Through capillary action, water is absorbed by the wooden peg and it swells and splits the rock.

99.   (a) When it is in the water, the force applied is

$F = mg - F_b = \rho V g - \rho_f g V$

$= (\rho - \rho_f)gV = (7.8 \times 10^3 \text{ kg/m}^3 - 1.0 \times 10^3 \text{ kg/m}^3)(9.80 \text{ m/s}^2)(0.25 \text{ m})(0.20 \text{ m})(10 \text{ m})$

$= \boxed{3.3 \times 10^4 \text{ N}}$.

(b) When it is out of water, the force applied is

$F = mg = \rho V g = (7.8 \times 10^3 \text{ kg/m}^3)(9.80 \text{ m/s}^2)(0.25 \text{ m})(0.20 \text{ m})(10 \text{ m}) = \boxed{3.8 \times 10^4 \text{ N}}$.

100.   (a) The buoyant force is $F_B = 14.4 \text{ N} - 4.8 \text{ N} = 9.6 \text{ N} = \rho_f g V$.

So $V = \dfrac{9.6 \text{ N}}{(1000 \text{ kg/m}^3)(9.80 \text{ m/s}^2)} = \boxed{9.8 \times 10^{-4} \text{ m}^3}$.

(b) $\rho = \dfrac{m}{V} = \dfrac{w}{gV} = \dfrac{14.4 \text{ N}}{(9.80 \text{ m/s}^2)(9.8 \times 10^{-4} \text{ m}^3)} = \boxed{1.5 \times 10^3 \text{ kg/m}^3}$.

(c) $\boxed{\text{Yes}}$, but less precisely—the sphere would float, and you would have to estimate the portion of its

volume that was submerged.

CHAPTER 10

1. $T_F = \frac{9}{5} T_C + 32 = \frac{9}{5}(15) + 32 = 59°F$. So (d) is the closest.

2. $\boxed{\text{Fahrenheit}}$. $9\Delta T_F = 5\Delta T_C$.

3. Not necessarily. Internal energy does not solely depend on temperature. It also depends on mass.

4. An incandescent lamp filament, when turned on, has a temperature of thousands of degrees Celsius.

5. (a) $T_C = \frac{5}{9}(T_F - 32) = \frac{5}{9}(1000 - 32) = \boxed{538°C}$.   (b) $T_C = \frac{5}{9}(0 - 32) = \boxed{-18°C}$.

    (c) $T_C = \frac{5}{9}(-20 - 32) = \boxed{-29°C}$.   (d) $T_C = \frac{5}{9}(-40 - 32) = \boxed{-40°C}$.

6. (a) $T_F = \frac{9}{5} T_C + 32 = \frac{9}{5}(150) + 32 = \boxed{302°F}$.   (b) $T_F = = \frac{9}{5}(32) + 32 = \boxed{90°F}$.

    (c) $T_F = \frac{9}{5}(-25) + 32 = \boxed{-13°C}$.   (d) $T_F = = \frac{9}{5}(-273) + 32 = \boxed{-459°F}$.

7. $T_C = \frac{5}{9}(T_F - 32) = \frac{5}{9}(172 - 32) = \boxed{77.8°C}$.

8. $T_F = \frac{9}{5} T_C + 32 = \frac{9}{5}(39.4) + 32 = \boxed{103°F}$.

9. $T_C = \frac{5}{9}(T_F - 32) = \frac{5}{9}(134 - 32) = \boxed{56.7°C}$. $T_C = \frac{5}{9}(-80 - 32) = \boxed{-62°C}$.

10. (a) $T_F = \frac{9}{5} T_C + 32 = \frac{9}{5}(245) + 32 = 473°F$. So $\boxed{245°F}$ is lower.

    (b) $T_F = \frac{9}{5}(200) + 32 = 392°F$. So $\boxed{375°F}$ is lower.

11. $T_F = \frac{9}{5} T_C + 32 = \frac{9}{5}(58) + 32 = \boxed{136°F}$. $T_F = \frac{9}{5}(-89) + 32 = \boxed{-128°F}$.

12. $T_F = \frac{9}{5} T_C + 32 = T_C$,   ☞ $T_C = \dfrac{32}{1 - 9/5} = -40°C = -40°F$.

13. (a) Since $T_F = \frac{9}{5} T_C + 32$, $\Delta T_F = \frac{9}{5}\Delta T_C = \frac{9}{5}[-49 - 7)] = \boxed{-101 \text{ F}°}$.

    (b) $\Delta T_C = \frac{5}{9}\Delta T_F = \frac{5}{9}[45 - (-4)] = \boxed{27 \text{ C}°}$.

14.   (a) The x intercept is found at $T_F = \frac{9}{5} T_C + 32 = 0$, ☞ $T_C = \boxed{-18°\text{C}}$.

(b) Comparing $T_C = \frac{5}{9}(T_F - 32)$ with the standard equation of a line $y = mx + b$, the slope is $\frac{5}{9}$ and the intercept is $-18°\text{F}$.

15.   (c).

16.   (d).

17.   (a) If pressure is held constant, the volume will decrease as temperature decreases, according to the ideal gas law. So the density $\boxed{\text{increases}}$.

(b) If the volume is held constant, the density is $\boxed{\text{constant}}$.

18.   The volume of the gas is held constant. So if the temperature increases, so does the pressure and vice versa, according to the ideal gas law. Therefore temperature is determined from pressure.

19.   The pressure of the gas is held constant. So if the temperature increases, so does the volume and vice versa, according to the ideal gas law. Therefore temperature is determined from volume.

20.   (a) $\boxed{\text{zero pressure or volume}}$.

(b) $\boxed{\text{negative pressure or volume}}$.

21. $\boxed{\text{The balloons collapsed}}$. Due to the decrease in temperature, the volume also decreases.

22.   (a) $T_K = T_C + 273.15 = 0 + 273.15 = \boxed{273 \text{ K}}$.   (b) $T_K = 100 + 273.15 = \boxed{373 \text{ K}}$.

(c) $T_K = 20 + 273.15 = \boxed{293 \text{ K}}$.   (d) $T_K = -35 + 273.15 = \boxed{238 \text{ K}}$.

23.   (a) $T_C = T_K - 273.15 = 0 - 273.15 = \boxed{-273°\text{C}}$.   (b) $T_C = 250 - 273.15 = \boxed{-23°\text{C}}$.

(c) $T_C = 273.15 - 273.15 = \boxed{0°\text{C}}$.   (d) $T_C = 325 - 273 = \boxed{52°\text{C}}$.

24.   (a) $-40°\text{F} = -40°\text{C}$ (from Exercise 10.12). $T_K = T_C + 273 = -40 + 273 = \boxed{233 \text{ K}}$.

(b) $\boxed{233 \text{ K}}$.

25. $T_C = \frac{5}{9}(T_F - 32) = \frac{5}{9}(300 - 32) = 149°\text{C} = 422 \text{ K}$.   So $\boxed{300\text{K}}$ is lower.

26. (a) $T_C = T_K - 273 = 6000 - 273 = \boxed{5727°C}$. $T_F = \frac{9}{5}T_C + 32 = \frac{9}{5}(5727) + 32 = \boxed{10\,340°F}$.

   (b) The percentage error is $\dfrac{6000 - 5727}{6000} = \boxed{4.6\%}$.

27. (a) H_2O has a molar mass of $(2 + 16)$ h/mole $= 18$ g/mole. $n = \dfrac{m}{M} = \dfrac{40\ g}{18\ g/mole} = \boxed{2.2\ moles}$.

   (b) H_2SO_4 has a molar mass of $(2 + 32 + 64)$ h/mole $= 98$ g/mole. $n = \dfrac{245\ g}{98\ g/mole} = \boxed{2.5\ moles}$.

   (c) NO_2 has a molar mass of $(14 + 32)$ g/mole $= 46$ h/mole. $n = \dfrac{138\ g}{46\ g/mole} = \boxed{3.0\ moles}$.

   (d) At STP, 1 mole occupies 22.4 L.   So $n = \dfrac{56\ L}{22.4\ L} = \boxed{2.5\ moles}$.

28. $\dfrac{p_1 V_1}{T_1} = \dfrac{p_2 V_2}{T_2}$.   Since $V_1 = V_2$, $T_2 = \dfrac{p_2}{p_1} T_1 = \dfrac{1500\ Pa}{1000\ Pa} \times [(273 + 20)K] = 439.5K = \boxed{167°C}$.

29. $\dfrac{p_1 V_1}{T_1} = \dfrac{p_2 V_2}{T_2}$.   Since $T_1 = T_2$, $p_2 = \dfrac{V_1}{V_2} \times p_1 = \dfrac{0.10\ m^3}{0.12\ m^3} \times (1.4 \times 10^5\ Pa) = \boxed{1.2 \times 10^5\ Pa}$.

30. $pV = nRT$,   ☞ $V = \dfrac{nRT}{p} = \dfrac{(1\ mol)[8.31\ /(mol \cdot K)](273\ K)}{1.01 \times 10^5\ Pa} = \boxed{0.0224\ m^3 = 22.4\ L}$.

31. $n = \dfrac{4.00\ g}{2.00\ g/mol} = 2.00\ mol$.

   $pV = nRT$,   ☞ $V = \dfrac{nRT}{p} = \dfrac{(2.00\ mol)[8.31\ /(mol \cdot K)](300\ K)}{2.00(1.01 \times 10^5\ Pa)} = \boxed{0.0247\ m^3}$.

32. (a) $pV = Nk_B T$,   ☞ $N = \dfrac{pV}{k_B T} = \dfrac{(1.01 \times 10^5\ Pa)(1.00 \times 10^{-3}\ m^3)}{(1.38 \times 10^{-23}\ J/K)(273\ K)} = \boxed{2.68 \times 10^{22}}$.

   (b) $N = \dfrac{(1.01 \times 10^5\ Pa)(1.00 \times 10^{-6}\ m^3)}{(1.38 \times 10^{-23}\ J/K)(273\ K)} = \boxed{2.68 \times 10^{19}}$.

33. $\dfrac{p_1 V_1}{T_1} = \dfrac{p_2 V_2}{T_2}$,   ☞ $\dfrac{p_2}{p_1} = \dfrac{V_1}{V_2}\dfrac{T_2}{T_1} = (2)(2) = 4$. So pressure $\boxed{increases\ by\ 4\ times}$.

34. $T_1 = 92°F = \frac{5}{9}(92 - 32)\ °C = 33.3°C = 306.3\ K$, $T_2 = 32°F = 0°C = 273\ K$.

   $\dfrac{p_1 V_1}{T_1} = \dfrac{p_2 V_2}{T_2}$,   ☞ $V_2 = \dfrac{p_1 V_1 T_2}{T_1 p_2} = \dfrac{(20.0\ lb/in^2)(0.20\ m^3)(273\ K)}{(306.3\ K)(14.7\ lb/in^2)} = \boxed{0.24\ m^3}$.

   Here lb/in^2 can be used since it is in a ratio.

35. $T_1 = 61°F = \frac{5}{9}(61 - 32)°C = 16.1°C = 289.1 \text{ K}, \quad T_2 = 100°F = 310.8 \text{ K},$

$p_1 = 30.0 \text{ lb/in}^2 + 14.7 \text{ lb/in}^2 = 44.7 \text{ lb/in}^2. \quad \dfrac{p_1 V_1}{T_1} = \dfrac{p_2 V_2}{T_2}.$

Since $V_1 = V_2, \quad p_2 = \dfrac{p_1 T_2}{T_1} = \dfrac{(44.7 \text{ lb/in}^2)(310.8 \text{ K})}{289.1 \text{ K}} = 48.1 \text{ lb/in}^2.$

So the gauge pressure is $48.1 \text{ lb/in}^2 - 14.7 \text{ lb/in}^2 = \boxed{33.4 \text{ lb/in}^2}$.

36. $\dfrac{p_1 V_1}{T_1} = \dfrac{p_2 V_2}{T_2}, \quad \text{☞} \quad p_2 = \dfrac{p_1 V_1 T_2}{T_1 V_2} = \dfrac{(1 \text{ atm})(2.4 \text{ m}^3)(303 \text{ K})}{(273 \text{ K})(1.6 \text{ m}^3)} = \boxed{1.7 \text{ atm}}.$

37. (a) The gas $\boxed{\text{expands}}$ according to ideal gas law.

(b) $\dfrac{p_0 V_0}{T_0} = \dfrac{pV}{T}, \quad \text{☞} \quad \dfrac{V}{V_0} = \dfrac{T p_0}{T_0 p} = \dfrac{T}{T_0} = \dfrac{313 \text{ K}}{283 \text{ K}} = 1.106.$

So the fractional change is $\dfrac{V - V_0}{V_0} = \dfrac{V}{V_0} - 1 = 0.106 = \boxed{10.6\%}$.

38. The pressure 5 m below the surface is

$p_1 = p_a + \rho g h = 1.01 \times 10^5 \text{ Pa} + (1000 \text{ kg/m}^3)(9.80 \text{ m/s}^2)(15 \text{ m}) = 2.48 \times 10^5 \text{ Pa}.$

$\dfrac{p_1 V_1}{T_1} = \dfrac{p_2 V_2}{T_2}, \quad \text{☞} \quad V_2 = \dfrac{p_1 T_2}{p_2 T_1} \times V_1 = \dfrac{(2.48 \times 10^5 \text{ Pa})(293 \text{ K})}{(1.01 \times 10^5 \text{ Pa})(280 \text{ K})} \times (2.0 \text{ cm}^3) = \boxed{5.1 \text{ cm}^3}.$

39. (d).

40. (c).

41. (a) Aluminum has a larger α and so it contracts more. Therefore the ice moves $\boxed{\text{upward}}$.

(b) Copper has a larger α so the ice moves $\boxed{\text{downward}}$.

(c) Brass has a larger α and so it will expand more. Therefore $\boxed{\text{copper}}$ should be on the top for the strip to curve upward.

42. (a) When the ball alone is heated, it expands and cannot go through the ring.
(b) When the ring is heated, it expands and the hole gets larger so the ball can go through again.

43. Water expands when cooled from 4°C to 2°C as it exhibits abnormal expansion between 0°C and 4°C.

44. When the disk is heated, it expands and so the mass is farther from the axis of rotation. This increases the moment of inertia. According to angular momentum conservation, the angular speed $\boxed{\text{decreases}}$.

45.   No , it will not be distorted because both the ring and the bar are made of iron so they will expand at the same rate as one single piece. Yes , the circular ring will be distorted, if the bar is made of aluminum.

46.   At $-30°C$, $\Delta L = \alpha L_o \Delta T = (12 \times 10^{-6} \, C°^{-1})(10 \text{ m})(-30°C - 20°C) = -6.0 \times 10^{-3} \text{ m} = \boxed{-6.0 \text{ mm}}$.

At $45°C$, $\Delta L = (12 \times 10^{-6} / C°)(10 \text{ m})(45°C - 20°C) = 3.0 \times 10^{-3} \text{ m} = \boxed{3.0 \text{ mm}}$.

47. $\Delta L = \alpha L_o \Delta T$,   ☞ $\dfrac{\Delta L}{L_o} = \alpha \Delta T = (24 \times 10^{-6} \, C°^{-1})(-5.0°C - 20°C) = -6.0 \times 10^{-4}$, or $\boxed{0.06\%}$.

48.   Only the higher temperature needs to be considered because the slabs will not touch under the lower temperature $\Delta L = \alpha L_o \Delta T = (12 \times 10^{-6} \, C°^{-1})(10.0 \text{ m})[45°C - (20°C)] = 3.0 \times 10^{-3} \text{ m} = \boxed{3.0 \text{ mm}}$.

49. $\Delta L = \alpha L_o \Delta T = (14 \times 10^{-6} \, C°^{-1})(2.4 \text{ cm})(100°C - 20°C) = \boxed{0.0027 \text{ cm}}$.

50. $\dfrac{\Delta V}{V} = 0.0010 = \beta \Delta T$,   ☞ $\Delta T = \dfrac{0.0010}{2.1 \times 10^{-4} \, C°^{-1}} = \boxed{4.8 \, C°}$.

51.   (a) $L' = L_o + \Delta L = L_o(1 + \alpha\Delta T) = (60 \text{ cm})[1 + (17 \times 10^{-6} \, C°^{-1})(85°C - 20°C)] = \boxed{60.07 \text{ cm}}$.

(b) $A_o = \pi r^2 = \pi(0.75 \text{ cm})^2 = 1.77 \text{ cm}^2$.

$\Delta A = 2\alpha A_o \Delta T = 2(17 \times 10^{-6} \, C°^{-1})(1.77 \text{ cm}^2)(85°C - 20°C) = \boxed{3.91 \times 10^{-3} \text{ cm}^2}$.

Yes, the flow speed will be affected according to the equation of continuity.

52.   (a) Larger due to expansion.

(b) $A_o = \pi r^2 = \pi(4.00 \text{ cm})^2 = 50.27 \text{ cm}^2$.

$\Delta A = 2\alpha A_o \Delta T = 2(24 \times 10^{-6} \, C°^{-1})(50.27 \text{ cm}^2)(150°C - 20°C) = 0.314 \text{ cm}^2$.

So the final area is $50.27 \text{ cm}^2 + 0.314 \text{ cm}^2 = \boxed{50.6 \text{ cm}^2}$.

53.   The ring should be heated so the ball can go through.

$\Delta L = \alpha L_o \Delta T$,   ☞ $\Delta T = \dfrac{\Delta L}{\alpha L_o} = \dfrac{0.10 \text{ mm}}{(12 \times 10^{-6} / C°)(25 \text{ mm})} = 333°C$.

So the required temperature is $333°C + 20°C = \boxed{353°C}$.

54. $\dfrac{\Delta A}{A_o} = \dfrac{\beta A_o \Delta T}{A_o} = 2\alpha\Delta T = 2(12 \times 10^{-6} \, C°^{-1})(0°C - 350°C) = -7.9 \times 10^{-3} = -\boxed{0.79\%}$.

55. $\Delta V = \beta V_o \Delta T = (9.5 \times 10^{-4}\ \text{C}^{\circ-1})(25\ \text{gal})(30^\circ\text{C} - 10^\circ\text{C}) = \boxed{0.48\ \text{gal}}$. It is better to buy gas in the morning.

56. $\rho = \dfrac{m}{V} = \dfrac{m}{V_o + \Delta V} = \dfrac{m}{V_o(1 + 3\alpha\Delta T)} = \rho_o \dfrac{1}{1 + 3\alpha\Delta T}$.

   Since $3\alpha\Delta T \ll 1$, $\dfrac{1}{3\alpha\Delta T} \approx 1 - 3\alpha\Delta T$ $\left(\dfrac{1}{1+x} \approx 1 - x \text{ for small } x\right)$.

   So $\rho = \rho_o(1 - 3\alpha\Delta T) = \rho_o(1 - \beta\Delta T)$.

57. $\rho = \dfrac{m}{V}$, ☞ $\dfrac{\rho}{\rho_o} = \dfrac{V_o}{V} = \dfrac{V_o}{V_o(1 + \beta\Delta T)} = \dfrac{1}{1 + \beta\Delta T}$.

   $\rho = \dfrac{1}{1 + \beta\Delta T}\rho_o = \dfrac{1}{1 + (1.8 \times 10^{-4}\ \text{C}^{\circ-1})(100^\circ\text{C} - 0^\circ\text{C})} \times (13.6 \times 10^3\ \text{kg/m}^3) = \boxed{13.4 \times 10^3\ \text{kg/m}^3}$.

58. (a) $\boxed{\text{Larger}}$ as it expands.

   (b) $V_o = \dfrac{4\pi}{3}r_o^3 = \dfrac{4\pi}{3}(0.050\ \text{m})^3 = 5.24 \times 10^{-4}\ \text{m}^3$.

   $\Delta V = 3\alpha V_o \Delta T = 3(17 \times 10^{-6}\ \text{C}^{\circ-1})(5.24 \times 10^{-4}\ \text{m}^3)(500\ \text{K} - 293\ \text{K})] = \boxed{5.5 \times 10^{-6}\ \text{m}^3}$.

59. (a) At 20°C, $A_{ob} = \pi(0.500\ \text{cm})^2 = 0.78540\ \text{cm}^2$ and $A_{oc} = \pi(0.501\ \text{cm})^2 = 0.78854\ \text{cm}^2$.

   At a temperature T, both will have the same area or radius, $A_b = A_c$.

   $\Delta A = 2\alpha L_o \Delta T$, ☞ $A = A_o + \Delta A = A_o(1 + 2\alpha\Delta T)$. So $A_{ob}(1 + 2\alpha_b \Delta T) = A_{oc}(1 + 2\alpha_c \Delta T)$,

   $\Delta T = \dfrac{A_{oc} - A_{ob}}{2(A_{ob}\alpha_b - A_{oc}\alpha_c)} = \dfrac{0.78854\ \text{cm}^2 - 0.78540\ \text{cm}^2}{2[(0.78540\ \text{cm}^2)(19 \times 10^{-6}\ \text{C}^{\circ-1}) - (0.78854\ \text{cm}^2)(17 \times 10^{-6}\ \text{C}^{\circ-1})]}$

   $= 1.03 \times 10^3\ \text{C}^\circ$. Thus the temperature is $1.03 \times 10^3\ \text{C}^\circ + 20^\circ\text{C} = \boxed{1.05 \times 10^3\ ^\circ\text{C}}$.

   (b) $\boxed{\text{No}}$, since brass has a higher α, the hole will be even larger at a higher temperature.

60. At 20°C, $V_{ob} = 1000\ \text{cm}^3$ and $V_{om} = 990\ \text{cm}^3$.

   At a temperature T, both the beaker and the mercury have the same volume, $V_b = V_m$.

   $V = V_o + \Delta V = V_o(1 + 3\alpha\Delta T) = V_o(1 + \beta\Delta T)$, ☞ $V_{ob}(1 + 3\alpha_b \Delta T) = V_{om}(1 + \beta\Delta T)$.

   $\Delta T = \dfrac{V_{ob} - V_{om}}{V_{om}\beta_m - 3V_{ob}\alpha_b} = \dfrac{1000\ \text{cm}^3 - 990\ \text{cm}^3}{(990\ \text{cm}^3)(1.8 \times 10^{-4}\ \text{C}^{\circ-1}) - 3(1000\ \text{cm}^3)(3.3 \times 10^{-6}\ \text{C}^{\circ-1})} = 59.4\ \text{C}^\circ$.

   So the temperature is $T = 20^\circ\text{C} + 59.4\ \text{C}^\circ = \boxed{79.4^\circ\text{C}}$.

61. (c) because $20^\circ\text{C} = 293\ \text{K}$ and $2 \times 293\ \text{K} = 586\ \text{K} = 313^\circ\text{C}$.

62. (d). Internal energy is proportional to the Kelvin temperature.

63. The gases diffuse through the porous membrane, but the helium gas diffuses faster because its atoms have a smaller mass. Eventually there will be equal concentrations of gases on both sides of the container.

64. Since the average speed of the additive is greater than that of the gas, $m_{additive} < m_{gas}$.

65. (a) $K = \frac{3}{2} k_B T = \frac{3}{2}(1.38 \times 10^{-23} \text{ J/K})(293 \text{ K}) = \boxed{6.1 \times 10^{-21} \text{ J}}$.

    (b) $K = \frac{3}{2}(1.38 \times 10^{-23} \text{ J/K})(373 \text{ K}) = \boxed{7.7 \times 10^{-21} \text{ J}}$.

66. $U = \frac{3}{2} nRT$, ☞ $\Delta U = \frac{3}{2} nR\Delta T = \frac{3}{2}(2.0 \text{ mol})[8.31 \text{ J/(mol·K)}](50°C - 20°C) = \boxed{7.5 \times 10^2 \text{ J}}$.

67. (a) $K = \frac{3}{2} k_B T = \frac{3}{2}(1.38 \times 10^{-23} \text{ J/K})(300 \text{ K}) = \boxed{6.21 \times 10^{-21} \text{ J}}$.

    (b) $v_{rms} = \sqrt{\frac{3k_B T}{m_o}} = \sqrt{\frac{3(1.38 \times 10^{-23} \text{ J/K})(300 \text{ K})}{6.65 \times 10^{-27} \text{ kg}}} = \boxed{1.37 \times 10^3 \text{ m/s}}$.

68. $v_{rms} = \sqrt{\frac{3k_B T}{m}} = \sqrt{\frac{3(1.38 \times 10^{-23} \text{ J/K})(273 \text{ K})}{5.31 \times 10^{-26} \text{ kg}}} = \boxed{4.61 \times 10^2 \text{ m/s}}$.

69. O_2 has a greater rms speed because it has a smaller mass.

    $v_{rms} = \sqrt{\frac{3k_B T}{m}}$, ☞ $\frac{(v_{rms})_2}{(v_{rms})_3} = \sqrt{\frac{m_3}{m_2}} = \sqrt{\frac{3}{2}} = 1.22$. So $\boxed{O_2 \text{ by } 1.22 \text{ times}}$.

70. $v_{rms} = \sqrt{\frac{3k_B T}{m_o}}$, ☞ $\frac{(v_{rms})_2}{(v_{rms})_1} = \sqrt{\frac{T_2}{T_1}} = \sqrt{\frac{373 \text{ K}}{298 \text{ K}}} = \boxed{1.12}$.

71. $T_2 = 2T_1 = 2(273 \text{ K}) = 546 \text{ K} = \boxed{273°C}$.

72. (a).

73. (b).

74. For monatomic gas, $U_1 = \frac{3}{2} nRT$.

    For diatomic gas, $U_2 = \frac{5}{2} nRT$. So $U_2 = \frac{5}{3} U_1 = \frac{5}{3}(5.0 \times 10^3 \text{ J}) = \boxed{8.3 \times 10^3 \text{ J}}$.

75. For diatomic gas, $U = \frac{5}{2} nRT = \frac{5}{2}(1.0 \text{ mol})[8.31 \text{ J/(mol·K)}](293 \text{ K}) = \boxed{6.1 \times 10^3 \text{ J}}$.

76.   (a) $U_t = \frac{3}{2} k_B T = \frac{3}{2} (1.38 \times 10^{-23} \text{ J/K})(273 \text{ K}) = \boxed{5.65 \times 10^{-21} \text{ J}}$.

(b) $U_r = \frac{2}{2} k_B T = \frac{2}{2} (1.38 \times 10^{-23} \text{ J/K})(273 \text{ K}) = \boxed{3.77 \times 10^{-21} \text{ J}}$.

(c) $U_{total} = U_t + U_r = 5.65 \times 10^{-21} \text{ J} + 3.77 \times 10^{-21} \text{ J} = \boxed{9.42 \times 10^{-21} \text{ J}}$.

77. $\Delta V_{gas} = \beta V_o \Delta T = (9.5 \times 10^{-4} \text{ C}^{\circ -1})(25 \text{ gal})(30°C - 10°C) = 0.48 \text{ gal}$.

$\Delta V_{tank} = 3\alpha V_o \Delta T = 3(12 \times 10^{-6} \text{ C}^{\circ -1})(25 \text{ gal})(30°C - 10°C) = 0.018 \text{ gal}$.

So the spilled volume is $\Delta V_{gas} - \Delta V_{tank} = 0.48 \text{ gal} - 0.018 \text{ gal} = \boxed{0.46 \text{ gal}}$.

78. $T_C = \frac{5}{9}(T_F - 32) = \frac{5}{9}(78 - 32) = \boxed{26°C}$. $T_C = \frac{5}{9}(65 - 32) = \boxed{18°C}$.

79. $\Delta L = \alpha L_o \Delta T = (17 \times 10^{-6} \text{ C}^{\circ -1})(0.500 \text{ m})(100°C - 20°C) = \boxed{6.8 \times 10^{-4} \text{ m}}$.

80.   First find the temperature of the gas.

$pV = nRT$,   ☞ $T = \dfrac{pV}{nR} = \dfrac{6.0(1.01 \times 10^5 \text{ Pa})(0.010 \text{ m}^3)}{(2.0 \text{ mol})[8.31 \text{ J/mol·K}]}) = 364.6 \text{ K}$.

$K = \frac{3}{2} k_B T = \frac{3}{2}(1.38 \times 10^{-23} \text{ J/K})(364.6 \text{ K}) = \boxed{7.5 \times 10^{-21} \text{ J}}$.

81. $\Delta V = \beta V_o \Delta T = (1.8 \times 10^{-4} \text{ C}^{\circ -1})(0.130 \text{ cm}^3)(50°C - 10°C) = 9.36 \times 10^{-4} \text{ cm}^3$.

Also $V = Ah$,   ☞ $\Delta h = \dfrac{\Delta V}{A} = \dfrac{9.36 \times 10^{-4} \text{ cm}^3}{0.012 \times 10^{-2} \text{ cm}^2} = \boxed{7.8 \text{ cm}}$.

82.   (a) $V = V_o + \Delta V = V_o(1 + 3\alpha\Delta T) = (0.100 \text{ m})^3 [1 + 3(24 \times 10^{-6} \text{ C}^{\circ -1})(300°C - 20°C)]$

$= \boxed{1.0202 \times 10^{-3} \text{ m}^3}$.

(b) $L = \sqrt[3]{V} = \sqrt[3]{1.02016 \times 10^{-3} \text{ m}^3} = \boxed{0.10068 \text{ m}}$.

83. $\Delta L = \alpha L_o \Delta T$,   ☞ $\dfrac{\Delta L}{L_o} = \alpha\Delta T$.   So $\dfrac{F}{A} = Y\dfrac{\Delta L}{L_o} = Y\alpha\Delta T$.

Therefore $\Delta T = \dfrac{F/A}{Y\alpha} = \dfrac{8.0 \times 10^7 \text{ N/m}^2}{(20 \times 10^{10} \text{ N/m}^2)(12 \times 10^{-6} \text{ C}^{\circ -1})} = \boxed{33 \text{ C}^\circ}$.

84. $\dfrac{p_0 V_0}{T_0} = \dfrac{pV}{T}$,   ☞ $\dfrac{V}{V_0} = \dfrac{Tp_0}{T_0 p}$.

Also $V = V_0 + \Delta V = V_0(1 + \beta \Delta T)$,   ☞ $\dfrac{V}{V_0} = 1 + \beta \Delta T = 1 + \beta(T - T_0)$.

So $1 + \beta(T - T_0) = \dfrac{Tp_0}{T_0 p}$,   or $\boxed{\beta = \dfrac{Tp_0 - T_0 p}{T_0 p(T - T_0)}}$.

85.   (a) One mole occupies 22.4 Liters.

So $n = \dfrac{0.75 \text{ L}}{22.4 \text{ L}} = \boxed{3.3 \times 10^{-2} \text{ moles}}$.

(b) $N = nN_A = (3.35 \times 10^{-2} \text{ moles})(6.02 \times 10^{23} \text{ /mole}) = \boxed{2.0 \times 10^{22}}$.

(c) CO has a molar mass of $12 + 16 = 28$ g/mole.

So the mass is $(3.35 \times 10^{-2} \text{ moles})(28 \text{ g/mole}) = \boxed{0.94 \text{ g}}$.

86.   Steel: $L = L_0(1 + \alpha \Delta T) = (1.0 \text{ m})[1 + (12 \times 10^{-6} \text{ C}^{\circ -1})(40^\circ\text{C} - 0^\circ\text{C}) = 1.00048$ m.

Aluminum: $L = (1.0 \text{ m})[(1 + (24 \times 10^{-6} \text{ C}^{\circ -1})(40^\circ\text{C} - 0^\circ\text{C}) = 1.00096$ m.

On the aluminum tape, it still reads 1.0 m for 1.00096 m of true length. The true length of the steel is

1.00048 m so its reading is $\dfrac{1.00048 \text{ m}}{1.00096 \text{ m}} \times (1.0 \text{ m}) = \boxed{0.999\,52 \text{ m}}$.

87.   (a) $T_F = \frac{9}{5} T_C + 32$,   ☞ $\Delta T_F = \frac{9}{5} \Delta T_C = \frac{9}{5}(10) = \boxed{18 \text{ F}^\circ}$.

(b) $\Delta T_C = \frac{5}{9} \Delta T_F = \frac{5}{9}(10) = \boxed{5.6 \text{ C}^\circ}$.

88. $\Delta L = \alpha L_0 \Delta T$,   ☞ $\alpha = \dfrac{\Delta L}{L_0 \Delta T} = \dfrac{0.044 \text{ cm}}{(50 \text{ cm})(250^\circ\text{C} - 20^\circ\text{C})} = \boxed{3.8 \times 10^{-6} \text{ C}^{\circ -1}}$.

$\boxed{\text{Yes}}$, it is a very good alloy with a very low coefficient of linear expansion.

89. $pV = Nk_B T$,   ☞ $N = \dfrac{pV}{k_B T} = \dfrac{(20 \text{ Pa})(0.20 \text{ m}^3)}{(1.38 \times 10^{-23} \text{ J/K})(293 \text{ K})} = \boxed{9.9 \times 10^{20}}$.

90. $T_K = T_C + 273 = \frac{5}{9}(T_F - 32) + 273.15 = \frac{5}{9} T_F + 255.37$.

Since $T_K = T_F = T$,   we have $T = \dfrac{255.37}{1 - 5/9} = \boxed{574.58 \text{ K}}$.

91. Assuming a rectangular block. $L = L_o + \Delta L = L_o(1 + \alpha\Delta T)$,

so $V = L^3 = L_o^3(1 + \alpha\Delta T)^3 = V_o(1 + 2\alpha\Delta T + \alpha^2\Delta T^2 + \alpha\Delta T + 2\alpha^2\Delta T^2 + \alpha^3\Delta T^3)$.

Since $\alpha\Delta T$ is small, $\alpha^2\Delta T^2$ and $\alpha^3\Delta T^3$ are even smaller. So they can be ignored.

Therefore $V = V_o(1 + 3\alpha\Delta T) = V_o(1 + \beta\Delta T)$, ☞ $\beta = 3\alpha$.

92. (a) The temperature is $T = 20°C - (6.5\ C°/km)(11\ km) = \boxed{-51.5°C}$.

(b) $T = 20°C - (6.5\ C°/km)(34\,000\ ft) \times \dfrac{1\ m}{3.28\ ft} \times \dfrac{1\ km}{1000\ m} = \boxed{-47.4°C}$.

93. $\Delta V = \beta V_o\Delta T = (1.8 \times 10^{-4}\ C°^{-1})(0.200\ cm^3)(30\ C°) = 1.08 \times 10^{-3}\ cm^3$.

$V = Ah = \pi r^2 h$, ☞ $\Delta h = \dfrac{\Delta V}{\pi r^2} = \dfrac{1.08 \times 10^{-3}\ cm^3}{\pi(0.0325\ cm)^2} = \boxed{3.3\ cm}$.

94. $\Delta L = \alpha L_o\Delta T = (17 \times 10^{-6}\ C°^{-1})(150\ m)[40°C - (-10°C)] = \boxed{0.13\ m}$.

95. $\dfrac{p_1 V_1}{T_1} = \dfrac{p_2 V_2}{T_2}$.

Since $T_2 = T_1$, we have $p_2 = \dfrac{V_1}{V_2}p_1 = 2(1\ atm) = 2\ atm = 2(1.013 \times 10^5\ Pa) = \boxed{2.026 \times 10^5\ Pa}$.

96. $L_1 = L_o(1 - \alpha\Delta T)$ and $L_2 = L_1(1 + \alpha\Delta T) = L_o(1 - \alpha\Delta T)(1 + \alpha\Delta T) = L_o(1 - \alpha^2\Delta T^2) < L_o$.

So the discrepancy is $L_o\alpha^2\Delta T^2$.

CHAPTER 11

1.   (d).

2.   (b).

3.   240 Btu = (240 Btu)(252 cal/Btu)(4.186 J/cal) = $\boxed{2.54 \times 10^5 \text{ J}}$.

4.   1500 Cal = 1500×10^3 cal = $(1500 \times 10^3 \text{ cal})(4.186 \text{ J/cal})$ = $\boxed{6.279 \times 10^6 \text{ J}}$.

5. $P = \dfrac{Q}{\Delta t} = \dfrac{20\,000 \text{ Btu}}{1 \text{ h}} = \dfrac{(20\,000 \text{ Btu})(252 \text{ cal/Btu})(4.186 \text{ J/cal})}{3600 \text{ s}} = \boxed{5.86 \times 10^3 \text{ W}}$.

6.   1 Btu = 252 cal = (252 cal)(4.186 J/cal) = 1.055×10^3 J.

      So it is $\boxed{1 \text{ Btu} = 1.06 \times 10^3 \text{ J}}$.

7.   (a) Work done in each lift: $W = Fd = (20 \text{ kg})(9.80 \text{ m/s}^2)(1.0 \text{ m}) = 196$ J.

      Energy input: $E = 2800 \text{ Cal} = 2800 \times 10^3 \text{ cal} = (2800 \times 10^3 \text{ cal})(4.186 \text{ J/cal}) = 1.17 \times 10^7$ J.

      So the number of lifts is $\dfrac{1.17 \times 10^7 \text{ J}}{196 \text{ J}} = \boxed{60\,000 \text{ times}}$.

      (b) $t = 60\,000(5.0 \text{ s}) = 3.0 \times 10^5 \text{ s} = \boxed{83 \text{ h}}$.

8.   (a).

9.   Water has higher specific heat so it takes longer to cool off.

10. $\boxed{\text{No}}$. A negative specific heat corresponds to an increase in temperature when heat is removed.

11. $\boxed{\text{Yes}}$. A negative heat corresponds to removal of heat.

12.   It will be $\boxed{\text{toward the water}}$, because the water cools slower due to its specific heat. The "warmer" air above the water rises and the cooler air above the water moves in to fill the void. See Figure 11.13 in the text book.

13.   Heat flow depends $\boxed{\text{only on the temperature difference}}$ ($Q = cm\Delta T$).

14.   This question is wrong because water has no weight in space (zero or negligible gravity). 3 lb of water on the Earth weighs 0 lb in space. This illustrates the limitation of the British system. Had the question been asked as "How many joules does it take to increase the temperature of 3 kg of …", we would have an answer for it.

15.   (a) $\boxed{\text{copper}}$ requires more heat as $c_{\text{copper}} = 390$ J/(kg·C°) $> c_{\text{lead}} = 130$ J/(kg·C°).

        (b) $Q = cm\Delta T$, ☞ $\Delta Q = \Delta cm\Delta T = [390$ J/(kg·C°) $- 130$ J/(kg·C°)$](1.0$ kg$)(190$ K $- 110$ K$)$

$$= \boxed{2.1 \times 10^4 \text{ J}}.$$

16. $Q = mc\Delta T$, ☞ $\Delta T = \dfrac{Q}{cm} = \dfrac{(200 \text{ J})}{[920 \text{ J/(kg·C°)}](5.0 \times 10^{-3} \text{ kg})} = 43°C.$

        So the final temperature is $43°C + 20°C = \boxed{63°C}$.

17.   1 liter of water has a mass of 1 kg.

$Q = cm\Delta T = [4186$ J/(kg·C°)$](5.0$ kg$)(100°C - 20°C) = \boxed{1.7 \times 10^6 \text{ J}}$.

18.   The heat gained by the cup is $Q_c = c_c m_c \Delta T_c = c_c (0.250 \text{ kg})(80°C - 20°C) = (15 \text{ kg·C°})c_c$,

        The heat lost by the coffee is $Q_{\text{cof}} = [4186$ J/(kg·C°)$](0.250$ kg$)(80°C - 100°C) = -2.093 \times 10^4$ J.

        From calorimetry: $-Q_{\text{lost}} = Q_{\text{gained}}$, ☞ 2.093×10^4 J $= (15$ kg·C°$)c_c$,

        so: $c_c = \boxed{1.40 \times 10^3 \text{ J/(kg·C°)}}$.

19.   The heat lost by the spoon is $Q_s = c_s m_s \Delta T_s = [920$ J/(kg·C°)$]m(30°C - 100°C) = -6.44 \times 10^4 \, m$ J/kg.

        The heat gained by water is $Q_w = [4186$ J/(kg·C°)$](0.200$ kg$)(30°C - 20°C) = 8.37 \times 10^3$ J.

        From calorimetry: $-Q_{\text{lost}} = Q_{\text{gained}}$, ☞ $6.44 \times 10^4 \, m$ J/kg $= 8.37 \times 10^3$ J,

        so: $m = \boxed{0.13 \text{ kg}}$.

20. $Q = cm\Delta T$, ☞ $m = \dfrac{Q}{c\Delta T}$.

        So $\dfrac{m_a}{m_c} = \dfrac{\dfrac{Q}{c_a \Delta T}}{\dfrac{Q}{c_c \Delta T}} = \dfrac{c_c}{c_a} = \dfrac{390 \text{ J/(kg·C°)}}{920 \text{ J/(kg·C°)}} = 0.424.$

        Therefore: $m_a = 0.424(3.00 \text{ kg}) = \boxed{1.27 \text{ kg}}$.

21. The gravitational energy of m kg of water at the top of the waterfall is $U = mgh$.

$$U = Q = cm\Delta T, \quad \text{☞} \quad \Delta T = \frac{U}{cm} = \frac{mgh}{cm} = \frac{gh}{c} = \frac{(9.80 \text{ m/s}^2)(75 \text{ m})}{4186 \text{ J/(kg·C°)}} = \boxed{0.18 \text{ C°}}.$$

22. $Q = cm\Delta T, \quad \text{☞} \quad \Delta T = \dfrac{Q}{cm}.$

So, $\dfrac{\Delta T_c}{|\Delta T_a|} = \dfrac{\dfrac{Q}{c_c m_a}}{\dfrac{Q}{c_a m_a}} = \dfrac{c_a m_a}{c_c m_c} = \dfrac{c_a \rho_a}{c_c \rho_c} = \dfrac{[920 \text{ J/(kg·C°)}](2.7 \times 10^3 \text{ kg/m}^3)}{[390 \text{ J/(kg·C°)}](8.9 \times 10^3 \text{ kg/m}^3)} = 0.716.$

Therefore, $\Delta T_c = 0.716(100°C - 20°C) = 57.3 \text{ C°}.$

Hence the final temperature is $20°C + 57.3 \text{ C°} = \boxed{77°C}$.

23. 1 liter of water has a mass of 1 kg.

The heat lost by the boiling water is $Q_1 = cm_1 \Delta T_1 = c(30 \text{ kg})(45°C - 100°C) = -(1650 \text{ kg·C°})c.$

The heat gained by the stream water is $Q_2 = cm_2 \Delta T_2 = cm_2 (45°C - 15°C) = (30 \text{ C°})cm_2.$

From calorimetry: $-Q_{\text{lost}} = Q_{\text{gained}}, \quad \text{☞} \quad (1650 \text{ kg·C°})c = (30 \text{ C°})cm_2.$

Solving, $m_2 = 55$ kg. Therefore $\boxed{55 \text{ L}}$ must be added.

24. The metal loses heat and the water and the cup gain heat.

The heat lost by the metal is $Q_m = cm\Delta T = c(0.150 \text{ kg})(30.5°C - 400°C) = -(55.43 \text{ kg·C°})c.$

The heat gained by the water and the cup is

$Q_G = [4186 \text{ J/(kg·C°)}](0.400 \text{ kg})(30.5°C - 10.0°C) + [920 \text{ J/(kg.C°)}](0.200 \text{ kg})(30.5°C - 10.0°C)$

$\quad = 3.810 \times 10^4 \text{ J}.$

From calorimetry: $-Q_{\text{lost}} = Q_{\text{gained}}, \quad \text{☞} \quad (55.43 \text{ kg·C°})c = 3.810 \times 10^4 \text{ J}.$

Solving, $c = \boxed{687 \text{ J/(kg·C°)}}.$

25. (a) The metal loses heat and the water and the cup gain heat.

The heat lost by the metal is $Q_m = cm\Delta T = c (0.50 \text{ kg})(25°C - 100°C) = -(37.5 \text{ kg·C°})c.$

The heat gained by the water and the cup is

$Q_G = [4186 \text{ J/(kg·C°)}](0.50 \text{ kg})(25°C - 20°C) + [920 \text{ J/(kg.C°)}](0.250 \text{ kg})(25°C - 20°C) = 1.162 \times 10^4 \text{ J}.$

From calorimetry: $-Q_{\text{lost}} = Q_{\text{gained}}, \quad \text{☞} \quad (37.5 \text{ kg·C°})c = 1.162 \times 10^4 \text{ J}.$

Solving, $c = \boxed{3.1 \times 10^2 \text{ J/(kg·C°)}}.$

(b) If some water splashed out, there will be less water to absorb the heat. So the final temperature will be higher and the measured specific heat value will be in error and higher than accepted value.

26. First calculate the heat required. 1 liter of water has a mass of 1 kg.

$Q = cm\Delta T = [4186 \text{ J/(kg·C°)}](1.0 \text{ kg})(100°\text{C} - 20°\text{C}) = 3.35 \times 10^5$ J.

Then: $P = \dfrac{Q}{\Delta t}$ ☞ $\Delta t = \dfrac{Q}{P} = \dfrac{3.35 \times 10^5 \text{ J}}{1500 \text{ W}} = 223 \text{ s} = \boxed{3.72 \text{ min}}$.

27. Assume the final temperature is T. $Q = cm\Delta T$.

The heat lost by aluminum is $Q_a = [920 \text{ J/(kg·C°)}](0.100 \text{ kg})(T - 90.0°\text{C}) = (92 \text{ J/C°})(T - 90.0°\text{C})$.

The heat gained by water is $Q_w = [4186 \text{ J/(kg·C°)}](1.00 \text{ kg})(T - 20°\text{C}) = (4186 \text{ J/C°})(T - 20°\text{C})$.

From calorimetry: $-Q_{\text{lost}} = Q_{\text{gained}}$, ☞ $-92(T - 90.0°\text{C}) = 4186(T - 20°\text{C})$.

Solving, $T = \boxed{21.5°\text{C}}$.

28. (a) First calculate the heat required. 1 liter of water has a mass of 1 kg.

$Q = cm\Delta T = [4186 \text{ J/(kg·C°)}](1.5 \text{ kg})(0°\text{C} - 20°\text{C}) = -1.26 \times 10^5$ J.

So: $P = \dfrac{-Q}{\Delta t} = \dfrac{1.26 \times 10^5 \text{ J}}{3.0(60 \text{ s})} = \boxed{7.0 \times 10^2 \text{ W}}$.

(b) 1 liter of mercury has a mass of 13.6 kg (the density of mercury is 13.6 times that of water).

$Q = [140 \text{ J/(kg·C°)}](1.5)(13.6 \text{ kg}))(-39°\text{C} - 20°\text{C}) = -1.69 \times 10^5$ J.

$P = \dfrac{1.69 \times 10^5 \text{ J}}{3.0(60 \text{ s})} = \boxed{9.4 \times 10^2 \text{ W}}$.

29. (d).

30. (d).

31. Different substances have different internal energies, different molecular structures, and different intrinsic heat values. These quantities affect the temperature at which phase changes take place due to the different effects the addition or removal of heat has on different substances. Latent heats will also be different for different substances because of different molecular structures, or bonds. The latent heat energy goes into breaking these bonds.

32. $\boxed{\text{No}}$, nothing is wrong with the thermometer. Extra heat is needed to melt the ice (latent heat of fusion). Once the ice is completely melted, the temperature of water increases.

33. This is due to the $\boxed{\text{high value of the latent heat of vaporization}}$. When steam condenses, it releases 2.26×10^6 J/kg of heat. When 100°C water drops its temperature by 1 C°, it releases only 4186 J/kg.

34. $Q = mL_v = (0.500 \text{ kg})(22.6 \times 10^5 \text{ J/kg}) = \boxed{1.13 \times 10^6 \text{ J}}$.

35. Heat needed to vaporize is $Q_1 = mL_v = (1.0 \text{ kg})((22.6 \times 10^5 \text{ J/kg}) = 2.26 \times 10^6 \text{ J}$.

Heat needed to raise T is: $Q_2 = cm\Delta T = [4186 \text{ J/(kg·C°)}](1.0 \text{ kg})(100°C - 0°C) = 4.186 \times 10^5 \text{ J}$.

So $\Delta Q = Q_1 - Q_2 = 2.26 \times 10^6 \text{ J} - 4.186 \times 10^5 \text{ J} = \boxed{1.84 \times 10^6 \text{ J more}}$.

36. The melting point of lead is 328°C. So the temperature of the lead has to be increased to 328°C first. The total heat required is then

$Q = cm\Delta T + mL_f = [130 \text{ J/(kg.C°)}](0.75 \text{ kg})(328°C - 20°C) + (0.75 \text{ kg})(0.25 \times 10^5 \text{ J/kg}) = \boxed{4.9 \times 10^4 \text{ J}}$.

37. 1 liter of nitrogen has a mass of 0.80 kg (the density of nitrogen is 0.80 times that of water).

$Q = mL_v = 0.50(0.80 \text{ kg})(2.0 \times 10^5 \text{ J/kg}) = \boxed{8.0 \times 10^4 \text{ J}}$.

38. $Q = cm\Delta T + mL_v = [4186 \text{ J/(kg·C°)}](0.50 \text{ kg})(100°C - 50°C) + (0.50 \text{ kg})(22.6 \times 10^5 \text{ J/kg}) = \boxed{1.2 \times 10^6 \text{ J}}$.

39. The boiling point of mercury is 357°C = 630 K. So $Q = mL_v = (0.015 \text{ kg})(2.7 \times 10^5 \text{ J/kg}) = \boxed{4.1 \times 10^3 \text{ J}}$.

40. (a) The heat needed to raise the temperature of ice from −20°C to 0°C is

$Q_1 = cm\Delta T = [2100 \text{ J/(kg.C°)}](0.500 \text{ kg})[0°C - (-20°C)] = 2.1 \times 10^4 \text{ J}$,

the heat needed to melt the ice at 0°C is $Q_2 = mL_f = (0.500 \text{ kg})(3.3 \times 10^5 \text{ J/kg}) = 1.65 \times 10^5 \text{ J}$,

the heat needed to raise the temperature of water from 0°C to 100°C is

$Q_3 = [4186 \text{ J/(kg.C°)}](0.500 \text{ kg})(100°C - 0°C) = 2.09 \times 10^5 \text{ J}$,

the heat needed to evaporate the water at 100°C is $Q_4 = (0.500 \text{ kg})(22.6 \times 10^5 \text{ J/kg}) = 1.13 \times 10^6 \text{ J}$,

the heat needed to raise the temperature of the steam from 100°C to 115°C is

$Q_5 = [2010 \text{ J/(kg·C°)}](0.500 \text{ kg})(115°C - 100°C) = 1.51 \times 10^4 \text{ J}$.

So the total heat required is $\Sigma Q = \boxed{1.54 \times 10^6 \text{ J}}$.

(b) The heat required to increase the temperature of ice from −20°C to −5°C is

$Q = (2100 \text{ J/kg.C°})(0.500 \text{ kg})[-5°C - (-20°C)] = 1.58 \times 10^4 \text{ J}$.

So the heat needed to be removed is $1.54 \times 10^6 \text{ J} - 1.58 \times 10^4 \text{ J} = \boxed{1.52 \times 10^6 \text{ J}}$.

41. The heat needed to be removed from water is

$Q_{lost} = mc\Delta T = [4186 \text{ J/(kg·C°)}](1.0 \text{ kg})(20°C - 100°C) = -3.35 \times 10^5 \text{ J}$.

The ice and the melt water have to absorb that much heat. Let the mass of ice be m.

$Q_{gained} = mL_f + mc\Delta T = m(3.3 \times 10^5 \text{ J/kg}) + m[4186 \text{ J/(kg.C°)}](20°C - 0°C) = 4.14 \times 10^5 \ m \text{ J/kg}$.

From calorimetry: $-Q_{lost} = Q_{gained}$, ☞ $m = \dfrac{3.35 \times 10^5 \text{ J}}{4.14 \times 10^5 \text{ J/kg}} = \boxed{0.81 \text{ kg}}$.

42. To completely melt the ice to water at 0°C it requires

$Q_1 = cm\Delta T + mL_f = [2100 \text{ J/(kg·C°)}](0.60 \text{ kg})[0°\text{C} - (-10°\text{C})] + (0.60 \text{ kg})(3.3 \times 10^5 \text{ J/kg}) = 2.11 \times 10^5 \text{ J}$.

For 0.30 kg of water not to freeze into ice, it can only release

$Q_2 = [4186 \text{ J/(kg)}](0.30 \text{ kg})(0°\text{C} - 50°\text{C}) = -6.28 \times 10^4 \text{ J} < Q_1$.

So the temperature of the ice will increase to 0°C and then a portion of it will be melted.

Let the amount of ice melted be M.

From calorimetry: $-Q_{lost} = Q_{gained}$,

so: $6.28 \times 10^4 \text{ J} = [2100 \text{ J/(kg·C°)}](0.60 \text{ kg})[0°\text{C} - (-10°\text{C})] + M(3.3 \times 10^5 \text{ J/kg})$,

therefore $M = 0.15$ kg. Hence the total amount of water is 0.30 kg + 0.15 kg = $\boxed{0.45 \text{ kg}}$.

43. Ice gains heat and water and the cup loses heat. Let T be the final temperature. There is a phase change (fusion for ice).   The heat gained by ice is

$Q_i = m_i L_f + c_w m_i \Delta T_i = (0.050 \text{ kg})(3.3 \times 10^5 \text{ J/kg}) + [4186 \text{ J/(kg·C°)}](0.050 \text{ kg})(T - 0°\text{C})$

   $= 1.65 \times 10^4 \text{ J} + (209 \text{ J/C°})T$.

The heat lost by the water and the aluminum cup is

$Q_L = [4186 \text{ J/(kg.C°)}](0.300 \text{ kg})(T - 25°\text{C}) + [920 \text{ J/(kg·C°)}](0.100 \text{ kg})(T - 25°\text{C})$

   $= (1348 \text{ J/C°})(T - 25°\text{C})$.

From calorimetry: $-Q_{lost} = Q_{gained}$, ☞ $-(1348 \text{ J/C°})(T - 25°\text{C}) = 1.65 \times 10^4 \text{ J} + (209 \text{ J/C°})T$.

Solving, $T = \boxed{11°\text{C}}$.

44. The heat required to raise the temperature of water to 60°C is

$Q_{gained} = cm\Delta T = [4186 \text{ J/(kg·C°)}](0.250 \text{ kg})(60°\text{C} - 20°\text{C}) = 4.19 \times 10^4 \text{ J}$.

Let the mass of steam be M. The steam condensates first and then lowers its temperature to 60°C.

$Q_{lost} = -ML_v + cM\Delta T = -M(22.6 \times 10^5 \text{ J/kg}) + M[4186 \text{ J/(kg·C°)}](60°\text{C} - 100°\text{C}) = -2.43 \times 10^6 M \text{ J/kg}$.

From calorimetry: $-Q_{lost} = Q_{gained}$, ☞ $M = \dfrac{4.19 \times 10^4 \text{ J}}{2.34 \times 10^6 \text{ J/kg}} = \boxed{1.72 \times 10^{-2} \text{ kg}}$.

45. If enough ice is added, the equilibrium temperature is 0°C. Note 1 Liter of water has a mass of 1 kg.

The heat lost by the tea is $Q_{lost} = cm\Delta T = [4186 \text{ J/(kg·C°)}](0.75 \text{ kg})(0°\text{C} - 20°\text{C}) = 6.279 \times 10^4 \text{ J}$.

Let the mass of ice melted be M. $Q_{gained} = ML_f = 3.3 \times 10^5 M \text{ J/kg}$.

From calorimetry: $-Q_{lost} = Q_{gained}$, ☞ $M = \dfrac{6.279 \times 10^4 \text{ J}}{3.3 \times 10^5 \text{ J/kg}} = 0.190$ kg.

So the total amount of liquid is 0.75 kg + 0.19 kg = $\boxed{0.94 \text{ kg or } 0.94 \text{ L}}$.

46.   1 L of water has a mass of 1 kg. The heat removed from water is

$$Q_w = c_w \, m\Delta T_w - mL_f + c_i \, m\Delta T_i = [4186 \text{ J/(kg·C°)}](0.50 \text{ kg})(0°C - 16°C) - (0.50 \text{ kg})(3.33 \times 10^5 \text{ J/kg})$$

$$+ [2100 \text{ J/(kg·C°)}](0.50 \text{ kg})(-8.0°C - 0°C) = -2.083 \times 10^5 \text{ J}.$$

The heat removed from the aluminum tray is

$$Q_a = [920 \text{ J/(kg·C°)}](0.250 \text{ kg})(-8.0°C - 16°C) = -5.52 \times 10^3 \text{ J}.$$

So the total heat that must be removed is $Q = 2.083 \times 10^5 \text{ J} + 5.52 \times 10^3 \text{ J} = \boxed{2.14 \times 10^5 \text{ J}}$.

47.   The mass of rain is $m = \rho V = (1.0 \times 10^3 \text{ kg/m}^3)(2.0 \times 10^3 \text{ m})(3.0 \times 10^3 \text{ m})(0.030 \text{ m}) = 1.8 \times 10^8 \text{ kg}$.

The heat required to condensate that much water and lower its temperature to 10°C is

$$Q = mL_v + cm\Delta T = (1.8 \times 10^8 \text{ kg})\{(22.6 \times 10^5 \text{ J/kg}) + [4186 \text{ J/(kg·C°)}](100°C - 10°C)\} = \boxed{4.7 \times 10^{14} \text{ J}}.$$

Yes, a very large amount. This is equivalent to 10^8 kWh. For a family of 4, the average electric usage is 600 kWh per month, so this is enough energy to supply 10^5 such households for a month.

48.   (a) $\boxed{110°C \text{ and } 140°C}$.

     (b) For solid: $c_1 = \dfrac{Q}{m\Delta T} = \dfrac{0.20 \times 10^4 \text{ J}}{(1.0 \text{ kg})(110°C - 100°C)} = \boxed{2.0 \times 10^2 \text{ J/(kg·C°)}}$,

     for liquid, $c_2 = \dfrac{(1.2 - 0.60) \times 10^4 \text{ J}}{(1.0 \text{ kg})(140°C - 110°C)} = \boxed{2.0 \times 10^2 \text{ J/(kg·C°)}}$,

     for gas: $c_3 = \dfrac{(2.0 - 1.8) \times 10^4 \text{ J}}{(1.0 \text{ kg})(160°C - 140°C)} = \boxed{1.0 \times 10^2 \text{ J/(kg·C°)}}$.

     (c) For fusion: $L_f = \dfrac{Q}{m} = \dfrac{(0.60 - 0.20) \times 10^4 \text{ J}}{1.0 \text{ kg}} = \boxed{4.0 \times 10^3 \text{ J/kg}}$,

     for vaporization: $L_v = \dfrac{(1.8 - 1.2) \times 10^4 \text{ J}}{1.0 \text{ kg}} = \boxed{6.0 \times 10^3 \text{ J/kg}}$.

49.   The heat lost by the ceramic is $Q_{lost} = cm\Delta T = [840 \text{ J/(kg·C°)}](0.150 \text{ kg})(-196°C - 20°C) = 2.72 \times 10^4 \text{ J}$.

Let the mass of nitrogen boiled be M. $Q_{gained} = ML_v = 2.0 \times 10^5 \, M$ J/kg.

From calorimetry: $-Q_{lost} = Q_{gained}$,   ☞ $M = \dfrac{2.72 \times 10^4 \text{ J}}{2.0 \times 10^5 \text{ J/kg}} = 0.136 \text{ kg}$.

Note that 1 liter of liquid nitrogen has a mass of 0.80 kg (the density of liquid nitrogen is 0.80 kg/L).

$$\rho = \frac{m}{V}, \quad ☞ \quad V = \frac{m}{\rho} = \frac{0.136 \text{ kg}}{0.80 \text{ kg/L}} = \boxed{0.17 \text{ L}}.$$

50.   (d).

51. Water can be heated relatively quickly because of $\boxed{\text{convection}}$. The warm (less dense) water rises to the top and the cooler (more dense) water sinks to the bottom.

52. Metal has a higher heat conductivity so it $\boxed{\text{conducts heat away from your hand faster}}$.

53. (a) This convects the heat from the hot soup to the cooler air.
(b) No. The ice blocks air flow and cooling of the air (Also, the air conditioner is less efficient and runs more, increasing electric cost.) Also, ice is a poor conductor.

54. The bridge is exposed to the cold air above and below while the road is exposed only above. So more heat is removed from the bridge than the road. This results in a fast freeze of the water on the bridge.

55. It is to increase the surface area for better conduction and radiation.

56. It will stay hot longer if cream is added right away because the heat loss is proportional to the temperature difference. By adding the cream right away, the temperature difference is less and so is the heat loss.

57. The double-walled and partially evacuated container is to counteract conduction and convection because both processes depend on a medium to transfer the heat (the double-walls are more for holding the partially evacuated region than for reducing conduction and convection). The mirrored interior minimizes the loss by radiation.

58. This is because $\boxed{\text{the pan is a much better heat conductor than air}}$ so more heat is transferred to your hand more quickly through the pan.

59. $\dfrac{\Delta Q}{\Delta t} = \dfrac{kA\Delta T}{d}$, ☞ $\dfrac{(\Delta Q/\Delta t)_t}{(\Delta Q/\Delta t)_o} = \dfrac{k_t}{k_o} = \dfrac{0.67 \text{ J/(m·s·C°)}}{0.15 \text{ J/(m·s·C°)}} = \boxed{4.5 \text{ times}}$.

60. $P = \sigma A e T^4 = [5.67 \times 10^{-8} \text{ W/(m}^2\text{·K}^4)](0.20 \text{ m}^2)(0.75)(293 \text{ K})^4 = \boxed{63 \text{ J/a}}$.

61. $\dfrac{\Delta Q}{\Delta t} = \dfrac{kA\Delta T}{d} = \dfrac{[0.84 \text{ J/(m·s·C°)}](2.00 \text{ m})(1.50 \text{ m})(2 \text{ C°})}{4.00 \times 10^{-3} \text{ m}} = 1260 \text{ J/s}$.

So $\Delta Q = (1.36 \times 10^3 \text{ W})(3600 \text{ s}) = \boxed{4.54 \times 10^6 \text{ J}}$.

62. The normal body temperature is 37°C.

$\dfrac{\Delta Q}{\Delta t} = \dfrac{kA\Delta T}{d} = \dfrac{[0.20 \text{ J/(m·s·C°)}](1.5 \text{ m}^2)(37°\text{C} - 33°\text{C})}{0.040 \text{ m}} = \boxed{30 \text{ J/s}}$.

63.   (a) $\dfrac{\Delta Q}{\Delta t} = \dfrac{kA\Delta T}{d} = \dfrac{[390 \text{ J/(m·s·C°)}](\pi)(0.15 \text{ m})^2(150°\text{C} - 100°\text{C})}{2.5 \times 10^{-3} \text{ m}} = \boxed{5.5 \times 10^5 \text{ J/s}}$.

     (b) In 5.0 min, the heat supplied to the water is

$\Delta Q = (5.5 \times 10^5 \text{ J/s})(5.0)(60 \text{ s}) = 1.65 \times 10^8 \text{ J}$.

The mass boiled away by ΔQ is $m = \dfrac{\Delta Q}{L_v} = \dfrac{1.65 \times 10^8 \text{ J}}{22.6 \times 10^5 \text{ kg}} = \boxed{73 \text{ kg}}$.

This answer is not reasonable because a lot of heat is lost.

64. $\dfrac{\Delta Q}{\Delta t} = \dfrac{kA\Delta T}{d}$,   ☞ $d = \dfrac{kA\Delta T}{(\Delta Q/\Delta t)}$. $\dfrac{d_{cu}}{d_{al}} = \dfrac{k_{Cu}}{k_{Ai}} = \dfrac{390 \text{ J/(m·s·C°)}}{240 \text{ J/(m·s·C°)}} = 1.6$.

     So $\boxed{d_{Cu} = 1.6 \, d_{Al}}$.

65.   The heat required to melt the ice is $Q = mL_f = (5.0 \text{ kg})(3.3 \times 10^5 \text{ J/kg}) = 1.65 \times 10^6 \text{ J}$.

$\dfrac{\Delta Q}{\Delta t} = \dfrac{kA\Delta T}{d} = \dfrac{[0.042 \text{ J/(m·s·C°)}](1.0 \text{ m}^2)(35 °\text{C} - 0°\text{C})}{0.025 \text{ m}}) = 58.8 \text{ J/s}$.

So the time is $\dfrac{1.65 \times 10^6 \text{ J}}{58.8 \text{ J/s}} = 2.8 \times 10^4 \text{ s} = \boxed{7.8 \text{ h}}$.

66.   (a) The greater the R-value, the greater the insulation value.

     (b)   (1) $R = \dfrac{L}{k}$,   ☞ $L = R k$.

So: $\dfrac{L_{\text{fiberboard}}}{L_{\text{foam plastic}}} = \dfrac{k_{\text{fiberboard}}}{k_{\text{foam plastic}}} = \dfrac{0.059 \text{ J/(m·s·C°)}}{0.042 \text{ J/(m·s·C°)}} = 1.40$.

Therefore $L_{\text{fiberboard}} = (1.40)(3.0 \text{ in}) = \boxed{4.2 \text{ in}}$.

     (2) $\dfrac{L_{\text{brick}}}{L_{\text{foam plastic}}} = \dfrac{0.71 \text{ J/(m·s·C°)}}{0.042 \text{ J/(m·s·C°)}} = 16.9$.

So $L_{\text{brick}} = 16.9(3.0 \text{ in}) = \boxed{51 \text{ in}}$.

67. $R = \dfrac{L}{k}$,   ☞ $L = R k$.

     (a) $\dfrac{L_{\text{glass wool}}}{L_{\text{pine wood}}} = \dfrac{k_{\text{glass wool}}}{k_{\text{pine wood}}} = \dfrac{0.042 \text{ J/(m·s·C°)}}{0.12 \text{ J/(m·s·C°)}} = 0.35$.

So $L_{\text{glass wool}} = 0.35(14 \text{ in}) = \boxed{4.9 \text{ in}}$.

     (b) $\dfrac{L_{\text{fiberboard}}}{L_{\text{pine wood}}} = \dfrac{0.059 \text{ J/(m·s·C°)}}{0.12 \text{ J/(m·s·C°)}} = 0.492$.

So $L_{\text{fiberboard}} = \boxed{6.9 \text{ in}}$.

68. (a) $\dfrac{\Delta Q}{\Delta t} = \dfrac{k\,A\,\Delta T}{d} = \dfrac{(0.84 \text{ J/m·s·C°})(2.0 \text{ m})(3.0 \text{ m})(20°\text{C} - 0°\text{C})}{4.0 \times 10^{-3} \text{ m}} = \boxed{2.5 \times 10^4 \text{ J/s}}$.

(b) From Example 11.8, $\dfrac{\Delta Q}{\Delta t} = \dfrac{A(T_2 - T_1)}{d_1/k_1 + d_2/k_2 + d_3/k_3}$

$= \dfrac{(2.0 \text{ m})(3.0 \text{ m})(20°\text{C} - 0°\text{C})}{(2.0 \times 10^{-3} \text{ m})/[0.84 \text{ J/(m·s·C°)}] + (1.0 \times 10^{-3} \text{ m})/[0.024 \text{ J/(m·s·C°)}] + (2.0 \times 10^{-3} \text{ m})/[0.84 \text{ J/(m·s·C°)}]}$

$= \boxed{2.6 \times 10^3 \text{ J/s}}$. No, because of losses due to radiation and convection. Also, temperature gradient across window is usually not as great as given by ambient temperatures.

69. $P = \sigma AeT^4$, ☞ $\dfrac{P_b}{P_o} = \dfrac{e_b}{e_o} = \dfrac{1}{0.60} = \boxed{1.7}$.

70. From Example 11.8, $\dfrac{\Delta Q}{\Delta t} = \dfrac{A(T_2 - T_1)}{d_1/k_1 + d_2/k_2 + d_3/k_3}$

$= \dfrac{(3.5 \text{ m})(5.0 \text{ m})[20°\text{C} - (-10°\text{C})]}{(0.020 \text{ m})/[0.059 \text{ J/(m·s·C°)}] + (0.150 \text{ m})/[1.3 \text{ J/(m·s·C°)}] + (0.070 \text{ m})/[0.71 \text{ J/(m·s·C°)}]} = 949 \text{ J/s}$.

In one hour $\Delta Q = (949 \text{ J/s})(3600 \text{ s}) = \boxed{3.4 \times 10^6 \text{ J}}$.

71. $\dfrac{\Delta Q}{\Delta t} = \dfrac{949 \text{ H/s}}{2} = 474.5 \text{ J/s} =$

$\dfrac{(3.5 \text{ m})(5.0 \text{ m})[20°\text{C} - (-10°\text{C})]}{(0.020 \text{ m})/[0.059 \text{ J/(m·s·C°)}] + d/[0.042 \text{ J/(m·s·C°)}] + (0.150 \text{ m})/[1.3 \text{ J/(m·s·C°)}] + (0.070 \text{ m})/[0.71 \text{ J/(m·s·C°)}]}$.

Solving, $d = 0.023 \text{ m} = \boxed{2.3 \text{ cm}}$.

72. (a) e is the $\boxed{\text{same}}$.

(b) $P = \sigma AeT^4$, ☞ $\dfrac{P}{P_o} = \dfrac{T^4}{T_o^4} = \dfrac{(273 + 40)^4}{(273 + 20)^4} = 1.3$. So $\boxed{\text{increases by 1.3 times}}$.

(c) $\dfrac{P}{P_o} = \dfrac{2^4}{1^4} = 16$. So increases by $\boxed{16 \text{ times}}$.

73. From Example 11.8,

$\dfrac{\Delta Q}{\Delta t} = \dfrac{A(T_2 - T_1)}{d_1/k_1 + d_2/k_2} = \dfrac{\pi(0.050 \text{ m})^2 (95°\text{C} - 15°\text{C})}{(0.040 \text{ m})/[46 \text{ J/(m·s·C°)}] + (0.040 \text{ m})/[390 \text{ J/(m·s·C°)}]} = 646 \text{ J/s}$.

In 10 min, $\Delta Q = (646 \text{ J/s})(20)(60 \text{ s}) = \boxed{7.8 \times 10^5 \text{ J}}$.

74. Let the temperature at the interface be T and consider steel.

$\dfrac{\Delta Q}{\Delta t} = \dfrac{\pi(0.050 \text{ m})^2 (95°\text{C} - T)}{(0.040 \text{ m})/[46 \text{ J/(m·s·C°)}]} = 646 \text{ J/s}$, solving, $T = \boxed{23°\text{C}}$.

75. Although the surface area of the collector is πrL, the sunlight is exposed to a rectangular cross-sectional area of $A = dL = 2\pi L = 2(0.50 \text{ m})(4.0 \text{ m}) = 4.0 \text{ m}^2$.

$E = IAt = [1000 \text{ J/(m}^2\cdot\text{s})](4.0 \text{ m}^2)(10)(3600 \text{ s}) = \boxed{1.4 \times 10^8 \text{ J}}$.

76. $Q = Q_a + Q_i = c_a\, m_a\, \Delta T = c_i\, m_i\, \Delta T$

$= [920 \text{ J/(kg}\cdot\text{C}°)](25 \text{ kg})(120°\text{C} - 20°\text{C}) + [460 \text{ J/(kg}\cdot\text{C}°)](80 \text{ kg})(120°\text{C} - 20°\text{C}) = \boxed{6.0 \times 10^6 \text{ J}}$.

77. 1 mL of water has mass of 1 g. Let the final temperature be T.

The heat lost by the shot is

$Q_{\text{lost}} = cm\Delta T = [920 \text{ J/(kg}\cdot\text{C}°)](0.35 \text{ kg})(T - 100°\text{C}) = (322 \text{ J/C}°)(T - 100°\text{C})$.

the heat gained by water is

$Q_{\text{gained}} = [4186 \text{ J/(kg}\cdot\text{C}°)](0.050 \text{ kg})(T - 10°\text{C}) = (209 \text{ J/C}°)(T - 10°\text{C})$.

From calorimetry: $-Q_{\text{lost}} = Q_{\text{gained}}$,   ☞ $-(322 \text{ J/C}°)(T - 100°\text{C}) = (209 \text{ J/C}°)(T - 10°\text{C})$.

Solving, $T = \boxed{65°\text{C}}$.

78. $P_{\text{net}} = \sigma Ae(T_s^4 - T^4)$,   ☞ $\dfrac{100 \text{ W}}{99.5 \text{ W}} = \dfrac{T_s^4 - (293 \text{ K})^4}{T_s^4 - (303 \text{ K})^4}$,

or $1.005T_s^4 - 8.47 \times 10^9 \text{ K}^4 = T_s^4 - 7.37 \times 10^9 \text{ K}^4$.   Solving, $T_s = 684 \text{ K} = \boxed{411°\text{C}}$.

79. Let the initial temperature of the shot be T.

The heat lost by the shot is

$Q_{\text{copper}} = cm\Delta T = [390 \text{ J/(kg}\cdot\text{C}°)](0.150 \text{ kg})(28°\text{C} - T) = (58.5 \text{ J/C}°)(28°\text{C} - T)$,

the heat gained by water is

$Q_{\text{water}} = [4186 \text{ J/(kg}\cdot\text{C}°)](0.200 \text{ kg})(28°\text{C} - 25°\text{C}) = 2512 \text{ J}$,

the heat gained by the cup is

$Q_{\text{cup}} = [920 \text{ J/(kg}\cdot\text{C}°)](0.375 \text{ kg})(28°\text{C} - 25°\text{C}) = 1035 \text{ J}$.

From calorimetry: $-Q_{\text{lost}} = Q_{\text{gained}}$,   ☞ $-(58.5 \text{ J/C}°)(28°\text{C} - T) = 2512 \text{ J} + 1035 \text{ J}$.

Solving, $T = \boxed{88.7°\text{C}}$.

80. Let the final temperature of the mixture be T. 1.0 L of water has a mass of 1.0 kg and 1.0 L of ethyl alcohol has a mass of 0.79 kg because the density of ethyl alcohol is 790 kg/m^3.

The heat lost by water is

$Q_{\text{water}} = cm\Delta T = [4186 \text{ J/(kg}\cdot\text{C}°)](1.0 \text{ kg})(T - 40°\text{C}) = (4186 \text{ J/C}°)(T - 40°\text{C})$.

The heat gained by alcohol is

$Q_{\text{alcohol}} = [2430 \text{ J/(kg·C°)}](0.79 \text{ kg})(T - 20°C) = (1920 \text{ J/C°})(T - 20°C).$

From calorimetry: $-Q_{\text{lost}} = Q_{\text{gained}},$ ☞ $-(4186 \text{ J/C°})(T - 40°C) = (1920 \text{ J/C°})(T - 20°C).$

Solving, $T = \boxed{34°C}$.

81.   25 km/h = 6.95 m/s.   The kinetic energy is $K = \frac{1}{2}mv^2 = \frac{1}{2}(65 \text{ kg})(6.95 \text{ m/s})^2 = 1.57 \times 10^3 \text{ J}.$

So $Q = 0.40K = 627 \text{ J}.$ $m = \dfrac{Q}{L_f} = \dfrac{627 \text{ J}}{3.3 \times 10^5 \text{ J/kg}} = 1.9 \times 10^{-3} \text{ kg} = \boxed{1.9 \text{ g}}.$

The rest of the energy goes to heating the skates and the environment.

82.   The kinetic energy of the bullet is $K = \frac{1}{2}mv^2.$

The heat that goes to melting the bullet is then $Q = 0.80K = 0.40mv^2.$

This heat goes into raising the temperature of lead and melting it.

$Q = cm\Delta T + mL_f = [130 \text{ J/(kg·C)}]m(328°C - 20°C) + m(0.25 \times 10^5 \text{ J/kg}) = 0.40mv^2.$

Solving, $v = \boxed{4.0 \times 10^2 \text{ m/s}}.$

83.   Since Al has a higher specific heat, it gains more heat.

$Q_{\text{Al}} = cm\Delta T = [920 \text{ J/(kg·C°)}](0.50 \text{ kg})(100°C - 20°C) = 3.68 \times 10^4 \text{ J},$

$Q_{\text{ir}} = [460 \text{ J/(kg·C°)}](0.50 \text{ kg})(100°C - 20°C) = 1.84 \times 10^4 \text{ J}.$

So the difference is 1.84×10^4 J, or $\boxed{\text{Al by } 1.8 \times 10^4 \text{ J}}$.

84. $Q = cm\Delta T,$ ☞ $\dfrac{m_{\text{Pb}}}{m_{\text{Cu}}} = \dfrac{Q/(c_{\text{Pb}}\Delta T_{\text{Pb}})}{Q/(C_{\text{Cu}}\Delta T_{\text{Cu}})} = \dfrac{c_{\text{Cu}}\Delta T_{\text{Cu}}}{c_{\text{Pb}}\Delta T_{\text{Pb}}} = \dfrac{[390 \text{ J/(kg·C°)}](5.0 \text{ C°})}{[130 \text{ J/(kg·C°)}](10 \text{ C°})} = 1.5.$

So $\boxed{\text{lead by 1.5 times}}$.

85.   The heat needed to raise the temperature of ice from −10°C to 0°C is

$Q_1 = cm\Delta T = [2100 \text{ J/(kg.C°)}](0.75 \text{ kg})[0°C - (-10°C)] = 1.575 \times 10^4 \text{ J},$

the heat needed to melt the ice at 0°C is $Q_2 = mL_f = (0.75 \text{ kg})(3.3 \times 10^5 \text{ J/kg}) = 2.475 \times 10^5 \text{ J},$

the heat needed to raise the temperature of water from 0°C to 100°C is

$Q_3 = [4186 \text{ J/(kg.C°)}](0.75 \text{ kg})(100°C - 0°C) = 3.140 \times 10^5 \text{ J},$

the heat needed to evaporate the water at 100°C is $Q_4 = (0.75 \text{ kg})(22.6 \times 10^5 \text{ J/kg}) = 1.695 \times 10^6 \text{ J},$

the heat needed to raise the temperature of the steam from 100°C to 120°C is

$Q_5 = [2010 \text{ J/(kg·C°)}](0.75 \text{ kg})(120°C - 100°C) = 3.015 \times 10^4 \text{ J}.$

So the total heat required is $\Sigma Q = \boxed{2.3 \times 10^6 \text{ J}}.$

1.   (c).

2.   (d).

3.   (a).

4.   For an ideal gas, $pV = nRT$. So a plot of p vs. V will not be a straight line.

5.

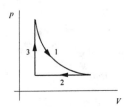

6.   (a) isothermal   (b) isobaric   (c) isometric

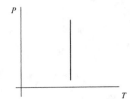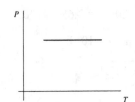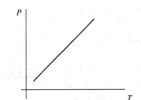

7.   (b).

8.   (c).

9.   (d).

10.   (a) A force is exerted to pump the air and does work on the system. After one cycle, the internal energy of the system returns to its original value so heat must leave the system. This causes the body of the pump to heat up.

        (b) The rapid "expansion" is almost adiabatic. Work is done at the expense of the internal energy of the gas. This lowers the temperature and cools the valve.

11.   This is an adiabatic compression. When the plunger is pushed in, the work done goes into increasing of the internal energy of the air. The increase in internal energy increases the temperature of the air and causes the paper to catch fire.

12. Since the container is rigid, $\Delta V = 0$, so $W = 0$. $Q = \Delta U + W = \Delta U = \boxed{2.0 \times 10^4 \text{ J}}$.

13. (a) For a cyclic process, $\Delta U = 0$.   So $Q = \Delta U + W = W = 400$ J. Therefore $\boxed{400 \text{ J added}}$.

    (b) T is a $\boxed{\text{constant}}$ since $\Delta U = 0$.

14. $Q = \Delta U + W$,   ☞ $W = Q - \Delta U = -50$ J $- 20$ J $= -70$ J.

    Since the work is negative, $\boxed{70 \text{ J of work is done on the system}}$.

15. (a) For an adiabatic process, $Q = 0$.   So $Q = \Delta U + W$,   ☞ $\Delta U = -W$.

    Since $\Delta V > 0$ ("expanded"), $W > 0$, or $\Delta U < 0$. So the temperature $\boxed{\text{decreases}}$.

    (b) For an adiabatic process, $Q = \boxed{0}$.

    (c) $\Delta U = -W = \boxed{-500 \text{ J}}$.

16. $W = p\Delta V = (1.01 \times 10^5 \text{ Pa})(3.0 \text{ m}^3 - 1.0 \text{ m}^3) = 2.02 \times 10^5$ J.

    $\Delta U = Q - W = 5.0 \times 10^4$ J $- 2.02 \times 10^5$ J $= \boxed{-1.5 \times 10^5 \text{ J}}$.

17. (a) $W = p\Delta V = (1.65 \times 10^4 \text{ Pa})(0.40 \text{ m}^3 - 0.20 \text{ m}^3) = \boxed{3.3 \times 10^3 \text{ J}}$.

    (b) $\boxed{\text{Yes}}$, the internal energy of the system changes.

    $Q = \Delta U + W$,   ☞ $\Delta U = Q - W = 1000$ J $- 3.3 \times 10^3$ J $= \boxed{-2.3 \times 10^3 \text{ J}}$.

18. $Q = \Delta U + W = \Delta U + mgh = -6.0 \times 10^4$ J $+ (145 \text{ kg})(9.80 \text{ m/s}^2)(2.1 \text{ m}) = -5.7 \times 10^4$ J.

    Since the heat is negative, $\boxed{5.7 \times 10^4 \text{ J flows out}}$.

19. (a) Since $pV = nRT$, $T \propto pV = 2p_1 (V_1/2) = p_1 V_1 = $ constant.   So $\Delta U = \boxed{0}$.

    (b) $W = p\Delta V = 2p_1 (V_1/2 - V_1) = \boxed{-p_1 V_1 \text{ (on the system)}}$.

    (c) $Q = \Delta U + W = 0 + (-p_1 V_1) = \boxed{-p_1 V_1 \text{ (out of the system)}}$.

20. (a) $U = \frac{3}{2} nRT$,   ☞ $\Delta U = \frac{3}{2} nR\Delta T = \frac{3}{2} (2.0 \text{ mole})(8.31 \text{ J/K·mole})(100 \text{ K}) = \boxed{2.5 \times 10^3 \text{ J}}$, independent of

    heat Q.

(b) $Q = \Delta U + W$, ☞ $W = Q - \Delta U$.

So $W_1 = 2500 \text{ J} - 2500 \text{ J} = 0$, $W_2 = 3000 \text{ J} - 2500 \text{ J} = 5.0 \times 10^2 \text{ J}$.

Therefore the $\boxed{\text{second pass by } 5.0 \times 10^2 \text{ J more}}$.

21. The heat required in the process is $Q = mL_v = (1.00 \times 10^{-3} \text{ kg})(22.6 \times 10^5 \text{ J/kg}) = 2260 \text{ J}$.

The work done in the process is

$W = p\Delta V = (1.01 \times 10^5 \text{ Pa})(1671 \text{ cm}^3 - 1.00 \text{ cm}^3) \times (10^{-6} \text{ m}^3/\text{cm}^3) = 169 \text{ J}$.

$Q = \Delta U + W$, ☞ $\Delta U = Q - W = 2260 \text{ J} - 169 \text{ J} = \boxed{2.09 \times 10^3 \text{ J}}$.

22. Work equals the area under the curve.

From 1–2, $W = \boxed{0}$; from 2–3, $W = (0.50 \times 10^5 \text{ Pa})(0.50 \text{ m}^3) = \boxed{2.5 \times 10^4 \text{ J}}$;

from 3–4, $W = \boxed{0}$; from 4–5, $W = (1.00 \times 10^5 \text{ Pa})(0.25 \text{ m}^3) = \boxed{2.5 \times 10^4 \text{ J}}$.

23. The work in addition to that in Exercise 12.24 is:

for isometric, $W = 0$; since $\Delta V = 0$; for isobaric, $W = (0.70 \times 10^5 \text{ Pa})(-0.20 \text{ m}^3) = -1.4 \times 10^4 \text{ J}$.

So the total work done is $\Sigma W = 0 + 2.5 \times 10^4 \text{ J} + 0 + 2.5 \times 10^4 \text{ J} + 0 - 1.4 \times 10^4 \text{ J} = \boxed{3.6 \times 10^4 \text{ J}}$.

24. The work done equals the area under the curve (the area of the trapezoid). The work is negative for

compression. $W = \frac{1}{2}(2.0 \times 10^5 \text{ Pa} + 5.0 \times 10^5 \text{ Pa})(0.50 \text{ m}^3) = \boxed{-1.8 \times 10^5 \text{ J}}$.

25. (a) First find the volumes from the ideal gas law. $pV = nRT$, ☞ $V = \dfrac{nRT}{p}$.

$V_1 = \dfrac{(1.0 \text{ mole})[8.31 \text{ J/(K·mole)}](200 \text{ K})}{1.01 \times 10^5 \text{ Pa}} = 0.0165 \text{ m}^3$;

$V_2 = \dfrac{(1.0 \text{ mole})[8.31 \text{ J/(K·mole)}](400 \text{ K})}{1.01 \times 10^5 \text{ Pa}} = 0.0329 \text{ m}^3$.

Path AB, $W = p\Delta V = (1.01 \times 10^5 \text{ Pa})(0.0165 \text{ m}^3 - 0.0329 \text{ m}^3) = \boxed{-1.66 \times 10^3 \text{ J}}$;

path BC, $W = \boxed{0}$ ($\Delta V = 0$ for isometric);

path CD, $W = (2 \times 1.01 \times 10^5 \text{ Pa})(0.0329 \text{ m}^3 - 0.0165 \text{ m}^3) = \boxed{3.31 \times 10^3 \text{ J}}$;

path DA, $W = \boxed{0}$.

(b) For a cyclic process, $\Delta U = \boxed{0}$. $Q = W = 3.31 \times 10^3 \text{ J} - 1.66 \times 10^3 \text{ J} = \boxed{1.65 \times 10^3 \text{ J}}$.

(c) $T_3 = \dfrac{(2 \times 1.01 \times 10^5 \text{ Pa})(0.0329 \text{ m}^3)}{(1.0 \text{ mole})[8.31 \text{ J/(K·mole)}]} = \boxed{800 \text{ K}}$.

26.   (c).

27.   (b).

28.   (a) [Increases] since heat is added.   (b) [Decreases] since heat is removed.

      (c) [Increases] since heat is added.   (d) [Decreases] since heat is removed.

29.   There must be energy created for the change in entropy to be negative.

30.   From the second law of thermodynamics, the entropy increases. The cold water gains more entropy than that lost by the hot water.

31. $\Delta S = \dfrac{Q}{T} = \dfrac{mL_f}{T} = \dfrac{(1.0 \text{ kg})(3.3 \times 10^5 \text{ J/kg})}{273 \text{ K}} = \boxed{1.2 \times 10^3 \text{ J/K}}$.

32. $\Delta S = \dfrac{Q}{T} = \dfrac{-mL_v}{T} = \dfrac{-(0.50 \text{ kg})(22.6 \times 10^5 \text{ J/kg})}{373 \text{ K}} = \boxed{-3.0 \times 10^3 \text{ J/K}}$.

33. $\Delta S = \dfrac{Q}{T} = \dfrac{-mL_v}{T} = \dfrac{-(0.50 \text{ kg})(2.7 \times 10^5 \text{ J/kg})}{630 \text{ K}} = \boxed{-2.1 \times 10^2 \text{ J/K}}$.

34. $\Delta S_i = \dfrac{Q}{T} = \dfrac{mL_f}{T} = \dfrac{(0.75 \text{ kg})(3.3 \times 10^5 \text{ J/kg})}{273 \text{ K}} = \boxed{9.1 \times 10^2 \text{ J/K}}$;

      $\Delta S_s = \dfrac{(0.25 \text{ kg})(22.6 \times 10^5 \text{ J/kg})}{373 \text{ K}} = \boxed{1.5 \times 10^3 \text{ J/K}}$.

      So [steam] has the greater change in entropy.

35.   For isothermal, $U = $ constant or $\Delta U = 0$.

      So $Q = \Delta U + W = W = -7.5 \times 10^3$ J (work done on system).

      Therefore $\Delta S = \dfrac{Q}{T} = \dfrac{-7.5 \times 10^3 \text{ J}}{293 \text{ K}} = \boxed{-26 \text{ J/K}}$.

36.   For an isothermal process, U is a constant or $\Delta U = 0$.   So $Q = \Delta U + W = W = 3.0 \times 10^3$ J.

      Therefore $\Delta S = \dfrac{Q}{T} = \dfrac{3.0 \times 10^3 \text{ J}}{273 \text{ K}} = \boxed{11 \text{ J/K}}$.

37. $\Delta S = \dfrac{Q}{T}$,   ☞ $T = \dfrac{Q}{\Delta S} = \dfrac{-1.67 \times 10^6 \text{J}}{-4.19 \times 10^3 \text{ J/K}} = 399 \text{ K} = \boxed{126°C}$.

38. (a) $\Delta S_h = \dfrac{Q_h}{T_h} = \dfrac{1000 \text{ J}}{373 \text{ K}} = \boxed{2.68 \text{ J/K}}$.

(b) $\Delta S_c = \dfrac{-1000 \text{ J}}{273 \text{ K}} = \boxed{-3.66 \text{ J/K}}$.

(c) $\Delta S = \Delta S_h + \Delta S_c = 2.68 \text{ J/K} - 3.66 \text{ J/K} = \boxed{-0.98 \text{ J/K}}$.

(d) $\boxed{\text{No}}$ because the entropy decreased and this is a violation of the second law of thermodynamics.

39. $\Delta S = \Delta S_1 + \Delta S_2 = \dfrac{Q_1}{T_1} + \dfrac{Q_2}{T_2} = \dfrac{-1.5 \times 10^3 \text{ J}}{473 \text{ K}} + \dfrac{1.5 \times 10^3 \text{ J}}{333 \text{ K}} = \boxed{1.33 \text{ J/K}}$.

40. For an isometric process, $\Delta V = 0$, so $W = 0$. Therefore $Q = \Delta U + W = \Delta U = -4.5 \times 10^3 \text{ J}$.

Use the average temperature in entropy calculation. $\Delta S = \dfrac{Q}{T} = \dfrac{-4.50 \times 10^3 \text{ J}}{(273 + 18) \text{ K}} = \boxed{-15.5 \text{ J/K}}$.

41. (a) The vertical line has $\Delta S = 0$. The horizontal line has $\Delta S = 100 \text{ J/K}$.

So $\Delta S = \dfrac{Q}{T}$, ☞ $Q = T\Delta S = (273 \text{ K})(100 \text{ J/K}) = \boxed{2.73 \times 10^4 \text{ J}}$.

(b) From b to c, $\Delta S = 0$, so $Q = 0$. Therefore it is adiabatic or isentropic.

42. Since the process returns to its original state, $\Delta S = \boxed{0}$.

Heat equals the area under the curve (the area of the triangle).

$Q = -\frac{1}{2}(100 \text{ J/K})(100 \text{ K}) = \boxed{-5.0 \times 10^3 \text{ J}}$.

43. (a) $\Delta S = \dfrac{Q}{T} = \dfrac{mL_f}{T} = \dfrac{(0.0500 \text{ kg})(3.33 \times 10^5 \text{ J/kg})}{273 \text{ K}} = \boxed{61.0 \text{ J/K}}$.

(b) From Calorimetry, the heat lost by water is also $(0.0500 \text{ kg})(3.33 \times 10^5 \text{ J/kg}) = 1.67 \times 10^4 \text{ J}$.

The temperature change of the water is $\Delta T = \dfrac{Q}{cm} = \dfrac{-1.67 \times 10^4 \text{ J}}{[4186 \text{ J/(kg·C°)}](0.500 \text{ kg})} = -7.98 \text{ C°}$.

So the final temperature of the water is 12.0°C. The average water temperature is $(20 + 12)/2 = 16°C$.

Use the average temperature of the water in entropy calculation. $\Delta S = \dfrac{-1.67 \times 10^4 \text{ J}}{289 \text{ K}} = \boxed{-57.8 \text{ J/K}}$.

(c) The total change in entropy is $\Delta S = 61.0 \text{ J/K} - 57.8 \text{ J/K} = \boxed{3.2 \text{ J/K}}$.

44. (d).

45. (b).

46. No, this is not a practical way to air condition a room. As a matter of fact, the room will be heated. The heat expelled to the room by the refrigerator is more than the heat removed by the refrigerator from the room.

47. Heat can be completely converted to work for a single process (not a cycle) such as an isothermal expansion process of an ideal gas.

48. No, this is not a violation. The heat output to the hot reservoir is the sum of the energy input and heat input from the cold reservoir.

49. No, as the warm air rises to the higher altitude, both gravity and buoyancy forces do work. Since it is a natural process with work input, the entropy increases and the second law is not violated.

50. (a) $\varepsilon_{th} = \dfrac{W_{net}}{Q_{in}}$, ☞ $W_{net} = \varepsilon_{th} Q_{in} = 0.28(2000 \text{ J}) = \boxed{560 \text{ J}}$.

   (b) $Q_{out} = Q_{in} - W_{net} = 2000 \text{ J} - 560 \text{ J} = \boxed{1440 \text{ J}}$.

51. $Q_{in} = Q_{out} + W_{net} = 600 \text{ J} + 200 \text{ J} = 800 \text{ J}$. $\varepsilon_{th} = \dfrac{W_{net}}{Q_{in}} = \dfrac{200 \text{ J}}{800 \text{ J}} = \boxed{25\%}$.

52. $\varepsilon_{th} = \dfrac{W_{net}}{Q_{in}}$, ☞ $Q_{in} = \dfrac{W_{net}}{\varepsilon_{th}} = \dfrac{800 \text{ J}}{0.40} = 2000 \text{ J}$.

   So $Q_{out} = Q_{in} - W_{net} = 2000 \text{ J} = 2000 \text{ J} - 800 \text{ J} = \boxed{1.20 \times 10^3 \text{ J}}$.

53. $\varepsilon_{th} = \dfrac{W_{net}}{Q_{in}}$, ☞ $Q_{in} = \dfrac{W_{net}}{\varepsilon_{th}} = \dfrac{2.60 \times 10^4 \text{ J}}{0.150} = 1.73 \times 10^5 \text{ J}$.

   So $Q_{out} = Q_{in} - W_{net} = 1.73 \times 10^5 \text{ J} - 2.60 \times 10^4 \text{ J} = \boxed{1.47 \times 10^5 \text{ J}}$.

54. $Q_{in} = W_{net} + Q_{out} = 4.0 \times 10^3 \text{ J} + 7.5 \times 10^3 \text{ J} = 11.5 \times 10^3 \text{ J}$.

   So $\varepsilon_{th} = \dfrac{W_{net}}{Q_{in}} = \dfrac{4.0 \times 10^3 \text{ J}}{11.5 \times 10^3 \text{ J}} = \boxed{35\%}$.

55. $Q_{in} = W_{net} + Q_{out} = 4500 \text{ J} + 500 \text{ J} + 6300 \text{ J} = 1.13 \times 10^4 \text{ J}$.

   So $\varepsilon_{th} = \dfrac{W_{net}}{Q_{in}} = \dfrac{4500 \text{ J}}{1.13 \times 10^4 \text{ J}} = \boxed{40\%}$.

56. (a) Since $\varepsilon_{th} = 1 - \dfrac{Q_{out}}{Q_{in}}$, so the ratio $\boxed{\text{decreases}}$.

(b) $\dfrac{Q_{out}}{Q_{in}} = 1 - \varepsilon_{th}$, so the change in $\dfrac{Q_{out}}{Q_{in}}$ is $\Delta\varepsilon_{th} = 0.25 - 0.20 = \boxed{0.05}$.

57. (a) $E = 2(3.3 \times 10^8 \text{ J}) = \boxed{6.6 \times 10^8 \text{ J}}$.

(b) In one hour, $W = Pt = (25 \times 10^3 \text{ J/s})(3600 \text{ s}) = 9.0 \times 10^7 \text{ J}$.

So $\varepsilon_{th} = \dfrac{W_{net}}{Q_{in}} = \dfrac{9.0 \times 10^7 \text{ J}}{3.3 \times 10^8 \text{ J}} = \boxed{27\%}$.

58. Since $Q_{in} = W_{net} + Q_{out}$, ☞ $P_{in} = P_{net} + P_{out} = 2.5 \text{ kW} + 7.5 \text{ kW} = \boxed{10 \text{ kW}}$.

59. (a) $\text{COP}_{ref} = \dfrac{Q_{in}}{Q_{out} - Q_{in}}$, ☞ $Q_{out} = Q_{in}\left(1 + \dfrac{1}{\text{COP}_{ref}}\right) = (4.2 \times 10^5 \text{ J})\left(1 + \dfrac{1}{2.2}\right) = \boxed{6.1 \times 10^5 \text{ J}}$.

(b) $W_{in} = Q_{out} - Q_{in} = 6.1 \times 10^5 \text{ J} - 4.2 \times 10^5 \text{ J} = 1.9 \times 10^5 \text{ J}$.

So in 10 cycles the total work is $10(1.9 \times 10^5 \text{ J}) = \boxed{1.9 \times 10^6 \text{ J}}$.

60. (a) $W_{in} = Q_{out} - Q_{in} = 3.5 \times 10^3 \text{ J} - 2.0 \times 10^3 \text{ J} = \boxed{1.5 \times 10^3 \text{ J}}$.

(b) $\text{COP}_{hp} = \dfrac{Q_{out}}{W_{in}} = \dfrac{3.5 \times 10^3 \text{ J}}{1.5 \times 10^3 \text{ J}} = \boxed{2.3}$.

61. $\text{COP}_{ref} = \dfrac{Q_{in}}{W_{in}}$, ☞ $W_{out} = \dfrac{Q_{in}}{\text{COP}_{ref}} = \dfrac{1.0 \times 10^7 \text{ J}}{2.75} = 3.64 \times 10^6 \text{ J}$.

So $P = \dfrac{W}{\Delta t} = \dfrac{3.64 \times 10^6 \text{ J}}{(20 \text{ min})(60 \text{ s/min})} = \boxed{3.0 \text{ kW}}$.

62. (a) $Q_{in} = mL_v = (8.00 \text{ kg})(22.6 \times 10^5 \text{ J/kg}) = 1.81 \times 10^7 \text{ J}$.

$\varepsilon_{th} = \dfrac{W_{net}}{Q_{in}}$, ☞ $W_{net} = \varepsilon_{th} Q_{in} = 0.300(1.81 \times 10^7 \text{ J}) = \boxed{5.42 \times 10^6 \text{ J}}$.

(b) $Q_{out} = Q_{in} - W_{net} = 1.81 \times 10^7 \text{ J} - 5.42 \times 10^6 \text{ J} = \boxed{1.27 \times 10^7 \text{ J}}$.

63. (a) $Q_{out} = W_{in} + Q_{in} = 3.0 \times 10^4 \text{ J} + 2.1 \times 10^5 \text{ J} = \boxed{2.4 \times 10^5 \text{ J}}$.

(b) The heat lost by water is equal to $Q_{in} = -2.1 \times 10^5 \text{ J} = cm\Delta T$,

so $\Delta T = \dfrac{-2.1 \times 10^5 \text{ J}}{[4186 \text{ J/(kg·C°)}](5.0 \text{ kg})} = \boxed{-10 \text{ C°}}$.

64.   (a) $\varepsilon_{th} = \dfrac{W_{net}}{Q_{in}} = \dfrac{P_{net}}{P_{in}}$,   ☞ $P_{in} = \dfrac{P_{net}}{\varepsilon_{th}} = \dfrac{900 \text{ MW}}{0.35} = \boxed{2.57 \times 10^3 \text{ MW}}$.

     (b) $P_{out} = P_{in} - P_{net} = 2.57 \times 10^3 \text{ MW} - 900 \text{ MW} = \boxed{1.67 \times 10^3 \text{ MW}}$.

     (c) This is to minimize thermal pollution to the river.

65.   (a) $P_{net} = 150 \text{ hp} = (150 \text{ hp})(746 \text{ W/hp}) = 1.12 \times 10^5 \text{ W} = 1.12 \times 10^5 \text{ J/s}$.

     So in one second, $W_{net} = 1.12 \times 10^5 \text{ J}$.

     $\varepsilon_{th} = \dfrac{W_{net}}{Q_{in}}$,   ☞ $Q_{in} = \dfrac{W_{net}}{\varepsilon_{th}} = \dfrac{1.12 \times 10^5 \text{ J}}{0.20} = 5.6 \times 10^5 \text{ J}$ (in each second).

     So the rate of energy input is $P_{in} = \boxed{5.6 \times 10^5 \text{ W}}$.

     (b) $P_{out} = P_{in} - P_{net} = 5.6 \times 10^5 \text{ J} - 1.12 \times 10^5 \text{ W} = \boxed{4.5 \times 10^5 \text{ W}}$.

66.   (c).

67.   (a).

68.   (a) No, the product of p and V has to be a constant for T to be constant. $Q_{in} = +Q_4$.

     (b) No. $Q_{out} = -Q_2$.

     (c) Compression, negative work.   Expansion, positive work.   Net work

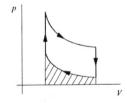   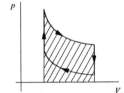   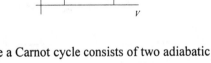

69.   (a) No, this change does not make the cycle a Carnot cycle because a Carnot cycle consists of two adiabatic and two isothermal processes.

     (b) There are heat transfers for all four legs. There are heat inputs for Q_3 and Q_4 and heat outputs for Q_1 and Q_2. The transfers at legs 1 and 3 occur at constant temperatures as the processes are isothermal.

70.   Water-cooled is more effective. The efficiency of cooling depends on the temperature difference and water can have higher temperature differences. Also water has high specific heat so it can absorb more heat.

71. $\boxed{\text{Diesel}}$ engines run hotter as diesel fuel burns at a higher temperature. According to Carnot efficiency, the higher the hot reservoir temperature, the higher the efficiency.

72. $\varepsilon_C = 1 - \dfrac{T_{cold}}{T_{hot}} = 1 - \dfrac{(273 + 20) \text{ K}}{(273 + 100) \text{ K}} = \boxed{21\%}$.

73. $\varepsilon_C = 1 - \dfrac{T_{cold}}{T_{hot}}$,   ☞ $T_{cold} = (1 - \varepsilon_C)T_{hot} = (1 - 0.35)(273 + 147)\ K = 273\ K = \boxed{0°C}$.

74. $\varepsilon_C = 1 - \dfrac{T_{cold}}{T_{hot}}$,   ☞ $T_{hot} = \dfrac{T_{cold}}{1 - \varepsilon_C} = \dfrac{(273 + 20)\ K}{1 - 0.30} = 419\ K = \boxed{146°C}$.

75.   (a) $\varepsilon_c = 1 - \dfrac{T_{cold}}{T_{hot}} = 1 - \dfrac{(273 + 5)\ K}{(273 + 25)\ K} = \boxed{6.7\%}$.

       (b) Probably not, due to the poor return. Fossil fuels are much better.

76. $\varepsilon_c = 1 - \dfrac{T_{cold}}{T_{hot}}$,   ☞ $T_{cold} = (1 - \varepsilon_c)T_{hot} = (1 - 0.40)(273 + 350)\ K = 374\ K = \boxed{101°C}$.

77.   First find the efficiency. $\varepsilon_c = 1 - \dfrac{T_{cold}}{T_{hot}} = 1 - \dfrac{(273 + 120\ )\ K}{(273 + 320)\ K} = 0.338$.

       Also $\varepsilon_{th} = \dfrac{W_{net}}{Q_{in}}$,   ☞ $W_{net} = \varepsilon_{th}\, Q_{in} = 0.338(2.7 \times 10^4\ J) = \boxed{9.1 \times 10^3\ J}$.

78.   (a) $\varepsilon_{th} = 1 - \dfrac{Q_{out}}{Q_{in}}$,   ☞ $Q_{in} = \dfrac{Q_{out}}{1 - \varepsilon_{th}} = \dfrac{1200\ J}{1 - 0.40} = \boxed{2000\ J}$.

       (b) $\varepsilon_C = 1 - \dfrac{T_{cold}}{T_{hot}}$,   ☞ $T_{hot} = \dfrac{T_{cold}}{1 - \varepsilon_c} = \dfrac{(273 + 50)\ K}{1 - 0.40} = 538\ K = \boxed{265°C}$.

79. $\varepsilon_c = 1 - \dfrac{T_{cold}}{T_{hot}}$,   ☞ $T_{hot} = \dfrac{T_{cold}}{1 - \varepsilon_c}$.

       So $\dfrac{T'_{hot}}{T_{hot}} = \dfrac{1 - \varepsilon_c}{1 - \varepsilon'_c} = \dfrac{1 - 0.30}{1 - 0.40} = 1.17$.

       Therefore $\Delta T_{hot} = \dfrac{T'_{hot} - T_{hot}}{T_{hot}} = 0.17 T_{hot} = 0.17(273 + 327)\ K = \boxed{100\ C°}$.

80.   The upper limit of efficiency is $\varepsilon_c = 1 - \dfrac{T_{cold}}{T_{hot}} = 1 - \dfrac{(273 + 125)\ K}{(273 + 400)\ K} = 59.1\%$.

       $\varepsilon_{th} = 1 - \dfrac{Q_{out}}{Q_{in}} = 1 - \dfrac{2.0 \times 10^5\ J}{5.0 \times 10^5\ J} = 60\%$. $\boxed{\text{No}}$, not possible.

81.   If T_{hot} is raised by ΔT, $\varepsilon_1 = 1 - \dfrac{T_{cold}}{T_{hot} + \Delta T}$;   if T_{cold} is lowered by ΔT, $\varepsilon_2 = 1 - \dfrac{T_{cold} - \Delta T}{T_{hot}}$.

       $\varepsilon_1 - \varepsilon_2 = \dfrac{T_{cold}}{T_{hot} + \Delta T} - \dfrac{T_{cold} - \Delta T}{T_{hot}} = \dfrac{T_{hot} T_{cold} - (T_{cold} - \Delta T)(T_{hot} + \Delta T)}{T_{hot}(T_{hot} + \Delta T)} = \dfrac{(T_{hot} - T_{cold})\Delta T + (\Delta T)^2}{T_{hot}(T_{hot} + \Delta T)} > 0$.

       So $\varepsilon_1 > \varepsilon_2$, i.e., $\boxed{\text{raising the high temperature reservoir temperature}}$.

82. The ideal efficiency is $\varepsilon_c = 1 - \dfrac{T_{\text{cold}}}{T_{\text{hot}}} = 1 - \dfrac{(273 + 100)\text{ K}}{(273 + 400)\text{ K}} = \boxed{44.6\%}$.

So the thermal efficiency is $\varepsilon_{\text{th}} = \varepsilon_{\text{rel}}\varepsilon_C = 0.45(44.6\%) = \boxed{20.1\%}$.

83. (a) $\varepsilon_{\text{th}} = \varepsilon_{\text{rel}}\varepsilon_C = 0.50\varepsilon_{\text{th}}$, ☞ $\varepsilon_{\text{rel}} = \boxed{50\%}$.

(b) $\varepsilon_c = 1 - \dfrac{T_{\text{cold}}}{T_{\text{hot}}} = 1 - \dfrac{(273 + 100)\text{ K}}{(273 + 375)\text{ K}} = 0.424$.

So $\varepsilon_{\text{th}} = 0.50\varepsilon_C = 0.212 = 1 - \dfrac{Q_{\text{out}}}{Q_{\text{in}}} = 1 - \dfrac{P_{\text{out}}}{P_{\text{in}}}$,

$P_{\text{out}} = (1 - \varepsilon_{\text{th}})P_{\text{in}} = (1 - 0.212)(50\text{ kW}) = \boxed{39\text{ kW}}$.

84. From ideal gas law, $pV = nRT$, ☞ $T = \dfrac{pV}{nR}$.

$T_{\text{hot}} = \dfrac{(250 \times 10^3\text{ Pa})(2.25 \times 10^{-2}\text{ m}^3)}{nR} = \dfrac{5625\text{ N·m}}{nR}$,

$T_{\text{cold}} = \dfrac{(150 \times 10^3\text{ Pa})(1.75 \times 10^{-2}\text{ m}^3)}{nR} = \dfrac{2625\text{ N·m}}{nR}$.

So $\varepsilon_c = 1 - \dfrac{T_{\text{cold}}}{T_{\text{hot}}} = 1 - \dfrac{2625}{5625} = 0.53\ (\times 100\%) = \boxed{53\%}$.

85. (a) $\varepsilon_c = 1 - \dfrac{Q_{\text{out}}}{Q_{\text{in}}} = 1 - \dfrac{600\text{ J}}{800\text{ J}} = \boxed{25\%}$.

(b) $\varepsilon_c = 0.25 = 1 - \dfrac{T_{\text{cold}}}{T_{\text{hot}}}$, ☞ $\dfrac{T_{\text{hot}}}{T_{\text{cold}}} = \dfrac{1}{1 - 0.25} = \boxed{4/3}$.

86. (a) $\varepsilon_c = 1 - \dfrac{T_{\text{cold}}}{T_{\text{hot}}} = 1 - \dfrac{(273 + 27)\text{ K}}{(273 + 227)\text{ K}} = \boxed{40\%}$.

(b) For a cyclic process, everything such as pressure, volume, and temperature, etc., returns to their original values. So $\Delta S = \boxed{0}$.

87. (a) $\varepsilon_c = 1 - \dfrac{T_{\text{cold}}}{T_{\text{hot}}} = 1 - \dfrac{(273 + 20)\text{ K}}{(273 + 540)\text{ K}} = \boxed{64\%}$.

(b) ε_c is the upper limit of the efficiency. In reality, a lot more energy is lost than ideally predicted.

88. (a) $\text{COP}_C = \dfrac{Q_{\text{hot}}}{Q_{\text{hot}} - Q_{\text{cold}}} = \dfrac{T_{\text{hot}}}{T_{\text{hot}} - T_{\text{cold}}}$.

(b) The efficiency improves as the temperature difference between the two reservoirs decreases. The COP_C of a refrigerator should be $\dfrac{T_{\text{cold}}}{T_{\text{hot}} - T_{\text{cold}}}$

89. (a) $\text{COP}_{\text{ref}} = \dfrac{Q_{\text{in}}}{Q_{\text{out}} - Q_{\text{in}}} = \dfrac{2.6 \times 10^3 \text{ J}}{2.8 \times 10^3 \text{ J} - 2.6 \times 10^3 \text{ J}} = \boxed{13}.$

(b) From Exercise 12.88, $\text{COP}_{\text{C}} = \dfrac{T_{\text{cold}}}{T_{\text{hot}} - T_{\text{cold}}} = \dfrac{(273 + 5.0) \text{ K}}{30°\text{C} - 5.0°\text{C}} = 11 < 13.$

$\boxed{\text{No}}$, this is not possible.

90. Since $\varepsilon_{\text{C}} = \dfrac{T_{\text{hot}} - T_{\text{cold}}}{T_{\text{hot}}}$, and from Exercise 12.88, $\text{COP}_{\text{C}} = \dfrac{T_{\text{hot}}}{T_{\text{hot}} - T_{\text{cold}}}.$

So $\text{COP}_{\text{C}} = \dfrac{T_{\text{hot}}}{T_{\text{hot}} - T_{\text{cold}}} = \dfrac{1}{\varepsilon_{\text{c}}} = \dfrac{1}{0.40} = \boxed{2.5}.$

91. $\varepsilon_{\text{C}} = 1 - \dfrac{T_{\text{cold}}}{T_{\text{hot}}} = 1 - \dfrac{Q_{\text{cold}}}{Q_{\text{hot}}},$ ☞ $Q_{\text{hot}} = Q_{\text{cold}} \dfrac{T_{\text{hot}}}{T_{\text{cold}}}.$

So $W = Q_{\text{hot}} - Q_{\text{cold}} = Q_{\text{cold}} \dfrac{T_{\text{hot}}}{T_{\text{cold}}} - Q_{\text{cold}} = Q_{\text{cold}} \left(\dfrac{T_{\text{hot}}}{T_{\text{cold}}} - 1 \right).$

92. $W = p\Delta V,$ ☞ $\Delta V = \dfrac{W}{p} = \dfrac{-900 \text{ J}}{300 \times 10^3 \text{ Pa}} = -3.0 \times 10^{-3} \text{ m}^3 = -3.0 \text{ L}.$

So $V_{\text{f}} = V_{\text{i}} + \Delta V = \boxed{7.0 \text{ L}}.$

93. For the hot reservoir, $\Delta S_{\text{hot}} = \dfrac{-Q}{T_{\text{hot}}};$ for the cold reservoir, $\Delta S_{\text{cold}} = \dfrac{Q}{T_{\text{cold}}}.$

For the universe, $\Delta S = \Delta S_{\text{hot}} + \Delta S_{\text{cold}} = Q \left(\dfrac{1}{T_{\text{cold}}} - \dfrac{1}{T_{\text{Hot}}} \right).$ Since $T_{\text{hot}} > T_{\text{cold}},\ \Delta S > 0.$

94. For the hot reservoir, $\Delta S_{\text{hot}} = \dfrac{-Q_{\text{hot}}}{T_{\text{hot}}};$ for the cold reservoir, $\Delta S_{\text{cold}} = \dfrac{Q_{\text{cold}}}{T_{\text{cold}}}.$

Also $\Delta S_{\text{hot}} = -\Delta S_{\text{cold}}$ for a cyclic process (everything returns to its original value so $\Delta S = 0$).

Therefore $\varepsilon_{\text{th}} = \dfrac{W_{\text{net}}}{Q_{\text{in}}} = \dfrac{Q_{\text{in}} - Q_{\text{out}}}{Q_{\text{in}}} = 1 - \dfrac{Q_{\text{out}}}{Q_{\text{in}}} = 1 - \dfrac{\Delta S_{\text{cold}} T_{\text{cold}}}{-\Delta S_{\text{hot}} T_{\text{hot}}} = 1 - \dfrac{T_{\text{cold}}}{T_{\text{hot}}} = \varepsilon_{\text{C}}.$

95. (a) It is an $\boxed{\text{isobaric expansion}}.$

(b) $Q = \Delta U + W,$ ☞ $\Delta U = Q - W = Q - p\Delta V = Q - pA\Delta x$

$= 420 \text{ J} - (1.01 \times 10^5 \text{ Pa})(\pi)(0.120 \text{ m})^2 (0.0600 \text{ m}) = \boxed{146 \text{ J}}.$

96. $\varepsilon_{\text{C}} = 1 - \dfrac{T_{\text{cold}}}{T_{\text{hot}}} = 1 - \dfrac{(273 + 20) \text{ K}}{(273 + 250) \text{ K}} = \boxed{44\%}.$ No, it could never be achieved.

97. $90 \text{ km/h} = 25 \text{ m/s}.$ $Q = K = 2 \times \frac{1}{2} mv^2 = mv^2 = (1.5 \times 10^3 \text{ kg})(25 \text{ m/s})^2 = 9.375 \times 10^5 \text{ J}.$

$$\Delta S = \frac{Q}{T} = \frac{9.375 \times 10^5 \text{ J}}{(273 + 20) \text{ K}} = \boxed{3.2 \times 10^3 \text{ J/K}}.$$

98.   (a) $\Delta S_u = \Delta S_{\text{hot}} + \Delta S_{\text{cold}} = \frac{-Q}{T_{\text{hot}}} + \frac{Q}{T_{\text{cold}}} = Q\left(\frac{1}{T_{\text{cold}}} - \frac{1}{T_{\text{hot}}}\right),$ so $W = T_{\text{cold}} \Delta S_u = Q\left(1 - \frac{T_{\text{cold}}}{T_{\text{hot}}}\right).$

(b) It is $\boxed{\text{Carnot efficiency}}$.

99.   In an isothermal process, $\Delta U = 0$ for an ideal gas.   So $Q = \Delta U + W = W = 30 \text{ J}.$

$$\Delta S = \frac{Q}{T} = \frac{30 \text{ J}}{(273 + 27) \text{ K}} = \boxed{0.10 \text{ J/K}}.$$

100.   For an adiabatic process, $Q = 0.$ So $\Delta U = Q - W = -W = -(-1500 \text{ J}) = \boxed{1500 \text{ J}}.$

The temperature $\boxed{\text{increases}}$ since U increases.

101. $\Delta U = Q - W = (2500 \text{ J}) - (-1000 \text{ J}) = \boxed{3500 \text{ J}}.$

102. $\Delta S = \dfrac{Q}{T} = \dfrac{mL_f}{T} = \dfrac{(0.75 \text{ kg})(3.3 \times 10^5 \text{ J/kg})}{273 \text{ K}} = \boxed{9.1 \times 10^2 \text{ J/K}}.$

103.   The process is an adiabatic free expansion. There is no transfer of heat and the gas does no work. So the internal energy of the gas remains unchanged, according to the first law of thermodynamics.

CHAPTER 13

VIBRATIONS AND WAVES

1.   (b).

2.   (d).

3.   (a) $E = \frac{1}{2}kA^2$, so $\boxed{\text{four times as large}}$.   (b) $v_{max} = \sqrt{\dfrac{k}{m}}\ A$, so $\boxed{\text{twice as large}}$.

4.   At the equilibrium position the elastic potential energy is zero and so all the energy is kinetic. Therefore the speed $\boxed{\text{increases}}$ as it approaches the equilibrium position.

5.   (b), because $f = \dfrac{1}{T}$.

6.   (a), because $U = \frac{1}{2}kx^2$.

7.   In each T, it travels $A + A + A + A = \boxed{4A}$.

8. $f = \dfrac{1}{T} = \dfrac{1}{0.50\ \text{s}} = \boxed{2.0\ \text{Hz}}$.

9. $T = \dfrac{1}{f} = \dfrac{1}{40\ \text{Hz}} = \boxed{0.025\ \text{s}}$.

10. $T = \dfrac{1}{f}$, ☞ $\Delta T = \dfrac{1}{f_2} - \dfrac{1}{f_1} = \dfrac{1}{0.50\ \text{s}} - \dfrac{1}{0.25\ \text{s}} = -2.0\ \text{s} = \boxed{\text{decrease of 2.0 s}}$.

11. $k = \dfrac{F}{x} = \dfrac{mg}{x} = \dfrac{(0.25\ \text{kg})(9.80\ \text{m/s}^2)}{0.060\ \text{m}} = \boxed{41\ \text{N/m}}$.

12. $v_{max} = \sqrt{\dfrac{k}{m}}\ A = \sqrt{\dfrac{10\ \text{N/m}}{0.50\ \text{kg}}}\ (0.050\ \text{m}) = \boxed{0.22\ \text{m/s}}$.

13.   (a) $T = \dfrac{1}{f} = \dfrac{1}{10^{12}\ \text{Hz}} = \boxed{10^{-12}\ \text{s}}$.

        (b) $v_{max} = \sqrt{\dfrac{k}{m}}\ A = \omega A = 2\pi f A = 2\pi(10^{12}\ \text{Hz})(10^{-11}\ \text{m}) = \boxed{63\ \text{m/s}}$.

---

14.   (a) $F = kx = (150 \text{ N/m})(0.150 \text{ m}) = \boxed{22.5 \text{ N}}$; $a = \dfrac{F}{m} = \dfrac{22.5 \text{ N}}{0.500 \text{ kg}} = \boxed{45.0 \text{ m/s}^2}$.

        (b) $F = (150 \text{ N/m})(0.050 \text{ m}) = \boxed{7.50 \text{ N}}$; $a = \dfrac{7.50 \text{ N}}{0.500 \text{ kg}} = \boxed{15.0 \text{ m/s}^2}$.

        (c) $F = \boxed{0}$; $a = \boxed{0}$.

15.   (a) The force is maximum at $x = \pm A$, because $F = kx$.

        (b) The speed is maximum at $x = 0$, because $v_{\max} = \sqrt{\dfrac{k}{m}(A^2 - x^2)}$.

        (c) The acceleration is maximum at $x = \pm A$, because $a \propto F = kx$.

16. $T = 2\pi\sqrt{\dfrac{m}{k}}$,   ☞ $m = \dfrac{T^2 k}{4\pi^2} = \dfrac{(0.91 \text{ s})^2 (12 \text{ N/m})}{4\pi^2} = \boxed{0.25 \text{ kg}}$.

17.   (a) $v_{\max} = \sqrt{\dfrac{k}{m}}\,A = \sqrt{\dfrac{12 \text{ N/m}}{0.25 \text{ kg}}}\,(0.15 \text{ m}) = \boxed{1.0 \text{ m/s}}$.

        (b) $\boxed{\text{At the equilibrium position}}$.

        (c) $v = \sqrt{\dfrac{k}{m}(A^2 - x^2)} = \sqrt{\dfrac{k}{m}[(0.15 \text{ m})^2 - (0.075 \text{ m})^2]} = \boxed{0.90 \text{ m/s}}$.

18. $T = 2\pi\sqrt{\dfrac{m}{k}} \propto \sqrt{m}$, so the ratio is $\boxed{\sqrt{2}}$.

19. $T = 2\pi\sqrt{\dfrac{m}{k}} \propto \dfrac{1}{\sqrt{k}}$, so the period $\boxed{\text{decreases by a factor of } \dfrac{1}{\sqrt{2}}}$.

20. $f = \dfrac{1}{2\pi}\sqrt{\dfrac{k}{m}}$,   ☞ $\dfrac{f_2}{f_1} = \sqrt{\dfrac{m_1}{m_2}} = \sqrt{\dfrac{0.25 \text{ kg}}{0.50 \text{ kg}}} = 0.707$.

        So $f_2 = (0.707)(1.0 \text{ Hz}) = \boxed{0.71 \text{ Hz}}$.

21.   Since $T = \dfrac{1}{2\pi}\sqrt{\dfrac{m}{k}}$ and $E = \tfrac{1}{2}kA^2$,

        $\dfrac{E_b}{E_a} = \dfrac{m_b\, T_a^2 A_b^2}{m_a\, T_b^2 A_a^2} = \tfrac{1}{4} \times \dfrac{(8.0 \text{ s})^2}{(0.60 \text{ s})^2} \times \dfrac{10^2}{5.0^2} = \boxed{1.8 \times 10^2 \text{ times more}}$.

22.   (a) $E = \tfrac{1}{2}kA^2 = \tfrac{1}{2}(80 \text{ N/m})(0.15 \text{ m})^2 = \boxed{0.90 \text{ J}}$.

        (b) $\boxed{\text{No}}$.

23. (a) $v = \sqrt{\dfrac{k}{m}(A^2 - x^2)} = \sqrt{\dfrac{80\text{ N/m}}{0.25\text{ kg}}[(0.15\text{ m})^2 - (0.050\text{ m})^2]} = \boxed{2.5\text{ m/s}}$.

(b) $v = \sqrt{\dfrac{80\text{ N/m}}{0.25\text{ kg}}[(0.15\text{ m})^2 - (-0.050\text{ m})^2]} = \boxed{2.5\text{ m/s}}$.

(c) $v_{\max} = \sqrt{\dfrac{k}{m}}\,A = \sqrt{\dfrac{80\text{ N/m}}{0.25\text{ kg}}}\,(0.15\text{ m}) = \boxed{2.7\text{ m/s, equilibrium position}}$.

24. (a) From conservation of energy (choose the bottom of the trampoline when stretched as $U = 0$):

$E = \frac{1}{2}kA^2 = U = mgh$, ☞ $k = \dfrac{2mgh}{A^2} = \dfrac{2(75\text{ kg})(9.80\text{ m/s}^2)(5.0\text{ m} + 0.30\text{ m})}{(0.30\text{ m})^2} = 8.66 \times 10^4\text{ N/m}$.

For the jump from 8.0 m high, $\frac{1}{2}(8.66 \times 10^4\text{ N/m})A^2 = (75\text{ kg})(9.80\text{ m/s}^2)(8.0\text{ m} + A)$.

Reduce to a quadratic equation: $4.33 \times 10^4\,A^2 - 735A - 5880 = 0$.

Solve for $A = \boxed{0.38\text{ m}}$ or -0.36 m, which is discarded.

(b) From Hooke's law, $x = \dfrac{F}{k} = \dfrac{mg}{k} = \dfrac{(75\text{ kg})(9.80\text{ m/s}^2)}{8.66 \times 10^4\text{ N/m}} = \boxed{8.5 \times 10^{-3}\text{ m}}$.

25. (a) From conservation of energy (choose the position of the object when the spring is compressed as $U_g = 0$): $E = \frac{1}{2}kA^2 = U = mgh$, ☞ $\frac{1}{2}(60.0\text{ N/m})A^2 = (0.250\text{ kg})(9.80\text{ m/s}^2)(0.100\text{ m} + A)$.

Reduce to a quadratic equation: $30.0A^2 - 2.45A - 0.245 = 0$.

Solve for $A = \boxed{0.14\text{ m}}$ or -0.058 m, which is discarded.

(b) From energy conservation, the object will go to a height of $\boxed{10.0\text{ cm}}$ (original position).

26. (d).

27. $T = 2\pi\sqrt{\dfrac{L}{g}} \propto \sqrt{L}$, so the period is $\boxed{\sqrt{2}\ \text{times as large}}$.

28. This could be done by tracing out the path of the object on a scrolling horizontal paper.

29. $\boxed{\text{No}}$, tan 90° goes to ∞.

30. In an upward accelerating elevator, the effective gravitational acceleration increases. This decreases the period according to $T = 2\pi\sqrt{\dfrac{L}{g}}$.

31. $T = 2\pi\sqrt{\dfrac{m}{k}}$, ☞ $m = \dfrac{T^2 k}{4\pi^2} = \dfrac{(2.0\text{ s})^2(10\text{ N/m})}{4\pi^2} = \boxed{1.0\text{ kg}}$.

32. (a) $T = 2\pi\sqrt{\dfrac{m}{k}} = 2\pi\sqrt{\dfrac{0.50 \text{ kg}}{200 \text{ N/m}}} = \boxed{0.31 \text{ s}}$.

(b) $f = \dfrac{1}{T} = \dfrac{1}{0.31 \text{ s}} = \boxed{3.2 \text{ Hz}}$.

33. (a) $T = 2\pi\sqrt{\dfrac{L}{g}} = 2\pi\sqrt{\dfrac{1 \text{ m}}{9.80 \text{ m/s}^2}} = \boxed{2.0 \text{ s}}$.

(b) $f = \dfrac{1}{T} = \dfrac{1}{2.0 \text{ s}} = \boxed{0.50 \text{ Hz}}$.

34. $T = 2\pi\sqrt{\dfrac{L}{g}}$, ☞ $L = \dfrac{T^2 g}{4\pi^2} = \dfrac{(1.0 \text{ s})^2 (9.80 \text{ m/s}^2)}{4\pi^2} = \boxed{0.25 \text{ m}}$.

35. (a) The position right after the push is positive and the initial position is zero.

So $x = A \sin \omega t$.

(b) The initial position is at $x = A$.

So $x = A \cos \omega t$.

36. (a) Compare to $y = A \sin\omega t$. $A = \boxed{0.10 \text{ m}}$.

(b) $\omega = 2\pi f = 100$ rad/s,   ☞ $f = \dfrac{100}{2\pi} = \boxed{16 \text{ Hz}}$.

(c) $T = \dfrac{1}{f} = \dfrac{1}{16 \text{ Hz}} = \boxed{0.063 \text{ s}}$.

37. (a) Compare to $y = A \sin 2\pi ft$. $A = \boxed{5.0 \text{ cm}}$.

(b) $\omega = 2\pi f = 20\pi$ rad/s,   ☞ $f = \boxed{10 \text{ Hz}}$.

(c) $T = \dfrac{1}{f} = \dfrac{1}{10 \text{ Hz}} = \boxed{0.10 \text{ s}}$.

38. (a) $y = (025 \text{ m}) \cos 314t = (0.25 \text{ m}) \cos 0 = \boxed{0.25 \text{ m}}$.

(b) $y = (0.25 \text{ m}) \cos[(314 \text{ rad/s})(5.0 \text{ s})] = \boxed{0.17 \text{ m}}$.

(c) $y = (0.25 \text{ m}) \cos[(314 \text{ rad/s})(15 \text{ s})] = \boxed{-0.18 \text{ m}}$.

39. $\omega = \sqrt{\dfrac{k}{m}}$,   ☞ $k = \omega^2 m$.   So $E = \tfrac{1}{2} kA^2 = \tfrac{1}{2} m\omega^2 A^2$.

40. $T = 2\pi\sqrt{\dfrac{m}{k}} = 2\pi\sqrt{\dfrac{L}{g}}$,   ☞ $L = \dfrac{mg}{k}$.

41. $T = 2\pi \sqrt{\dfrac{L}{g}}$, ☞ $g = \dfrac{4\pi^2 L}{T^2} = \dfrac{4\pi^2 (0.3690 \text{ m})}{(1.220 \text{ s})^2} = \boxed{9.787 \text{ m/s}^2}$.

42. (a) $y = (10 \text{ cm}) \sin 0.50t = (10 \text{ cm}) \sin[(0.50 \text{ rad/s})(1.0 \text{ s})] = \boxed{4.8 \text{ cm}}$.

(b) $v = A\omega \cos \omega t = (10 \text{ cm})(0.50 \text{ rad/s}) \cos[(0.50 \text{ rad/s})(1.0 \text{ s})] = \boxed{4.4 \text{ cm/s}}$.

(c) $a = -\omega^2 y = -(0.50 \text{ rad/s})^2 (4.8 \text{ cm}) = \boxed{-1.2 \text{ cm/s}^2}$.

43. (a) $\omega = \sqrt{\dfrac{k}{m}} = \sqrt{\dfrac{6.0 \text{ N/m}}{0.15 \text{ kg}}} = 6.3 \text{ rad/s}$.

$y = A \sin(\omega t + \delta)$.   At $t = 0$, $y = 8.0 \text{ cm}$,   so $\delta = 90°$ or $\pi/2$ rad.

Therefore $y = (8.0 \text{ cm}) \sin[(6.3 \text{ rad/s})t + 90°] = \boxed{(8.0 \text{ cm}) \cos(6.3 \text{ rad/s})t}$.

(b) As in (a), $\delta = \boxed{90° \text{ or } \pi/2 \text{ rad}}$.

(c) $y = (8.0 \text{ cm}) \cos[(6.3 \text{ rad/s})(0.50 \text{ s})] = \boxed{-8.0 \text{ cm, or at the other amplitude}}$.

44. $T = 2\pi \sqrt{\dfrac{m}{k}}$, ☞ $\dfrac{T_1}{T_2} = \sqrt{\dfrac{k_2}{k_1}} = \sqrt{2}$. So $\boxed{\text{the first one by } \sqrt{2} \text{ times}}$.

45. $T = 2\pi \sqrt{\dfrac{L}{g}}$, ☞ $\dfrac{T_M}{T_E} = \sqrt{\dfrac{g_E}{g_M}} = \sqrt{\dfrac{g}{g/6}} = \sqrt{6} = 2.4$.

So the period $\boxed{\text{increases by 2.4 times}}$.

46. $T = 2\pi \sqrt{\dfrac{L}{g}} = 2\pi \sqrt{\dfrac{m}{k}}$, ☞ $k = \dfrac{mg}{L} = \dfrac{(0.075 \text{ kg})(9.80 \text{ m/s}^2)}{0.30 \text{ m}} = \boxed{2.5 \text{ N/m}}$.

47. $T = 8.0 \text{ s}$, $A = 5.0 \text{ cm}$,   and $y = 5.0 \text{ cm}$ at $t = 0$.

$\omega = 2\pi f = \dfrac{2\pi}{T} = \dfrac{2\pi}{8.0 \text{ s}} = \dfrac{\pi}{4}$ rad/s.

So $y = A \cos (\omega t + \delta) = \boxed{(5.0 \text{ cm}) \cos (\pi t/4)}$.

48. (a) $T = 0.60 \text{ s}$, $A = 10 \text{ cm} = 0.10 \text{ m}$,   and $y = 0$ and v is negative when $t = 0$.

$\omega = 2\pi f = \dfrac{2\pi}{T} = \dfrac{2\pi}{0.60 \text{ s}} = \dfrac{10\pi}{3}$ rad/s   So $y = A \sin (\omega t + \delta) = \boxed{(-0.10 \text{ m}) \sin (10\pi/3) \, t}$.

(b) $T = 2\pi \sqrt{\dfrac{m}{k}}$, ☞ $k = \dfrac{4\pi^2 m}{T^2} = \dfrac{4\pi^2 (0.35 \text{ kg})}{(0.60 \text{ s})^2} = \boxed{38 \text{ N/m}}$.

49.   (a) In the tangential direction, $\Sigma F = mg \sin\theta \approx mg\,\theta = mg\dfrac{x}{L} = \dfrac{mg}{L}x = kx.$

        (b) Since the effective spring constant is $k = \dfrac{mg}{L}$,

        then $T = 2\pi\sqrt{\dfrac{m}{k}} = 2\pi\sqrt{\dfrac{m}{mg/L}} = 2\pi\sqrt{\dfrac{L}{g}}\,.$

50.   (a) Since $T = 2\pi\sqrt{\dfrac{L}{g}}$ and the length is shorter, so T is smaller.

        So the clock runs faster or $\boxed{\text{gains time}}$.

        (b) $\Delta T = 2\pi\sqrt{\dfrac{0.7500\ \text{m}}{9.80\ \text{m/s}^2}} - 2\pi\sqrt{\dfrac{0.7480\ \text{m}}{9.80\ \text{m/s}^2}} = 2.32 \times 10^{-3}$ s.

        So in 24 hours = 86 400 s (or 43 200 periods), the time difference is

        $43\,200(2.32 \times 10^{-3}\ \text{s}) = 100\ \text{s} = \boxed{1.7\ \text{min}}$.

        (c) $\boxed{\text{Yes}}$.   Because of linear thermal expansion, the length depends on the temperature.

51.   (d).

52.   (a).

53.   (a) $\boxed{\text{Transverse and longitudinal}}$.   (b) $\boxed{\text{Longitudinal}}$.   (c) $\boxed{\text{Longitudinal}}$.

54.   (a) $\boxed{\text{Transverse}}$.   (b) $\boxed{\text{Longitudinal}}$.

55. $\lambda = \dfrac{v}{f} = \dfrac{340\ \text{m/s}}{1000\ \text{Hz}} = \boxed{0.34\ \text{m}}$.

56. $v = \lambda f = (0.50\ \text{m})(20\ \text{Hz}) = \boxed{10\ \text{m/s}}$.

57. $v = \dfrac{2.4\ \text{m}}{1.6\ \text{s}} = \boxed{1.5\ \text{m/s}}$.

58. $\lambda = \dfrac{v}{f} = \dfrac{3.00 \times 10^8\ \text{m/s}}{5 \times 10^{14}\ \text{Hz}} = \boxed{6 \times 10^{-7}\ \text{m}}$.

59. $f = \dfrac{v}{\lambda} = \dfrac{3.00 \times 10^8\ \text{m/s}}{633 \times 10^{-9}\ \text{m}} = \boxed{4.7 \times 10^{14}\ \text{Hz}}$.

60. $\lambda_{max} = \dfrac{v}{f} = \dfrac{345 \text{ m/s}}{20 \text{ Hz}} = \boxed{17 \text{ m}}, \quad \lambda_{min} = \dfrac{345 \text{ m/s}}{20 \times 10^3 \text{ Hz}} = \boxed{0.017 \text{ m}}.$

61. (a) $\lambda_{max} = \dfrac{v}{f} = \dfrac{3.00 \times 10^8 \text{ m/s}}{550 \times 10^3 \text{ Hz}} = \boxed{545 \text{ m}}, \quad \lambda_{min} = \dfrac{3.00 \times 10^8 \text{ m/s}}{1600 \times 10^3 \text{ Hz}} = \boxed{188 \text{ m}}.$

    (b) $\lambda_{max} = \dfrac{3.00 \times 10^8 \text{ m/s}}{88.0 \times 10^6 \text{ Hz}} = \boxed{3.41 \text{ m}}, \quad \lambda_{max} = \dfrac{3.00 \times 10^8 \text{ m/s}}{108 \times 10^6 \text{ Hz}} = \boxed{2.78 \text{ m}}.$

62. $v = \lambda f = (4.80 \times 10^{-4} \text{ m})(2.50 \times 10^6 \text{ Hz}) = 1200 \text{ m/s}.$

    So the depth is $\frac{1}{2}(1200 \text{ m/s})(10 \text{ s}) = \boxed{6.00 \times 10^3 \text{ m}}.$

63. In between 13 crests, there are only 12 wavelengths. So the frequency is $f = \dfrac{12}{3.0 \text{ s}} = 4.0 \text{ Hz}.$

    Therefore $\quad v = \lambda f = (0.75 \text{ m})(4.0 \text{ Hz}) = \boxed{3.0 \text{ m/s}}.$

64. (a) $15 \text{ cm} = \boxed{0.15 \text{ m}}.$

    (b) $T = 0.80 \text{ s}, \quad \text{☞} \quad f = \dfrac{1}{T} = \dfrac{1}{0.80 \text{ s}} = 1.25 \text{ Hz}.$

    So $\quad v = \lambda f = (0.12 \text{ m})(1.25 \text{ Hz}) = \boxed{0.15 \text{ m/s}}.$

65. (a) 90° in latitude covers one quarter of the Earth's circumference. The straight line distance between the locations is $d = \sqrt{R^2 + R^2} = \sqrt{2}\, R = \sqrt{2}\,(6.4 \times 10^3 \text{ km}) = 9.05 \times 10^3 \text{ km}.$

    $\Delta t = \dfrac{d}{v_S} - \dfrac{d}{v_P} = \dfrac{9.05 \times 10^3 \text{ km}}{6.0 \text{ km/s}} - \dfrac{9.05 \times 10^3 \text{ km}}{8.0 \text{ km/s}} = \boxed{3.8 \times 10^2 \text{ s}}.$

    (b) $r = R \cos 45°.$ So the depth under the surface is

    $R - r = R(1 - \cos 45°) = (6.4 \times 10^3 \text{ km})(1 - \cos 45°) = 1.9 \times 10^3 \text{ km} > 30 \text{ km}.$

    So $\boxed{\text{yes}}.$

    (c) $t = \dfrac{2(6.4 \times 10^3 \text{ km})}{8.0 \text{ km/s}} = \boxed{1.6 \times 10^3 \text{ s; S waves do not go through the liquid core}}.$

66. (a) $v = \sqrt{\dfrac{Y}{\rho}} = \sqrt{\dfrac{7.0 \times 10^{10} \text{ N/m}^2}{2.7 \times 10^3 \text{ kg/m}^3}} = 5091 \text{ m/s}. \quad \lambda = \dfrac{v}{f} = \dfrac{5091 \text{ m/s}}{40 \text{ Hz}} = \boxed{1.3 \times 10^2 \text{ m}}.$

    (b) $v = \sqrt{\dfrac{11 \times 10^{10} \text{ N/m}^2}{8.9 \times 10^3 \text{ kg/m}^3}} = 3516 \text{ m/s}. \quad \lambda = \dfrac{3516 \text{ m/s}}{40 \text{ Hz}} = \boxed{88 \text{ m}}.$

67. (a) $v = \sqrt{\dfrac{Y}{\rho}} = \sqrt{\dfrac{20 \times 10^{10} \ \text{N/m}^2}{7.8 \times 10^3 \ \text{kg/m}^3}} = 5064 \ \text{m/s}.$

So the time is $t = \dfrac{1.0 \times 10^3 \ \text{m}}{5064 \ \text{m/s}} = \boxed{0.20 \ \text{s}}.$

(b) $T = \dfrac{1}{f} = \dfrac{1}{0.50 \ \text{Hz}} = \boxed{2.0 \ \text{s}}.$

68. (d).

69. (b).

70. $\boxed{\text{Waveform}}$ is destroyed. Energy is not destroyed.

71. $\boxed{\text{Reflection}}$, because the sound is reflected by the prey.

72. Sound from different frequencies would arrive at different times.

73. (d).

74. (c).

75. At a frequency of $f_0/2$ (or a period of $2T_0$), the swing is pushed every other oscillation. So only half the energy is going into the swing, but it is pushed smoothly.

76. $\boxed{5}$.

77. (a) $f_2 = 2f_0 = 2(100 \ \text{Hz}) = \boxed{200 \ \text{Hz}}.$

(b) $f_3 = 3f_0 = 3(100 \ \text{Hz}) = \boxed{300 \ \text{Hz}}.$

78. $f_3 = 3f_0,$ ☞ $f_0 = \dfrac{f_3}{3} = \dfrac{450 \ \text{Hz}}{3} = \boxed{150 \ \text{Hz}}.$

79. (a) $L = \dfrac{\lambda_1}{2},$ ☞ $\lambda_1 = 2L = 2(3.0 \ \text{m}) = \boxed{6.0 \ \text{m}}.$

(b) $L = 1.5\lambda_3,$ ☞ $\lambda_3 = \dfrac{L}{1.5} = \dfrac{3.0 \ \text{m}}{1.5} = \boxed{2.0 \ \text{m}}.$

80. (a) $f_0 = \dfrac{v}{2L} = \dfrac{12 \text{ m/s}}{2(4.0 \text{ m})} = 1.5$ Hz. So $\boxed{\text{yes}}$, 15 Hz is the 10th harmonic.

   (b) $\boxed{\text{No}}$, 20 Hz is not a harmonic.

81. $f = \dfrac{v}{\lambda} = \dfrac{250 \text{ m/s}}{0.80 \text{ m}} = 312.5$ Hz. $\quad f_0 = \dfrac{v}{2L} = \dfrac{250 \text{ m/s}}{2(2.0 \text{ m})} = 62.5$ Hz.

   So $n = \dfrac{f}{f_0} = \dfrac{312.5 \text{ Hz}}{62.5 \text{ Hz}} = \boxed{5}$.

82. (a) $v = \sqrt{\dfrac{F_T}{\mu}} = \sqrt{\dfrac{9.00 \text{ N}}{0.125 \text{ kg/m}}} = \boxed{8.49 \text{ m/s}}$.

   (b) $f_n = \dfrac{nv}{2L} = n\,\dfrac{8.49 \text{ m/s}}{2(10.0 \text{ m})} = \boxed{(0.425)n \text{ Hz; } n = 1, 2, 3, \ldots}$.

83. $v = \sqrt{\dfrac{F_T}{\mu}} = \sqrt{\dfrac{40 \text{ N}}{2.5 \times 10^{-2} \text{ kg/m}}} = 40$ m/s. $\quad f_n = \dfrac{nv}{2L} = \dfrac{40 \text{ m/s}}{2(2.0 \text{ m})}\,n = 10n$ Hz.

   So the frequencies of the first four harmonics are $\boxed{10 \text{ Hz, } 20 \text{ Hz, } 30 \text{ Hz, and } 40 \text{ Hz}}$.

84. (a) The wave speeds in the two strings are the same. Since $f_n = \dfrac{v}{2L}$, $\dfrac{(f_n)_{1.0}}{(f_n)_{3.0}} = \dfrac{3.0 \text{ m}}{1.0 \text{ m}} = 3$.

   So $\boxed{3^{\text{rd}} \text{ harmonic of } 3.0 \text{ m} = 1^{\text{st}} \text{ harmonic of } 1.0}$

   and $\boxed{6^{\text{th}} \text{ harmonic of } 3.0 \text{ m} = 2^{\text{nd}} \text{ harmonic of } 1.0 \text{ m}}$.

   (b) $\dfrac{(f_n)_{1.5}}{(f_n)_{2.0}} = \dfrac{2.0 \text{ m}}{1.5 \text{ m}} = \dfrac{4}{3}$. So $\boxed{3^{\text{rd}} \text{ harmonic of } 2.0 \text{ m} = 4^{\text{th}} \text{ harmonic of } 1.5 \text{ m}}$.

85. There is a node where the finger is placed. So the longest possible wavelength is $\dfrac{\lambda}{2} = \dfrac{7}{8}L$.

   $f = \dfrac{v}{\lambda} = \dfrac{v}{7L/4} = \dfrac{4v}{7L} = \dfrac{8}{7}\dfrac{v}{2L} = \dfrac{8}{7}f_0 = \dfrac{8}{7}(440 \text{ Hz}) = \boxed{503 \text{ Hz}}$.

86. The first harmonic, $\quad \lambda_1 = 4L$. $\quad f_1 = \dfrac{v}{\lambda} = \dfrac{v}{4L} = 1 \times \dfrac{v}{4L}$;

   the next harmonic (3rd), $\quad \lambda_3 = \dfrac{4L}{3}$, $\quad f_3 = \dfrac{3\,v}{4L} = 3 \times \dfrac{v}{4L}$;

   the next harmonic (5th), $\quad \lambda_5 = \dfrac{4L}{5}$, $\quad f_5 = \dfrac{5\,v}{4L} = 5 \times \dfrac{v}{4L}$;

   Therefore $\quad f_m = \dfrac{mv}{4L} = m\,\dfrac{3.5 \times 10^3 \text{ m/s}}{4(1.0 \text{ m})} = \boxed{m(8.8 \times 10^2 \text{ Hz}), m = 1, 3, 5, \ldots}$.

87. $v = \lambda f = \sqrt{\dfrac{F_T}{\mu}} = \sqrt{\dfrac{Mg}{m/L}}$, ☞ $M = \dfrac{m\lambda^2 f^2}{gL} = \dfrac{(0.10 \times 10^{-3}\ \text{kg})(60\ \text{Hz})^2}{(9.80\ \text{m/s}^2)(1.5\ \text{m})}\lambda^2 = 0.0245\lambda^2.$

$\lambda_1 = 2L = 2(1.5\ \text{m}) = 3.0\ \text{m},$ $\quad \lambda_2 = L = 1.5\ \text{m},$ $\quad \lambda_3 = \dfrac{2L}{3} = 1.0\ \text{m},$ $\quad \lambda_4 = \dfrac{L}{2} = 0.75\ \text{m}.$

So $\quad M_1 = \boxed{0.22\ \text{kg}},$ $\quad M_2 = \boxed{0.055\ \text{kg}},$ $\quad M_3 = \boxed{0.024\ \text{kg}},$ $\quad M_4 = \boxed{0.014\ \text{kg}}.$

88. $v_{\max} = \sqrt{\dfrac{k}{m}}\,A = \omega A.$

$v = \sqrt{\dfrac{k}{m}(A^2 - x^2)} = \omega A\sqrt{1 - \dfrac{x^2}{A^2}} = v_{\max}\sqrt{1 - \dfrac{x^2}{A^2}}$

$= (0.40\ \text{m/s})\sqrt{1 - \dfrac{(0.040\ \text{m})^2}{(0.080\ \text{m})^2}} = \boxed{0.35\ \text{m/s}}.$

89. (a) The distance between two successive nodes is $\dfrac{\lambda}{2}$. So $\lambda = 2(6.0\ \text{cm}) = \boxed{12\ \text{cm}}.$

(b) The anti-nodes are halfway between the nodes. So they are at $\boxed{3.0\ \text{cm},\ 9.0\ \text{cm},\ 15\ \text{cm}}.$

90. (a) $T = \dfrac{10\ \text{s}}{5} = \boxed{2.0\ \text{s}}.$ $\quad f = \dfrac{1}{T} = \dfrac{1}{2.0\ \text{s}} = \boxed{0.50\ \text{Hz}}.$

(b) $T = 2\pi\sqrt{\dfrac{L}{g}},$ ☞ $L = \dfrac{T^2 g}{4\pi^2} = \dfrac{(2.0\ \text{s})^2(9.80\ \text{m/s}^2)}{4\pi^2} = \boxed{0.99\ \text{m}}.$

91. $x = A\cos\omega t = A\sin(\omega t + 90°).$

So $\quad v = \omega A\cos(\omega t + 90°) = -\omega A\sin\omega t$

and $\quad a = -\omega^2 x = -\omega^2 A\cos\omega t.$

$v_{\max} = \omega A = (50\ \text{rad/s})(0.10\ \text{m}) = \boxed{5.0\ \text{m/s}}.$

$a_{\max} = \omega^2 A = (50\ \text{rad/s})^2(0.10\ \text{m}) = \boxed{2.5 \times 10^2\ \text{m/s}^2}.$

92. $v = \sqrt{\dfrac{F_T}{\mu}} = \sqrt{\dfrac{550\ \text{N}}{(3.0 \times 10^{-3}\ \text{kg})/(0.60\ \text{m})}} = 332\ \text{m/s}.$

$f_1 = \dfrac{v}{2L} = \dfrac{332\ \text{m/s}}{2(0.60\ \text{m})} = \boxed{2.8 \times 10^2\ \text{Hz}}.$

$\lambda_1 = \dfrac{v}{f_1} = \dfrac{332\ \text{m/s}}{276\ \text{Hz}} = \boxed{1.2\ \text{m}},$ $\quad$ or $\quad \lambda_1 = 2L = 1.2\ \text{m}.$

93. The 4th harmonic and the 2nd harmonic vibrate in 4 and 2 loops, respectively.

So $\quad f_2 = \dfrac{f_4}{2} = \dfrac{420\ \text{Hz}}{2} = \boxed{210\ \text{Hz}}.$

94. $f_n = \dfrac{n}{2L}\sqrt{\dfrac{F_T}{\mu}}$, ☞ $\dfrac{F_T'}{F_T} = \dfrac{(f_1')^2}{(f_1)^2} = \dfrac{(440 \text{ Hz})^2}{(450 \text{ Hz})^2} = 0.956$.

So $F_T' = 0.956(500 \text{ N}) = \boxed{478 \text{ N}}$.

95. Since $v = \sqrt{\dfrac{F_T}{\mu}}$, doubling the tension will make the speed $\sqrt{2}$ times as large.

The wavelength is unchanged as it is determined by the length of the string and the mode of vibration.

However, the frequency is increased by a factor of $\sqrt{2}$ due to the speed increase.

96. $f_3 = 3\dfrac{v}{2L}$, $L = \dfrac{3v}{2f_3} = \dfrac{3(45 \text{ m/s})}{2(27 \text{ Hz})} = \boxed{2.5 \text{ m}}$.

97. $y = A\sin(\omega t + \delta) = (0.20 \text{ cm})\sin 1.8\pi t$.

$v = \omega A \cos(\omega t + \delta) = (1.8\pi \text{ rad/s})(0.20 \text{ cm})\cos[(1.8\pi \text{ rad/s})(10 \text{ s})] = \boxed{1.1 \text{ cm/s}}$.

98. (a) $\boxed{20 \text{ cm from the equilibrium position}}$ according to the definition of amplitude.

(b) $v_{max} = \omega A = 2\pi f A = 2\pi(0.50 \text{ Hz})(0.20 \text{ m}) = \boxed{0.63 \text{ m/s}}$.

(c) $a_{max} = \omega^2 A = (2\pi f)^2 A = 4\pi^2 f^2 A = 4\pi^2 (0.50 \text{ Hz})^2 (0.20 \text{ m}) = \boxed{2.0 \text{ m/s}^2}$.

99. The equation of motion is $x = A\sin(\omega t + \delta) = (16 \text{ cm})\sin(\omega t + 90°) = (16 \text{ cm})\cos\omega t$.

So $8.0 \text{ cm} = (16 \text{ cm})\cos[\omega(0.50 \text{ s})]$, $\omega(0.50 \text{ s}) = \dfrac{2\pi}{T}(0.50 \text{ s}) = \cos^{-1} 0.50 = 1.05 \text{ rad}$.

Therefore $T = \dfrac{2\pi(0.50 \text{ s})}{1.05 \text{ rad}} = \boxed{3.0 \text{ s}}$.

CHAPTER 14

SOUND

1. (b).

2. (a).

3. (a).

4. (d).

5. Some insects produce sounds that are not in our audible range.

6. Sound is a traveling disturbance like any other wave. The speed of the air molecules is greater in warmer air so the air molecules can pass the disturbance along faster.

7. They arrive at the same time because sound is not dispersive, i.e., speed not depending on frequency.

8. At the same temperature and pressure, water vapor has a smaller density than air. The speed of sound is inversely proportional to the square root of the density of the medium. Generally, the less dense air (O_2 and N_2 molecules replaced by H_2O molecules), the faster sound travels. So the speed increases with increasing humidity.

9. The unit of v in a liquid is $\sqrt{\dfrac{N/m^2}{kg/m^3}} = \sqrt{\dfrac{N \cdot m}{kg}} = \sqrt{\dfrac{kg \cdot m^2/s^2}{kg}} = \sqrt{\dfrac{m^2}{s^2}} = m/s$.

   Y has the same unit as B, so the unit of v in a solid is also m/s.

10. (a) $v = (331 + 0.6T_C)$ m/s $= [331 + 0.6(10)]$ m/s $= \boxed{337 \text{ m/s}}$.

    (b) $v = [331 + 0.6(20)]$ m/s $= \boxed{343 \text{ m/s}}$.

11. $v = (331 + 0.6T_C)$ m/s, ☞ $T_C = \dfrac{v - 331 \text{ m/s}}{0.6} = \dfrac{350 \text{ m/s} - 331 \text{ m/s}}{0.6} = \boxed{32°C}$.

12. (a) Neglect the time taken by the lightning since light travels at a much faster speed.

    $t \approx (1/3 \text{ km/s})(3.0 \text{ s}) = \boxed{1.0 \text{ km}}$.

    (b) $t \approx (1/5 \text{ mi/s})(3.0 \text{ s}) = \boxed{0.60 \text{ mi}}$.

13. The sound travels through the distance twice. $d = \dfrac{vt}{2} = \dfrac{(1.5 \text{ km/s})(2.0 \text{ s})}{2} = \boxed{1.5 \text{ km}}$.

14. $f = \dfrac{v}{\lambda} = \dfrac{1500 \text{ m/s}}{3.0 \times 10^{-4} \text{ m}} = \boxed{5.0 \times 10^6 \text{ Hz}}$, where $v = 1500$ m/s is the speed of sound in water.

15. (a) $\lambda = \dfrac{v}{f} = \dfrac{331 \text{ m/s}}{256 \text{ Hz}} = \boxed{1.29 \text{ m}}$.

    (b) $\lambda = \dfrac{(331 + 0.6T_C) \text{ m/s}}{f} = \dfrac{[331 + 0.6(20)] \text{ m/s}}{256 \text{ Hz}} = \boxed{1.34 \text{ m}}$.

16. From Table 14.1, the speed of sound in copper is 3500 m/s while the speed of sound in zinc is 3200 m/s. So adding zinc to copper will $\boxed{\text{decrease}}$ the speed of sound in the alloy, i.e., brass.

17. (a) $\Delta t = \dfrac{d}{v_a} - \dfrac{d}{v_s} = \dfrac{300 \text{ m}}{343 \text{ m/s}} - \dfrac{300 \text{ m}}{4500 \text{ m/s}} = \boxed{0.81 \text{ s}}$.

    (b) 36 km/h = 10 m/s. So $\Delta t = \dfrac{300 \text{ m}}{343 \text{ m/s} + 10 \text{ m/s}} - \dfrac{300 \text{ m}}{4500 \text{ m/s}} = \boxed{0.78 \text{ s}}$.

18. $v = (331 + 0.6T_C) \text{ m/s} = [331 + 0.6(16)] \text{ m/s} = 341 \text{ m/s}$. $d = vt = (341 \text{ m/s})(0.25 \text{ s}) = \boxed{85 \text{ m}}$.

19. $\lambda_{20} = \dfrac{v_{20}}{f} = \dfrac{[331 + 0.6(20)] \text{ m/s}}{2000 \text{ Hz}} = 0.1715 \text{ m}$, $\lambda_{10} = \dfrac{[331 + 0.6(10)] \text{ m/s}}{2000 \text{ Hz}} = 0.1685 \text{ m}$.

    So the percentage difference is $\dfrac{0.1685 \text{ m} - 0.1715 \text{ m}}{0.1715 \text{ m}} = \boxed{-1.75\%}$.

20. $T_C = \tfrac{5}{9}(T_F - 32) = \tfrac{5}{9}(72 - 32) = 22.22°C$. $v_s = (331 + 0.6T_C) \text{ m/s} = [331 + 0.6(22.22)] \text{ m/s} = 344.3 \text{ m/s}$.

    $\Delta t = \dfrac{d}{v_b} + \dfrac{d}{v_s} = d\left(\dfrac{1}{v_b} + \dfrac{1}{v_s} \right)$. So $d = \dfrac{\Delta t}{\dfrac{1}{v_b} + \dfrac{1}{v_s}} = \dfrac{1.00 \text{ s}}{\dfrac{1}{200 \text{ m/s}} + \dfrac{1}{344.3 \text{ m/s}}} = \boxed{127 \text{ m}}$.

21. $v = (331 + 0.6T_C) \text{ m/s} = [331 + 0.6(20)] \text{ m/s} = 343 \text{ m/s}$.

    So $d = \dfrac{vt}{2} = \dfrac{(343 \text{ m/s})(3.40 \text{ s})}{2} = \boxed{583 \text{ m}}$.

22. $v = \dfrac{2d}{t} = \dfrac{2(760 \text{ m})}{4.50 \text{ s}} = 338 \text{ m/s}$.   Also $v = (331 + 0.6T_C) \text{ m/s}$,

    so $T_C = \dfrac{v - 331}{0.6} °C = \dfrac{338 - 331}{0.6} °C = \boxed{12°C}$.

23. Since $\lambda = \dfrac{v}{f}$ and $v = (331 + 0.6T_C)$ m/s, the percentage change in wavelength is

$$\frac{\lambda_{30} - \lambda_{4.0}}{\lambda_{30}} = \frac{0.6(4.0 - 30)}{331 + 0.6(30)} = \boxed{-4.5\%}.$$

24. (c).

25. (b).

26. They are used to compress a large range into a smaller numerical scale.

27. $\boxed{\text{Yes}}$. Since $\beta = 10 \log \dfrac{I}{I_o}$ and $\log x < 0$ for $x < 1$, if $I < I_o$, an intensity is below the threshold intensity, β is negative.

28. (a) $I = \dfrac{P}{4\pi r^2} = \dfrac{1.0 \text{ W}}{4\pi(3.0 \text{ m})^2} = \boxed{8.8 \times 10^{-3} \text{ W/m}^2}.$

    (b) $I = \dfrac{1.0 \text{ W}}{4\pi(6.0 \text{ m})^2} = \boxed{2.2 \times 10^{-3} \text{ W/m}^2}.$

29. Since $I = \dfrac{P}{4\pi r^2} \propto \dfrac{1}{r^2}$, the intensity will be $\boxed{\text{four times as large}}$ if the distance is halved.

30. $I_2 = \frac{1}{2} I_1.$ $\dfrac{I_2}{I_1} = \dfrac{R_1^2}{R_2^2}$,   ☞ $\dfrac{R_2}{R_1} = \sqrt{\dfrac{I_1}{I_2}} = \sqrt{2} = \boxed{1.4 \text{ times}}.$

31. (a) $\beta = 10 \log \dfrac{I}{I_o} = 10 \log \dfrac{10^{-12} \text{ W/m}^2}{10^{-12} \text{ W/m}^2} = 10 \log 1 = \boxed{0}.$

    (b) $\beta = 10 \log \dfrac{1 \text{ W/m}^2}{10^{-12} \text{ W/m}^2} = 10 \log 10^{12} = 10(12) = \boxed{120 \text{ dB}}.$

32. (a) $\beta = 10 \log \dfrac{I}{I_o} = 10 \log \dfrac{10^{-2}}{10^{-12}} = \boxed{100 \text{ dB}}.$

    (b) $\beta = 10 \log \dfrac{10^{-6}}{10^{-12}} = \boxed{60 \text{ dB}}.$

    (c) $\beta = 10 \log \dfrac{10^{-15}}{10^{-12}} = \boxed{-30 \text{ dB}}.$

33. $\beta = 10 \log \dfrac{I}{I_o}$, ☞ $\Delta\beta = 10\left(\log \dfrac{I_2}{I_o} - \log \dfrac{I_1}{I_o}\right) = 10 \log \dfrac{I_2}{I_1} = 10 \log \dfrac{10^{-2}}{10^{-4}} = \boxed{20 \text{ dB}}$.

   $(\log x - \log y = \log \dfrac{x}{y})$

34. The 100 W speaker will generate twice as much intensity. However, it will not generate twice as much intensity level (decibel level) because $\log 2x = \log 2 + \log x = 0.3 + \log x \neq 2(\log x)$. So the answer is $\boxed{\text{no}}$.

35. (a) $\beta = 10 \log \dfrac{I}{I_o}$, ☞ $\dfrac{I}{I_o} = 10^{\beta/10}$, so $I = 10^{\beta/10} I_o = 10^5 (10^{-12} \text{ W/m}^2) = \boxed{10^{-7} \text{ W/m}^2}$.

   (b) $I = 10^9 (10^{-12} \text{ W/m}^2) = \boxed{10^{-3} \text{ W/m}^2}$.

36. (a) $\beta = 10 \log \dfrac{I}{I_o}$, ☞ $\dfrac{I}{I_o} = 10^{\beta/10}$, so $I = 10^{\beta/10} I_o$.

   Therefore $I_{\min} = 10^{8.57} (10^{-12} \text{ W/m}^2) = \boxed{3.72 \times 10^{-4} \text{ W/m}^2}$,

   $I_{\max} = 10^{11.0} (10^{-12} \text{ W/m}^2) = \boxed{1.00 \times 10^{-1} \text{ W/m}^2}$.

   (b) $I_{\min} = 10^{9.98} (10^{-12} \text{ W/m}^2) = \boxed{9.55 \times 10^{-3} \text{ W/m}^2}$, $I_{\max} = 10^{10.78} (10^{-12} \text{ W/m}^2) = \boxed{6.03 \times 10^{-2} \text{ W/m}^2}$.

37. (a) $\beta = 10 \log \dfrac{10,000\, I}{I_o} = 10 \log 10,000 + 10 \log \dfrac{I}{I_o} = 40 + 23 = \boxed{63 \text{ dB}}$.

   $(\log xy = \log x + \log y)$

   (b) $\beta = 10 \log \dfrac{10^6 I}{I_o} = 10 \log 10^6 + 10 \log \dfrac{I}{I_o} = 60 + 23 = \boxed{83 \text{ dB}}$.

   (c) $\beta = 10 \log \dfrac{10^9 I}{I_o} = 10 \log 10^9 + 10 \log \dfrac{I}{I_o} = 90 + 23 = \boxed{113 \text{ dB}}$.

38. $\beta = 10 \log \dfrac{I_s}{I_n}$, ☞ $\dfrac{I_s}{I_n} = 10^{\beta/10} = 10^{5.3} = \boxed{2.0 \times 10^5 \text{ times greater}}$.

39. (a) $\beta = 10 \log \dfrac{I}{I_o}$, ☞ $\dfrac{I}{I_o} = 10^{\beta/10}$, so $I = 10^{\beta/10} I_o$.

   $I_M = 10^9 (10^{-12} \text{ W/m}^2) = \boxed{10^{-3} \text{ W/m}^2}$ and $I_L = 10^4 (10^{-12} \text{ W/m}^2) = \boxed{10^{-8} \text{ W/m}^2}$.

   (b) $\dfrac{I_M}{I_L} = \dfrac{10^{-3}}{10^{-8}} = \boxed{10^5}$.

40. $\beta_2 = 10 \log \dfrac{2I}{I_o} = 10 \log \left(2 \dfrac{I}{I_o}\right) = 10 \left(\log 2 + \log \dfrac{I}{I_o}\right) = 10\,(0.3) \text{ dB} + 40 \text{ dB} = \boxed{43 \text{ dB}}$.

   $(\log xy = \log x + \log y.)$

41.   Assume n bands. $\beta_n = 10 \log \dfrac{nI}{I_0} = 10 \log n + 10 \log \dfrac{I}{I_0} = 10 \log n + 110$ dB. ($\log xy = \log x + \log y$.)

So $10 \log n = 120$ dB $- 110$ dB $= 10$ dB,   ☞ $\log n = 1$,   so $n = \boxed{10}$.

42. $\beta = 10 \log \dfrac{I}{I_0}$,   ☞ $\Delta\beta = \beta_2 - \beta_1 = 10 \log \dfrac{I_2}{I_0} - 10 \log \dfrac{I_1}{I_0} = 10 \log \dfrac{I_2}{I_1}$ ($\log x - \log y = \log \dfrac{x}{y}$).

So $\dfrac{I_2}{I_1} = 10^{\Delta\beta/10} = 10^{-3}$.   Also $\dfrac{I_2}{I_1} = \dfrac{R_1^2}{R_2^2}$,   ☞ $R_2 = \sqrt{\dfrac{I_1}{I_2}}\, R_1 = \sqrt{10^3}\,(10.0 \text{ m}) = \boxed{316 \text{ m}}$.

43. $\dfrac{I_B}{I_A} = \dfrac{R_A^2}{R_B^2} = \dfrac{(150 \text{ m})^2}{(200 \text{ m})^2} = 0.56$. So $\boxed{I_B = 0.56I_A}$;

$\dfrac{I_C}{I_A} = \dfrac{R_A^2}{R_C^2} = \dfrac{(150 \text{ m})^2}{(300 \text{ m})^2} = 0.25$. So $\boxed{I_C = 0.25I_A}$;

$\dfrac{I_D}{I_A} = \dfrac{R_A^2}{R_D^2} = \dfrac{(150 \text{ m})^2}{(200 \text{ m})^2 + (300 \text{ m})^2} = 0.17$. So $\boxed{I_D = 0.17I_A}$.

44.   Just before reflection, $\beta_1 = 10 \log \dfrac{I_1}{I_0} = 10 \log \dfrac{2.5 \times 10^{-4} \text{ W/m}^2}{10^{-12} \text{ W/m}^2} = \boxed{84 \text{ dB}}$.

Just after reflection, $\beta_2 = 10 \log \dfrac{0.80(2.0 \times 10^{-4} \text{ W/m}^2)}{10^{-12} \text{ W/m}^2} = \boxed{83 \text{ dB}}$.

45.   (a) $\beta = 10 \log \dfrac{I}{I_0}$,   ☞ $I = 10^{\beta/10} I_0 = 10^{9.5} (10^{-12} \text{ W/m}^2) = \boxed{3.2 \times 10^{-3} \text{ W/m}^2}$.

(b) From Exercise 14.42, $\dfrac{I_2}{I_1} = 10^{\Delta\beta/10} = 10^{1.2} = \boxed{16}$.

46.   (a) From Exercise 14.42, $\dfrac{I_2}{I_1} = 10^{\Delta\beta/10} = 10^{-4.0} = 10^{-4}$.

Also $\dfrac{I_2}{I_1} = \dfrac{R_1^2}{R_2^2}$,   ☞ $R_2 = \sqrt{\dfrac{I_1}{I_2}}\, R_1 = 10^2 (2.5 \text{ m}) = \boxed{2.5 \times 10^2 \text{ m}}$.

(b) The threshold of hearing is at 0 dB. $\dfrac{I_2}{I_1} = 10^{-10.0}$.

$R_2 = \sqrt{10^{10.0}}\, R_1 = 10^{5.0} (2.5 \text{ m}) = \boxed{2.5 \times 10^5 \text{ m}}$.

This number is a bit unrealistic because we ignored loss of sound during propogation.

47.   For one bee, $I = I_0$. Assume it takes n bees.

$\beta = 10 \log \dfrac{nI}{I_0} = 10 \log n$,   ☞ $n = 10^{\beta/10} = 10^{5.0} = \boxed{10^5 \text{ bees}}$.

48.   (a).

49.   (b).

50.   No . The beat of music has to do with tempo. Beats are physical phenomena related to the frequency difference between two tones.

51.   (a) No , there is no relative velocity between the observer and the source.

        (b) An increasing sound frequency is observed since the source is moving toward the observer and its speed increases.

52.   It must be faster than the speed of sound in water.

53.   The varying sound intensity is caused by the interference effect. At certain locations there is constructive interference and at other locations, there are destructive interference.

54.   (a) $\Delta L = 3.75$ m $- 2.50$ m $= 1.25$ m $= 2.5$ $(0.50$ m$) = 2.5\lambda$. So destructive .

        (b) $\Delta L = 8.25$ m $- 3.25$ m $= 5.00$ m $= 10(0.50$ m$) = 10\lambda$. So constructive .

55.   At the first destructive point, $\Delta L = \frac{1}{2}\lambda = \frac{1}{2}\frac{v}{f} = \frac{343 \text{ m/s}}{2(1000 \text{ Hz})} = \boxed{0.172 \text{ m}}$.

56.   The beat frequency is $f_b = |f_2 - f_1| = 440$ Hz $- 436$ Hz $= \boxed{4 \text{ Hz}}$.

57. $f_2 = f_1 \pm f_b = 264$ Hz ± 3 Hz $= \boxed{267 \text{ Hz or } 261 \text{ Hz}}$.

58.   (a) Since the heard frequency is higher than the siren frequency, the person is moving toward the siren.

        (b)$f_o = \frac{v + v_o}{v}f_s$,   ☞ $v_o = \frac{f_o - f_s}{f_s} v = \frac{520 \text{ Hz} - 500 \text{ Hz}}{500 \text{ Hz}} (343 \text{ m/s}) = \boxed{13.7 \text{ m/s}}$.

59.   The observer moves with a speed of 50 km/h $= 13.9$ m/s.

        So $f_o = \frac{v + v_o}{v}f_s = \frac{331 \text{ m/s} + 13.9 \text{ m/s}}{331 \text{ m/s}} (800 \text{ Hz}) = \boxed{834 \text{ Hz}}$.

60. $v = (331 + 0.6T_C)$ m/s $= [331 + 0.6(25)]$ m/s $= 346$ m/s, $v_s = 90$ km/h $= 25$ m/s. Source is in motion.

(a) $f_o = \dfrac{v}{v - v_s} f_s = \dfrac{346 \text{ m/s}}{346 \text{ m/s} - 25 \text{ m/s}} (400 \text{ Hz}) = \boxed{431 \text{ Hz}}$.

(b) $f_o = \dfrac{v}{v + v_s} f_s = \dfrac{346 \text{ m/s}}{346 \text{ m/s} + 25 \text{ m/s}} (400 \text{ Hz}) = \boxed{373 \text{ Hz}}$.

61. $f = \dfrac{v}{\lambda} = \dfrac{\sqrt{\dfrac{F}{\mu}}}{\lambda}$,   ☞ $\dfrac{f_2}{f_1} = \sqrt{\dfrac{F_2}{F_1}} = \sqrt{0.985} = 0.9925$.

So $f_2 = 0.9925 f_1$,   or $f_b = |f_1 - f_2| = f_1 - f_2 = 0.0075 f_1 = (0.0075)(440 \text{ Hz}) = \boxed{3.3 \text{ Hz}}$.

62. The source is in motion. $f_o = \dfrac{v}{v - v_s} f_s$,   ☞ $1.050 = \dfrac{v}{v - v_s}$.

So $v_s = \dfrac{0.050v}{1.050} = \dfrac{0.050(340 \text{ m/s})}{1.050} = 16.2$ m/s $= \boxed{58 \text{ km/h}}$.

63. $\sin\theta = \dfrac{v}{v_s}$,   ☞ $\theta = \sin^{-1}\left(\dfrac{v}{v_s}\right) = \sin^{-1} 1 = \boxed{90°}$.

64. $M = \dfrac{1}{\sin\theta}$,   ☞ $\theta = \sin^{-1}\left(\dfrac{1}{M}\right) = \sin^{-1}\left(\dfrac{1}{1.5}\right) = \sin^{-1} 0.667 = \boxed{42°}$.

65. (a) $M = \dfrac{1}{\sin\theta} = \dfrac{1}{\sin 35°} = \boxed{1.74}$.

(b) $M = \dfrac{v}{v_s}$,   ☞ $v = Mv_s = 1.74\{[331 + 0.6(-20)] \text{ m/s}\} = \boxed{555 \text{ m/s}}$.

66. The minimum separation for destructive interference corresponds to $\Delta L = \dfrac{\lambda}{2}$.

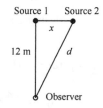

$\Delta L = d - 12 \text{ m} = \sqrt{x^2 + (12.0 \text{ m})^2} - 12.0 \text{ m} = \dfrac{\lambda}{2} = \dfrac{v}{2f} = \dfrac{340 \text{ m/s}}{2(1000 \text{ Hz})} = 0.170$ m.

So $x^2 + (12.0 \text{ m})^2 = (12.17 \text{ m})^2$,   ☞ $x = \boxed{2.03 \text{ m}}$.

67. When the source is approaching, $f_{oA} = \dfrac{v}{v - v_s} f_s$,   Eq. (1)

When the source is moving away, $f_{oM} = \dfrac{v}{v + v_s} f_s$ Eq. (2)

$\dfrac{\text{Eq. (2)}}{\text{Eq. (1)}}$ gives $\dfrac{f_{oM}}{f_{oA}} = \dfrac{v - v_s}{v + v_s}$,   ☞ $f_{oM}(v + v_s) = f_{oA}(v - v_s)$.

So $v_s = \dfrac{(f_{oA} - f_{oM})v}{f_{oA} + f_{oM}} = \dfrac{(476 \text{ Hz} - 404 \text{ Hz})(343 \text{ m/s})}{476 \text{ Hz} + 404 \text{ Hz}} = \boxed{28 \text{ m/s}}$.

68.　　(b).

69.　　(a).

70.　　(a) The snow absorbs sound so there is little reflection.

(b) In an empty room, there is less absorption. So the reflections die out more slowly and therefore the sound sounds hollow and echoing.

(c) Sound is reflected by the shower walls and standing waves are set up, giving rise to more harmonics and therefore richer sound quality.

71.　　$f_1 = \dfrac{v}{2L}$, ☞ $L = \dfrac{v}{2f_1}$.　For two notes A and B, the spacing between the frets is

$$\Delta L = f_{1B} - f_{1A} = \frac{v}{2f_{1B}} - \frac{v}{2f_{1A}} = \frac{v}{2f_{1A}f_{1B}}(f_{1A} - f_{1B}) = \frac{v}{2f_{1A}f_{1B}}\Delta f.$$ So the spacing (change in length)

depends not only on the frequency difference Δf, but also on the values of the frequencies themselves. For different frequencies, ΔL is therefore different.

72.　　For an open pipe,　　$f_n = \dfrac{nv}{2L}$　　for $n = 1, 2, 3, \ldots$

For a closed pipe,　　$f_m = \dfrac{mv}{4L}$　　for $m = 1, 3, 5, \ldots$

So　$\dfrac{f_n}{f_m} = \dfrac{n/2}{m/4} = \dfrac{2n}{m}$.　　For $f_n = f_m$, $2n = m$.

This is $\boxed{\text{not possible}}$ because $2n$ is an even integer and m is an odd integer.

73.　　As the level of water increases in the bottle, the length of the air column above the water decreases. This decrease in length of the air column decreases the wavelength and increases the frequency.

74.　　(a) 378 Hz = 3(126 Hz) and 630 Hz = 5(126 Hz), so it is a $\boxed{\text{closed pipe}}$.

(b) $f_n = \dfrac{mv}{4L}$,　☞　$L = \dfrac{v}{4f_1} = \dfrac{340 \text{ m/s}}{4(126 \text{ Hz})} = \boxed{0.675 \text{ m}}$; here we take $m = 1$.

75.　　$f = \dfrac{v}{\lambda}$,　☞　$\dfrac{f_2}{f_1} = \dfrac{v_2}{v_1} = \dfrac{331 \text{ m/s}}{343 \text{ m/s}} = 0.965$.　　So　$f_2 = 0.965(528 \text{ Hz}) = \boxed{510 \text{ Hz}}$.

76.　　For a closed pipe, $f_1 = \dfrac{v}{4L} = f_n = \dfrac{343 \text{ m/s}}{4(0.025 \text{ m})} = \boxed{3.4 \text{ kHz}}$.

The ear is also the most sensitive to this frequency.

77. (a) Since $f_m = \dfrac{mv}{4L}$ for $m = 1, 3, 5, \ldots$, $\boxed{f_2 \text{ does not exist}}$—only odd harmonics.

(b) $f_3 = \dfrac{3v}{4L} = \dfrac{3(343 \text{ m/s})}{4(0.800 \text{ m})} = \boxed{322 \text{ Hz}}$.

78. For the open pipe, $(f_1)_o = \dfrac{(1)v}{2L} = \dfrac{343 \text{ m/s}}{2(0.52 \text{ m})} = \boxed{330 \text{ Hz}}$.

For the closed pipe, $(f_1)_c = \dfrac{(1)v}{4L} = \dfrac{(f_1)_o}{2} = \boxed{165 \text{ Hz}}$.

79. If the observer were stationary, the frequency heard by the observer would have been $(f_o)_1 = \dfrac{v}{v \mp v_s} f_s$, which would be the frequency of the "source" to the moving observer. $(f_s)_2 = (f_o)_1$.

So $(f_o)_2 = f_o = \dfrac{v \pm v_o}{v}(f_s)_2 = \dfrac{v \pm v_o}{v} \dfrac{v}{v \mp v_s} f_s = \dfrac{v \pm v_o}{v \mp v_s} f_s$.

80. (a) $v_s = 90$ km/h $= -25$ m/s and $v_o = 65$ km/h $= 18.1$ m/s. Both the source and the observer are moving toward each other. From Exercise 14.79 and according to the sign conventions:

$f_o = \dfrac{v + v_o}{v - v_s} f_s = \dfrac{354 \text{ m/s} + 18.1 \text{ m/s}}{354 \text{ m/s} - 25 \text{ m/s}}(500 \text{ Hz}) = \boxed{566 \text{ Hz}}$.

(b) Both the source and the observer are moving away from each other.

So $f_o = \dfrac{354 \text{ m/s} - 18.1 \text{ m/s}}{354 \text{ m/s} + 25 \text{ m/s}}(500 \text{ Hz}) = \boxed{443 \text{ Hz}}$.

81. The distance between node–antinode is $\lambda/4$ and the distance between node–node is $\lambda/2$.

So for the mth ($m = 1, 3, 5, \ldots$) resonant position, $L_m = \dfrac{m\lambda}{4} = \dfrac{mv/f}{4} = \dfrac{mv}{4f}$.

So $L_1 = \dfrac{(1)(342 \text{ m/s})}{4(440 \text{ Hz})} = \boxed{0.194 \text{ m}}$, $L_3 = 3L_1 = \boxed{0.583 \text{ m}}$, and $L_5 = 5L_1 = \boxed{0.972 \text{ m}}$, …

82. $f_1 = \dfrac{(1)v}{4L}$, ☞ $\dfrac{(f_1)_{He}}{(f_1)_{air}} = \dfrac{v_{He}}{v_{air}} = \dfrac{965 \text{ m/s}}{331 \text{ m/s}} = 2.915$.

So $(f_1)_{He} = 2.915(660 \text{ Hz}) = \boxed{1.92 \times 10^3 \text{ Hz}}$.

83. $\lambda = \dfrac{v}{f} = \dfrac{[331 + 0.6(15)] \text{ m/s}}{440 \text{ Hz}} = 0.773 \text{ m}$.

$\Delta L = 8.90 \text{ m} - 6.97 \text{ m} = 1.93 \text{ m} = 2.5 (0.773) = 2.5\lambda$.

So they will interfere $\boxed{\text{destructively}}$.

84. $v = (331 + 0.6T_C)$ m/s $= [331 + 0.6(30)]$ m/s $= 349$ m/s.

So $t = \dfrac{d}{v} = \dfrac{3.5 \times 10^3 \text{ m}}{349 \text{ m/s}} = \boxed{10 \text{ s}}$.

85. $\dfrac{I_2}{I_1} = \dfrac{R_1^{\,2}}{R_2^{\,2}} = \dfrac{(30.0 \text{ m})^2}{(25.0 \text{ m})^2} = 1.44.$

So it $\boxed{\text{increases to 1.44 times}}$.

86. $\boxed{\text{No}}$, the manager does achieve his goal. Removing 25 computers will cut the intensity in half, but won't cut the intensity level in half.

With $\beta = 10 \log \dfrac{I}{I_o}$, $\beta_{1/2} = \beta_1 - 10(\log 2)$ because $\log x = \log 2 + \log x/2$.

So $\beta_2 = 40$ dB $- 10(\log 2)$ dB $= 40$dB $- 10(0.3)$ dB $= \boxed{37 \text{ dB}}$.

87. $f_o = \dfrac{v + v_o}{v} f_s$, ☞ $v_o = \dfrac{f_o - f_s}{f_s} v = \dfrac{2f_s - f_s}{f_s} v = v$, which is at $\boxed{\text{speed of sound}}$.

88. $\beta = 10 \log \dfrac{I}{I_o}$, ☞ $\dfrac{I}{I_o} = 10^{\beta/10}$. So $\dfrac{I_1}{I_o} = 10^{6.00}$ and $\dfrac{I_2}{I_o} = 10^{6.50}$.

Therefore the intensity level heard by another person is

$\beta_{\text{tot}} = 10 \log \dfrac{I_1 + I_2}{I_o} = 10 \log (10^{6.00} + 10^{6.50}) = \boxed{66.2 \text{ dB}}$.

89. $\beta = 10 \log \dfrac{I}{I_o}$, ☞ $\dfrac{I}{I_o} = 10^{\beta/10}$. So $I = 10^{9.0} (10^{-12} \text{ W/m}^2) = 10^{-3}$ W/m^2.

In 5.0 s, the energy is $E = IAt = (10^{-3} \text{ W/m}^2)(1.5 \text{ m}^2)(5.0 \text{ s}) = \boxed{7.5 \times 10^{-3} \text{ J}}$.

90. $M = \dfrac{1}{\sin \theta}$, ☞ $\theta = \sin^{-1}\left(\dfrac{1}{M}\right) = \sin^{-1}\left(\dfrac{1}{2.0}\right) = \sin^{-1} 0.50 = \boxed{30°}$.

$\boxed{\text{Yes}}$, you can tell its speed if you know the air temperature or the speed of sound.

91. The period (time for one vibration) is $T = \dfrac{1}{f} = \dfrac{1}{440 \text{ Hz}} = 2.273 \times 10^{-3}$ s.

The time taken for sound to travel 30 m is $t = \dfrac{d}{v} = \dfrac{30 \text{ m}}{343 \text{ m/s}} = 0.08746$ s.

So the number of vibrations is $n = \dfrac{t}{T} = \dfrac{0.08746 \text{ s}}{2.273 \times 10^{-3} \text{ s}} = \boxed{38 \text{ vibrations}}$.

92. $v_s = (331 + 0.6T_C)$ m/s $= [331 + 0.6(10)]$ m/s $= 337$ m/s. Assume the depth is d. The stone first free falls to the bottom and then the sound travels up to the person. The time taken for the free fall is

$$\sqrt{\frac{2d}{g}} \quad (y = d = \tfrac{1}{2}gt^2). \qquad \text{So} \quad 3.16 \text{ s} = \sqrt{\frac{2d}{g}} + \frac{d}{v_s} = \sqrt{\frac{2d}{9.80 \text{ m/s}^2}} + \frac{d}{337 \text{ m/s}} .$$

Reducing to a quadratic equation: $\quad d^2 - 2.531 \times 10^4 \, d + 1.134 \times 10^6 = 0$.

Solving, $\quad d = \boxed{45 \text{ m}}$.

93. 90.0 km/h = 25 m/s.

Approaching: $\quad f_o = \dfrac{v}{v - v_s} f_s = \dfrac{343 \text{ m/s}}{343 \text{ m/s} - 25 \text{ m/s}} (700 \text{ Hz}) = \boxed{755 \text{ Hz}}$.

Moving away: $\quad f_o = \dfrac{v}{v + v_s} f_s = \dfrac{343 \text{ m/s}}{343 \text{ m/s} + 25 \text{ m/s}} (700 \text{ Hz}) = \boxed{652 \text{ Hz}}$.

94. Neglect the time taken by the light since light travels at a much faster speed.

$$t = \frac{d}{v} = \frac{d}{(331 + 0.6T_C) \text{ m/s}} = \frac{300 \text{ m}}{[331 + 0.6(5)] \text{ m/s}} = \boxed{0.90 \text{ s}} .$$

95. For the open pipe, $\quad (f_1)_o = \dfrac{(1)\,v}{2L_o}$. For the closed pipe, $\quad (f_3)_c = \dfrac{(3)v}{4L_c}$.

If $\quad (f_1)_o = (f_3)_c, \quad L_c = \tfrac{3}{2}L_o = \tfrac{3}{2}(0.75 \text{ m}) = \boxed{1.1 \text{ m}}$.

CHAPTER 15

ELECTRIC CHARGE, FORCE, AND FIELD

1.   (c).

2.   (b).

3.   (a) We know there are two types of charges because attractive and repulsive forces can be produced by different combinations of just two types of charges.

        (b) There would be $\boxed{\text{no effect}}$.

4. $\boxed{\text{No}}$. Charges are simply moved from the object to another object, which will have opposite charge.

5.   If an object is positively charged, its mass $\boxed{\text{decreases}}$ because it loses electrons. If an object is negatively charged, its mass $\boxed{\text{increases}}$ because it gains electrons.

6. $q = ne = (10^6)(1.60 \times 10^{-19} \text{ C}) = \boxed{-1.60 \times 10^{-13} \text{ C}}$.

7. $n = \dfrac{q}{e} = \dfrac{-50 \times 10^{-6} \text{ C}}{-1.60 \times 10^{-19} \text{ C}} = \boxed{3.1 \times 10^{14} \text{ electrons}}$.

8.   (a) $\boxed{-8.0 \times 10^{-10} \text{ C}}$ according to charge conservation.

        (b) $n = \dfrac{q}{e} = \dfrac{8.0 \times 10^{-10} \text{ C}}{1.6 \times 10^{-19} \text{ C}} = \boxed{5.0 \times 10^9 \text{ electrons}}$.

9.   (a) $\boxed{+4.8 \times 10^{-9} \text{ C}}$ according to charge conservation.

        (b) $n = \dfrac{q}{e} = \dfrac{4.8 \times 10^{-9} \text{ C}}{1.6 \times 10^{-19} \text{ C}} = 3.0 \times 10^{10}$ electrons.

        So the mass is $(3.0 \times 10^{10})(9.11 \times 10^{-31} \text{ kg}) = \boxed{2.7 \times 10^{-20} \text{ kg}}$.

10.   There are two protons in each α particle.

        So the charge is $q = ne = (2)(2)(1.60 \times 10^{-19} \text{ C}) = \boxed{+6.40 \times 10^{-19} \text{ C}}$.

11.   When the positively charged fur is brought near an electroscope, the leaves are charged by induction. So the charges on the leaves are $\boxed{\text{positive}}$.

12.   (a), since there will be more negative charges on the leaves by induction.

13. $\boxed{\text{No}}$, the wall is still neutral but polarized. That is why there is a *net* attractive force between the balloon and the wall.

14.   If you bring a negatively charged object near the electroscope, the induction process will charge the electroscope with positive charges. You can prove the charges are positive by bringing the negatively charged object near the leaves and seeing if the leaves fall.

15.   The spheres can be charged through polarization by induction. For example, if you bring a positively charged object near one of the two spheres, the sphere near the charged object will have a net negative charge and the other sphere will have a net positive charge (polarization by induction). Then you separate the two spheres (while keep the positively charged object nearby) and the spheres will have opposite charges according to charge conservation.

16.   (c).

17.   (d).

18.   Although the electric force is fundamentally much stronger than the gravitational force, both the Earth and our bodies are electrically neutral so there are no noticeable electric forces.

19.   Both the Sun and the planets are electrically neutral.

20.   (a) Since $F = \dfrac{kq_1 q_2}{r^2} \propto \dfrac{1}{r^2}$, F is $\boxed{\text{1/4 as large}}$ if r is doubled.

        (b) F is $\boxed{\text{9 times as large}}$ if r is reduced to one-third.

21.   (a) Since $F = \dfrac{kq_1 q_2}{r^2} \propto q_1 q_2$, F is $2 \times \frac{1}{2} = 1$, i.e., the $\boxed{\text{same}}$.

        (b) $F = \frac{1}{2} \times \frac{1}{2} = \boxed{\text{1/4 as large}}$.

        (c) $F = \frac{1}{2} \times 1 = \boxed{\text{1/2 as large}}$.

22. $F = \dfrac{kq_1 q_2}{r^2} = \dfrac{k(6e)(6e)}{r^2} = \dfrac{(9.0 \times 10^9 \text{ N·m}^2/\text{C}^2)(6)^2 (1.6 \times 10^{-19} \text{ C})^2}{(0.25 \times 10^{-9} \text{ m})^2} = \boxed{1.3 \times 10^{-7} \text{ N}}$.

23.   (a) $F = \dfrac{kq_1 q_2}{r^2} = \dfrac{(9.0 \times 10^9 \text{ N·m}^2/\text{C}^2)(1.6 \times 10^{-19} \text{ C})^2}{(2.0 \times 10^{-9} \text{ m})^2} = \boxed{5.8 \times 10^{-11} \text{ N}}$.

(b) $\boxed{\text{Zero}}$ because they are internal forces of the system.

24. $F = \dfrac{kq_1 q_2}{r^2}$,   ☞ $\dfrac{F_2}{F_1} = \dfrac{r_1^{\,2}}{r_2^{\,2}}$,   so $r_2 = \sqrt{\dfrac{F_1}{F_2}}\,r_1 = \sqrt{10}\ (30 \text{ cm}) = \boxed{95 \text{ cm}}$.

25. $F = \dfrac{kq_1 q_2}{r^2}$,   ☞ $\dfrac{F_2}{F_1} = \dfrac{r_1^{\,2}}{r_2^{\,2}}$,   so $r_1 = \sqrt{\dfrac{F_2}{F_1}}\,r_2 = \sqrt{5}\ (100 \text{ cm}) = \boxed{2.24 \text{ m}}$.

26. $F = \dfrac{kq_1 q_2}{r^2}$,   ☞ $\dfrac{F_2}{F_1} = \dfrac{r_1^{\,2}}{r_2^{\,2}}$,   so $F_2 = \dfrac{r_1^{\,2}}{r_2^{\,2}}\,F_1 = \dfrac{(10 \text{ cm})^2}{(50 \text{ cm})^2}\,(25 \text{ N}) = \boxed{1.0 \text{ N}}$.

27.   (a) By symmetry, the electron has to be at the $\boxed{50 \text{ cm}}$ mark since both forces are repulsive and in opposite directions.

(b) By symmetry, the proton has to be at the $\boxed{50 \text{ cm}}$ mark since both forces are attractive and in opposite directions.

28.   (a) $\boxed{\text{Nowhere}}$ since both forces are in the same direction.

(b) $\boxed{\text{Nowhere}}$ since both forces are in the same direction.

29.   (a) If q_1 and q_2 are like charges, the third charge must be placed in between q_1 and q_2 for it to be in electrostatic equilibrium. Also q_1 and q_2 have the same magnitude; it must be at $\boxed{0.25 \text{ m}}$ from symmetry.

(b) If q_1 and q_2 are unlike charges, the third charge could be placed outside q_1 and q_3 ($x < 0$ and $x > 0.50$ m). However, since the magnitudes of q_1 and q_2 are equal, there will be $\boxed{\text{nowhere}}$ for it to happen according to Coulomb's law.

(c) Since $q_1 = +3.0\ \mu\text{C}$ and $q_2 = -7.0\ \mu\text{C}$, a third charge of either type can be placed outside q_1 ($x < 0$) for it to be in electrostatic equilibrium. It cannot be placed to right of q_2

($x > 0.50$ m) since the force by q_2 will always be larger due to the closer distance from it. Assume the third charge is placed at d from q_1 (or $x = -d$).

From Coulomb's law, we have $\dfrac{kq_1 q_3}{r_{13}^2} = \dfrac{k|q_2|q_3}{r_{23}^2}$, ☞ $\dfrac{q_1}{d^2} = \dfrac{|q_2|}{(d + 0.50\ \text{m})^2}$.

Taking the square root on both sides gives $\dfrac{\sqrt{3.0}}{d} = \dfrac{\sqrt{7.0}}{d + 0.50}$, so $1.73(d + 0.50) = 2.65d$.

Solving, $d = 0.94$ m. Thus $\boxed{x = -0.94\ \text{m for either } \pm q_3}$.

30.   (a) $F = \dfrac{kq_1 q_2}{r^2} = \dfrac{(9.0 \times 10^9\ \text{N·m}^2/\text{C}^2)(1.6 \times 10^{-19}\ \text{C})^2}{(5.3 \times 10^{-11}\ \text{m})^2} = \boxed{8.2 \times 10^{-8}\ \text{N}}$.

(b) The electric force provides the required centripetal force. $F = m\dfrac{v^2}{r}$,

so $v = \sqrt{\dfrac{Fr}{m}} = \sqrt{\dfrac{(8.2 \times 10^{-8}\ \text{N})(5.3 \times 10^{-11}\ \text{m})}{9.11 \times 10^{-31}\ \text{kg}}} = \boxed{2.2 \times 10^6\ \text{m/s}}$.

(c) $a_c = \dfrac{v^2}{r} = \dfrac{F}{m} = \dfrac{8.2 \times 10^{-8}\ \text{N}}{9.11 \times 10^{-31}\ \text{kg}} = 9.0 \times 10^{22}\ \text{m/s}^2 = \boxed{9.2 \times 10^{21}\ g}$, where $g = 9.80\ \text{m/s}^2$.

31.   From Exercise 30(a), $F_e = 8.2 \times 10^{-8}$ N.

$F_g = \dfrac{Fm_1 m_2}{r^2} = \dfrac{(6.67 \times 10^{-11}\ \text{N·m}^2/\text{kg}^2)(9.11 \times 10^{-31}\ \text{kg})(1.67 \times 10^{-27}\ \text{kg})}{(5.3 \times 10^{-11}\ \text{m})^2} = 3.6 \times 10^{-47}$ N.

So $\dfrac{F_e}{F_g} = \dfrac{8.2 \times 10^{-8}\ \text{N}}{3.6 \times 10^{-47}\ \text{N}} = \boxed{2.3 \times 10^{39}}$.

32. $F_2 = F_3 = \dfrac{kq_1 q_2}{r^2} = \dfrac{(9.0 \times 10^9\ \text{N·m}^2/\text{C}^2)(4.0 \times 10^{-6}\ \text{C})^2}{(0.20\ \text{m})^2} = 3.6$ N.

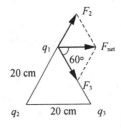

According to symmetry, the net force on q_1 points in the $+x$ direction.

$F_{net} = F_x = F_2 \cos 60° + F_3 \cos 60°$

$= 2(3.6\ \text{N}) \cos 60° = \boxed{3.6\ \text{N in the } +x \text{ direction}}$.

33.   (a) From Coulomb's law: $F_1 = \dfrac{kq_1 q_2}{r^2} = \dfrac{(9.0 \times 10^9\ \text{N·m}^2/\text{C}^2)(10 \times 10^{-6}\ \text{C})(10 \times 10^{-6}\ \text{C})}{(0.10\ \text{m})^2} = 90$ N.

So $\mathbf{F}_1 = (90\ \text{N})\ \hat{\mathbf{x}}$.

$F_3 = \dfrac{(9.0 \times 10^9\ \text{N·m}^2/\text{C}^2)(5.0 \times 10^{-6}\ \text{C})(10 \times 10^{-6}\ \text{C})}{(0.10\ \text{m})^2} = 45$ N.

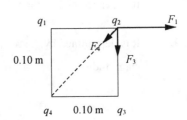

So $\mathbf{F}_3 = (-45\ \text{N})\ \hat{\mathbf{y}}$.

$F_4 = \dfrac{(9.0 \times 10^9\ \text{N·m}^2/\text{C}^2)(5.0 \times 10^{-6}\ \text{C})(10 \times 10^{-6}\ \text{C})}{(0.10\ \text{m})^2 + (0.10\ \text{m})^2} = 22.5$ N.

So $\mathbf{F}_4 = -F_4 (\cos 45°)\ \hat{\mathbf{x}} + (\sin 45°)\ \hat{\mathbf{y}} = (-15.9\ \text{N})\ (\hat{\mathbf{x}} + \hat{\mathbf{y}})$.

Therefore the net force is $\mathbf{F}_2 = \mathbf{F}_1 + \mathbf{F}_3 + \mathbf{F}_4 = (74.1 \text{ N}) \mathbf{x} - (60.9 \text{ N}) \hat{\mathbf{y}}$.

Thus $F_2 = \sqrt{(74.1 \text{ N})^2 + (60.9 \text{ N})^2} = \boxed{96 \text{ N}}$, $\theta = \tan^{-1}\left(\dfrac{60.9}{74.1}\right) = \boxed{39° \text{ below the } +x \text{ axis}}$.

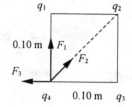

(b) $F_1 = \dfrac{(9.0 \times 10^9 \text{ N·m}^2/\text{C}^2)(10 \times 10^{-6} \text{ C})(5.0 \times 10^{-6} \text{ C})}{(0.10 \text{ m})^2} = 45 \text{ N}$.

So $\mathbf{F}_1 = (45 \text{ N}) \hat{\mathbf{y}}$.

$F_2 = \dfrac{(9.0 \times 10^9 \text{ N·m}^2/\text{C}^2)(10 \times 10^{-6} \text{ C})(5.0 \times 10^{-6} \text{ C})}{(0.10 \text{ m})^2 + (0.10 \text{ m})^2} = 22.5 \text{ N}$.

So $\mathbf{F}_2 = F_2 (\cos 45°) \hat{\mathbf{x}} + (\sin 45°) \hat{\mathbf{y}} = (15.9 \text{ N}) (\hat{\mathbf{x}} + \hat{\mathbf{y}})$.

$F_3 = \dfrac{(9.0 \times 10^9 \text{ N·m}^2/\text{C}^2)(5.0 \times 10^{-6} \text{ C})(5.0 \times 10^{-6} \text{ C})}{(0.10 \text{ m})^2} = 22.5 \text{ N}$. So $\mathbf{F}_3 = (-22.5 \text{ N}) \hat{\mathbf{x}}$.

Therefore the net force is $\mathbf{F}_4 = \mathbf{F}_1 + \mathbf{F}_2 + \mathbf{F}_3 = (-6.6 \text{ N}) \hat{\mathbf{x}} + (60.9 \text{ N}) \hat{\mathbf{y}}$.

Thus $F_2 = \sqrt{(6.6 \text{ N})^2 + (60.9 \text{ N})^2} = \boxed{61 \text{ N}}$, $\theta = \tan^{-1}\left(\dfrac{60.9}{6.6}\right) = \boxed{84° \text{ above the } -x \text{ axis}}$.

34. $F = \dfrac{kq_1 q_2}{r^2} = \dfrac{kq^2}{r^2}$. $\sin \theta = \dfrac{9.0 \text{ cm}}{30 \text{ cm}}$, ☞ $\theta = 17.5°$.

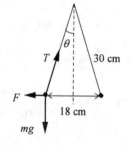

In the vertical direction, $T \cos\theta = mg$, ☞ $T = \dfrac{mg}{\cos\theta}$,

in the horizontal direction, $F = T \sin\theta = \dfrac{mg}{\cos\theta} \sin\theta = mg \tan\theta$.

Therefore $\dfrac{kq^2}{r^2} = mg \tan\theta$, ☞ $q = \sqrt{\dfrac{mg \tan\theta}{k}} \, r$.

Thus $q = \sqrt{\dfrac{(0.10 \times 10^{-3} \text{ kg})(9.80 \text{ m/s}^2) \tan 17.5°}{9.0 \times 10^9 \text{ N·m}^2/\text{C}^2}} \, (0.18 \text{ m}) = \boxed{3.3 \times 10^{-8} \text{ C}}$.

35. (b).

36. (b).

37. (b), because the electron has negative charge.

38. It is determined by the relative lengths of the electric field vectors (the lengths of the arrows).

39. It is determined by the relative density or spacing of the field lines. The closer the lines, the greater the magnitude.

40. $\boxed{\text{No}}$. Electric field is defined as the ratio of force to charge at a given point in space. The force on a charge can only point in one direction, so does the electric field. Therefore the field lines never cross, since that would indicate two different directions at the crossing point.

41. If a positive charge is at center of the spherical shell, the electric field is *not* zero inside. The field lines run radially outward to the inside surface of the shell where they stop at the induced negative charges on this surface. The field lines reappear on the outside shell surface (positively charged), and continue radially outward as if emanating from the point charge at center. If the charge were negative, the field lines would reverse their directions.

42. $E = \dfrac{kq}{r^2} \propto \dfrac{1}{r^2}$. So doubling the distance will make the electric field $\boxed{\text{1/4 as large}}$.

43. $E = \dfrac{F}{q} = \dfrac{3.2 \times 10^{-14}\,\text{N}}{1.6 \times 10^{-19}\,\text{C}} = \boxed{2.0 \times 10^5\,\text{N/C}}$.

44. $E = \dfrac{kq}{r^2} = \dfrac{(9.0 \times 10^9\,\text{N·m}^2/\text{C}^2)(2.0 \times 10^{-6}\,\text{C})}{(0.25 \times 10^{-2}\,\text{m})^2} = \boxed{2.9 \times 10^9\,\text{N/C}}$.

45. $E = \dfrac{kq}{r^2}$, ☞ $r = \sqrt{\dfrac{kq}{E}} = \sqrt{\dfrac{(9.00 \times 10^9\,\text{N·m}^2/\text{C}^2)(1.67 \times 10^{-27}\,\text{kg})}{1.0 \times 10^5\,\text{N/C}}} = \boxed{1.2 \times 10^{-7}\,\text{m}}$.

46. The electric fields by the two charges are opposite in direction.

$E_{4.0} = \dfrac{kq}{r^2} = \dfrac{(9.0 \times 10^9\,\text{N·m}^2/\text{C}^2)(4.0 \times 10^{-6}\,\text{C})}{(0.10\,\text{m})^2} = 3.6 \times 10^6\,\text{N/C}$,

$E_{5.0} = \dfrac{(9.0 \times 10^9\,\text{N·m}^2/\text{C}^2)(5.0 \times 10^{-6}\,\text{C})}{(0.10\,\text{m})^2} = 4.5 \times 10^6\,\text{N/C}$.

So the net field is $E = E_{5.0} - E_{4.0} = \boxed{9.0 \times 10^5\,\text{N/C toward the } -5.0\ \mu\text{C charge}}$.

47. Proton: $E = \dfrac{F}{q} = \dfrac{mg}{q} = \dfrac{(1.67 \times 10^{-27}\,\text{kg})(9.80\,\text{m/s}^2)}{1.6 \times 10^{-19}\,\text{C}} = \boxed{1.0 \times 10^{-7}\,\text{N/C upward}}$.

Electron: $E = \dfrac{(9.11 \times 10^{-31}\,\text{kg})(9.80\,\text{m/s}^2)}{1.6 \times 10^{-19}\,\text{C}} = \boxed{5.6 \times 10^{-11}\,\text{N/C downward}}$.

48. (a) Since both charges are negative, a point between the two charges could have zero electric field. Assume the point is d from the $-3.0\ \mu$C charge. For the electric field to be zero, $E_{3.0} = E_{4.0}$.

So $E_{3.0} = \dfrac{kq}{r^2} = \dfrac{k(3.0\ \mu\text{C})}{d^2} = E_{4.0} = \dfrac{k(4.0\ \mu\text{C})}{(1.25 - d)^2}$.

Taking the square root on both sides gives

$$\frac{\sqrt{3.0}}{d} = \frac{\sqrt{4.0}}{1.25 - d}. \qquad \text{Or} \quad 1.73(1.25 - d) = 2.0d.$$

Solving for $\quad d = 0.580$ m. $\quad$ Therefore the coordinates of the point are $\boxed{(0.080\ \text{m},\ 0)}$.

(b) $\boxed{\text{Yes}}$. There are an infinite number of points where the electric field has only a y component. Basically, any point above or below the x axis where $\mathbf{E}_x = 0$ satisfies.

49. $\qquad r = \sqrt{x^2 + y^2}, \quad$ and $\quad \theta = \tan^{-1}\left(\dfrac{y}{x}\right).$

The electric field by the +2.5 μC charge is

$$E_{2.5} = \frac{kq}{r^2} = \frac{(9.0 \times 10^9\ \text{N·m}^2/\text{C}^2)(2.5 \times 10^{-6}\ \text{C})}{(0.20\ \text{m})^2 + (0.15\ \text{m})^2} = 3.6 \times 10^5\ \text{N/C},$$

$\theta_{2.5} = 36.9°,$

so $\mathbf{E}_{2.5} = (3.6 \times 10^5\ \text{N/C})[(\cos 36.9°)\ \hat{\mathbf{x}} - (\sin 36.9°)\ \hat{\mathbf{y}}] = (2.88 \times 10^5\ \text{N/C})\ \hat{\mathbf{x}} - (2.16 \times 10^5\ \text{N/C})\ \hat{\mathbf{y}};$

the electric field by the –4.8 μC charge is

$$E_{4.8} = \frac{(9.0 \times 10^9\ \text{N·m}^2/\text{C}^2)(4.8 \times 10^{-6}\ \text{C})}{(0.50\ \text{m})^2 + (0.35\ \text{m})^2} = 1.16 \times 10^5\ \text{N/C}, \quad \theta_{4.8} = 35.0°,$$

so $\mathbf{E}_{4.8} = (1.16 \times 10^5\ \text{N/C})[(\cos 35.0°)\ \hat{\mathbf{x}} - (\sin 35.0°)\ \hat{\mathbf{y}}] = (9.50 \times 10^4\ \text{N/C})\ \hat{\mathbf{x}} - (6.65 \times 10^4\ \text{N/C})\ \hat{\mathbf{y}};$

the electric field by the –6.3 μC charge is

$$E_{6.3} = c\frac{(9.0 \times 10^9\ \text{N·m}^2/\text{C}^2)(6.3 \times 10^{-6}\ \text{C})}{(0.42\ \text{m})^2 + (0.32\ \text{m})^2} = 2.03 \times 10^5\ \text{N/C}, \quad \theta_{2.5} = 37.3°,$$

so $\mathbf{E}_{6.3} = (2.03 \times 10^5\ \text{N/C})(-\cos 37.3°)\ \hat{\mathbf{x}} - (\sin 37.3°)\ \hat{\mathbf{y}}] = -(1.61 \times 10^5\ \text{N/C})\ \hat{\mathbf{x}} + (1.23 \times 10^5\ \text{N/C})\ \hat{\mathbf{y}}.$

Therefore the net electric field is $\mathbf{E} = \mathbf{E}_{2.5} + \mathbf{E}_{4.8} + \mathbf{E}_{6.3} = \boxed{(2.2 \times 10^5\ \text{N/C})\ \hat{\mathbf{x}} - (4.1 \times 10^5\ \text{N/C})\ \hat{\mathbf{y}}}.$

Or $\qquad E = \sqrt{(2.22 \times 10^5\ \text{N/C})^2 + (4.06 \times 10^5\ \text{N/C})^2} = \boxed{4.6 \times 10^5\ \text{N/C}},$

$$\theta = \tan^{-1}\left(\frac{4.06}{2.22}\right) = \boxed{61° \text{ below } +x \text{ axis}}.$$

50. The point has to be between the two charges. Assume it is d from the +4.0 μC charge.

For the electric field to be zero, $\quad \dfrac{kq_1}{r_1^2} = \dfrac{kq_2}{r_2^2}, \quad \Rightarrow \quad \dfrac{4.0\ \mu\text{C}}{d^2} = \dfrac{9.0\ \mu\text{C}}{(0.30\ \text{m} - d)^2}.$

Taking the square root on both sides gives $\quad \dfrac{2}{d} = \dfrac{3}{0.30 - d}.$ $\quad$ Therefore $\quad 3d = 2(0.30 - d).$

Solving, $\quad d = 0.12$ m $= \boxed{12\ \text{cm from the 4.0 }\mu\text{C charge (between the charges)}}.$

51. $r = \dfrac{0.10 \text{ m}}{\cos 30°} = 0.115 \text{ m}.$

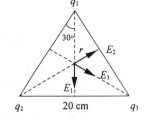

$E_1 = E_2 = E_3 = \dfrac{kq}{r^2} = \dfrac{(9.0 \times 10^9 \text{ N·m}^2/\text{C}^2)(4.0 \times 10^{-6} \text{ C})}{(0.115 \text{ m})^2} = 2.72 \times 10^6 \text{ N/C}.$

Due to symmetry, the resultant of $\mathbf{E}_1$ and $\mathbf{E}_2$ will point toward q_3.

So the net electric field

$E = E_3 + E_1 \cos 60° + E_2 \cos 60° = 2.72 \times 10^6 \text{ N/C} + 2(2.72 \times 10^6 \text{ N/C}) \cos 60°$

$= \boxed{5.4 \times 10^6 \text{ N/C toward } -4.0 \ \mu\text{C charge}}.$

52. Due to symmetry, E_1 and E_2 cancel out.

So the net electric field is the electric field by q_3.

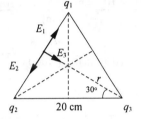

$E = E_3 = \dfrac{kq_3}{r^2} = \dfrac{(9.0 \times 10^9 \text{ N·m}^2/\text{C}^2)(4.0 \times 10^{-6} \ \mu\text{C})}{[(0.20 \text{ m}) \cos 30°]^2}$

$= \boxed{1.2 \times 10^6 \text{ N/C toward the } -4.0 \ \mu\text{C charge}}.$

53. $E_1 = E_2 = \dfrac{kq}{r^2} = \dfrac{(9.0 \times 10^9 \text{ N·m}^2/\text{C}^2)(10 \times 10^{-6} \text{ C})}{(0.05 \text{ m})^2 + (0.05 \text{ m})^2} = 1.8 \times 10^7 \text{ N/C}.$

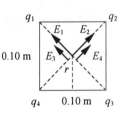

$E_3 = E_4 = \dfrac{(9.0 \times 10^9 \text{ N·m}^2/\text{C}^2)(5.0 \times 10^{-6} \text{ C})}{(0.05 \text{ m})^2 + (0.05 \text{ m})^2} = 9.0 \times 10^6 \text{ N/C}.$

Due to symmetry, the net electric field will be upward and it is equal to

$E = (E_1 + E_3) \cos 45° + (E_2 + E_3) \cos 45°$

$= 2(1.8 \times 10^7 \text{ N/C} + 9.0 \times 10^6 \text{ N/C}) \cos 45° = \boxed{3.8 \times 10^7 \text{ N/C in the } +y \text{ direction}}.$

54. (a) First find the acceleration. $a = \dfrac{F}{m} = \dfrac{qE}{m} = \dfrac{(2.0 \times 10^{-6} \text{ C})(12 \text{ N/C})}{2.0 \times 10^{-5} \text{ kg}} = 1.2 \text{ m/s}^2.$

$x = v_0 t + \tfrac{1}{2} a t^2 = \tfrac{1}{2}(1.2 \text{ m/s}^2)(0.50 \text{ s})^2 = \boxed{0.15 \text{ m}}.$

(b) $v = v_0 + at = (1.2 \text{ m/s}^2)(0.50 \text{ s}) = \boxed{0.60 \text{ m/s}}.$

(c) $E = \dfrac{4\pi kQ}{A}$,   so $Q = \dfrac{EA}{4\pi k} = \dfrac{(12 \text{ N/C})(0.050 \text{ m})^2}{4\pi(9.00 \times 10^9 \text{ N·m}^2/\text{C}^2)} = 2.7 \times 10^{-13} \text{ C} = \boxed{0.27 \text{ pC}}.$

55. $E = \dfrac{4\pi kQ}{A}$,   ☞ $\dfrac{Q}{A} = \dfrac{E}{4\pi k} = \dfrac{1.7 \times 10^6 \text{ N/C}}{4\pi(9.00 \times 10^9 \text{ N·m}^2/\text{C}^2)} = \boxed{15 \ \mu\text{C/m}^2}.$

56. (a) $E = \dfrac{4\pi kQ}{A} = \dfrac{4\pi(9.00 \times 10^9 \text{ N·m}^2/\text{C}^2)(4.0 \times 10^{-9} \text{ C})}{(0.20 \text{ m})^2} = \boxed{1.1 \times 10^4 \text{ N/C}}.$

(b) $F = qE = (1.60 \times 10^{-19} \text{ C})(1.1 \times 10^4 \text{ N/C}) = \boxed{1.8 \times 10^{-15} \text{ N}}.$

57. $E_1 = \dfrac{kq}{r^2} = \dfrac{(9.0 \times 10^9 \text{ N·m}^2/\text{C}^2)(10 \times 10^{-6} \text{ C})}{(0.10 \text{ m})^2 + (0.040 \text{ m})^2} = 7.76 \times 10^6 \text{ N/C},$

$\theta_1 = \tan^{-1}\left(\dfrac{4.0}{10}\right) = 21.8°, \quad$ so

$\mathbf{E}_1 = (7.76 \times 10^6 \text{ N/C})[(-\cos 21.8°)\,\hat{x} + (\sin 21.8°)\,\hat{y}]$

$\quad = (-7.20 \times 10^6 \text{ N/C})\,\hat{x} + (2.88 \times 10^6 \text{ N/C})\,\hat{y};$

$E_2 = \dfrac{(9.0 \times 10^9 \text{ N·m}^2/\text{C}^2)(10 \times 10^{-6} \text{ C})}{(0.040 \text{ m})^2} = 5.63 \times 10^7 \text{ N/C}, \qquad$ so $\qquad \mathbf{E}_2 = (5.63 \times 10^7 \text{ N/C})\,\hat{y};$

$E_3 = \dfrac{(9.0 \times 10^9 \text{ N·m}^2/\text{C}^2)(5.0 \times 10^{-6} \text{ C})}{(0.060 \text{ m})^2} = 1.25 \times 10^7 \text{ N/C}, \qquad$ so $\qquad \mathbf{E}_3 = (1.25 \times 10^7 \text{ N/C})\,\hat{y};$

$E_4 = \dfrac{(9.0 \times 10^9 \text{ N·m}^2/\text{C}^2)(5.0 \times 10^{-6} \text{ C})}{(0.10 \text{ m})^2 + (0.060 \text{ m})^2} = 3.31 \times 10^6 \text{ N/C}, \qquad \theta_4 = \tan^{-1}\left(\dfrac{6.0}{10}\right) = 31.0°,$

so $\quad \mathbf{E}_4 = (3.31 \times 10^6 \text{ N/C})[(\cos 31.0°)\,\hat{x} + (\sin 31.0°)\,\hat{y}] = (2.84 \times 10^6 \text{ N/C})\,\hat{x} + (1.70 \times 10^6 \text{ N/C})\,\hat{y}.$

Therefore $\quad \mathbf{E} = \mathbf{E}_1 + \mathbf{E}_2 + \mathbf{E}_3 + \mathbf{E}_4 = (-4.4 \times 10^6 \text{ N/C})\,\hat{x} + (7.3 \times 10^7 \text{ N/C})\,\hat{y}).$ Or

$E = \sqrt{(4.36 \times 10^6 \text{ N/C})^2 + (7.34 \times 10^7 \text{ N/C})^2} = \boxed{7.4 \times 10^7 \text{ N/C}}, \quad \theta = \tan^{-1}\left(\dfrac{73.4}{4.36}\right) = \boxed{87°}.$

58. (a) From symmetry, the net electric field is in the $\boxed{-y}$ direction.

(b) $r = \sqrt{(d/2)^2 + x^2}, \quad \sin\theta = \dfrac{d/2}{r} = \dfrac{d/2}{\sqrt{(d/2)^2 + x^2}}.$

$E_- = E_+ = \dfrac{kq}{r^2} = \dfrac{kq}{(d/2)^2 + x^2}.$

$E = E_y = E_- \sin\theta + E_+ \sin\theta = 2E_+ \sin\theta = \dfrac{2kq}{(d/2)^2 + x^2}\,\dfrac{d/2}{\sqrt{(d/2)^2 + x^2}} = \boxed{\dfrac{kqd}{[(d/2)^2 + x^2]^{3/2}}}.$

(c) If $x \gg d$, we can ignore the term $(d/2)^2$ in $(d/2)^2 + x^2$.

So $\quad E = \dfrac{kqd}{[(d/2)^2 + x^2]^{3/2}} \approx \dfrac{kqd}{(x^2)^{3/2}} = \dfrac{kqd}{x^3}.$

59. (b) since there is no electric field inside a conductor in electrostatic equilibrium.

60. $\boxed{\text{Yes}}$, because the car (a metal frame) skeeps the electric field from reaching you.

61. $\boxed{\text{No}}$. There are conduction electrons inside the conductor. However, these conduction electrons are neutralized by the protons inside.

62. (a) since there is no electric field inside a conductor in electrostatic equilibrium.

---

63.   (a) $\boxed{\text{Zero}}$ since all excess charge resides on the surface of the conductor in electrostatic equilibrium.

(b) $\boxed{+Q}$ since all excess charge resides on the surface of the conductor in electrostatic equilibrium.

(c) $\boxed{-Q}$ by induction and the conservation of charge.

(d) $\boxed{+Q}$ by induction and the conservation of charge.

64.   (a) There is $\boxed{\text{none}}$ since the electric field is zero.

(b) $\boxed{\text{Outward}}$ from the center of the sphere since the charge on the surface of the sphere is positive.

(c) There is $\boxed{\text{none}}$ since the electric field is zero. The field by the sphere cancels out the field by the inner surface of the shell.

(d) $\boxed{\text{Outward}}$ from the center of the sphere. The net excess charge is positive on the outer surface of the shell.

65.   (a) Again it is $\boxed{\text{zero}}$ since there is no electric field inside a conductor in electrostatic equilibrium.

(b) The charge on the surface of the sphere can be considered as if it were concentrated at the center.

So $E = \dfrac{k\,(-Q)}{r^2} = -\boxed{\dfrac{k\,Q}{r^2}}$, the negative sign indicates it is toward the center.

(c) Again it is $\boxed{\text{zero}}$.

(d) All charges can be considered as if they were concentrated at the center.

So $E = \dfrac{k\,(-Q)}{r^2} + \dfrac{k\,Q}{r^2} + \dfrac{k\,(-Q)}{r^2} = -\boxed{\dfrac{k\,Q}{r^2}}$, the negative sign indicates it is toward the center.

66.   More charges accumulate at sharper points and the electric field lines are perpendicular to the surface.

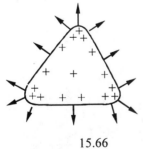

15.66

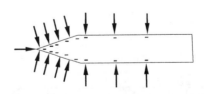

15.67

67.   See diagram above on the right.

68.	$\boxed{0}$, since the number of lines going into the surface equals the number of lines coming out of the surface.

69.	(a) Since field lines point away from positive charge.

70.	The $\boxed{\text{same}}$, since both enclose the same charge.

71.	Since the number of lines is proportional to charge, the net charges are $\boxed{\text{equal and opposite in sign}}$.

72.	Since the number of lines is proportional to charge $\quad q_2 = \dfrac{75}{16}(+10.0 \ \mu C) = \boxed{+46.9 \ \mu C}$.

73.	A dipole consists of a pair of equal and opposite charges.

	So there will be $\boxed{\text{10 field lines entering (negative)}}$.

74.	The net number of field lines is $\quad +6 - 2 \times 6 = -6$ or $\boxed{\text{6 lines entering}}$.

75.	$\boxed{\text{No}}$. All it means is that there is more positive charge than negative. A special case would be no negative charge and only positive charge.

76.	(a) $F = q E = (-1.6 \times 10^{-19} \ C)(3.5 \times 10^3 \ N/C) = -5.6 \times 10^{-16} \ N = \boxed{5.6 \times 10^{-16} \ N \text{ in } -y}$.

	(b) First find the acceleration. $\quad a = \dfrac{F}{m}$, $\quad$ and $\quad v^2 = v_0^2 + 2ax = \dfrac{2Fx}{m}$ (since $v_o = 0$).

	So $\quad K = \frac{1}{2}mv^2 = Fx = (5.6 \times 10^{-16} \ N)(0.10 \ m) = \boxed{5.6 \times 10^{-17} \ J}$.

77.	$n = \dfrac{q}{e} = \dfrac{-0.50 \times 10^{-6} \ C}{-1.60 \times 10^{-19} \ C/electron} = \boxed{3.1 \times 10^{12} \text{ electrons}}$.

78.	(a) The charge has to be placed in between the two charges. Assume it is d from the $-3.0 \ \mu C$ charge.

	So $\quad \dfrac{kq(3.0 \ \mu C)}{d^2} = \dfrac{k q (5.0 \ \mu C)}{(0.40 \ m - d)^2}$.

	Taking the square root on both sides gives $\quad \dfrac{\sqrt{3}}{d} = \dfrac{\sqrt{5}}{0.40 \ m - d}$. $\quad$ Or $\quad 2.24d = 1.73(0.40 - d)$.

	Solve for $\quad d = \boxed{0.17 \ m \text{ from the } -3.0 \ \mu C \text{ charge (in between the charges)}}$.

	(b) In (a), the result is independent of q. So the answer is still $\boxed{0.17 \ m \text{ from the } -3.0 \ \mu C \text{ charge}}$.

79. (a) First find the acceleration. $a = \dfrac{F}{m} = \dfrac{eE}{m}$. $x = v_o t + \frac{1}{2}at^2 = \frac{1}{2}at^2$,

so $t = \sqrt{\dfrac{2x}{a}} = \sqrt{\dfrac{2x}{eE/m}} = \sqrt{\dfrac{2xm}{eE}} = \sqrt{\dfrac{2(1.0\ \text{m})(9.11 \times 10^{-31}\ \text{kg})}{(1.6 \times 10^{-19}\ \text{C})(450\ \text{N/C})}} = \boxed{1.6 \times 10^{-7}\ \text{s}}$.

(b) $x = \frac{1}{2}at^2 = \frac{1}{2}\dfrac{(-1.6 \times 10^{-19}\ \text{C})(450\ \text{N/C})}{9.11 \times 10^{-31}\ \text{kg}} \times (7.95 \times 10^{-8}\ \text{s})^2 = -0.25\ \text{m},\ y = 0.$

So it is at $\boxed{(-0.25\ \text{m},\ 0)}$.

80. $E_x = \dfrac{kq}{r^2} = \dfrac{(9.00 \times 10^9\ \text{N·m}^2/\text{C}^2)(4.0 \times 10^{-6}\ \text{C})}{(4.0\ \text{m})^2} = (2.25 \times 10^3\ \text{N/C})\ \hat{\textbf{x}}.$

$E_y = -\dfrac{(9.00 \times 10^9\ \text{N·m}^2/\text{C}^2)(5.0 \times 10^{-6}\ \text{C})}{(3.0\ \text{m})^2} = -(5.00 \times 10^3\ \text{N/C})\ \hat{\textbf{y}}.$

So $E = \sqrt{(2.25 \times 10^3\ \text{N/C})^2 + (5.00 \times 10^3\ \text{N/C})^2} = \boxed{5.5 \times 10^3\ \text{N/C}}.$

$\theta = \tan^{-1}\left(\dfrac{-5.00}{2.25}\right) = \boxed{66^\circ\ \text{below}\ +x\ \text{axis}}.$

81. $F = \dfrac{kq_1 q_2}{r^2},$ ☞ $q_2 = \dfrac{Fr^2}{kq_1} = \dfrac{(1.8\ \text{N})(0.30\ \text{m})^2}{(9.0 \times 10^9\ \text{N·m}^2/\text{C}^2)(6.0 \times 10^{-6}\ \text{C})} = 3.0 \times 10^{-6}\ \text{C} = 3.0\ \mu\text{C}.$

So the charge could be $\boxed{+3.0\ \mu\text{C on the}\ -y\ \text{axis or}\ -3.0\ \mu\text{C on the}\ +y\ \text{axis}}$ from the charge-force law.

82. $E_1 = \dfrac{kq}{r^2} = \dfrac{(9.0 \times 10^9\ \text{N·m}^2/\text{C}^2)(10 \times 10^{-6}\ \text{C})}{(0.050\ \text{m})^2} = 3.6 \times 10^7\ \text{N/C},$

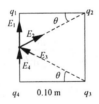

so $\textbf{E}_1 = (3.6 \times 10^7\ \text{N/C})\ \hat{\textbf{y}};$

$E_2 = \dfrac{(9.0 \times 10^9\ \text{N·m}^2/\text{C}^2)(10 \times 10^{-6}\ \text{C})}{(0.050\ \text{m})^2 + (0.10\ \text{m})^2} = 7.2 \times 10^6\ \text{N/C},$

$\theta = \tan^{-1}\left(\dfrac{0.05}{0.10}\right) = 26.6^\circ,$

so $\textbf{E}_2 = (7.2 \times 10^6\ \text{N/C})[(\cos 26.6^\circ)\ \hat{\textbf{x}} + (\sin 26.6^\circ)\ \hat{\textbf{y}}] = (6.44 \times 10^6\ \text{N/C})\ \hat{\textbf{x}} + (3.22 \times 10^6\ \text{N/C})\ \hat{\textbf{y}},$

$E_3 = \dfrac{(9.0 \times 10^9\ \text{N·m}^2/\text{C}^2)(5.0 \times 10^{-6}\ \text{C})}{(0.050\ \text{m})^2 + (0.10\ \text{m})^2} = 3.6 \times 10^6\ \text{N/C},$

so $\textbf{E}_3 = (3.6 \times 10^6\ \text{N/C})[(-\cos 26.6^\circ)\ \hat{\textbf{x}} + (\sin 26.6^\circ)\ \hat{\textbf{y}}] = (-3.22 \times 10^6\ \text{N/C})\ \hat{\textbf{x}} + (1.61 \times 10^6\ \text{N/C})\ \hat{\textbf{y}},$

$E_4 = \dfrac{(9.0 \times 10^9\ \text{N·m}^2/\text{C}^2)(5.0 \times 10^{-6}\ \text{C})}{(0.050\ \text{m})^2} = 1.8 \times 10^7\ \text{N/C},$ so $\textbf{E}_4 = (1.8 \times 10^7\ \text{N/C})\ \hat{\textbf{y}}.$

Therefore $\textbf{E} = \textbf{E}_1 + \textbf{E}_2 + \textbf{E}_3 + \textbf{E}_4 = \boxed{(3.2 \times 10^6\ \text{N/C})\ \hat{\textbf{x}} + (5.9 \times 10^7\ \text{N/C})\ \hat{\textbf{y}}},$ or

$E = \sqrt{(3.22 \times 10^6\ \text{N/C})^2 + (5.88 \times 10^7\ \text{N/C})^2} = \boxed{5.9 \times 10^7\ \text{N/C}},\quad \theta = \tan^{-1}\left(\dfrac{5.8.8}{3.22}\right) = \boxed{87^\circ\ \text{above}\ +x\ \text{axis}}.$

83.   See diagram below.

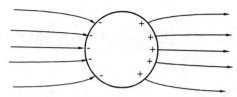

84. $Q_{net} = -10 \times 10^{-6}\,C - 10 \times 10^{-6}\,C + 5.0 \times 10^{-6}\,C + 5.0 \times 10^{-6}\,C = -10 \times 10^{-6}\,C$.

The net lines are $\boxed{\text{negative}}$.

85.   If d is zero, the positive charge and the negative overlap and so the electric field is zero.

86.

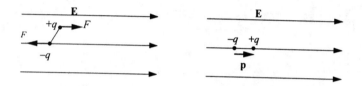

87.   It will still rotate, but it will be drawn into the region where the field is highest, negative end first.

88.   Same field except zero inside slab. Induced charges on slab create exactly opposite field cancel the original field and to create zero net field inside slab.

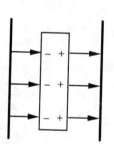

89. $t = \dfrac{x}{v_x} = \dfrac{0.10\ \text{m}}{6.0 \times 10^7\,\text{m/s}} = 1.67 \times 10^{-9}\ \text{s}$.

$a_y = \dfrac{F}{m} = \dfrac{qE}{m} = \dfrac{(1.60 \times 10^{-19}\,\text{C})(2.0 \times 10^4\,\text{N/C})}{9.11 \times 10^{-31}\,\text{kg}} = 3.51 \times 10^{15}\ \text{m/s}^2$.

$d = \frac{1}{2}a_y t^2 = \frac{1}{2}(3.51 \times 10^{15}\,\text{m/s}^2)(1.67 \times 10^{-9}\,\text{s})^2 = 4.9 \times 10^{-3}\ \text{m} = \boxed{4.9\ \text{mm}}$.

90.   From $\quad E = \dfrac{4\pi k Q}{A}$, $\quad Q = \dfrac{EA}{4\pi k} = \dfrac{(2.0 \times 10^4\,\text{N/C})(0.10\,\text{m})^2}{4\pi(9.00 \times 10^9\,\text{N·m}^2/\text{C}^2)} = 1.8 \times 10^{-9}\ \text{C} = \boxed{1.8\ \text{nC}}$.

CHAPTER 16

ELECTRIC POTENTIAL, ELECTRIC ENERGY, AND CAPACITORS

1.   (d).

2.   (a) Electrical potential is the electrostatic potential energy *per unit charge*, i.e., $V = \dfrac{U}{q_0}$.

       (b) $\boxed{\text{No difference}}$.

3.   (a).

4.   (a), since potential energy is inversely proportional to the distance between the charges.

5.   Approaching a negative charge means moving towards a region of larger negative potential values, that is losing potential. Positive charges tend to move towards regions of lower potential, thus losing potential energy and gaining kinetic energy (speeding up)

6.   (b), because electron has negative charge.

7.   The electron still $\boxed{\text{loses}}$ potential energy. Without external work, charges will always move toward regions of lower potential energy. However, for positive charges, the potential energy is lower if the potential is lower; for negative charges, the potential energy is higher if the potential is lower (electron has negative charge).

8.   (b).

9.   (b), since electron has negative charge.

10. $W_{\text{ext}} = q\Delta V = (-4.0 \times 10^6 \text{ C})(-24 \text{ V}) = \boxed{9.6 \times 10^{-5} \text{ J}}$.

11.   (a) $W_{\text{ext}} = q\Delta V$,   ☞ $q = \dfrac{W_{\text{ext}}}{\Delta V} = \dfrac{1.6 \times 10^{-5} \text{ J}}{6 \text{ V}} = 2.7 \times 10^{-6} \text{ C} = \boxed{2.7 \ \mu\text{C}}$.

       (b) For a negative charge, it moves from $\boxed{\text{positive to negative}}$ since work is done by an external source or the electric field does negative work.

12.   From $W = qEd$,

$$E = \frac{W}{qd} = \frac{\Delta V}{d} = \frac{6.0 \text{ V}}{4.0 \times 10^{-3} \text{ m}} = \boxed{1.5 \times 10^3 \text{ V/m from positive to negative}}.$$

13. $W = q\Delta V = \Delta K = K - K_0 = K = \frac{1}{2}mv^2,$

So $v = \sqrt{\dfrac{2q\Delta V}{m}} = \sqrt{\dfrac{2(1.60 \times 10^{-19}\ \text{C})(10 \times 10^3\ \text{V})}{1.67 \times 10^{-27}\ \text{kg}}} = \boxed{1.4 \times 10^6\ \text{m/s}}.$

14.   The electron will accelerate downward because it is negatively charged.

$a = \dfrac{F}{m} = \dfrac{qE}{m},$ and $v^2 = v_0^2 + 2ax = 2ax.$

So $v = \sqrt{2ax} = \sqrt{\dfrac{2qEx}{m}} = \sqrt{\dfrac{2(1.6 \times 10^{-19}\ \text{C})(1000\ \text{V/m})(0.0050\ \text{m})}{9.11 \times 10^{-31}\ \text{kg}}}$

$= \boxed{1.3 \times 10^6\ \text{m/s down}}.$

15.   (a) The electron will accelerate downward because it is negatively charged.

From the work-energy theorem: $|W_{\text{elec}}| = q\Delta V = eE\Delta x = \Delta K = K - K_0 = K = \frac{1}{2}mv^2,$

so $v = \sqrt{\dfrac{2eE\Delta x}{m}} = \sqrt{\dfrac{2(1.6 \times 10^{-19}\ \text{C})(1000\ \text{V/m})(0.0050\ \text{m})}{9.11 \times 10^{-31}\ \text{kg}}} = \boxed{1.3 \times 10^6\ \text{m/s down}}.$

(b) The electron does not move from high to low potential. It $\boxed{\text{loses potential energy}}$.

16.   (a) $\Delta V = \dfrac{kq}{r_B} - \dfrac{kq}{r_A} = \dfrac{(9.0 \times 10^9\ \text{N·m}^2/\text{C}^2)(5.5 \times 10^{-6}\ \text{C})}{0.20\ \text{m}} - \dfrac{(9.0 \times 10^9\ \text{N·m}^2/\text{C}^2)(5.5 \times 10^{-6}\ \text{C})}{0.40\ \text{m}}$

$= \boxed{1.2 \times 10^5\ \text{V}}.$

(b) $\boxed{\text{The nearer point}}$ (20 cm) has a higher potential.

17.   (a) $V = \dfrac{kq}{r},$ ☞ $r = \dfrac{kq}{V} = \dfrac{(9.0 \times 10^9\ \text{N·m}^2/\text{C}^2)(1.0 \times 10^{-6}\ \text{C})}{10 \times 10^3\ \text{V}} = \boxed{0.90\ \text{m}}.$

(b) $\Delta V = \dfrac{kq}{r_B} - \dfrac{kq}{r_A} = \dfrac{(9.0 \times 10^9\ \text{N·m}^2/\text{C}^2)(1.0 \times 10^{-6}\ \text{C})}{3(0.90\ \text{m})} - \dfrac{(9.0 \times 10^9\ \text{N·m}^2/\text{C}^2)(1.0 \times 10^{-6}\ \text{C})}{0.90\ \text{m}}$

$= \boxed{-6.7 \times 10^3\ \text{V}}.$

Since the potential difference is negative, it is a potential decrease.

18.   (a) $\Delta V = \dfrac{kq}{r_B} - \dfrac{kq}{r_A} = \dfrac{(9.0 \times 10^9\ \text{N·m}^2/\text{C}^2)(1.6 \times 10^{-19}\ \text{C})}{0.48 \times 10^{-9}\ \text{m}} - \dfrac{(9.0 \times 10^9\ \text{N·m}^2/\text{C}^2)(1.6 \times 10^{-19}\ \text{C})}{0.21 \times 10^{-9}\ \text{m}}$

$= -3.9\ \text{V}.$

So the difference is $\boxed{3.9\ \text{V}}$.

(b) $\boxed{\text{The closer orbit}}$ (0.21 nm) is at a higher potential.

19. (a) $\Delta U_e = q\Delta V_{\text{L-H}} = (-1.6 \times 10^{-19}\text{ C})(-3.86\text{ V}) = \boxed{+6.2 \times 10^{-19}\text{ J}}$. The electron gains potential energy.

(b) $\Delta U_e = q\Delta V_{\text{H-L}} = q(-\Delta V_{\text{L-H}}) = (-1.6 \times 10^{-19}\text{ C})(3.86\text{ V}) = \boxed{-6.2 \times 10^{-19}\text{ J}}$.

The electron loses potential energy.

(c) $\Delta V = \dfrac{kq}{\infty} - \dfrac{(9.0 \times 10^9\text{ N·m}^2/\text{C}^2)(1.6 \times 10^{-19}\text{ C})}{0.48 \times 10^{-9}\text{ m}} = -3.0\text{ V}$.

$\Delta U = (-1.6 \times 10^{-19}\text{ C})(-3.0\text{ V}) = \boxed{+4.8 \times 10^{-19}\text{ J}}$. The electron gains potential energy.

20. Field does work. $W_{\text{elec}} = -U_t = -\dfrac{kq_1 q_2}{r} = -\dfrac{(9.0 \times 10^9\text{ N·m}^2/\text{C}^2)(-1.4 \times 10^{-6}\text{ C})^2}{8.0 \times 10^{-3}\text{ m}} = \boxed{-2.2\text{ J}}$.

21. From conservation of energy, each will have half of the total potential energy.

So the kinetic energy is $\boxed{1.1\text{ J}}$.

22. (a) External source does work. $W_{\text{ext}} = U_t = \dfrac{kq_1 q_2}{r} = \dfrac{kq^2}{r}$,

so $q = \sqrt{\dfrac{Wr}{k}} = \sqrt{\dfrac{(5.5\text{ J})(0.010\text{ m})}{9.0 \times 10^9\text{ N·m}^2/\text{C}^2}} = 2.5 \times 10^{-6}\text{ C} = \boxed{2.5\ \mu\text{C}}$.

(b) Since q^2 is a positive quantity, all you know is that the charges are of the $\boxed{\text{same sign}}$.

23. (a) $W = \Delta U_e = \dfrac{kq_1 q_2}{r_2} - \dfrac{kq_1 q_2}{r_1} = \dfrac{(9.0 \times 10^9\text{ N·m}^2/\text{C}^2)(-5.0 \times 10^{-6}\text{ C})(2.0 \times 10^{-6}\text{ C})}{0.50\text{ m}}$

$- \dfrac{(9.0 \times 10^9\text{ N·m}^2/\text{C}^2)(-5.0 \times 10^{-6}\text{ C})(2.0 \times 10^{-6}\text{ C})}{0.20\text{ m}} = \boxed{+0.27\text{ J}}$.

(b) $\boxed{\text{No}}$, since electric force is a conservative force.

24. (a) $W = \Delta U_{\text{A-C}} = q\Delta V = qEd = (-1.60 \times 10^{-19}\text{ C})(15\text{ V/m})(0.25\text{ m}) = -\boxed{6.0 \times 10^{-19}\text{ J}}$.

(b) $\Delta V_{\text{A-C}} = \dfrac{\Delta U_{\text{A-C}}}{q} = \dfrac{-6.0 \times 10^{-19}\text{ J}}{-1.60 \times 10^{-19}\text{ C}} = \boxed{3.8\text{ V}}$.

(c) Since $\Delta V_{\text{A-C}}$ is positive, $\boxed{\text{point C}}$ is at a higher potential.

25. $W_{\text{ext}} = U_t = \dfrac{(9.0 \times 10^9\text{ N·m}^2/\text{C}^2)(4.0 \times 10^{-6}\text{ C})(-4.0 \times 10^{-6}\text{ C})}{0.20\text{ m}}$

$+ \dfrac{(9.0 \times 10^9\text{ N·m}^2/\text{C}^2)(4.0 \times 10^{-6}\text{ C})(4.0 \times 10^{-6}\text{ C})}{0.20\text{ m}}$

$+ \dfrac{(9.0 \times 10^9\text{ N·m}^2/\text{C}^2)(4.0 \times 10^{-6}\text{ C})(-4.0 \times 10^{-6}\text{ C})}{0.20\text{ m}} = \boxed{-0.72\text{ J}}$.

26. $W_{ext} = U_t = \dfrac{(9.0 \times 10^9 \text{ N·m}^2/\text{C}^2)(-10 \times 10^{-6} \text{ C})(-10 \times 10^{-6} \text{ C})}{0.10 \text{ m}}$

$+ \dfrac{(9.0 \times 10^9 \text{ N·m}^2/\text{C}^2)(-10 \times 10^{-6} \text{ C})(5.0 \times 10^{-6} \text{ C})}{0.10 \text{ m}}$

$+ \dfrac{(9.0 \times 10^9 \text{ N·m}^2/\text{C}^2)(-10 \times 10^{-6} \text{ C})(5.0 \times 10^{-6} \text{ C})}{0.10 \text{ m}}$

$+ \dfrac{(9.0 \times 10^9 \text{ N·m}^2/\text{C}^2)(5.0 \times 10^{-6} \text{ C})(5.0 \times 10^{-6} \text{ C})}{0.10 \text{ m}}$

$+ \dfrac{(9.0 \times 10^9 \text{ N·m}^2/\text{C}^2)(-10 \times 10^{-6} \text{ C})(5.0 \times 10^{-6} \text{ C})}{\sqrt{(0.10 \text{ m})^2 + (0.10 \text{ m})^2}}$

$+ \dfrac{(9.0 \times 10^9 \text{ N·m}^2/\text{C}^2)(-10 \times 10^{-6} \text{ C})(5.0 \times 10^{-6} \text{ C})}{\sqrt{(0.10 \text{ m})^2 + (0.10 \text{ m})^2}}$

$= \boxed{-4.1 \text{ J}}$.

27. The distance from the center to the corner is $r = \dfrac{10 \text{ cm}}{\cos 30°} = 11.5 \text{ cm}$.

$V = \Sigma \dfrac{kq}{r} = \dfrac{(9.0 \times 10^9 \text{ N·m}^2/\text{C}^2)(4.0 \times 10^{-6} \text{ C})}{0.115 \text{ m}} + \dfrac{(9.0 \times 10^9 \text{ N·m}^2/\text{C}^2)(4.0 \times 10^{-6} \text{ C})}{0.115 \text{ m}}$

$+ \dfrac{(9.0 \times 10^9 \text{ N·m}^2/\text{C}^2)(-4.0 \times 10^{-6} \text{ C})}{0.115 \text{ m}} = \boxed{3.1 \times 10^5 \text{ V}}$.

28. The distance from q_1 to the point is $r = (20 \text{ cm}) \cos 30° = 17.3 \text{ cm}$.

$V = \Sigma \dfrac{kq}{r} = \dfrac{(9.0 \times 10^9 \text{ N·m}^2/\text{C}^2)(4.0 \times 10^{-6} \text{ C})}{0.173 \text{ m}} + \dfrac{(9.0 \times 10^9 \text{ N·m}^2/\text{C}^2)(-4.0 \times 10^{-6} \text{ C})}{0.10 \text{ m}}$

$+ \dfrac{(9.0 \times 10^9 \text{ N·m}^2/\text{C}^2)(4.0 \times 10^{-6} \text{ C})}{0.10 \text{ m}} + \dfrac{(9.0 \times 10^9 \text{ N·m}^2/\text{C}^2)(5.0 \times 10^{-6} \text{ C})}{0.112 \text{ m}} = \boxed{2.1 \times 10^5 \text{ V}}$.

29. The distance from the charges to the center of the square is

$r = \sqrt{(0.05 \text{ m})^2 + (0.05 \text{ m})^2} = 0.0707 \text{ m}$.

$V = \Sigma \dfrac{kq}{r} = 2 \dfrac{(9.0 \times 10^9 \text{ N·m}^2/\text{C}^2)(-10 \times 10^{-6} \text{ C})}{0.0707 \text{ m}} + 2 \dfrac{(9.0 \times 10^9 \text{ N·m}^2/\text{C}^2)(5.0 \times 10^{-6} \text{ C})}{0.0707 \text{ m}}$

$= \boxed{-1.3 \times 10^6 \text{ V}}$.

30. The distance from q_2 and q_3 to the point is $r = \sqrt{(0.10 \text{ m})^2 + (0.05 \text{ m})^2} = 0.112 \text{ m}$.

$V = \Sigma \dfrac{kq}{r} = \dfrac{(9.0 \times 10^9 \text{ N·m}^2/\text{C}^2)(-10 \times 10^{-6} \text{ C})}{0.05 \text{ m}} + \dfrac{(9.0 \times 10^9 \text{ N·m}^2/\text{C}^2)(-10 \times 10^{-6} \text{ C})}{0.112 \text{ m}}$

$+ \dfrac{(9.0 \times 10^9 \text{ N·m}^2/\text{C}^2)(5.0 \times 10^{-6} \text{ C})}{0.112 \text{ m}} + \dfrac{(9.0 \times 10^9 \text{ N·m}^2/\text{C}^2)(5.0 \times 10^{-6} \text{ C})}{0.05 \text{ m}} = \boxed{-1.3 \times 10^6 \text{ V}}$.

31. (a) $\Delta K = K - K_o = K = \frac{1}{2}mv^2$,

also from work-energy theorem: $\quad W = \Delta K = -\Delta U_e = -q\Delta V = e\Delta V$.

So $\quad v = \sqrt{\dfrac{2e\Delta V}{m}} = \dfrac{2(1.6 \times 10^{-19}\ \text{C})(10 \times 10^3\ \text{V})}{9.11 \times 10^{-31}\ \text{kg}} = \boxed{5.9 \times 10^7\ \text{m/s}}$.

(b) $t = \dfrac{\Delta x}{v} = \dfrac{0.35\ \text{m}}{5.93 \times 10^7\ \text{m/s}} = \boxed{5.9 \times 10^{-9}\ \text{s}}$.

32. The distance from q_2 to the point is $\ r_2 = \sqrt{(0.10\ \text{m})^2 + (0.06\ \text{m})^2} = 0.117\ \text{m}$.

The distance from q_3 to the point is $\ r_3 = \sqrt{(0.10\ \text{m})^2 + (0.04\ \text{m})^2} = 0.108\ \text{m}$.

$V = \Sigma\ \dfrac{kq}{r} = \dfrac{(9.0 \times 10^9\ \text{N·m}^2/\text{C}^2)(-10 \times 10^{-6}\ \text{C})}{0.06\ \text{m}} + \dfrac{(9.0 \times 10^9\ \text{N·m}^2/\text{C}^2)(-10 \times 10^{-6}\ \text{C})}{0.117\ \text{m}}$

$+ \dfrac{(9.0 \times 10^9\ \text{N·m}^2/\text{C}^2)(5.0 \times 10^{-6}\ \text{C})}{0.108\ \text{m}} + \dfrac{(9.0 \times 10^9\ \text{N·m}^2/\text{C}^2)(5.0 \times 10^{-6}\ \text{C})}{0.04\ \text{m}} = \boxed{-7.3 \times 10^5\ \text{V}}$.

33. (a).

34. (b).

35.

36. A point in space can have only one potential value. If two equipotential surfaces intersect in space, the intersection will have two different potential values. Therefore, the equipotential surfaces cannot intersect.

37. $\boxed{\text{Yes}}$. There is no change in kinetic or potential energy. So the work done is zero.

38. They are $\boxed{\text{planes, parallel to the plate surfaces}}$.

39. (a).

40. Since $V = \dfrac{kq}{r}$ and $V = $ constant, $r = $ constant.

So the equipotential surfaces are $\boxed{\text{concentric spheres centered on the charge}}$.

41. Since $V = \dfrac{kq}{r}$, V increases as r decreases. So the potential boxed{increases} to a larger positive value.

42. $V/m = \dfrac{J/C}{m} = \dfrac{J}{C \cdot m} = \dfrac{N \cdot m}{C \cdot m} = N/C$.

43. The electron volt unit is gotten from $e\Delta V = q\Delta V = \Delta U_e$. It is also the kinetic energy gained by an electron when it goes through a potential difference of 1 V. So it is a unit of energy. A GeV is larger than a MeV by 1000 times.

44. (b) since $W = -qE\Delta x$, ☞ $E = -\dfrac{W}{q\,\Delta x} = -\dfrac{\Delta V}{\Delta x}$.

45. From Exercise 16.40, equipotential surfaces cannot cross. Since electric field lines are perpendicular to the equipotential surfaces, electric field lines cannot cross either.

46. boxed{Yes}. Electric field is a measure of the change in electric potential over a distance. Inside a conductor in electrostatic equilibrium, the electric field is zero, yet the electrical potential could be at a *constant* value.

47. The distance is $d = \dfrac{10\text{ V}}{100\text{ V/m}} = 10^{-2}\,m = \boxed{1.0 \text{ cm}}$.

48. $d = \dfrac{7.0 \times 10^3\text{ V}}{10 \times 10^3\text{ V/m}} = 0.70\text{ m} = \boxed{70 \text{ cm}}$.

49. $E = -\dfrac{\Delta V}{\Delta x}$, ☞ $\dfrac{E_2}{E_1} = \dfrac{\Delta x_2}{\Delta x_1}$ since E is constant.

So $E_2 = \dfrac{\Delta x_2}{\Delta x_1} E_1 = \dfrac{2.5\text{ mm}}{10\text{ mm}}(24\text{ V}) = 6.0$ V.

If we choose the negative plate as the reference point ($V = 0$), then $V = \boxed{+6.0 \text{ V}}$.

50. From Exercise 16.49, $\Delta x_2 = \dfrac{E_2}{E_1}\Delta x_1 = \dfrac{20\text{ V}}{24\text{ V}}(10\text{ mm}) = 8.3$ mm from the negative plate.

So it is $10\text{ mm} - 8.3\text{ mm} = \boxed{1.7 \text{ mm away from the positive plate toward the negative plate}}$.

51. $V = \dfrac{kq}{r}$, ☞ $r = \dfrac{kq}{V} = \dfrac{(9.0 \times 10^9\text{ N} \cdot m^2/C^2)(3.50 \times 10^{-6}\text{ C})}{2.50 \times 10^3\text{ V}} = \boxed{12.6 \text{ m}}$.

52. $V = \dfrac{kq}{r}$, ☞ $q = \dfrac{Vr}{k} = \dfrac{(2.20 \times 10^3\text{ V})(14.3\text{ m})}{9.0 \times 10^9\text{ N} \cdot m^2/C^2} = \boxed{3.50 \ \mu C}$.

53. $\Delta V = 2.50 \times 10^3$ V $- 2.20 \times 10^3$ V $= +300$ V. $\quad 1$ eV $= 1.60 \times 10^{-19}$ J.

So $W = q\Delta V = \boxed{+300 \text{ eV} = 4.8 \times 10^{-17} \text{ J}}$.

54. (a) $W = \Delta K = K - K_o = K = -(0.20)\Delta U_e = -(0.20)q\Delta V = (0.20)e\Delta V = (0.20)e(100 \times 10^6 \text{ V})$

$= \boxed{2.00 \times 10^7 \text{ eV}}$.

(b) $(2.00 \times 10^7 \text{ eV}) \times \dfrac{1.60 \times 10^{-19} \text{ J}}{1 \text{ eV}} = \boxed{3.20 \times 10^{-12} \text{ J}}$.

55. (a) $W = \Delta K = K - K_o = K = -\Delta U_e = -q\,(-\Delta V) = e\Delta V = e(20 \text{ MV}) = \boxed{2.0 \times 10^7 \text{ eV}}$.

(b) 2.0×10^7 eV $= \boxed{2.0 \times 10^4 \text{ keV}}$.

(c) 2.0×10^7 eV $= \boxed{20 \text{ MeV}}$.

(d) 2.0×10^7 eV $= \boxed{2.0 \times 10^{-2} \text{ GeV}}$.

(e) $(2.0 \times 10^7 \text{ eV}) \times \dfrac{1.6 \times 10^{-19} \text{ J}}{1 \text{ eV}} = \boxed{3.2 \times 10^{-12} \text{ J}}$.

56. $\boxed{\text{They are all doubled}}$ since $K \propto q$.

57. From the work-energy theorem: $\quad W = \Delta K = \frac{1}{2}mv^2 = q\Delta V, \quad$ ☞ $\quad v = \sqrt{\dfrac{2q\Delta V}{m}}$.

So $\quad v_p = \sqrt{\dfrac{2(1.6 \times 10^{-19} \text{ C})(20 \times 10^6 \text{ V})}{1.67 \times 10^{-27} \text{ kg}}} = \boxed{6.2 \times 10^7 \text{ m/s}}$;

$v_\alpha = \sqrt{\dfrac{2[2(1.6 \times 10^{-19} \text{ C})](20 \times 10^6 \text{ V})}{4(1.67 \times 10^{-27} \text{ kg})}} = \boxed{4.4 \times 10^7 \text{ m/s}}$.

58. (a) $\Delta V = \dfrac{\Delta U_e}{q} = \dfrac{\Delta U_e}{e} = \dfrac{3.5 \text{ eV}}{e} = \boxed{3.5 \text{ V}}$.

$\frac{1}{2}mv^2 = K = |\Delta U_e|, \quad$ ☞ $\quad v = \sqrt{\dfrac{2|\Delta U_e|}{m}} = \sqrt{\dfrac{2(3.5 \text{ eV})(1.6 \times 10^{-19} \text{ J/eV})}{1.67 \times 10^{-27} \text{ kg}}} = \boxed{2.6 \times 10^4 \text{ m/s}}$.

(b) $\Delta V = \boxed{4.1 \text{ kV}}$. $\quad v = \sqrt{\dfrac{2(4.1 \times 10^3 \text{ eV})(1.6 \times 10^{-19} \text{ J/eV})}{1.67 \times 10^{-27} \text{ kg}}} = \boxed{8.9 \times 10^5 \text{ m/s}}$.

(c) 8.0×10^{-16} J $= (8.0 \times 10^{-16} \text{ J}) \times \dfrac{1 \text{ eV}}{1.60 \times 10^{-19} \text{ J}} = 5.0 \times 10^3$ eV $= 5.0$ keV.

So $\quad \Delta V = \boxed{5.0 \text{ kV}}$. $\quad v = \sqrt{\dfrac{2(5.0 \times 10^3 \text{ eV})(1.6 \times 10^{-19} \text{ J/eV})}{1.67 \times 10^{-27} \text{ kg}}} = \boxed{9.8 \times 10^5 \text{ m/s}}$.

59. (a) $\Delta V = \boxed{3.5 \text{ V}}$ $v = \sqrt{\dfrac{2|\Delta U_e|}{m}} = \sqrt{\dfrac{2(3.5 \text{ eV})(1.6 \times 10^{-19} \text{ J/eV})}{9.11 \times 10^{-31} \text{ kg}}} = \boxed{1.1 \times 10^6 \text{ m/s}}$.

   (b) $\Delta V = \boxed{4.1 \text{ kV}}$. $v = \sqrt{\dfrac{2(4.1 \times 10^3 \text{ eV})(1.6 \times 10^{-19} \text{ J/eV})}{9.11 \times 10^{-31} \text{ kg}}} = \boxed{3.8 \times 10^7 \text{ m/s}}$.

   (c) $\Delta V = \boxed{5.0 \text{ kV}}$. $v = \sqrt{\dfrac{2(5.0 \times 10^3 \text{ eV})(1.6 \times 10^{-19} \text{ J/eV})}{9.11 \times 10^{-31} \text{ kg}}} = \boxed{4.2 \times 10^7 \text{ m/s}}$.

60. $\Delta V = E \Delta x \cos\theta = \dfrac{12 \text{ V}}{0.030 \text{ m}} (0.010 \text{ m}) \cos 45° = \boxed{+2.8 \text{ V}}$.

61. If it is moved parallel to the plates, $\theta = 90°$, so $\Delta V = 0$ for this move. Therefore it is still $\boxed{+2.8 \text{ V}}$.

62. (d).

63. (b) as the capacitance is directly proportional to the plate area, $C = \dfrac{\varepsilon_o A}{d}$.

6c4. Charge Q remains constant. $U_C = \tfrac{1}{2}\dfrac{Q^2}{C} = \tfrac{1}{2}\dfrac{Q^2}{\varepsilon A/d} = \tfrac{1}{2}\dfrac{Q^2}{\varepsilon A} d \propto d$.

   So $\boxed{\text{it decreases}}$.

65. $Q = CV = (2.0 \times 10^{-6} \text{ F})(12 \text{ V}) = \boxed{2.4 \times 10^{-5} \text{ C}}$.

66. $C = \dfrac{\varepsilon_o A}{d} = \dfrac{(8.85 \times 10^{-12} \text{ F/m})(0.50 \text{ m}^2)}{2.0 \times 10^{-3} \text{ m}} = \boxed{2.2 \times 10^{-9} \text{ F}}$.

67. $C = \dfrac{\varepsilon_o A}{d}$, ☞ $d = C = \dfrac{\varepsilon_o A}{C} = \dfrac{(8.85 \times 10^{-12} \text{ F/m})(0.40 \text{ m}^2)}{5.0 \times 10^{-9} \text{ F}} = \boxed{0.71 \text{ mm}}$.

68. $C = \dfrac{\varepsilon_o A}{d}$, ☞ $A = \dfrac{Cd}{\varepsilon_o} = \dfrac{(2.5 \times 10^{-9} \text{ F})(3.0 \times 10^{-3} \text{ m})}{8.85 \times 10^{-12} \text{ F/m}} = \boxed{0.85 \text{ m}^2}$.

69. (a) $Q = CV = \dfrac{\varepsilon_o A}{d} V = \dfrac{\varepsilon_o AV}{d} = \dfrac{(8.85 \times 10^{-12} \text{ C}^2/\text{N·m}^2)(0.20 \text{ m}^2)(12 \text{ V})}{5.0 \times 10^{-3} \text{ m}} = \boxed{4.2 \times 10^{-9} \text{ C}}$.

   (b) $U_C = \tfrac{1}{2}CV^2 = \tfrac{1}{2}QV = \tfrac{1}{2}(4.25 \times 10^{-9} \text{ C})(12 \text{ V}) = \boxed{2.5 \times 10^{-8} \text{ J}}$.

70. (a) Charge remains constant and so it is the $\boxed{\text{same}}$.

(b) $U_C = \frac{1}{2}\frac{Q^2}{C}$. Now C is only half as large because d doubles.

So the energy stored $\boxed{\text{doubles to } 5.0 \times 10^{-8} \text{ J}}$.

71. The energy supplied is $E = U = Pt = (0.50 \text{ W})(5.0 \text{ s}) = 2.5 \text{ J}$.

Also $U_C = \frac{1}{2}CV^2$, ☞ $V = \sqrt{\frac{2U_C}{C}} = \sqrt{\frac{2(2.5 \text{ J})}{1.0 \text{ F}}} = \boxed{2.2 \text{ V}}$.

72. (b).

73. (d), because the dielectric increases the capacitance and, therefore, the charge.

74. We cannot maintain a nonzero voltage on a conductor; charges will move from the positive to the negative immediately.

75. The charged rubber rod polarizes the stream of water, and the stream is attracted to it.

76. $K = \frac{C}{C_o} = \frac{150 \text{ pF}}{50 \text{ pF}} = \boxed{3.0}$.

77. $Q = CV = KC_o V = 2.6(50 \times 10^{-12} \text{ F})(24 \text{ V}) = \boxed{3.1 \times 10^{-9} \text{ C}}$,

$U_C = \frac{1}{2}CV^2 = \frac{1}{2}KC_o V^2 = \frac{1}{2}2.6(50 \times 10^{-12} \text{ C})(24 \text{ V})^2 = \boxed{3.7 \times 10^{-8} \text{ J}}$.

78. (a) $C = \frac{K\varepsilon_o A}{d}$, ☞ $d = \frac{K\varepsilon_o A}{C} = \frac{4.6(8.85 \times 10^{-12} \text{ F/m})(0.50 \text{ m}^2)}{0.10 \times 10^{-6} \text{ F}} = \boxed{020 \text{ mm}}$.

(b) $Q = CV = (0.10 \times 10^{-6} \text{ F})(12 \text{ V}) = \boxed{1.2 \ \mu\text{C}}$.

79. The charge Q remains constant.

$K = \frac{C}{C_o} = \frac{Q/V}{Q/V_o} = \frac{V_o}{V} = \frac{12 \text{ V}}{5.0 \text{ V}} = \boxed{2.4}$.

80. $U_C = \frac{1}{2}CV^2$, ☞ $C = \frac{2U_C}{V^2} = \frac{2(20.0 \text{ J})}{(400 \text{ V})^2} = 2.50 \times 10^{-4} \text{ F}$.

$C = KC_o$, ☞ $K = \frac{C}{C_o} = \frac{2.50 \times 10^{-4} \text{ F}}{100 \times 10^{-6} \text{ F}} = \boxed{2.50}$.

81. (b).

82. (a).

83.   When they are $\boxed{\text{equal in capacitance}}$.

84.   (a) $\dfrac{1}{C_s} = \dfrac{1}{C_1} + \dfrac{1}{C_2}$, ☞ $C_s = \dfrac{C_1 C_2}{C_1 + C_2} = \dfrac{(0.40\ \mu F)(0.60\ \mu F)}{0.40\ \mu F + 0.60\ \mu F} = \boxed{0.24\ \mu F}$.

        (b) $C_p = C_1 + C_2 = 0.40\ \mu F + 0.60\ \mu F = \boxed{1.0\ \mu F}$.

85.   The charge is the same for both capacitors.

        $U_t = \tfrac{1}{2} C_s V^2$, ☞ $C_s = \dfrac{2U_t}{V^2} = \dfrac{2(173\ \mu J)}{(12\ V)^2} = 2.40\ \mu F$.

        Also $\dfrac{1}{C_s} = \dfrac{1}{C_1} + \dfrac{1}{C_2}$, ☞ $C_2 = \dfrac{C_1 C_s}{C_1 - C_s} = \dfrac{(4.0\ \mu C)(2.40\ \mu F)}{4.0\ \mu F - 2.40\ \mu F} = \boxed{6.0\ \mu F}$.

86.   All three are in parallel.   So $C_p = C_1 + C_2 + C_3 = 1.7\ \mu F$.

        Therefore $C_1 = 1.7\ \mu F - 0.20\ \mu F - 0.30\ \mu F = \boxed{1.2\ \mu F}$.

87.   (a) The voltage is the same for all three capacitors. $Q_1 = Q_2 = Q_3 = C_1 V = (0.25\ \mu F)(12\ V) = \boxed{3.0\ \mu C}$.

        (b) $Q_t = Q_1 + Q_2 + Q_3 = 3(3.0\ \mu C) = \boxed{9.0\ \mu C}$.

88.   Three in series: $\dfrac{1}{C_s} = \dfrac{1}{C_1} + \dfrac{1}{C_2} + \dfrac{1}{C_2} = \dfrac{3}{1.0\ \mu F}$,   so $C_s = \boxed{0.33\ \mu F}$.

        Two in series: $\dfrac{1}{C_s} = \dfrac{1}{C_1} + \dfrac{1}{C_2} = \dfrac{2}{1.0\ \mu F}$,   so $C_s = \boxed{0.50\ \mu F}$.

        Two parallel, then series: $C_p = C_1 + C_2 = 2.0\ \mu F$.

        $\dfrac{1}{C_s} = \dfrac{1}{C_1} + \dfrac{1}{C_2}$, ☞ $C_s = \dfrac{C_1 C_2}{C_1 + C_2} = C_s = \dfrac{(2.0\ \mu F)(1.0\ \mu F)}{2.0\ \mu F + 1.0\ \mu F} = \boxed{0.67\ \mu F}$.

        Just one: $C = \boxed{1.0\ \mu F}$.

        Two in series, then parallel: $C_p = 0.50\ \mu F + 1.0\ \mu F = \boxed{1.5\ \mu F}$.

        Two in parallel: $C_p = 1.0\ \mu F + 1.0\ \mu F = \boxed{2.0\ \mu F}$.

        Three in parallel: $C_p = 1.0\ \mu F + 1.0\ \mu F + 1.0\ \mu F = \boxed{3.0\ \mu F}$.

        There are a total of $\boxed{7}$ different values.

89. Parallel combination gives maximum.

$$C_p = C_1 + C_2 + C_3 = 1.5\ \mu F + 2.0\ \mu F + 3.0\ \mu F = \boxed{6.5\ \mu F}.$$

Series combination gives minimum.

$$\frac{1}{C_s} = \frac{1}{C_1} + \frac{1}{C_2} + \frac{1}{C_3} = \frac{1}{1.5\ \mu F} + \frac{1}{2.0\ \mu F} + \frac{1}{3.0\ \mu F} = \frac{1}{1.5\ \mu F}.$$

So $C_s = \boxed{0.67\ \mu F}$.

90. The voltage is the same for all capacitors in parallel. $Q_1 = C_1 V = (0.10\ \mu F)(6.0\ V) = \boxed{0.60\ \mu C}$,

$Q_2 = (0.20\ \mu F)(6.0\ V) = \boxed{1.2\ \mu C}$, $\quad Q_3 = (0.30\ \mu F)(6.0\ V) = \boxed{1.8\ \mu C}$.

91. (a) Charge is the same for series combination and voltage is the same for parallel combination.

C_1 and C_2 are in parallel: $\qquad C_{p1} = C_1 + C_2 = 0.40\ \mu F + 0.40\ \mu F = 0.80\ \mu F.$

C_3 and C_4 are in parallel: $\qquad C_{p3} = C_3 + C_4 = 0.20\ \mu F + 0.60\ \mu F = 0.80\ \mu F.$

C_{p1} and C_{p3} are in series: $\qquad \dfrac{1}{C_s} = \dfrac{1}{C_{p1}} + \dfrac{1}{C_{p3}},$

$$C_s = \frac{C_{p1}\,C_{p3}}{C_{p1} + C_{p3}} = \frac{(0.80\ \mu F)(0.80\ \mu F)}{0.80\ \mu F + 0.80\ \mu F} = 0.40\ \mu F.$$

So the total charge on C_S is $Q_s = C_s V = (0.40\ \mu F)(12\ V) = 4.8\ \mu C.$

Therefore C_{p1} and C_{p3} have the same charge as C_s, which is 4.8 μC.

The voltage across C_{p1} (C_1 and C_2) is $V_1 = \dfrac{Q_{p1}}{C_{p1}} = \dfrac{4.8\ \mu C}{0.80\ \mu F} = 6.0\ V.$

Thus the charge on C_1 and C_2 is $Q_1 = C_2 = (0.40\ \mu F)(6.0\ V) = 2.4\ \mu C.$

The voltage across C_{p3} (C_3 and C_4) is $V_3 = \dfrac{Q_{p3}}{C_{p3}} = \dfrac{4.8\ \mu C}{0.80\ \mu F} = 6.0\ V.$

Thus the charges on C_3 and C_4 are $Q_3 = (0.20\ \mu F)(6.0\ V) = 1.2\ \mu F,$ $\quad Q_4 = (0.60\ \mu F)(6.0\ V) = 3.6\ \mu C.$

Hence the answers are $\boxed{2.4\ \mu C \text{ for } C_1,\ 2.4\ \mu C \text{ for } C_2,\ 1.2\ \mu C \text{ for } C_3,\ 3.6\ \mu C \text{ for } C_4}.$

(b) As found in (a), the voltages are $\boxed{6.0\ V \text{ for all the capacitors}}.$

92. The direction of the field is upward.

$$E = -\frac{\Delta V}{\Delta x} = -\frac{-200\ V}{10 \times 10^{-3}\ m} = 2.0 \times 10^4\ V/m = \boxed{20\ kV/m\ up}.$$

$$V = V_0 + \Delta V = V_0 + |E\Delta x| = 116\ kV + (200\ kV/m)(0.10\ m) = \boxed{+118\ kV}.$$

93. $W = \Delta U_e = U - U_0 = \dfrac{kq_1 q_2}{r} = \dfrac{k(+q)(-q)}{d} = \boxed{-\dfrac{kq^2}{d}}.$

94.   Electric field lines are pointing toward the wire.

Looking at the end of the wire   Side view

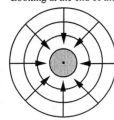
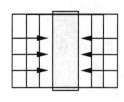

95. $U_e = \dfrac{kq_1 q_2}{r} = \dfrac{(9.0 \times 10^9 \text{ N·m}^2/\text{C}^2)[2(1.6 \times 10^{-19} \text{ C})](-e)}{0.027 \times 10^{-9} \text{ m}} = -107 \text{ eV} = \boxed{-1.1 \times 10^2 \text{ eV}}$.

96.   (a) C_1 and C_2 are in parallel: $C_p = C_1 + C_2 = 0.15 \ \mu\text{F} + 0.25 \ \mu\text{F} = 0.40 \ \mu\text{F}$.

        This C_p and C_3 are in series: $\dfrac{1}{C_s} = \dfrac{1}{C_p} + \dfrac{1}{C_3}$,

        so $C_s = \dfrac{C_p C_3}{C_p + C_3} = \dfrac{(0.40 \ \mu\text{F})(0.30 \ \mu\text{F})}{0.40 \ \mu\text{F} + 0.30 \ \mu\text{F}} = \boxed{0.17 \ \mu\text{F}}$.

        (b) $Q = C_s V = (0.171 \ \mu\text{F})(12 \text{ V}) = \boxed{2.1 \ \mu\text{C}}$.

        (c) Charge is the same for series combination and voltage is the same for parallel combination.

        So the charge on C_3 is 2.1 μC.   Therefore $V_3 = \dfrac{Q_3}{C_3} = \dfrac{2.06 \ \mu\text{F}}{0.30 \ \mu\text{F}} = 6.9 \text{ V}$.

        Thus the voltage on C_1 and C_2 is 12 V − 6.9 V = 5.1 V.

        Hence the answers are $\boxed{V_1 = V_2 = 5.1 \text{ V and } V_3 = 6.9 \text{ V}}$.

97.   (a) The electric force must balance the gravitational force.

        $|F| = qE = q \dfrac{\Delta V}{\Delta x} = mg,$ ☞ $\Delta V = \dfrac{mg\Delta x}{q} = \dfrac{(9.11 \times 10^{-31} \text{ kg})(9.80 \text{ m/s}^2)(0.015 \text{ m})}{1.6 \times 10^{-19} \text{ C}}$

        $= \boxed{8.4 \times 10^{-13} \text{ V}}$.

        (b) $\Delta V = \dfrac{(1.67 \times 10^{-27} \text{ kg})(9.80 \text{ m/s}^2)(0.015 \text{ m})}{1.6 \times 10^{-19} \text{ C}} = \boxed{1.5 \times 10^{-9} \text{ V}}$.

        (c) $\boxed{\text{In (a), top is +; in (b), top is −}}$.

98.   (a) $C_o = \dfrac{\varepsilon_0 A_0}{d}$, ☞ $A_o = \dfrac{Cd}{\varepsilon_0} = \dfrac{(1.0 \text{ F})(0.50 \times 10^{-3} \text{ m})}{8.85 \times 10^{-12} \text{ C}^2/\text{N·m}^2} = \boxed{5.6 \times 10^7 \text{ m}^2}$.

        (b) $C = C_o = K \dfrac{\varepsilon_0 A}{d}$, ☞ $A = \dfrac{A_o}{K} = \dfrac{5.65 \times 10^7 \text{ m}^2}{2.6} = \boxed{2.2 \times 10^7 \text{ m}^2}$.

99. $\Delta U_e = -q\Delta V = eE\Delta x = (1.6 \times 10^{-19} \text{ C})(5.5 \times 10^4 \text{ V/m})(0.030 \text{ m}) = \boxed{2.6 \times 10^{-16} \text{ J}}$.

CHAPTER 17

ELECTRIC CURRENT AND RESISTANCE

1.   (b).

2.   (d).

3.   (a).

4.   The chemical membrane is to prevent the two ions from each electrode from mixing. If the ions mix, one ion can be attracted to the other electrode along with that electrode's ion. The result is that it could "coat" the other electrode and then essentially the two electrodes are identical. From Exercise 17.4, there will be no potential difference.

5.   As the internal resistance increases, the voltage across it also increases. This decreases the terminal voltage.

6. $\boxed{\text{No}}$, this is not possible. Any battery has internal resistance and there will be a voltage across the internal resistance when the battery is in use.

7.   (a) $\mathscr{E} = \mathscr{E}_1 + \mathscr{E}_2 = 1.5 \text{ V} + 1.5 \text{ V} = \boxed{3.0 \text{ V}}$.

   (b) $\boxed{1.5 \text{ V}}$.

7.   (a) $\mathscr{E} = 6(1.5 \text{ V}) = \boxed{9.0 \text{ V}}$.

   (b) $\boxed{1.5 \text{ V}}$.

9.   (a) $\mathscr{E} = \mathscr{E}_1 + \mathscr{E}_2 + \mathscr{E}_3 = 2(6.0 \text{ V}) + 12 \text{ V} = \boxed{24 \text{ V}}$.

   (b) The two 6.0 V in series, then combined in parallel with the 12 V.

10.   Using just one battery at a time gives three voltages: 1.0 V, 3.0 V, and 12 V.

   Using just two batteries at a time gives six voltages:

   two in series at a time, 4.0 V, 13 V, and 15 V;

   two in parallel at a time, 1.0 V, 3.0 V, 1.0 V;

   so three more different voltages of 4.0 V, 13 V, and 15 V.

Using three batteries at a time gives eight voltages:

> two in parallel, then in series with the third, 13 V, 4.0 V, and 4.0 V;
>
> all three in series, 18 V; all three in parallel, 1.0 V;
>
> two in series then parallel to the third, 4.0 V, 3.0 V, 1.0 V;
>
> so there is one new different voltage of 18 V.

Therefore there are $\boxed{7}$ different voltages and they are

$$\boxed{1.0\ \text{V},\ 3.0\ \text{V},\ 4.0\ \text{V},\ 12\ \text{V},\ 13\ \text{V},\ 15\ \text{V, and }18\ \text{V}}.$$

11. (d).

12. $I = \dfrac{q}{t} = \dfrac{30\ \text{C}}{120\ \text{s}} = \boxed{0.25\ \text{A}}$.

13. $I = \dfrac{q}{t}$, ☞ $t = \dfrac{q}{I} = \dfrac{2.5\ \text{C}}{5.0 \times 10^{-3}\ \text{A}} = 500\ \text{s} = \boxed{8.3\ \text{min}}$.

14. (a) $q = It = (0.50 \times 10^{-3}\ \text{A})(600\ \text{s}) = \boxed{0.30\ \text{C}}$.

   (b) $E = \Delta U = q\Delta V = (0.30\ \text{C})(3.0\ \text{V}) = \boxed{0.90\ \text{J}}$.

15. $q = It = (50\ \text{A})(1.5\ \text{s}) = 75\ \text{C}$. $n = \dfrac{q}{e} = \dfrac{75\ \text{C}}{1.60 \times 10^{-19}\ \text{C}}) = \boxed{4.7 \times 10^{20}}$ electrons.

16. $I_1 = \dfrac{q_1}{t_1} = \dfrac{20\ \text{C}}{1.25(60\ \text{s})} = 0.267\ \text{A}$, $I_2 = \dfrac{30\ \text{C}}{1.52(60\ \text{s})} = 0.329\ \text{A}$.

   So $\Delta I = I_2 - I_1 = 0.061\ \text{A}$. Therefore the $\boxed{2^{\text{nd}}\ \text{wire by } 0.062\ \text{A}}$.

17. $q = It = (5.0\ \text{A})(20\ \text{h})(3600\ \text{s/h}) = \boxed{3.6 \times 10^5\ \text{C}}$.

18. $I = \dfrac{q_{\text{net}}}{t} = \dfrac{-6.7\ \text{C} - (+8.3\ \text{C})}{45\ \text{s}} = -0.33\ \text{A} = \boxed{0.33\ \text{A to the left}}$.

19. (a) In each second.

   $q = It = (9.5 \times 10^{-3}\ \text{A})(1.0\ \text{s}) = 9.5 \times 10^{-3}\ \text{C} = (9.5 \times 10^{-3}\ \text{C}) \times \dfrac{1\ e}{1.6 \times 10^{-19}\ \text{C}} = \boxed{5.9 \times 10^{16}\ \text{protons}}$.

   (b) $P = \dfrac{E}{t} = \dfrac{(5.9 \times 10^{16}\ \text{protons})(20 \times 10^6\ \text{eV/proton})(1.6 \times 10^{-19}\ \text{J/eV})}{1.0\ \text{s}} = \boxed{1.9 \times 10^5\ \text{J/s}}$.

20. (a).

21.   (d).

22.   Since $V = (R)I$ $(y = mx)$ so the one with the $\boxed{\text{smaller slope}}$ is less resistive.

23.   (a) $V = IR = (1.9 \text{ A})(6.0 \text{ } \Omega) = \boxed{11.4 \text{ V}}$.

        (b) $\mathscr{E} = V + Ir$,   ☞ $r = \dfrac{\mathscr{E} - V}{I} = \dfrac{12 \text{ V} - 11.4 \text{ V}}{1.9 \text{ A}} = \boxed{0.32 \text{ } \Omega}$.

24. $\mathscr{E} = V + Ir = IR + Ir = I(R + r) = (1.5 \text{ A})(5.0 \text{ } \Omega + 0.15 \text{ } \Omega) = \boxed{7.7 \text{ V}}$.

25.   (a) $R = \dfrac{\rho L}{A}$,   ☞ $\dfrac{R_2}{R_1} = \dfrac{L_2}{L_1} \dfrac{A_1}{A_2} = (2) \left(\tfrac{1}{2}\right) = 1$.   Also $I = \dfrac{V}{R}$.

        So the current is the $\boxed{\text{same}}$.

        (b) Since $A = \dfrac{\pi d^2}{4}$, half the diameter means $\tfrac{1}{4}$ the area, so $\dfrac{A_2}{A_1} = \tfrac{1}{4}$.

        Therefore $\dfrac{R_2}{R_1} = (1)(4) = 4$.   Thus $\dfrac{I_2}{I_1} = \dfrac{R_1}{R_2} = \tfrac{1}{4}$, i.e., $\boxed{1/4 \text{ the current}}$.

26.   The number of charge carriers rises as the temperature increases. There are also more collisions (more resistance) among the charge carriers. However the former dominates.

27. $R = \dfrac{\rho L}{A}$,   ☞ $A = \pi r^2 = \dfrac{\rho L}{R}$.   So $\dfrac{r_{\text{Al}}}{r_{\text{Cu}}} = \sqrt{\dfrac{\rho_{\text{Al}}}{\rho_{\text{Cu}}}} = \sqrt{\dfrac{2.82 \times 10^{-8} \text{ } \Omega \cdot \text{m}}{1.70 \times 10^{-8} \text{ } \Omega \cdot \text{m}}} = 1.29$.

        Therefore $\boxed{\text{alunimum is thicker by 29\%}}$.

28. $I = \dfrac{V}{R} = \dfrac{12 \text{ V}}{15 \text{ } \Omega} = \boxed{0.80 \text{ A}}$.

29. $V = IR = (0.50 \text{ A})(2.0 \text{ } \Omega) = \boxed{1.0 \text{ V}}$.

30. $I = \dfrac{V}{R} \propto V$.   So $\dfrac{I_2}{I_1} = \dfrac{V_2}{V_1}$,   ☞ $I_2 = \dfrac{V_2}{V_1} I_1 = \dfrac{10 \text{ V}}{6.0 \text{ V}} (0.25 \text{ A}) = \boxed{0.42 \text{ A}}$.

31. $R = \dfrac{\rho L}{A} = \dfrac{\rho L}{\pi r^2} = \dfrac{(1.70 \times 10^{-8} \text{ } \Omega \cdot \text{m})(0.60 \text{ m})}{\pi (0.05 \times 10^{-2} \text{ m})^2} = \boxed{1.3 \times 10^{-2} \text{ } \Omega}$.

32. $V = IR = (1.5 \text{ A})(100 \text{ } \Omega) = 150 \text{ V}$.

        The terminal voltage of one battery is $\dfrac{150 \text{ V}}{2} = \boxed{75 \text{ V}}$ since they are in series.

33. $I = \dfrac{V}{R} = \dfrac{12 \text{ V}}{2.5 \text{ }\Omega} = 4.8 \text{ A} = (4.8 \text{ C/s}) \times \dfrac{1 \text{ electron}}{1.6 \times 10^{-19} \text{ C}} = \boxed{3.0 \times 10^{19} \text{ electrons/s}}$.

34. (a) $R = \dfrac{V}{I} = \dfrac{\rho L}{A}$, $\mathscr{F}$ $\rho = \dfrac{VA}{IL} = \dfrac{(100 \text{ V})(0.50 \times 10^{-2} \text{ m})^2}{(5.0 \text{ A})(2.0 \text{ m})} = \boxed{2.5 \times 10^{-4} \text{ }\Omega\cdot\text{m}}$.

(b) $\sigma = \dfrac{1}{\rho} = \dfrac{1}{2.5 \times 10^{-4} \text{ }\Omega\cdot\text{m}} = \boxed{4.0 \times 10^{3} \text{ }(\Omega\cdot\text{m})^{-1}}$.

This is a value associated with a typical semiconductor.

35. $I = \dfrac{V}{R} = \dfrac{V}{\rho L/A} = \dfrac{VA}{\rho L}$, $\mathscr{F}$ $I \propto \dfrac{1}{L}$.

$\dfrac{I_{0.50}}{I_{2.0}} = \dfrac{L_{2.0}}{L_{0.50}} = \dfrac{2.0 \text{ m}}{0.50 \text{ m}} = \boxed{4}$. That is, the shorter wire carries 4 times the current.

36. $R = \dfrac{\rho L}{A} = \dfrac{\rho L}{\pi d^2/4} = \dfrac{4\rho}{\pi d^2}$, $\mathscr{F}$ $R \propto \dfrac{1}{d^2}$.

$\dfrac{R_{\text{thick}}}{R_{\text{thin}}} = \left(\dfrac{d_{\text{thin}}}{d_{\text{thick}}}\right)^2 = \left(\dfrac{1}{3}\right)^2 = \boxed{1/9}$.

37. $R = R_0 (1 + \alpha\Delta T) = \dfrac{\rho_0 L (1 + \alpha\Delta T)}{A}$

$= \dfrac{(10 \times 10^{-8} \text{ }\Omega\cdot\text{m})(0.75 \text{ m})[1 + (6.51 \times 10^{-3} \text{ C°}^{-1})(360 \text{ C°})]}{2.0 \times 10^{-6} \text{ m}^2} = \boxed{0.13 \text{ }\Omega}$.

38. $\rho = \rho_0 (1 + \alpha\Delta T) = \rho_0 [1 + (6.80 \times 10^{-3} \text{ C°}^{-1})(80 \text{ C°})] = 1.544\rho_0$.

So the percentage variation is $\dfrac{\rho - \rho_0}{\rho_0} = \dfrac{\rho}{\rho_0} - 1 = 0.544 = \boxed{54\%}$ increase.

39. $\Delta R = R_0 \, \alpha\Delta T = (25 \text{ m}\Omega)(6.80 \times 10^{-3} \text{ C°}^{-1})(27 \text{ C°}) = \boxed{4.6 \text{ m}\Omega}$.

40. $\Delta R = R_0 \, \alpha\Delta T = (10.00 \text{ }\Omega)(4.29 \times 10^{-3} \text{ C°}^{-1})(100 \text{ C°}) = \boxed{0.429 \text{ }\Omega}$.

4.29 Ω

41. $R_1 = \dfrac{V_1}{I_1} = \dfrac{12 \text{ V}}{0.185 \text{ A}} = 65 \text{ }\Omega$, $R_2 = \dfrac{90 \text{ V}}{1.25 \text{ A}} = 72 \text{ }\Omega$.

$\boxed{\text{No}}$, it is not ohmic since $R \neq$ constant..

42. $R = \dfrac{\rho L}{A}$, $\mathscr{F}$ $L = \dfrac{RA}{\rho} = \dfrac{(20 \text{ }\Omega)(\pi)(2.588 \times 10^{-3} \text{ m})^2/4}{100 \times 10^{-8} \text{ }\Omega\cdot\text{m}} = \boxed{105 \text{ m}}$.

43.   The volume (material) of the wire remains constant. $A_1 L_1 = A_2 L_2$,   ☞ $\dfrac{A_1}{A_2} = \dfrac{L_2}{L_1}$.

$R = \dfrac{\rho L}{A}$,   ☞ $\dfrac{R_2}{R_1} = \dfrac{L_2}{L_1} \dfrac{A_1}{A_2} = \left(\dfrac{L_2}{L_1}\right)^2 = \left(\dfrac{1.25}{1}\right)^2 = 1.6$.

No, the resistance of the wire is different before and after.   It increases by a factor of 1.6 times.

44. $R = \dfrac{\rho L}{A}$,   ☞ $A = \dfrac{\pi d^2}{4} = \dfrac{\rho L}{R}$.

So $d = \sqrt{\dfrac{4\rho L}{\pi R}} = \sqrt{\dfrac{4(2.82 \times 10^{-8} \ \Omega \cdot m)(20 \ m)}{\pi(0.25 \times 10^{-3} \ \Omega)}} = 5.4 \times 10^{-2} \ m$.

45. $\Delta R = R_0 \alpha \Delta T$,   ☞ $\Delta T = \dfrac{\Delta R}{R_0 \alpha} = \dfrac{\Delta R}{R_0 \alpha} \dfrac{1}{\alpha} = \pm 0.050 \dfrac{1}{\alpha} = \pm 0.050 \dfrac{1}{4.29 \times 10^{-3} \ C°^{-1}} = \pm 11.7 \ C°$.

So $T_{max} = 20°C + 11.7 \ C° = 32°C$ and $T_{min} = 20°C - 11.7 \ C° = 8.3°C$.

Therefore the range is from   8.2°C to 32°C.

46.   (a)   Yes, the resistor is an ohmic resistor because the V vs. I graph is a straight line (constant slope).

(b) $R = $ slope $ = \dfrac{\Delta V}{\Delta I} = \dfrac{40V - 10 \ V}{20 \ A - 5.0 \ A} = 2.0 \ \Omega$.

47. $I = \dfrac{V}{R} = \dfrac{V}{R_0 (1 + \alpha \Delta T)}$,   ☞ $\dfrac{I}{I_0} = \dfrac{1}{1 + \alpha \Delta T}$.

So $I = \dfrac{1}{1 + \alpha \Delta T} I_0 = \dfrac{1}{1 + (-7.0 \times 10^{-2} \ C°^{-1})(5 \ C°)} (0.50 \ A) = 0.77 \ A$.

48. $I_0 = \dfrac{V}{R_0} = \dfrac{1.5 \ V}{5.0 \ \Omega} = 0.30 \ A$.

$I = \dfrac{V}{R} = \dfrac{V}{R_0 (1 + \alpha \Delta T)} = \dfrac{1.5 \ V}{(5.0 \ \Omega)[1 + (3.93 \times 10^{-3} \ C°^{-1})(2000 \ C°)]} = 0.0334 \ A$.

So $\Delta I = 0.0334 \ A - 0.30 \ A = -0.27 \ A = 0.27 \ A \ decrease$.

49.   (d).

50.   (b) since $P = \dfrac{V^2}{R}$.

51.   (d), because $P = I^2 R$.

52. $P = \dfrac{V^2}{R}$. So its $\boxed{\text{power output would quadruple}}$ and it would overheat at least.

53. Since $P = \dfrac{V^2}{R}$, the bulb of higher power has smaller resistance or thicker wire.

So $\boxed{\text{the wire in a 60 W bulb is thicker}}$.

54. $P = \dfrac{V^2}{R} = \dfrac{(110 \text{ V})^2}{10 \text{ }\Omega} = \boxed{1.2 \times 10^3 \text{ W}}$.

55. $P = I^2 R = (13 \text{ A})^2 (12 \text{ }\Omega) = \boxed{2.0 \times 10^3 \text{ W}}$.

56. $P = \dfrac{V^2}{R}$, ☞ $R = \dfrac{V^2}{P} = \dfrac{(120 \text{ V})^2}{100 \text{ W}} = \boxed{144 \text{ }\Omega}$.

57. $\dfrac{V^2}{\Omega} = \dfrac{V^2}{\text{V/A}} = \text{V A} = \dfrac{\text{J}}{\text{C}} \dfrac{\text{C}}{\text{s}} = \text{J/s} = \text{W}$.

58. $P = \dfrac{V^2}{R}$, ☞ $R = \dfrac{V^2}{P} = \dfrac{(240 \text{ V})^2}{50 \times 10^3 \text{ W}} = \boxed{1.2 \text{ }\Omega}$.

59. The heat (energy) needed is

$Q = cm\Delta T = [4186 \text{ J/(kg·C°)}](50 \text{ gal})(3.785 \text{ kg/gal})(60 \text{ C°}) = 4.75 \times 10^7 \text{ J}$.

At 90% efficiency, the energy input is $\dfrac{4.75 \times 10^7 \text{ J}}{0.90} = 5.28 \times 10^7 \text{ J}$.

So $t = \dfrac{E}{P} = \dfrac{5.28 \times 10^7 \text{ J}}{50 \times 10^3 \text{ W}} = 1.05 \times 10^3 \text{ s} = \boxed{18 \text{ min}}$.

60. (a) $I = \dfrac{V}{R} = \dfrac{4(1.5 \text{ V})}{15 \text{ }\Omega} = \boxed{0.40 \text{ A}}$.

(b) $P = IV = (0.40 \text{ A})(4)(1.5 \text{ V}) = \boxed{2.4 \text{ W}}$.

61. (a) $E = Pt = IVt = (18 \text{ A})(240 \text{ V})(1.0 \text{ s}) = \boxed{4.3 \times 10^3 \text{ J}}$.

(b) $R = \dfrac{V}{I} = \dfrac{240 \text{ V}}{18 \text{ A}} = \boxed{13 \text{ }\Omega}$.

62. (a) $E = P t = (4.5 \text{ kW})(2.0 \text{ h/d})(30 \text{ d}) = 270 \text{ kWh}$.

So it costs $(270 \text{ kWh})(15 \text{ ¢/kWh}) = \boxed{\$40.50}$.

(b) $P = \dfrac{V^2}{R}$, ☞ $R = \dfrac{V^2}{P} = \dfrac{(120 \text{ V})^2}{4500 \text{ W}} = \boxed{3.2 \text{ }\Omega}$.

63. $P = \dfrac{V^2}{R}$, ☞ $R = \dfrac{V^2}{P} = \dfrac{(120 \text{ V})^2}{(15 \times 10^3 \text{ J/min})(1 \text{ min})/(60 \text{ s})} = \boxed{58 \text{ }\Omega}$.

64. $E = Pt = (0.200 \text{ kW})(10 \text{ h/d})(365 \text{ d/y}) = 730 \text{ kWh/y}$.

    So the annual cost is $(730 \text{ kWh})(15 \text{ ¢/kWh}) = \boxed{\$110}$.

65. (a) $E = Pt = IVt = (15 \text{ A})(120 \text{ V})(1/3 \text{ h}) = 600 \text{ Wh} = \boxed{0.60 \text{ kWh}}$.

    (b) It costs $(0.60 \text{ kWh})(15 \text{ ¢/kWh}) = \boxed{\$0.09}$.

66. $P = \dfrac{V^2}{R}$, ☞ $V = \sqrt{PR}$.

    For $100 \text{ }\Omega$, $V = \sqrt{(1.5 \text{ W})(100 \text{ }\Omega)} = \boxed{12 \text{ V}}$;

    for $25 \text{ k}\Omega$, $V = \sqrt{(0.25 \text{ W})(25 \times 10^3 \text{ }\Omega)} = \boxed{79 \text{ V}}$.

67. (a) $I = \dfrac{V}{R} = \dfrac{15 \text{ V}}{100 \text{ }\Omega} = \boxed{0.15 \text{ A}}$.

    (b) $R = \dfrac{\rho L}{A}$, ☞ $\rho = \dfrac{RA}{L} = \dfrac{(100 \text{ }\Omega)(\pi)(1.5 \times 10^{-3} \text{ m})^2}{5.0 \text{ m}} = \boxed{1.4 \times 10^{-4} \text{ }\Omega\cdot\text{m}}$.

    (c) $P = VI = (15 \text{ V})(0.15 \text{ A}) = \boxed{2.3 \text{ W}}$.

68. $R = R_0(1 + \alpha \Delta T) = R_0[1 + (4.5 \times 10^{-3} \text{ C°}^{-1})(150 \text{ C°})] = 1.68 R_0$.

    $P = \dfrac{V^2}{R}$, ☞ $\dfrac{P}{P_0} = \dfrac{R_0}{R} = \dfrac{1}{1.68} = 0.595$.

    So $P = 0.595(500 \text{ W}) = 298 \text{ W}$.

    Therefore $\Delta P = 298 \text{ W} - 500 \text{ W} \approx \boxed{-202 \text{ W}}$ (a decrease).

69. (a) $E = Pt = \dfrac{V^2}{R} t = \dfrac{[4(1.5 \text{ V})]^2 (60 \text{ s})}{20 \text{ }\Omega} = \boxed{1.1 \times 10^2 \text{ J}}$.

    (b) $E = \dfrac{(1.5 \text{ V})^2 (60 \text{ s})}{20 \text{ }\Omega} = \boxed{6.8 \text{ J}}$.

70. (a) $I = \dfrac{P}{V} = \dfrac{5.5 \times 10^3 \text{ W}}{240 \text{ V}} = 23 \text{ A} > 20 \text{ A}$.

    So it should have a $\boxed{30\text{-amp}}$ circuit breaker.

(b) The heat (energy) required is

$$Q = cm\Delta T = [4190 \text{ J/(kg·C°)}](55 \text{ gal})(3.785 \text{ kg/gal})(60 \text{ C°}) = 5.23 \times 10^7 \text{ J}.$$

The energy input is $E = \dfrac{5.23 \times 10^7 \text{ J}}{0.85} = 6.16 \times 10^7 \text{ J}.$

$$t = \frac{E}{P} = \frac{6.16 \times 10^7 \text{ J}}{5.5 \times 10^3 \text{ W}} = 1.12 \times 10^4 \text{ s} = \boxed{3.1 \text{ h}}.$$

71. The heat required is $Q = cm\Delta T = [4190 \text{ J/(kg·C°)}](0.300 \text{ kg})(60 \text{ C°}) = 7.54 \times 10^4 \text{ J}.$

The energy input is $E = \dfrac{7.54 \times 10^4 \text{ J}}{0.75} = 1.01 \times 10^5 \text{ J}.$

$$P = \frac{E}{t} = \frac{V^2}{R}, \qquad ☞ \qquad R = \frac{V^2 t}{E} = \frac{(120 \text{ V})^2 (2.5)(60 \text{ s})}{1.01 \times 10^5 \text{ J}} = \boxed{21 \ \Omega}.$$

72. $P = \dfrac{V^2}{R}, \qquad ☞ \qquad \dfrac{P_2}{P_1} = \left(\dfrac{V_2}{V_1}\right)^2 = \left(\dfrac{0.95 \times 120 \text{ V}}{120 \text{ V}}\right)^2 = 0.90.$

So $P_2 = 0.90 P_1 = 0.90(100 \text{ W}) = \boxed{90 \text{ W}}.$

73. $P = \dfrac{V^2}{R}, \qquad ☞ \qquad R = \dfrac{V^2}{P}, \qquad \text{so} \qquad \dfrac{R_2}{R_1} = \dfrac{V_2^2}{V_1^2}\dfrac{P_1}{P_2}. \qquad \text{So} \qquad \dfrac{R_{120 \text{ V}}}{R_{90 \text{ V}}} = \dfrac{(120 \text{ V})^2}{(60 \text{ V})^2}\dfrac{20 \text{ W}}{60 \text{ W}} = \boxed{4/3}.$

74. (a) The input power to the pump is $P = \dfrac{2.00 \text{ kW}}{0.84} = 2.38 \text{ kW}.$

$$P = VI, \qquad ☞ \qquad I = \frac{P}{V} = \frac{2.38 \times 10^3 \text{ W}}{240 \text{ V}} = \boxed{9.9 \text{ A}}.$$

(b) $R = \dfrac{V}{I} = \dfrac{240 \text{ V}}{9.9 \text{ A}} = \boxed{24 \ \Omega}.$

75. $E = \Sigma Pt = (5.0 \text{ kW})(0.30)(24 \text{ h/d})(30 \text{ d}) + (0.8 \text{ kW})(0.50 \text{ h}) + (0.625 \text{ kW})(1/4 \text{ h/d})(30 \text{ d})$

$$+ (0.5 \text{ kW})(0.15)(24 \text{ h/d})(30 \text{ d}) + (10.5 \text{ kW})(10 \text{ h}) + (0.1 \text{ kW})(120 \text{ h}) = 1256 \text{ kWh}.$$

So it costs $(1256 \text{ kWh})(\$0.12 \text{ /kWh}) = \boxed{\$151}.$

76. (a) Since copper has a positive α and carbon has a negative α, $\boxed{\text{copper}}$ will have a greater resistance.

(b) $R = R_0 (1 + \alpha\Delta T), \qquad ☞ \qquad \dfrac{R_{Cu}}{R_C} = \dfrac{1 + \alpha_{Cu}\Delta T}{1 + \alpha_C \Delta T} = \dfrac{1 + (6.80 \times 10^{-3} \text{ C°}^{-1})(10.0 \text{ C°})}{1 + (-5.0 \times 10^{-4} \text{ C°}^{-1})(10.0 \text{ C°})} = \boxed{1.07}.$

77. $\dfrac{\Delta R}{R_0} = \alpha\Delta T = 0.25, \qquad ☞ \qquad \Delta T = \dfrac{0.25}{3.93 \times 10^{-3} \text{ C°}^{-1}} = \boxed{64 \text{ C°}}.$

78. $I_0 = \dfrac{V}{R_0} = \dfrac{12\ \text{V}}{1.75\ \Omega} = 6.86\ \text{A}.$ $R = R_0(1 + \alpha\Delta T) = (1.75\ \Omega)[1 + (6.51 \times 10^{-3}\ \text{C}°^{-1})(280\ \text{C}°)] = 4.94\ \Omega.$

So $I = \dfrac{12\ \text{V}}{4.94\ \Omega} = 2.43\ \text{A}.$ Therefore $\Delta I = 2.43\ \text{A} - 6.86\ \text{A} = -4.4\ \text{A} = \boxed{4.4\ \text{A less}}.$

79. (a) $I = \dfrac{P}{V} = \dfrac{40\ \text{W}}{120\ \text{V}} = \boxed{0.33\ \text{A}}.$

(b) $R = \dfrac{V}{I} = \dfrac{120\ \text{V}}{0.33\ \text{A}} = \boxed{3.6 \times 10^2\ \Omega}.$

80. $E = Pt = (0.075\ \text{kW})(8.0\ \text{h}) = 0.60\ \text{kWh}.$

So it costs $10 \times (0.60\ \text{kWh})(\$0.15/\text{KWh}) = \boxed{\$0.90}.$

81. $P = \dfrac{V^2}{R},$ ☞ $R_0 = \dfrac{V^2}{P_0} = \dfrac{(120\ \text{V})^2}{1600\ \text{W}} = 9.00\ \Omega.$

Since $R = \dfrac{\rho L}{A},$ R is $0.90R_0.$

So $P = \dfrac{(120\ \text{V})^2}{0.90(9.00\ \Omega)} = 1.78 \times 10^3\ \text{W} = \boxed{1.78\ \text{kW}}.$

82. $R = R_0(1 + \alpha\Delta T) = (200\ \Omega)[1 + (4.5 \times 10^{-3}\ \text{C}°^{-1})(1580\ \text{C}°)] = \boxed{1.62 \times 10^3\ \Omega}.$

83. $R = \dfrac{\rho L}{A}.$ If aluminum is at room temperature, $\dfrac{R_{\text{Cu}}}{R_{\text{Al}}} = 1 = \dfrac{\rho_{\text{Cu}}(1 + \alpha_{\text{Cu}}\Delta T)}{\rho_{\text{Al}}}.$

So $\Delta T = \dfrac{\rho_{\text{Al}}/\rho_{\text{Cu}} - 1}{\alpha_{\text{Cu}}} = \dfrac{(2.82 \times 10^{-8}\ \Omega\cdot\text{m})/(1.70 \times 10^{-8}\ \Omega\cdot\text{m}) - 1}{6.80 \times 10^{-3}\ \text{C}°^{-1}} = 96.9°\text{C}°.$

Therefore $20°\text{C} + 96.9\ \text{C}° = 117°\text{C},$ i.e., $\boxed{\text{copper at } 117°\text{C}}.$

If copper is at room temperature, $\dfrac{R_{\text{Cu}}}{R_{\text{Al}}} = 1 = \dfrac{\rho_{\text{Cu}}}{\rho_{\text{Al}}(1 + \alpha_{\text{Al}}\Delta T)}.$

So $\Delta T = \dfrac{\rho_{\text{Cu}}/\rho_{\text{Al}} - 1}{\alpha_{\text{Al}}} = \dfrac{(1.70 \times 10^{-8}\ \Omega\cdot\text{m})/(2.82 \times 10^{-8}\ \Omega\cdot\text{m}) - 1}{4.29 \times 10^{-3}\ \text{C}°^{-1}} = -92.6°\text{C}°.$

So $20°\text{C} - 92.6\ \text{C}° = -73°\text{C},$ i.e., $\boxed{\text{aluminum at } -73°\text{C}}.$

84. $R = \dfrac{\rho L}{A} = \dfrac{(2.82 \times 10^{-8}\ \Omega\cdot\text{m})(100\ \text{m})}{\pi(1.0 \times 10^{-3}\ \text{m})^2} = 0.898\ \Omega.$

$I = \dfrac{V}{R} = \dfrac{1.5\ \text{V}}{0.898\ \Omega} = \boxed{1.7\ \text{A}}.$

85. $E = Pt = \dfrac{V^2}{R}\ t = \dfrac{(120\ \text{V})^2(3600\ \text{s})}{15\ \Omega} = \boxed{3.5 \times 10^6\ \text{J}}$.

86. (a) $R = \dfrac{V}{I} = \dfrac{\rho L}{A}$, ☞ $\rho = \dfrac{VA}{IL} = \dfrac{(3.00\ \text{V})(\pi)(0.5 \times 10^{-3}\ \text{m})^2}{(11.8\ \text{A})(2.0\ \text{m})} = \boxed{1.0 \times 10^{-7}\ \Omega\text{·m}}$.

   (b) From Table 17.1, it could be $\boxed{\text{iron or platinum}}$.

87. (a) $P = I^2 R$, ☞ $I = \sqrt{\dfrac{P}{R}} = \sqrt{\dfrac{0.25\ \text{W}}{100\ \Omega}} = \boxed{5.0 \times 10^{-2}\ \text{A}}$.

   (b) $V = IR = (0.05\ \text{A})(100\ \Omega) = \boxed{5.0\ \text{V}}$.

88. $I = \dfrac{q}{t} = \dfrac{ne}{t}$, ☞ $n = \dfrac{It}{e} = \dfrac{(75 \times 10^{-3}\ \text{A})(2.0\ \text{s})}{1.6 \times 10^{-19}\ \text{C}} = \boxed{9.4 \times 10^{17}\ \text{electrons}}$.

89. (a) $R = \dfrac{V}{I} = \dfrac{40\ \text{V}}{0.10\ \text{A}} = \boxed{4.0 \times 10^2\ \Omega}$.

   (b) $P = IV = (0.10\ \text{A})(40\ \text{V}) = \boxed{4.0\ \text{W}}$.

   (c) $E = Pt = (4.0\ \text{W})(2.0)(60\ \text{s}) = \boxed{4.8 \times 10^2\ \text{J}}$.

90. (a) $R = \dfrac{\rho L}{A}$, ☞ $\dfrac{R_{\text{Cu}}}{R_{\text{Al}}} = \dfrac{\rho_{\text{Cu}}}{\rho_{\text{Al}}}\dfrac{L_{\text{Cu}}}{L_{\text{Al}}}\dfrac{A_{\text{Al}}}{A_{\text{Cu}}} = \dfrac{1.70 \times 10^{-8}\ \Omega\text{·m}}{2.82 \times 10^{-8}\ \Omega\text{·m}}(1)(1) = \boxed{0.60}$.

   (b) Half the diameter means $\frac{1}{4}$ the area $(A = \pi r^2)$, so $\dfrac{A_{\text{Al}}}{A_{\text{Cu}}} = 4$.

   $\dfrac{R_{\text{Cu}}}{R_{\text{Al}}} = \dfrac{\rho_{\text{Cu}}}{\rho_{\text{Al}}}(2)(4) = \boxed{4.8}$.

91. $P = IV$, ☞ $q = It = \dfrac{P}{V}\ t = \dfrac{(60\ \text{W})(3600\ \text{s})}{120\ \text{V}} = 1800\ \text{C}$.

   $n = \dfrac{q}{e} = \dfrac{1800\ \text{C}}{1.6 \times 10^{-19}\ \text{C}} = \boxed{1.1 \times 10^{22}\ \text{electrons}}$.

92. $V = IR = I\dfrac{\rho L}{A} = \dfrac{(3000\ \text{A})(1.70 \times 10^{-8}\ \Omega\text{·m})(1.5\ \text{m})}{(0.080\ \text{m})(0.040\ \text{m})} = \boxed{2.4 \times 10^{-2}\ \text{V}}$.

93. Since $P = IV$, a higher voltage means lower current if P is kept constant. The resistance of the transmission lines is a fixed number. With lower current, the power loss on the lines is reduced.

   $P_{\text{loss}} = I^2 R = \dfrac{P^2}{V^2}\ R \propto \dfrac{1}{V^2}$. So if V is raised by 10 times, P_{loss} will be reduced by a factor of 1/100.

94. (a) $\Delta Q = nVq = nAxq = (nAx)q$.

(b) $I = \dfrac{\Delta Q}{\Delta t} = nq\,\dfrac{x}{\Delta t}\,A = nqv_{\mathrm{d}}A$.

95. $1\ \mathrm{m}^3 = 10^6\ \mathrm{cm}^3$. From Exercise 17.94, $I = nqv_{\mathrm{d}}A$,

so $v_{\mathrm{d}} = \dfrac{I}{nqA} = \dfrac{1.2\ \mathrm{A}}{(8.5 \times 10^{28}\ /\mathrm{m}^3)(1.6 \times 10^{-19}\ \mathrm{C})(13.3 \times 10^{-6}\ \mathrm{m}^2)} = \boxed{6.6 \times 10^{-6}\ \mathrm{m/s}}$.

CHAPTER 18

In this chapter, the following convenient calculation of equivalent resistance for two resistors in parallel is used in many exercises. $\dfrac{1}{R_p} = \dfrac{1}{R_1} + \dfrac{1}{R_2}$, ☞ $R_p = \dfrac{R_1 R_2}{R_1 + R_2}$.

1.   (b).

2.   (a).

3. $\boxed{\text{No}}$, not generally. However $\boxed{\text{if all resistors are equal}}$, the voltages across them are the same.

4. $\boxed{\text{No}}$, not generally. However $\boxed{\text{if all resistors are equal}}$, the currents through each is the same.

5.   Since $P = IV$, the $\boxed{5\ \Omega}$ resistor gets the most power because it gets the most voltage and all resistors have the same current.

6.   Since $P = IV$, the $\boxed{1\ \Omega}$ resistor get the most power because it gets the most current and all resistors have the same voltage.

7.   (a) Series gives maximum resistance: $R_s = R_1 + R_2 + R_3 = 10\ \Omega + 20\ \Omega + 30\ \Omega = \boxed{60\ \Omega}$.

         (b) Parallel gives minimum resistance: $\dfrac{1}{R_p} = \dfrac{1}{R_1} + \dfrac{1}{R_2} + \dfrac{1}{R_3} = \dfrac{1}{10\ \Omega} + \dfrac{1}{20\ \Omega} + \dfrac{1}{30\ \Omega} = \dfrac{11}{60\ \Omega}$,

         so $R_p = \boxed{5.5\ \Omega}$.

8.   Series combination: $R_s = R_1 + R_2 = R + R = 2R.$

         Parallel combination: $\dfrac{1}{R_p} = \dfrac{1}{R_s} + \dfrac{1}{R_3}$,   ☞ $R_p = \dfrac{R_s R_3}{R_s + R_3} = 10\ \Omega = \dfrac{(2R)(20\ \Omega)}{2R + 20\ \Omega}$.

         Simplifying, $20R + 200 = 40R$.   Solving, $R = \boxed{10\ \Omega}$.

9.   Parallel combination: $\dfrac{1}{R_p} = \dfrac{1}{R_1} + \dfrac{1}{R_2}$,   ☞ $R_p = \dfrac{R_1 R_2}{R_1 + R_2} = \dfrac{R\,R}{R + R} = \dfrac{R}{2}$.

         Series combination: $R_s = R_p + R_3 = \dfrac{R}{2} + 40\ \Omega = 55\ \Omega$,   ☞ $R = \boxed{30\ \Omega}$.

10.   Parallel: $\dfrac{1}{R_p} = \dfrac{1}{R_1} + \dfrac{1}{R_2} + \dfrac{1}{R_3} = 3\,\dfrac{1}{4.0\ \Omega} = \dfrac{3}{4.0\ \Omega}$,   ☞ $R_p = \boxed{1.3\ \Omega \text{ for parallel}}$.

Series: $R_s = R_1 + R_2 + R_3 = 3(4.0\ \Omega) = \boxed{12\ \Omega \text{ for series}}$.

parallel   series   series-parallel   parallel-series

Two in series-parallel: $\dfrac{1}{R_p} = \dfrac{1}{R_s} + \dfrac{1}{R} = \dfrac{1}{R+R} + \dfrac{1}{R} = \dfrac{3}{2(4.0\ \Omega)}$,

so $R_p = \boxed{2.7\ \Omega \text{ for series-parallel}}$.

Two in parallel-series: $R_s = R + R_p = R + \dfrac{R\,R}{R+R} = \dfrac{3R}{2} = \dfrac{3(4.0\ \Omega)}{2} = \boxed{6.0\ \Omega \text{ for parallel-series}}$.

11.   (a) $R_s = R_1 + R_2 + R_3 = 5.0\ \Omega + 10\ \Omega + 15\ \Omega = \boxed{30\ \Omega}$.

(b) $I = \dfrac{V}{R_s} = \dfrac{9.0\ \text{V}}{30\ \Omega} = \boxed{0.30\ \text{A}}$.

(c) $P = I^2 R = (0.30\ \text{A})^2 (15\ \Omega) = \boxed{1.4\ \text{W}}$.

12.   Two or more in series: $R_s = R_1 + R_2 + R_3 = \boxed{15\ \Omega,\ 20\ \Omega,\ 25\ \Omega,\ 30\ \Omega}$.

Two or more in parallel: $\dfrac{1}{R_p} = \dfrac{1}{R_1} + \dfrac{1}{R_2} + \dfrac{1}{R_3}$,   ☞ $R_p = \boxed{3.3\ \Omega,\ 3.8\ \Omega,\ 6.0\ \Omega,\ 2.7\ \Omega}$.

Parallel-series: $R_s = \dfrac{R_1 R_2}{R_1 + R_2} + R_3 = \boxed{11\ \Omega,\ 14\ \Omega,\ 18\ \Omega}$.

Series-parallel: $\dfrac{1}{R_p} = \dfrac{1}{R_1 + R_2} + \dfrac{1}{R_3}$,   ☞ $R_p = \boxed{4.2\ \Omega,\ 6.7\ \Omega,\ 7.5\ \Omega}$.

13.   (a) $\dfrac{1}{R_p} = \dfrac{1}{R_1} + \dfrac{1}{R_2} + \dfrac{1}{R_3} = \dfrac{1}{1.0\ \Omega} + \dfrac{1}{2.0\ \Omega} + \dfrac{1}{4.0\ \Omega} = \dfrac{7}{4.0\ \Omega}$,   ☞ $R_p = \boxed{0.57\ \Omega}$.

(b) $\boxed{6.0\ \text{V}}$ for all three since they are in parallel combination.

(c) $P = \dfrac{V^2}{R} = \dfrac{(6.0\ \text{V})^2}{4.0\ \Omega} = \boxed{9.0\ \text{W}}$.

14. $1.5\ \Omega = 1.0\ \Omega + 0.5\ \Omega = 1.0\ \Omega + \dfrac{1.0\ \Omega}{2}$.

So $\boxed{\text{wire two in parallel, and then put that in series with one}}$.

15.   The series of three segments has a resistance of 27 $\mu\Omega$: $27 \; \mu\Omega = 3R,$ ☞ $R = \dfrac{27 \; \mu\Omega}{3} = 9.0 \; \mu\Omega.$

These three segments are in parallel now: $\dfrac{1}{R_p} = 3\dfrac{1}{9.0 \; \mu\Omega} = \dfrac{1}{3.0 \; \mu\Omega},$ ☞ $R_p = \boxed{3.0 \; \mu\Omega}.$

16.   When $\boxed{\text{three are connected in series and then parallel to the fourth one}}$, the equivalent resistance is

$$R_p = \dfrac{(5.0 \; \Omega + 5.0 \; \Omega + 5.0 \; \Omega)(5.0 \; \Omega)}{(5.0 \; \Omega + 5.0 \; \Omega + 5.0 \; \Omega) + 5.0 \; \Omega} = 3.75 \; \Omega.$$

17.   (a) $I = \dfrac{V}{R_s} = \dfrac{12 \; \text{V}}{2.0 \; \Omega + 4.0 \; \Omega + 6.0 \; \Omega} = \boxed{1.0 \; \text{A}}.$

(b) In series, all have the same current, $\boxed{1.0 \; \text{A}}$.

(c) $P = I^2 R,$ ☞ $P_{2\,\Omega} = (1.0 \; \text{A})^2 \, (2.0 \; \Omega) = \boxed{2.0 \; \text{W}};$ $P_{4\,\Omega} = (1.0 \; \text{A})^2 \, (4.0 \; \Omega) = \boxed{4.0 \; \text{W}};$

and $P_{6\,\Omega} = (1.0 \; \text{A})^2 \, (6.0 \; \Omega) = \boxed{6.0 \; \text{W}}.$

(d) $P_{\text{total}} = (1.0 \; \text{A})^2 \, (12 \; \Omega) = 12 \; \text{W},$ $P_{\text{sum}} = 2.0 \; \text{W} + 4.0 \; \text{W} + 6.0 \; \text{W} = 12 \; \text{W}.$

So $\boxed{P_{\text{sum}} = P_{\text{total}} = 12 \; \text{W}}.$

18.   (a) $\dfrac{1}{R_p} = \dfrac{1}{2.0 \; \Omega} + \dfrac{1}{4.0 \; \Omega} + \dfrac{1}{6.0 \; \Omega} = \dfrac{11}{12 \; \Omega},$ ☞ $R_p = 1.09 \; \Omega.$

So $I = \dfrac{V}{R_p} = \dfrac{12 \; \text{V}}{1.09 \; \Omega} = \boxed{11 \; \text{A}}.$

(b) $I_{2\,\Omega} = \dfrac{12 \; \text{V}}{2.0 \; \Omega} = \boxed{6.0 \; \text{A}};$ $I_{4\,\Omega} = \dfrac{12 \; \text{V}}{4.0 \; \Omega} = \boxed{3.0 \; \text{A}};$ $I_{6\,\Omega} = \dfrac{12 \; \text{V}}{6.0 \; \Omega} = \boxed{2.0 \; \text{A}}.$

(c) $P = I^2 R,$ ☞ $P_{2\,\Omega} = (6.0 \; \text{A})^2 \, (2.0 \; \Omega) = \boxed{72 \; \text{W}};$ $P_{4\,\Omega} = (3.0 \; \text{A})^2 \, (4.0 \; \Omega) = \boxed{36 \; \text{W}};$

and $P_{6\,\Omega} = (2.0 \; \text{A})^2 \, (6.0 \; \Omega) = \boxed{24 \; \text{W}}.$

(d) $P_{\text{total}} = (11 \; \text{A})^2 \, (1.09 \; \Omega) = 132 \; \text{W},$ $P_{\text{sum}} = 72 \; \text{W} + 36 \; \text{W} + 24 \; \text{W} = 132 \; \text{W}.$

So $\boxed{P_{\text{sum}} = P_{\text{total}} = 132 \; \text{W}}.$

19. $R_s = R_{p8} + R_{p4} = \dfrac{(8.0 \; \Omega)(8.0 \; \Omega)}{8.0 \; \Omega + 8.0 \; \Omega} + \dfrac{(4.0 \; \Omega)(4.0 \; \Omega)}{4.0 \; \Omega + 4.0 \; \Omega} = 6.0 \; \Omega.$

$I = \dfrac{V}{R_s} = \dfrac{12 \; \text{V}}{6.0 \; \Omega} = 2.0 \; \text{A}.$

So the current through each resistor is $\dfrac{2.0 \; \text{A}}{2} = \boxed{1.0 \; \text{A for all}}.$

$V_{8.0} = (1.0 \; \text{A})(8.0 \; \Omega) = \boxed{8.0 \; \text{V}},$ and $V_{4.0} = (1.0 \; \text{A})(4.0 \; \Omega) = \boxed{4.0 \; \text{V}}.$

20. R_1 and R_2 are in series: $R_s = 2.0\ \Omega + 2.0\ \Omega = 4.0\ \Omega$.

R_s, R_3, and R_4 are in parallel: $\dfrac{1}{R_p} = \dfrac{1}{4.0\ \Omega} + \dfrac{1}{2.0\ \Omega} + \dfrac{1}{2.0\ \Omega} = \dfrac{5}{4.0\ \Omega}$,

so $R_p = \dfrac{4.0\ \Omega}{5} = \boxed{0.80\ \Omega}$.

21. R_2 and R_3 are in series: $R_s = 6.0\ \Omega + 4.0\ \Omega = 10\ \Omega$.

R_s, R_1, and R_4 are in parallel: $\dfrac{1}{R_p} = \dfrac{1}{10\ \Omega} + \dfrac{1}{6.0\ \Omega} + \dfrac{1}{10\ \Omega} = \dfrac{22}{60\ \Omega}$, ☞ $R_p = \boxed{2.7\ \Omega}$.

22. R_2, R_3 and R_4 are in series: $R_s = 20\ \Omega + 5.0\ \Omega + 5.0\ \Omega = 30\ \Omega$.

R_s and R_1 are in parallel: $R_p = \dfrac{(30\ \Omega)(10\ \Omega)}{30\ \Omega + 10\ \Omega} = \boxed{7.5\ \Omega}$.

23. (a) See diagram.

(b) The current through each bulb is

$I = \dfrac{P}{V} = \dfrac{60\ \text{W}}{120\ \text{V}} = 0.50\ \text{A}$.

So it takes $\dfrac{15\ \text{A}}{0.50\ \text{A}} = 30$ bulbs to make 15 A. Therefore $\boxed{31}$ bulbs will blow the fuse.

24. (a) Parallel consumes maximum power:

parallel

$\dfrac{1}{R_p} = 3\,\dfrac{1}{50\ \Omega} = \dfrac{3}{50\ \Omega}$, ☞ $R_p = \dfrac{50\ \Omega}{3} = 16.7\ \Omega$.

So $P_{max} = \dfrac{V^2}{R_p} = \dfrac{(120\ \text{V})^2}{16.7\ \Omega} = \boxed{8.6 \times 10^2\ \text{W}}$.

(b) Series consumes minimum power:

series

$R_s = 3(50\ \Omega) = 150\ \Omega$. So $P_{min} = \dfrac{(120\ \text{V})^2}{150\ \Omega} = \boxed{96\ \text{W}}$.

25. The equivalent resistance is

$R_s = R_p + R_3 = \dfrac{R_1 R_2}{R_1 + R_2} + R_3 = \dfrac{(10\ \Omega)(2.0\ \Omega)}{10\ \Omega + 2.0\ \Omega} + 5.0\ \Omega = 6.67\ \Omega$.

The total current is $I = \dfrac{V}{R_s} = \dfrac{10\ \text{V}}{6.67\ \Omega} = 1.5\ \text{A}$.

The voltage drop across R_3 is $V_3 = (1.5\ \text{A})(5.0\ \Omega) = 7.5\ \text{V}$.

So the voltage drop across the 10 Ω is $10\ \text{V} - 7.5\ \text{V} = \boxed{2.5\ \text{V}}$,

and the current through it is $\dfrac{2.5\ \text{V}}{10\ \Omega} = \boxed{0.25\ \text{A}}$.

26.　(a) $P = IV$, ☞ $I_{50} = \dfrac{P}{V} = \dfrac{50\text{ W}}{120\text{ V}} = \boxed{0.42\text{ A}}$.

$I_{100} = \dfrac{100\text{ W}}{120\text{ V}} = \boxed{0.83\text{ A}}$,　$I_{150} = \dfrac{150\text{ W}}{120\text{ V}} = \boxed{1.25\text{ A}}$.

(b) $R_{50} = \dfrac{V}{I} = \dfrac{120\text{ V}}{0.417\text{ A}} = \boxed{290\ \Omega}$,　$R_{100} = \dfrac{120\text{ V}}{0.833\text{ A}} = \boxed{144\ \Omega}$,　$R_{150} = \dfrac{120\text{ V}}{1.25\text{ A}} = \boxed{96\ \Omega}$.

27.　(a) $I_1 = \dfrac{V}{R_1} = \dfrac{20\text{ V}}{20\ \Omega} = \boxed{1.0\text{ A}}$.　R_2 and R_3 are in series:　$R_s = 20\ \Omega + 20\ \Omega = 40\ \Omega$.

So　$I_2 = I_3 = \dfrac{20\text{ V}}{40\ \Omega} = \boxed{0.50\text{ A}}$.

(b) $V_1 = \boxed{20\text{ V}}$,　$V_2 = V_3 = I_2\,R_2 = (0.50\text{ A})(20\ \Omega) = \boxed{10\text{ V}}$.

(c) The total power is　$P = \dfrac{V^2}{R_1} + \dfrac{V^2}{R_s} = \dfrac{(20\text{ V})^2}{20\ \Omega} + \dfrac{(20\text{ V})^2}{40\ \Omega} = \boxed{30\text{ W}}$.

28.　$I = \dfrac{V}{R} = \dfrac{120\text{ V}}{300\ \Omega} = 0.40\text{ A}$.　So there can be only $(15\text{ A})/(0.40\text{ A}) = 37.5$ resistors.

So $\boxed{37}$ resistors could be connected in parallel without tripping the 15 A breaker.

29.　$P = 2(100\text{ W}) + 150\text{ W} + 300\text{ W} + 900\text{ W} + 200\text{ W} = 1750\text{ W}$.

$I = \dfrac{P}{V} = \dfrac{1750\text{ W}}{120\text{ V}} = 14.6\text{ A} < 15\text{ A}$.　$\boxed{\text{No}}$, the breaker will not trip.

30.　R_1 and R_2 are in series.　$R_s = 2.0\ \Omega + 2.0\ \Omega = 4.0\ \Omega$.

So　$I_1 = I_2 = \dfrac{V}{R_s} = \dfrac{12\text{ V}}{4.0\ \Omega} = \boxed{3.0\text{ A}}$,

$I_3 = \dfrac{12\text{ V}}{2.0\ \Omega} = \boxed{6.0\text{ A}}$,　$I_4 = \dfrac{12\text{ V}}{2.0\ \Omega} = \boxed{6.0\text{ A}}$.

(b) $V_1 = V_2 = I_1\,R_1 = (3.0\text{ A})(2.0\ \Omega) = \boxed{6.0\text{ V}}$,　$V_3 = V_4 = \boxed{12\text{ V}}$.

(c) From Exercise 18.20,　$P = \dfrac{V^2}{R_p} = \dfrac{(12\text{ V})^2}{0.80\ \Omega} = \boxed{1.8 \times 10^2\text{ W}}$.

31.　The heat required is　$Q = cm\Delta T = [4186\text{ J/(kg·C}°)](0.20\text{ kg})(80°\text{C} - 20°\text{C}) = 5.02 \times 10^4\text{ J}$.

$P = \dfrac{E}{t}$,　☞　$t = \dfrac{E}{P} = \dfrac{5.02 \times 10^4\text{ J}}{500\text{ W}} = \boxed{100\text{ s} = 1.7\text{ min}}$.

32.　(a) $I_1 = \dfrac{V}{R_1} = \dfrac{6.0\text{ V}}{6.0\ \Omega} = \boxed{1.0\text{ A}}$　R_2 and R_3 are in series.　$R_s = 4.0\ \Omega + 6.0\ \Omega = 10\ \Omega$.

So　$I_2 = I_3 = \dfrac{6.0\text{ V}}{10\ \Omega} = \boxed{0.60\text{ A}}$,　$I_4 = \dfrac{6.0\text{ V}}{10\ \Omega} = \boxed{0.60\text{ A}}$.

(b) $P_1 = I_1^2 R_1 = (1.0 \text{ A})^2 (6.0 \text{ }\Omega) = \boxed{6.0 \text{ W}}$, $P_2 = (0.60 \text{ A})^2 (4.0 \text{ }\Omega) = \boxed{1.4 \text{ W}}$,

$P_3 = (0.60 \text{ A})^2 (6.0 \text{ }\Omega) = \boxed{2.2 \text{ W}}$, $P_4 = (0.60 \text{ A})^2 (10 \text{ }\Omega) = \boxed{3.6 \text{ W}}$.

(c) $P_{\text{sum}} = 6.0 \text{ W} + 1.44 \text{ W} + 2.16 \text{ W} + 3.6 \text{ W} = 13 \text{ W}$.   From Exercise 18.21,

$P_{\text{total}} = \dfrac{(6.0 \text{ V})^2}{2.7 \text{ }\Omega} = 13 \text{ W}$.   So $\boxed{P_{\text{sum}} = P_{\text{tot}} = 13 \text{ W}}$.

33.   (a) The wattage ratings are based on 120 V. $P = \dfrac{V^2}{R}$,   ☞ $R = \dfrac{V^2}{P}$.

$R_{15} = \dfrac{(120 \text{ V})^2}{15 \text{ W}} = 960 \text{ }\Omega$, $R_{40} = \dfrac{(120 \text{ V})^2}{40 \text{ W}} = 360 \text{ }\Omega$, $R_{60} = \dfrac{(120 \text{ V})^2}{60 \text{ W}} = 240 \text{ }\Omega$,

and $R_{100} = \dfrac{(120 \text{ V})^2}{100 \text{ W}} = 144 \text{ }\Omega$.   So the equivalent resistance is

$R_{\text{eq}} = 960 \text{ }\Omega + 360 \text{ }\Omega + \dfrac{(240 \text{ }\Omega)(144 \text{ }\Omega)}{240 \text{ }\Omega + 144 \text{ }\Omega} = 1410 \text{ }\Omega$.   Therefore $I = \dfrac{V}{R_{\text{eq}}} = \dfrac{120 \text{ V}}{1410 \text{ }\Omega} = \boxed{0.085 \text{ A}}$.

(b) $P_{15} = I^2 R = (0.0851 \text{ A})^2 (960 \text{ }\Omega) = \boxed{7.0 \text{ W}}$, $P_{40} = (0.851 \text{ A})^2 (360 \text{ }\Omega) = \boxed{2.6 \text{ W}}$.

$V_{60} = V_{100} = 120 \text{ V} - (0.0851 \text{ A})(960 \text{ }\Omega + 360 \text{ }\Omega) = 7.67 \text{ V}$.

So $P_{60} = \dfrac{V^2}{R} = \dfrac{(7.67 \text{ V})^2}{240 \text{ }\Omega} = \boxed{0.24 \text{ W}}$, $P_{100} = \dfrac{(7.67 \text{ V})^2}{144 \text{ }\Omega} = \boxed{0.41 \text{ W}}$.

34. R_1 and R_2 are in series. $R_{s1} = 10 \text{ }\Omega + 5.0 \text{ }\Omega = 15 \text{ }\Omega$.

So $I_1 = I_2 = \dfrac{V}{R_{s1}} = \dfrac{10 \text{ V}}{15 \text{ }\Omega} = \boxed{0.67 \text{ A}}$ $I_3 = \dfrac{10 \text{ V}}{10 \text{ }\Omega} = \boxed{1.0 \text{ A}}$.

R_4 and R_5 are in series. $R_{s2} = 5.0 \text{ }\Omega + 20 \text{ }\Omega = 25 \text{ }\Omega$.   So $I_4 = I_5 = \dfrac{10 \text{ V}}{25 \text{ }\Omega} = \boxed{0.40 \text{ A}}$.

(b) $V_1 = I_1 R_1 = (0.667 \text{ A})(10 \text{ }\Omega) = \boxed{6.7 \text{ V}}$, $V_2 = (0.667 \text{ A})(5.0 \text{ }\Omega) = \boxed{3.3 \text{ V}}$, $V_3 = \boxed{10 \text{ V}}$,

$V_4 = (0.40 \text{ A})(5.0 \text{ }\Omega) = \boxed{2.0 \text{ V}}$, $V_5 = (0.40 \text{ A})(20 \text{ }\Omega) = \boxed{8.0 \text{ V}}$.

35.   6.0 Ω and 4.0 Ω are in parallel. $R_{p1} = \dfrac{(6.0 \text{ }\Omega)(4.0 \text{ }\Omega)}{6.0 \text{ }\Omega + 4.0 \text{ }\Omega} = 2.4 \text{ }\Omega$.

This R_{p1} and 2.0 Ω are in series. $R_{s1} = 2.4 \text{ }\Omega + 2.0 \text{ }\Omega = 4.4 \text{ }\Omega$.

This R_{s1} and 12 Ω are in parallel. $R_{p2} = \dfrac{(4.4 \text{ }\Omega)(12 \text{ }\Omega)}{4.4 \text{ }\Omega + 12 \text{ }\Omega} = 3.22 \text{ }\Omega$.

10 Ω (the one on the bottom) and 5.0 Ω are in parallel. $R_{p3} = \dfrac{(10 \text{ }\Omega)(5.0 \text{ }\Omega)}{10 \text{ }\Omega + 5.0 \text{ }\Omega} = 3.33 \text{ }\Omega$.

Finally, R_{p2}, R_{p3}, and 10 Ω (the one on the top) are in series, $R_{s2} = 3.22 \text{ }\Omega + 3.33 \text{ }\Omega + 10 \text{ }\Omega = 16.6 \text{ }\Omega$.

So $P = \dfrac{V^2}{R_{s2}} = \dfrac{(24 \text{ V})^2}{16.6 \text{ }\Omega} = \boxed{35 \text{ W}}$.

36.   8.0 Ω and 4.0 Ω are in parallel. $R_{p1} = \dfrac{(8.0\ \Omega)(4.0\ \Omega)}{8.0\ \Omega + 4.0\ \Omega} = 2.67\ \Omega$.

    This R_{p1} and 10 W are in series. $R_{s1} = 2.67\ \Omega + 10\ \Omega = 12.7\ \Omega$.

    6.0 Ω, 3.0 Ω, and 2.0 Ω are in parallel. $\dfrac{1}{R_{p2}} = \dfrac{1}{6.0\ \Omega} + \dfrac{1}{3.0\ \Omega} + \dfrac{1}{2.0\ \Omega} = \dfrac{1}{1.0\ \Omega}$,

    so $R_{p2} = 1.0\ \Omega$.

    This R_{p2} and 5.0 Ω are in series. $R_{s2} = 1.0\ \Omega + 5.0\ \Omega = 6.0\ \Omega$.

    R_{s1} and R_{s2} are in parallel. $R_{p3} = \dfrac{(12.7\ \Omega)(6.0\ \Omega)}{12.7\ \Omega + 6.0\ \Omega} = 4.07\ \Omega$.

    Finally, this R_{p3} and 4.0 Ω are in series. $R_{s3} = 4.07\ \Omega + 4.0\ \Omega = \boxed{8.1\ \Omega}$.

37. R_3 and R_4 are in series. $R_{s1} = 4.0\ \Omega + 6.0\ \Omega = 10\ \Omega$.

    This R_{s1} and R_1 are in parallel. $R_{p1} = \dfrac{(10\ \Omega)(2.0\ \Omega)}{10\ \Omega + 2.0\ \Omega} = 1.67\ \Omega$.

    Finally, this R_{p1} and R_2 are in series. $R_{s2} = 1.67\ \Omega + 2.0\ \Omega = 3.67\ \Omega$.

    So $I = \dfrac{V}{R_{s2}} = \dfrac{12\ \text{V}}{3.67\ \Omega} = 3.27\ \text{A}$.   The voltage on R_{p1} is $V_{p1} = (3.27\ \text{A})(1.67\ \Omega) = 5.46\ \text{V}$.

    Therefore $I_1 = \dfrac{5.46\ \text{V}}{2.0\ \Omega} = \boxed{2.7\ \text{A}}$, $I_2 = I = \boxed{3.3\ \text{A}}$, $I_3 = I_4 = \dfrac{V_{p1}}{R_{s1}} = \dfrac{5.46\ \text{V}}{10\ \Omega} = \boxed{0.55\ \text{A}}$.

38.   When it is balanced, point b and point c have the same potential, or $V_{ab} = V_{ac}$, and $V_{bd} = V_{cd}$.

    So $V_{ab} = I_1 R_s = I_2 R_1$ (1)   and $V_{bd} = I_1 R_x = I_2 R_2$ (2)

    $\dfrac{(2)}{(1)}$ gives $\dfrac{R_x}{R_s} = \dfrac{R_2}{R_1}$,   ☞ $R_x = \dfrac{R_2}{R_1} R_s$.

39.   (d).

40.   (c).

41. $\boxed{\text{Positive}}$ because you traverse from low potential to high potential so the potential difference is positive.

42.   Around loop 3, $-V_1 + I_1 R_1 + I_2 R_2 = 0$, or $V_1 - I_1 R_1 - I_2 R_2 = 0$, which is the result of the equations for loop 1 plus the equation for loop 2.

43.   Around loop 1 (reverse), $-V_1 + I_3 R_3 + V_2 + I_1 R_1 = 0$.

    If we multiply −1 on both sides, it is the same as the equation for loop 1 (forward).

    Around loop 2 (reverse), $I_2 R_2 - V_2 - I_3 R_3 = 0$.

    Again if we multiply by −1 on both sides, it is the same as the equation for loop 2 (forward).

44. Around the inner loop:

$10 \text{ V} - I_2(2.0 \ \Omega) - I_3(5.0 \ \Omega) = 0.$ Eq. (1)

Around the outer loop:

$10 \text{ V} - I_1(10 \ \Omega) - I_3(5.0 \ \Omega) = 0.$ Eq. (2)

From junction theorem:

$I_3 = I_1 + I_2.$ Eq. (3)

Substituting Eq. (3) into Eq. (1) and Eq. (2) gives

$(5.0 \ \Omega)I_1 + (7.0 \ \Omega)I_2 = 10 \text{ V}$ Eq. (3)

$(7.0 \ \Omega)I_1 + (5.0 \ \Omega)I_2 = 10 \text{ V}$ Eq. (4)

Solving, $I_1 = \boxed{0.25 \text{ A}}$, $I_2 = \boxed{1.25 \text{ A}}$, and $I_3 = \boxed{1.5 \text{ A}}$.

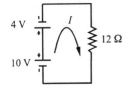

45. Around the left loop in a clockwise direction, $20 \text{ V} - I_1(20 \ \Omega) = 0$, ☞ $\boxed{I_1 = 1.0 \text{ A down}}$.

Around the outer loop (without R_1) in clockwise direction, $20 \text{ V} - I_2(20 \ \Omega) - I_2(20 \ \Omega) = 0$,

so $\boxed{I_2 = 0.50 \text{ A right}}$ and $\boxed{I_3 = 0.50 \text{ A down}}$.

46. (a) Around the loop, $10 \text{ V} - 4 \text{ V} - I(12 \ \Omega) = 0$,

so $I = \boxed{0.50 \text{ A}}$ and $P = I^2 R = (0.50 \text{ A})^2(12 \ \Omega) = \boxed{3.0 \text{ W}}$

(b) $P_{10} = \varepsilon I = (10 \text{ V})(0.50 \text{ A}) = \boxed{5.0 \text{ W output}}$,

$P_4 = (-4 \text{ V})(0.50 \text{ A}) = -2.0 \text{ W} = \boxed{2.0 \text{ W input}}$.

$P_{net} = 5.0 \text{ W} - 2.0 \text{ W} = \boxed{3.0 \text{ W to the resistor}}$

47. Around the loop in a counterclockwise direction, $20 \text{ V} - I(20 \ \Omega) - 10 \text{ V} - I(10 \ \Omega) = 0$,

so $I = I_1 = I_2 = 0.33 \text{ A}$. Therefore $\boxed{I_1 = 0.33 \text{ A left}}$ and $\boxed{I_2 = 0.33 \text{ A right}}$.

48. (a) For the R_1 and R_2 connecting junction: $I = I_1 + I_2$. Eq. (1)

Around the loop through R_1 in counterclockwise direction,

$12 \text{ V} - I(2.0 \ \Omega) - I(8.0 \ \Omega) + 6.0 \text{ V} - I(2.0 \ \Omega) - I_1(4.0 \ \Omega) = 0$,

or $-12I - 4I_1 + 18 = 0.$ Eq. (2)

Around the loop through R_2 in counterclockwise direction,

$12 \text{ V} - I(2.0 \ \Omega) - I(8.0 \ \Omega) + 6.0 \text{ V} - I(2.0 \ \Omega) - I_2(6.0 \ \Omega) = 0$,

or $-12I - 6I_2 + 18 = 0.$ Eq. (3)

Substituting Eq. (1) into Eq. (2) and Eq. (3) gives $\quad -16I_1 - 12I_2 + 18 = 0.$ $\qquad$ Eq. (4)

$$-12I_1 - 18I_2 + 18 = 0. \qquad \text{Eq. (5)}$$

Solving, $\quad \boxed{I_1 = 0.75 \text{ A left}}, \quad \boxed{I_2 = 0.50 \text{ A left}}, \quad I = I_3 = I_4 = I_5,$

so $\quad \boxed{I_3 = 1.25 \text{ A up}}, \quad \boxed{I_4 = 1.25 \text{ A right}}, \quad$ and $\quad \boxed{I_5 = 1.25 \text{ A down}}.$

(b) $P = I^2 R = (1.25 \text{ A})^2 (8.0 \ \Omega) = \boxed{13 \text{ W}}.$

49.   Around the left loop in clockwise direction, $\quad 10 \text{ V} - I_1 (4.0 \ \Omega) + 5.0 \text{ V} = 0, \quad \text{☞} \quad I_1 = 3.75 \text{ A}.$

Around the right loop in counterclockwise direction, $\quad 5.0 \text{ V} - I_3 (4.0 \ \Omega) + 5.0 \text{ V} - I_2 (4.0 \ \Omega) = 0.$

Also $\quad I_2 = I_3.$ So $\quad I_2 = I_3 = 1.25 \text{ A}.$

Therefore $\quad \boxed{I_1 = 3.75 \text{ A up}}, \quad \boxed{I_2 = 1.25 \text{ A left}}, \quad$ and $\quad \boxed{I_3 = 1.25 \text{ A right}}.$

50.   The equivalent resistance of the three 2.0 Ω in parallel is $\qquad R_p = \dfrac{2.0 \ \Omega}{3} = 0.667 \ \Omega.$

Assume the current through the parallel combination is I.   From junction theorem, $\quad I = I_1 + I_2 + I_3.$

Around the left loop in clockwise direction, $\qquad\qquad$ $20 \text{ V} - I_1 (5.0 \ \Omega) - I(0.667 \ \Omega) = 0,$

or $\quad 5.667I_1 + 0.667I_2 + 0.667I_3 = 20.$ $\qquad\qquad$ Eq. (1)

Around the middle loop in counterclockwise direction, $\qquad$ $10 \text{ V} - I_1 (5.0 \ \Omega) + I_2 (4.0 \ \Omega) = 0,$

or $\quad 5I_1 - 4I_2 = 10,$ $\qquad\qquad$ Eq. (2)

Around the right loop in counterclockwise direction, $\qquad$ $-I_2 (4.0 \ \Omega) + I_3 (6.0 \ \Omega) = 0,$

or $\quad 4I_2 - 6I_3 = 0.$ $\qquad\qquad$ Eq. (3).

Solve the simultaneous equations for $\quad I_1 = 3.23 \text{ A}, \quad I_2 = 1.54 \text{ A}, \quad I_3 = 1.02 \text{ A}.$

$V_p = I R_p = (I_1 + I_2 + I_3)R_p = (3.23 \text{ A} + 1.54 \text{ A} + 1.02 \text{ A})(0.667 \ \Omega) = 3.86 \text{ V}.$

So $\quad I_4 = I_5 = I_6 = \dfrac{3.86 \text{ V}}{2.0 \ \Omega} = 1.93 \text{ A}.$

Therefore $\quad \boxed{I_1 = 3.23 \text{ A down}}, \quad \boxed{I_2 = 1.54 \text{ A down}}, \quad \boxed{I_3 = 1.02 \text{ A down}},$

and $\quad \boxed{I_4 = I_5 = I_6 = 1.93 \text{ A left}}.$

51.   From the junction theorem, $\quad I_3 = I_1 + I_2, \quad$ and $\quad I_2 = I_4 + I_5. \quad$ So $\quad I_3 = I_1 + I_4 + I_5.$

Around the left loop in counterclockwise direction,

$\qquad\qquad 6.0 \text{ V} - I_1 (12 \ \Omega) + 12 \text{ V} - I_3 (6.0 \ \Omega) - I_1 (2.0 \ \Omega) = 0,$

or $\quad 14I_1 + 6I_3 = 18.$ $\qquad\qquad\qquad\qquad\qquad\qquad$ Eq. (1)

Around the middle loop in clockwise direction,

$\qquad\qquad 12 \text{ V} - I_3 (6.0 \ \Omega) - I_2 (4.0 \ \Omega) + 6.0 \text{ V} - I_4 (8.0 \ \Omega) = 0,$

or $\quad 4I_2 + 6I_3 + 8I_4 = 18, \quad$ or $\quad -4I_1 + 10I_3 + 8I_4 = 18.$ $\qquad\qquad$ Eq. (2)

Around the right loop in counterclockwise direction, $6.0\text{ V} - I_4(8.0\text{ }\Omega) + I_5(10\text{ }\Omega) = 0$,

or $8I_4 - 10I_5 = 6$,   or $10I_1 - 10I_3 + 18I_4 = 6$.   Eq. (3)

Solving, $\boxed{I_1 = 0.664\text{ A left}}$, $\boxed{I_2 = 0.786\text{ A right}}$, $\boxed{I_3 = 1.450\text{ A up}}$,

$\boxed{I_4 = 0.770\text{ A down}}$, $\boxed{I_5 = 0.016\text{ A down}}$,   and $\boxed{I_6 = 0.664\text{ A down}}$.

52.   (a). The voltage across the capacitor decreases exponentially when a capacitor is discharged.

53.   (c). The current through the capacitor decreases exponentially when a capacitor is charged.

54.   (d) because the time constant $\tau = RC$.

55.   (a) Just after the switch is closed, the capacitor is not charged.

So $V_C = \boxed{0}$ and $V_R = V_o - V_C = \boxed{V_o}$.

(b) After one time constant, $V_C = \boxed{0.63V_o}$ and $V_R = V_o - V_C = \boxed{0.37V_o}$.

(c) After many time constants, the capacitor is fully charged.

So $V_C = \boxed{V_o}$ and $V_R = \boxed{0}$.

56.   (a) By definition, $\tau = \boxed{1.5\text{ s}}$.

(b) $V_C = V_o\left(1 - e^{-t/\tau}\right) = V_o\left(1 - e^{-10}\right) = 0.99995$,

So the percentage is $\dfrac{V_C}{V_o} = \boxed{99.995\%}$.

57. $\tau = RC$,   ☞ $R = \dfrac{\tau}{C} = \dfrac{2.0\text{ s}}{1.0 \times 10^{-6}\text{ F}} = 2.0 \times 10^6\text{ }\Omega = \boxed{2.0\text{ M}\Omega}$.

58. $V_C = V_o e^{-t/\tau}$,   ☞ $0.5 = e^{-t/\tau}$,   or $\ln 0.5 = -\dfrac{t}{\tau}$.

So $t = \boxed{0.693\,\tau}$.

59.   (a) $\tau = RC$,   ☞ $R = \dfrac{\tau}{C} = \dfrac{1.50\text{ s}}{1.00 \times 10^{-6}\text{ F}} = 1.50 \times 10^6\text{ }\Omega = \boxed{1.50\text{ M}\Omega}$.

(b) $V_C = V_o\left(1 - e^{-t/\tau}\right) = (12.0\text{ V})\left(1 - e^{-3}\right) = \boxed{11.4\text{ V}}$.

60.   (a) The potential difference on the capacitor is zero immediately after the switch is closed because the capacitor is uncharged.

$V_C = V_0\left(1-e^{-t/\tau}\right) = V_0\left(1-e^0\right) = 0.$ So the potential difference across the resistor is $\boxed{24\ \text{V}}$.

(b) $\boxed{0}$.

(c) $I = \dfrac{\mathcal{E}}{R} = \dfrac{24\ \text{V}}{6.0\ \Omega} = \boxed{4.0\ \text{A}}$.

61.   (a) $V_C = V_0\left(1-e^{-t/\tau}\right) = (24\ \text{V})\left(1-e^{-4}\right) = 23.56\ \text{V}.$

So $Q = C\,V_C = (40\times 10^{-6}\ \text{F})(23.56\ \text{V}) = \boxed{9.4\times 10^{-4}\ \text{C}}$.

(b) After a long time, the capacitor is fully charged. $V_C = \boxed{24\ \text{V}}$ and $V_R = \boxed{0}$.

62.   At $t = 2\tau$, $V_C = V_0\left(1-e^{-t/\tau}\right) = (12\ \text{V})\left(1-e^{-2}\right) = 10.38\ \text{V}.$

At $t = 4\tau$, $V_C = (12\ \text{V})\left(1-e^{-4}\right) = 11.78\ \text{V}.$ So $\Delta V_C = 11.78\ \text{V} - 10.38\ \text{V} = \boxed{1.4\ \text{V}}$, an increase.

63.   (a) At $t = 0$, $V_C = \boxed{0}$, $I = \dfrac{\mathcal{E}}{R} = \dfrac{4(1.5\ \text{V})}{3.0\times 10^6\ \Omega} = 2.0\times 10^{-6}\ \text{A} = \boxed{2.0\ \mu\text{A}}$.

(b) $\tau = RC = (3.0\times 10^6\ \Omega)(0.28\times 10^{-6}\ \text{F}) = 0.84\ \text{s}.$ $V_C = V_0\left(1-e^{-t/\tau}\right) = (6.0\ \text{V})\left(1-e^{-4.0/0.84}\right) = 5.95\ \text{V}.$

So $Q = CV_C = (0.28\times 10^{-6}\ \text{F})(5.95\ \text{V}) = \boxed{1.7\times 10^{-6}\ \text{C}}$.

64.   (b).

65.   (c).

66.   (a).

67.   (a) An ammeter has very low resistance, so if it were connected in parallel in a circuit, the circuit current would be very high and the galvanometer could burn out.

(b) A voltmeter has very high resistance, so if it were connected in series in a circuit, it would read the voltage of the source because it has the highest resistance (most probably) and therefore the most voltage drop among the circuit elements.

68. $I_g = \dfrac{IR_s}{r + R_s}$,   ☞ $R_s = \dfrac{I_g r}{I - I_g} = \dfrac{(2000\times 10^{-6}\ \text{A})(100\ \Omega)}{30\ \text{A} - 2000\times 10^{-6}\ \text{A}} = 0.00667\ \Omega = \boxed{6.7\ \text{m}\Omega}$.

69. $I_g = \dfrac{V}{r + R_m}$,   ☞ $R_m = \dfrac{V}{I_g} - r = \dfrac{15\ \text{V}}{2000\times 10^{-6}\ \text{A}} - 100\ \Omega = 7.4\times 10^3\ \Omega = \boxed{7.4\ \text{k}\Omega}$.

70. $I_g = \dfrac{IR_s}{r + R_s}$, ☞ $R_s = \dfrac{I_g r}{I - I_g} = \dfrac{(600 \times 10^{-6}\ \text{A})(50\ \Omega)}{5.0\ \text{A} - 600 \times 10^{-6}\ \text{A}} = 6.0 \times 10^{-3}\ \Omega = \boxed{6.0\ \text{m}\Omega}$.

71. $I_g = \dfrac{V}{r + R_m}$, ☞ $R_m = \dfrac{V}{I_g} - r = \dfrac{10\ \text{V}}{200 \times 10^{-6}\ \text{A}} - 20\ \Omega = 4.998 \times 10^4\ \Omega = \boxed{50\ \text{k}\Omega}$.

72. Ammeter is connected in series. $\quad I = \dfrac{V}{R + R_a} = \dfrac{6.0\ \text{V}}{10\ \Omega + 1.0 \times 10^{-3}\ \Omega} = \boxed{0.59994\ \text{A}}$.

73. Voltmeter is connected in parallel. $\quad I = \dfrac{V}{R_v} = \dfrac{6.0\ \text{V}}{30 \times 10^3\ \Omega} = 2.0 \times 10^{-4}\ \text{A} = \boxed{0.20\ \text{mA}}$.

74. (a) The current reading I is the total current through the parallel combination R_p (R and R_v).

So the voltage reading is $V = IR_p = I\dfrac{R_v R}{R_v + R}$.

Therefore $\quad R = \dfrac{V}{I - (V/R_v)}$.

(b) If R_v is ∞, $R = \dfrac{V}{I}$, i.e., the measurement is "perfect."

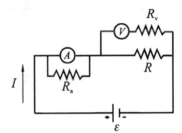

75. (a) The current reading I is the current through R and the voltage reading is the total voltage across R and R_a.

So $\quad V = I(R + R_a)$, ☞ $R = \dfrac{V}{I} - R_a$.

(b) If $R_a = 0$, $R = \dfrac{V}{I}$, i.e., the measurement is "perfect."

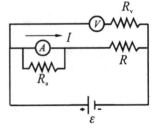

76. (a).

77. (c).

78. The fuse and the switch are on the ground side of the circuit. An open switch or blown fuse would potentially leave the motor at a high voltage if it were touched by a person.

79. Since current is caused by voltage (potential difference), a high voltage can produce high "harmful" current even though the resistance of a body is high.

80. A conductor has very low resistance. The resistance of the wire between the feet is very very small, so the voltage between the feet is also small and so is the current through the bird, most continues through the wire.

81. It is safer to jump. If you step off the car one foot at a time, there will be a high voltage between your feet. If you jump, the voltage between your feet is zero because your feet will be at the same potential all the time.

82. The case is grounded because if the hot wire accidentally touches the case, the potential of the case is zero.

83. $R_p = \dfrac{R_1 R_2}{R_1 + R_2} = \dfrac{(50\ \Omega)(50\ \Omega)}{50\ \Omega + 50\ \Omega} = 25\ \Omega.$ $R_s = R_p + R_3 = 25\ \Omega + 50\ \Omega = \boxed{75\ \Omega}.$

84. $R_s = R_1 + R_2 = 100\ \Omega + 100\ \Omega = 200\ \Omega.$ $R_p = \dfrac{R_s R_3}{R_s + R_3} = \dfrac{(200\ \Omega)(100\ \Omega)}{200\ \Omega + 100\ \Omega} = \boxed{66.7\ \Omega}.$

85. $R_s = R_1 + \dfrac{R_2 R_3}{R_2 + R_3} = 4.0\ \Omega + \dfrac{(6.0\ \Omega)R_3}{6.0\ \Omega + R_3} = 7.0\ \Omega.$

    Solving, $R_3 = \boxed{6.0\ \Omega}.$

86. From the junction theorem, $I_1 = I_2 + I_3.$

    Around the upper loop in clockwise direction, $6.0\ \text{V} - I_1(2.0\ \Omega) - I_2(4.0\ \Omega) + 6.0\ \text{V} = 0,$

    or $2I_1 + 4I_2 = 12.$ Eq. (1)

    Around the whole circuit in clockwise direction, $6.0\ \text{V} - I_1(2.0\ \Omega) - I_3(8.0\ \Omega) + 6.0\ \text{V} = 0,$

    or $10I_1 - 8I_2 = 12.$ Eq. (2)

    Solving, $\boxed{I_1 = 2.6\ \text{A right}}$, $\boxed{I_2 = 1.7\ \text{A left}}$,   and $\boxed{I_3 = 0.86\ \text{A left}}.$

87. The total power is $P = \dfrac{V^2}{R_1} + \dfrac{V^2}{R_2} = \dfrac{(9.0\ \text{V})^2}{30\ \Omega} + \dfrac{(9.0\ \text{V})^2}{15\ \Omega} = 8.1\ \text{W} = \boxed{8.1\ \text{J/s}}.$

88. (a) $\boxed{R_1 \text{ and } R_4}$ will dissipate the most power.

    The current through the $10\ \Omega$ resistor is $P = \dfrac{V^2}{R} = \dfrac{(90\ \text{V})^2}{10\ \Omega} = \boxed{8.1 \times 10^2\ \text{W}}.$

    (b) $\dfrac{1}{R_p} = \dfrac{1}{10\ \Omega} + \dfrac{1}{5.0\ \Omega + 10\ \Omega} + \dfrac{1}{10\ \Omega} = \dfrac{4}{15\ \Omega},$ ☞ $R_p = 3.75\ \Omega.$

    So the total power is $P = \dfrac{(90\ \text{V})^2}{3.75\ \Omega} = \boxed{2.2 \times 10^3\ \text{W}}.$

89.   (a) R_2, R_3, and R_4 are in parallel combination,

$$\frac{1}{R_p} = \frac{1}{25\ \Omega} + \frac{1}{50\ \Omega} + \frac{1}{25\ \Omega} = \frac{1}{10\ \Omega}, \quad \text{so} \quad R_p = 10\ \Omega.$$

So the total current is $I = I_1 = \frac{110\ \text{V}}{100\ \Omega + 10\ \Omega} = \boxed{1.0\ \text{A}}$.

The voltage on R_p is $(1.0\ \text{A})(10\ \Omega) = 10\ \text{V}$.

Therefore $\quad I_2 = I_4 = \frac{10\ \text{V}}{25\ \Omega} = \boxed{0.40\ \text{A}}, \quad I_3 = \frac{10\ \text{V}}{50\ \Omega} = \boxed{0.20\ \text{A}}$.

(b) $P_1 = I^2 R_1 = (1.0\ \text{A})^2\,(100\ \Omega) = \boxed{100\ \text{W}}, \quad P_2 = P_4 = (0.40\ \text{A})^2\,(25\ \Omega) = \boxed{4.0\ \text{W}}$,

$P_3 = (0.20\ \text{A})^2\,(50\ \Omega) = \boxed{2.0\ \text{W}}$.

90.   Three R are in series, $\quad R_{s1} = 3R$.

This R_{s1} and R are in parallel, $\quad R_{p1} = \frac{(3R)R}{3R + R} = \frac{3}{4}\,R$.

This R_{p1} and two R are in series, $\quad R_{s2} = 2R + \frac{3}{4}\,R = \frac{11}{4}\,R$.

This R_{s2} and R are in parallel, $\quad R_{p2} = \frac{\frac{11}{4}R\,R}{\frac{11}{4}R + R} = \frac{11}{15}\,R$.

Finally this R_{p2} and two R are in series, $\quad R_{s3} = 2R + \frac{11}{15}\,R = \boxed{\frac{41}{15}\,R = 2.73R}$.

91.   Use the results in Exercise 18.90,

The current through the first two R (from left) is

$$I_1 = I_2 = \frac{V}{R_{s3}} = \frac{12.0\ \text{V}}{2.73(10.0\ \Omega)} = \boxed{0.440\ \text{A}}\ .$$

The voltage across R_{p2} is $\quad V_{p2} = I_1 R_{p2} = (0.440\ \text{A})\frac{11}{15}\,(10.0\ \Omega) = 3.23\ \text{V}$.

So the current through the third R is $\quad I_3 = \frac{3.23\ \text{V}}{10.0\ \Omega} = \boxed{0.323\ \text{A}}\ .$

The current through the next two R is $\quad I_4 = I_5 = \frac{3.23\ \text{V}}{11(10.0\ \Omega)/4} = \boxed{0.117\ \text{A}}\ .$

The voltage across R_{p1} is $\quad V_{p1} = I_4 R_{p1} = (0.117\ \text{A})\frac{3}{4}\,(10.0\ \Omega) = 0.878\ \text{V}$.

So $\quad I_6 = \frac{0.878\ \text{V}}{10.0\ \Omega} = \boxed{0.0878\ \text{A}}\ , \quad I_7 = I_8 = I_9 = \frac{0.878\ \text{V}}{3(10.0\ \Omega)} = \boxed{0.0293\ \text{A}}.$

92. $V_C = V_o\left(1 - e^{-t/\tau}\right)$.　At V_m,　$V_m = V_o\left(1 - e^{-t_m/\tau}\right)$,　☞　$e^{-t_m/\tau} = 1 - \dfrac{V_m}{V_o}$.

So　$\dfrac{t_m}{\tau} = \ln \dfrac{V_o}{V_o - V_m}$,　i.e.,　$t_m = RC \ln \dfrac{V_o}{V_o - V_m}$.　Similarly,　$t_b = RC \ln \dfrac{V_o}{V_o - V_b}$.

Therefore　$T = T_b - T_m = RC \ln \dfrac{V_o(V_o - V_m)}{(V_o - V_b)V_o} = RC \ln \dfrac{V_o - V_m}{V_o - V_b}$.　$\left(\ln x - \ln y = \ln \dfrac{x}{y}\right)$.

93. When there is no current in the ammeter,　$\mathscr{E}_1 = IR_1$　and　$\mathscr{E}_2 = IR_2$.

Dividing the two equations gives　$\dfrac{\mathscr{E}_2}{\mathscr{E}_1} = \dfrac{R_2}{R_1}$,　or　$\mathscr{E}_2 = \dfrac{R_2}{R_1} = \mathscr{E}_1$.

94. (a) $P = \dfrac{V^2}{R}$,　☞　$R = \dfrac{V^2}{P} = \dfrac{(110\text{ V})^2}{100\text{ W}} = 121\ \Omega$.

So　$I_1 = I_2 = \dfrac{V}{2R} = \dfrac{110\text{ V}}{2(121\ \Omega)} = \boxed{0.45\text{ A}}$.　$P_1 = P_2 = (0.455\text{ A})^2(121\ \Omega) = \boxed{25\text{ W}}$.

(b) $I_1 = I_2 = \dfrac{110\text{ V}}{121\ \Omega} = \boxed{0.91\text{ A}}$　and　$P_1 = P_2 = \boxed{100\text{ W}}$.

95. Top loop:　$R_{p1} = \dfrac{(12\ \Omega)(6.0\ \Omega)}{12\ \Omega + 6.0\ \Omega} = 4.0\ \Omega$,　　　$R_{s1} = 4.0\ \Omega + 3.0\ \Omega = 7.0\ \Omega$.

$R_{p2} = \dfrac{(7.0\ \Omega)(4.0\ \Omega)}{7.0\ \Omega + 4.0\ \Omega} = 2.55\ \Omega$.

$R_{s2} = 2.545\ \Omega + 7.0\ \Omega + 10\ \Omega + 5.0\ \Omega = 24.55\ \Omega$.

Bottom loop:　$R_{p1} = \dfrac{(4.0\ \Omega)(4.0\ \Omega)}{4.0\ \Omega + 4.0\ \Omega} = 2.0\ \Omega$,　　　$R_{s1} = 2.0\ \Omega + 2.0\ \Omega = 4.0\ \Omega$,

$R_{p2} = \dfrac{(4.0\ \Omega)(6.0\ \Omega)}{4.0\ \Omega + 6.0\ \Omega} = 2.4\ \Omega$.

Top and bottom combination,　$R_p = \dfrac{(24.55\ \Omega)(2.4\text{ W})}{24.55\ \Omega + 2.4\ \Omega} = 2.19\ \Omega$.

Finally,　$R_s = 2.19\ \Omega + 6.0\ \Omega + 2.0\ \Omega = 10.2\ \Omega$.

$I = \dfrac{V}{R_s} = \dfrac{120\text{ V}}{10.2\ \Omega} = \boxed{11.8\text{ A}}$.

96. $P = \dfrac{V^2}{R}$,　☞　$R = \dfrac{V^2}{P} = \dfrac{(12\text{ V})^2}{3.2\text{ W}} = 45\ \Omega$.

Since　$30\ \Omega < 45\ \Omega < 60\ \Omega$, they cannot be connected in series or parallel.

Also　$45\ \Omega = 30\ \Omega + 15\ \Omega = 30\ \Omega + \dfrac{(30\ \Omega)(30\ \Omega)}{30\ \Omega + 30\ \Omega}$.

So the connection is $\boxed{\text{two in parallel and in series with the other resistor}}$.

97.   (a) $\mathcal{E} = 3(1.5 \text{ V}) = 4.5 \text{ V}.$ $I = \dfrac{\mathcal{E}}{R+r} = \dfrac{4.5 \text{ V}}{10 \text{ }\Omega + 3(0.02 \text{ }\Omega)} = 0.447 \text{ A}.$

So $V = IR = (0.447 \text{ A})(10 \text{ }\Omega) = \boxed{4.47 \text{ V}}.$

(b) As determined in (a), $I = \boxed{0.447 \text{ A}}.$

98. $I_g = \dfrac{V}{r + R_m},$ ☞ $R_m = \dfrac{V}{I_g} - r.$

So $R_1 = \dfrac{20 \text{ V}}{200 \times 10^{-6} \text{ A}} - 50 \text{ }\Omega = 9.995 \times 10^4 \text{ }\Omega = \boxed{99.95 \text{ k}\Omega},$

$R_2 = \dfrac{100 \text{ V}}{200 \times 10^{-6} \text{ A}} - 50 \text{ }\Omega = 4.9995 \times 10^5 \text{ }\Omega = \boxed{499.95 \text{ k}\Omega},$

$R_3 = \dfrac{200 \text{ V}}{200 \times 10^{-6} \text{ A}} - 50 \text{ }\Omega = 9.9995 \times 10^5 \text{ }\Omega = \boxed{0.99995 \text{ M}\Omega}.$

99. $I_g = \dfrac{IR_s}{r + R_s},$ ☞ $R_s = \dfrac{I_g r}{I - I_g}.$ So $R_{s1} = \dfrac{(100 \times 10^{-6} \text{ A})(100 \text{ }\Omega)}{1.0 \text{ A} - 100 \times 10^{-6} \text{ A}} = 1.0 \times 10^{-2} \text{ }\Omega = \boxed{10 \text{ m}\Omega},$

$R_{s2} = \dfrac{(100 \times 10^{-6} \text{ A})(100 \text{ }\Omega)}{5.0 \text{ A} - 100 \times 10^{-6} \text{ A}} = \boxed{2.0 \text{ m}\Omega},$ and $R_{s3} = \dfrac{(100 \times 10^{-6} \text{ A})(100 \text{ }\Omega)}{10 \text{ A} - 100 \times 10^{-6} \text{ A}} = \boxed{1.0 \text{ m}\Omega}.$

CHAPTER 19

1.   (e), as unlike poles attract.

2.   (b).

3.   (c).

4.   The magnet would attract the unmagnetized iron bar when a pole end is placed at the center of its long side. If the end of the unmagnetized bar were placed at the center of the long side of the magnet, it would not be attracted.

5.   Similarities: Two kinds of poles, north and south (charges, positive and negative); like poles (charges) repel and unlike poles (charges) attract.
    Differences: Poles come in pairs (single charge can exist).

6.   No . Charge must be in motion to experience magnetic force.

7.   (b), according to the right-hand rule.

8.   Into the page according to the right-hand rule.

9.   They are parallel .

10.   (a) According to the right-hand rule: (1) negative charge , (2) no charge , (3) positive charge .

    (b) The radius of the circular orbit is proportional to the mass, so $m_3 > m_1$.

11.   (a) The bottom half would have a magnetic field directed into the page and the top half would have a magnetic field directed out of the page.

    (b) They are the same since centripetal force does not change the speed of the particle.

12. $F = qvB \sin \theta,$ ☞ $B = \dfrac{F}{qB \sin \theta} = \dfrac{20 \text{ N}}{(0.25 \text{ C})(2.0 \times 10^2 \text{ m/s}) \sin 90°} = \boxed{0.40 \text{ T}}$.

13. $F = qvB \sin \theta,$ ☞ $v = \dfrac{F}{qB \sin \theta} = \dfrac{10 \text{ N}}{(0.05 \text{ C})(0.080 \text{ T}) \sin 90°} = \boxed{2.5 \times 10^3 \text{ m/s}}$.

14. If the charges are electrons (negative), an excess negative charge accumulates on the left side of the strip, and if positive, on the right side of the strip. The sign of the voltage drop across the strip would then indicate the type of charge.

15. The magnetic field has to be to the left, looking in the direction of the beam so the magnetic force points upward. $F = qvB \sin \theta = mg$,

so $B = \dfrac{mg}{qv \sin \theta} = \dfrac{(1.67 \times 10^{-27} \text{ kg})(9.80 \text{ m/s}^2)}{(1.6 \times 10^{-19} \text{ C})(5.0 \times 10^6 \text{ m/s}) \sin 90°} = \boxed{2.0 \times 10^{-14} \text{ T to the left}}$, looking in the

direction of the beam so the magnetic force points upward, opposite to gravity.

16. The magnetic field is in the $-z$ direction since electron has negative charge, according to the right-hand rule. $F = qvB \sin \theta$,

so $B = \dfrac{F}{qv \sin \theta} = \dfrac{5.0 \times 10^{-19} \text{ N}}{(1.6 \times 10^{-19} \text{ C})(3.0 \times 10^6 \text{ m/s}) \sin 90°} = \boxed{1.0 \times 10^{-6} \text{ T in } -z \text{ direction}}$.

17. (a) $F = qvB \sin \theta = (1.6 \times 10^{-19} \text{ C})(2.0 \times 10^4 \text{ m/s})(1.2 \times 10^{-3} \text{ T}) \sin 90° = \boxed{3.8 \times 10^{-18} \text{ N}}$.

(b) $F = (1.6 \times 10^{-19} \text{ C})(2.0 \times 10^4 \text{ m/s})(1.2 \times 10^{-3} \text{ T}) \sin 45° = \boxed{2.7 \times 10^{-18} \text{ N}}$.

(c) $F = \boxed{0}$ since $\sin 0° = 0$.

18. $F = qvB \sin \theta = F_0 \sin \theta$, ☞ $\sin \theta = \frac{1}{2}$, so $\theta = \boxed{30° \text{ or } 150°}$.

19. (a) $a = \dfrac{F}{m} = \dfrac{qvB \sin \theta}{m} = \dfrac{(1.6 \times 10^{-19} \text{ C})(3.0 \times 10^5 \text{ m/s})(0.50 \text{ T}) \sin 37°}{1.67 \times 10^{-27} \text{ kg}} = \boxed{8.6 \times 10^{12} \text{ m/s}^2}$.

The direction of initial acceleration is horizontal toward right, looking in direction of velocity.

(b) Since $F = qvB \sin \theta$ independent of mass, the force on the electron has the

$\boxed{\text{same magnitude but in the opposite direction}}$ because the electron has negative charge.

20. (a), according to the source right hand rule.

21. (b), according to the source right hand rule.

22. (b), according to the source right hand rule.

23. (b), according to the source right hand rule.

24. $B = \dfrac{\mu_0 I}{2\pi d} = \dfrac{(4\pi \times 10^{-7} \text{ T·m/A})(2.5 \text{ A})}{2\pi(0.25 \text{ m})} = \boxed{2.0 \times 10^{-6} \text{ T}}$.

25. $B = \dfrac{\mu_0 I}{2\pi d}$, ☞ $d = \dfrac{\mu_0 I}{2\pi B} = \dfrac{(4\pi \times 10^{-7}\ \text{T·m/A})(5.0\ \text{A})}{2\pi(4.0 \times 10^{-6}\ \text{T})} = \boxed{0.25\ \text{m}}$.

26. $B = N\dfrac{\mu_0 I}{2r}$, ☞ $I = \dfrac{2rB}{N\mu_0} = \dfrac{2(0.15\ \text{m})(0.80 \times 10^{-3}\ \text{T})}{(50)(4\pi \times 10^{-7}\ \text{T·m/A})} = \boxed{3.8\ \text{A}}$.

27. $n = \dfrac{100\ \text{turns}}{0.20\ \text{m}} = 500\ \text{turns/m}$. $B = \mu_0 n I$,   ☞ $I = \dfrac{B}{\mu_0 n} = \dfrac{1.5 \times 10^{-3}\ \text{T}}{(4\pi \times 10^{-7}\ \text{T·m/A})(500\ /\text{m})} = \boxed{2.4\ \text{A}}$.

28. (a) The fields by the two wires are equal in magnitude and opposite in direction. So the net field is $\boxed{0}$.

    (b) The fields by the two wires are equal in magnitude and in the same direction. So the net field is

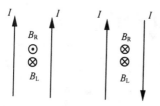

$$B = 2B_R = 2\,\dfrac{\mu_0 I}{2\pi d} = \dfrac{\mu_0 I}{\pi d} = \dfrac{(4\pi \times 10^{-7}\ \text{T·m/A})(4.0\ \text{A})}{\pi(0.25\ \text{m})} = \boxed{6.4 \times 10^{-6}\ \text{T}}.$$

29. The magnitudes at both locations are the same.

    Calculate for the location to the right of I_2. $B = \dfrac{\mu_0 I}{2\pi d}$.

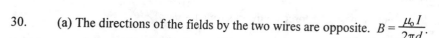

$$B_1 = \dfrac{(4\pi \times 10^{-7}\ \text{T·m/A})(1.5\ \text{A})}{2\pi(0.35\ \text{m})} = 8.57 \times 10^{-7}\ \text{T},$$

$$B_2 = \dfrac{(4\pi \times 10^{-7}\ \text{T·m/A})(1.5\ \text{A})}{2\pi(0.15\ \text{m})} = 2.0 \times 10^{-6}\ \text{T}.$$

So the net field is $B = B_1 + B_2 = 7.57 \times 10^{-7}\ \text{T} + 2.0 \times 10^{-6}\ \text{T} = \boxed{2.9 \times 10^{-6}\ \text{T}}$.

30. (a) The directions of the fields by the two wires are opposite. $B = \dfrac{\mu_0 I}{2\pi d}$.

$$B_1 = \dfrac{(4\pi \times 10^{-7}\ \text{T·m/A})(8.0\ \text{A})}{2\pi(0.060\ \text{m})} = 2.67 \times 10^{-5}\ \text{T},$$

$$B_2 = \dfrac{(4\pi \times 10^{-7}\ \text{T·m/A})(2.0\ \text{A})}{2\pi(0.060\ \text{m})} = 6.67 \times 10^{-6}\ \text{T}.$$

So the net field is $B = B_1 - B_2 = 2.67 \times 10^{-5}\ \text{T} - 6.67 \times 10^{-6}\ \text{T} = \boxed{2.0 \times 10^{-5}\ \text{T}}$.

    (b) Assume the net field is zero at x from wire 1.

$$B_1 = \dfrac{\mu_0 (8.0\ \text{A})}{2\pi x} = \dfrac{\mu_0 (2.0\ \text{A})}{2\pi(0.12\ \text{m} - x)},\quad \text{or}\quad x = 4(0.12\ \text{m} - x).$$

Solve for $x = 9.6 \times 10^{-2}\ \text{m} = \boxed{9.6\ \text{cm from wire 1}}$.

31. $d = \sqrt{(0.12 \text{ m})^2 + (0.090 \text{ m})^2} = 0.15 \text{ m}, \quad \theta = \tan^{-1} \dfrac{0.12 \text{ m}}{0.090 \text{ m}} = 53.1°.$

$$B_2 = \frac{\mu_0 I_2}{2\pi d_2} = \frac{(4\pi \times 10^{-7} \text{ T·m/A})(2.0 \text{ A})}{2\pi(0.090 \text{ m})} = 4.44 \times 10^{-6} \text{ T},$$

so $\quad \mathbf{B}_2 = -4.44 \times 10^{-6} \text{ T } \hat{\mathbf{x}},$

$$B_1 = \frac{(4\pi \times 10^{-7} \text{ T·m/A})(8.0 \text{ A})}{2\pi(0.15 \text{ m})} = 1.07 \times 10^{-5} \text{ T}.$$

$\mathbf{B}_1 = (1.07 \times 10^{-5} \text{ T})(-\cos 53.1° \, \hat{\mathbf{x}} - \sin 53.1° \, \hat{\mathbf{y}}) = (-6.42 \times 10^{-6} \text{ T } \hat{\mathbf{x}} - 8.56 \times 10^{-6} \text{ T } \hat{\mathbf{y}}).$

So the net field is $\mathbf{B} = \mathbf{B}_1 + \mathbf{B}_2 = (-1.09 \times 10^{-5} \text{ T } \hat{\mathbf{x}} - 8.56 \times 10^{-6} \text{ T } \hat{\mathbf{y}}),$

or $\quad B = \sqrt{(1.09 \times 10^{-5} \text{ T})^2 + (8.56 \times 10^{-6} \text{ T})^2} = \boxed{1.4 \times 10^{-5} \text{ T}}.$

The angle between the field and a horizontal to the left is

$\alpha = \tan^{-1} \dfrac{8.56 \times 10^{-6} \text{ T}}{1.09 \times 10^{-5} \text{ T}} = \boxed{38° \text{ below a horizontal line to the left}}.$

32. (a) The fields by the two wires are in the same direction.

$$B_1 = \frac{\mu_0 I_1}{2\pi d_1} = \frac{(4\pi \times 10^{-7} \text{ T·m/A})(8.0 \text{ A})}{2\pi(0.060 \text{ m})} = 2.67 \times 10^{-5} \text{ T},$$

$$B_2 = \frac{(4\pi \times 10^{-7} \text{ T·m/A})(2.0 \text{ A})}{2\pi(0.060 \text{ m})} = 6.67 \times 10^{-6} \text{ T}.$$

So the net field is $B = B_1 + B_2 = 2.67 \times 10^{-5} \text{ T} + 6.67 \times 10^{-6} \text{ T} = \boxed{3.3 \times 10^{-5} \text{ T}}.$

(b) Since the fields by the two wires in between the line perpendicular to and joining the wires are in the same direction, there is $\boxed{\text{no place}}$ where the magnetic field is zero. However, outside the two wires on the same line there is a location (closer to I_2) where the magnetic field is zero.

33. $B = \dfrac{\mu_0 I}{2r} = \dfrac{(4\pi \times 10^{-7} \text{ T·m/A})(1.8 \text{ A})}{0.12 \text{ m}} = \boxed{1.9 \times 10^{-5} \text{ T, toward observer (up)}}.$

34. The Earth's magnetic field at the equator is about 10^{-5} T.

$B = \dfrac{\mu_0 I}{2r}, \quad \Longrightarrow \quad I = \dfrac{2rB}{\mu_0} = \dfrac{2(0.10 \text{ m})(10^{-5} \text{ T})}{4\pi \times 10^{-7} \text{ T·m/A}} = \boxed{1.6 \text{ A}}.$

35. $B = N \dfrac{\mu_0 I}{2r} = \dfrac{4(4\pi \times 10^{-7} \text{ T·m/A})(2.0 \text{ A})}{2(0.050 \text{ m})} = \boxed{1.0 \times 10^{-4} \text{ T, away from observer}}.$

36. The currents are opposite and so the fields produced by the two loops are also opposite.

So $\quad B_1 = \dfrac{\mu_0 I_1}{2r_1} = \dfrac{\mu_0 I_2}{2r_2}, \quad \Longrightarrow \quad r_2 = \dfrac{I_2}{I_1} r_1 = \dfrac{2.0 \text{ A}}{1.0 \text{ A}} (5.0 \text{ cm}) = \boxed{10 \text{ cm}}.$

37. $n = \dfrac{1000}{0.10 \text{ m}} = 10\,000 \text{ /m}$. $B = \mu_0 nI$, ☞ $I = \dfrac{B}{\mu_0 n} = \dfrac{4.0 \times 10^{-4} \text{ T}}{(4\pi \times 10^{-7} \text{ T·m/A})(10\,000 \text{ /m})} = \boxed{3.2 \times 10^{-2} \text{ A}}$.

38. $n_1 = 200 \text{ /cm} = 200 \times 10^2 \text{ /m}$ and $n_2 = 180 \text{ /cm} = 180 \times 10^2 \text{ /m}$.

The fields by the two coils are opposite. So the net field is

$B = B_2 - B_1 = \mu_0 n_2 I_2 - \mu_0 n_1 I_1$

$= (4\pi \times 10^{-7} \text{ T·m/A})[(180 \times 10^2 \text{ /m})(15 \text{ A}) - (200 \times 10^2 \text{ /m})(10 \text{ A})] = \boxed{8.8 \times 10^{-2} \text{ T}}$.

39. The two fields by the two wires are perpendicular to each other.

$B_1 = \dfrac{\mu_0 I_1}{2\pi d_1} = \dfrac{(4\pi \times 10^{-7} \text{ T·m/A})(15 \text{ A})}{2\pi(0.10 \text{ m})} = 3.0 \times 10^{-5} \text{ T along the page out.}$

$B_2 = B_1 = 3.0 \times 10^{-5} \text{ T into the page.}$

So the net field is

$B = \sqrt{B_1^2 + B_2^2} = \sqrt{(3.0 \times 10^{-5} \text{ T})^2 + (3.0 \times 10^{-5} \text{ T})^2} = \boxed{4.2 \times 10^{-5} \text{ T}}$.

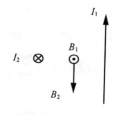

40. $d = \sqrt{(a/2)^2 + (a/2)^2} = \dfrac{a}{\sqrt{2}}$.

$B_1 = B_2 = B_3 = B_4 = \dfrac{\mu_0 I}{2\pi d} = \dfrac{\mu_0 I}{2\pi(a/\sqrt{2})} = \dfrac{\mu_0 I}{\sqrt{2}\,\pi a}$.

So the net field is $B = B_1 + B_4 = 2\,\dfrac{\mu_0 I}{\sqrt{2}\,\pi a} = \boxed{\dfrac{\sqrt{2}\,\mu_0 I}{\pi a}}$,

at 45° toward the lower-left wire (wire 3).

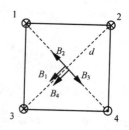

41. (a) Magnetic force provides centripetal force. $F = qvB \sin \theta = m\dfrac{v^2}{R}$,

so $R = \dfrac{mv}{qB \sin \theta} = \dfrac{mv}{qB}$ (sin 90° = 1).

The frequency is $f = \dfrac{1}{T} = \dfrac{1}{2\pi R/v} = \dfrac{v}{2\pi R} = \boxed{\dfrac{qB}{2\pi m}}$.

(b) $T = \dfrac{1}{f} = \boxed{\dfrac{2\pi m}{qB}}$, independent of m and v.

(c) $R = \dfrac{(9.11 \times 10^{-31} \text{ kg})(10^5 \text{ m/s})}{(1.6 \times 10^{-19} \text{ C})(10^{-4} \text{ T})} = \boxed{5.7 \times 10^{-3} \text{ m}}$.

$f = \dfrac{(1.6 \times 10^{-19} \text{ C})(10^{-4} \text{ T})}{2\pi(9.11 \times 10^{-31} \text{ kg})} = \boxed{2.8 \times 10^6 \text{ Hz}}$.

42. (b).

43.   (d).

44.   Toward you according to the source right-hand rule.

45.   Away from you according to the right-hand rule (electron has negative charge).

46.   (a) $B = \mu n I = K_m \mu_o n I = (2000)(4\pi \times 10^{-7} \text{ T·m/A})(100 \times 10^2 \text{ /m})(1.2 \text{ A}) = \boxed{30 \text{ T}}$.

       (b) $B_o = \mu_o n I$,   ☞ $\dfrac{B}{B_o} = K_m = \boxed{2000}$.

47.   Electric force provides centripetal force. $F = \dfrac{kq_1 q_2}{r^2} = \dfrac{ke^2}{r^2} = m \dfrac{v^2}{r}$,

       so $v = \sqrt{\dfrac{k}{m\,r}}\, e = \sqrt{\dfrac{9.0 \times 10^9 \text{ N·m}^2/\text{C}^2}{(9.11 \times 10^{-31} \text{ kg})(0.053 \times 10^{-9} \text{ m})}}\, (1.6 \times 10^{-19} \text{ C}) = 2.18 \times 10^6 \text{ m/s}$.

       $I = \dfrac{q}{T} = \dfrac{e}{2\pi r/v} = \dfrac{ev}{2\pi r}$.   Therefore

       $B = \dfrac{\mu_o I}{2r} = \dfrac{\mu_o\, ev/(2\pi r)}{2r} = \dfrac{\mu_o\, ev}{4\pi r^2} = \dfrac{(4\pi \times 10^{-7} \text{ T·m/A})(1.6 \times 10^{-19} \text{ C})(2.18 \times 10^6 \text{ m/s})}{4\pi (0.053 \times 10^{-9} \text{ m})^2} = \boxed{12 \text{ T}}$.

48.   (d) according to the force right-hand rule.

49.   Attract for currents in the same direction and repel for opposite currents.

50.   It shortens because the coils of the spring attract each other.

51.   Yes , with the plane of the loop perpendicular to the magnetic field.

52. $F = ILB \sin \theta = (5.0 \text{ A})(1.0 \text{ m})(0.30 \text{ T}) \sin 90° = \boxed{1.5 \text{ N, } +y \text{ direction}}$ (taking $+z$ as upward).

53. $F = ILB \sin \theta = (20 \text{ A})(2.0 \text{ m})(0.050 \text{ T}) \sin 37° = \boxed{1.2 \text{ N perpendicular to current and field}}$.

54.   (a) To the right .   (b) Toward top of page .

       (c) Into the page .   (d) To the left .

       (e) Into or out of the page .

55. $F = ILB \sin \theta$, ☞ $B = \dfrac{F}{IL \sin \theta} = \dfrac{1.0 \times 10^{-2}\,\text{N}}{(4.0\,\text{A})(0.50\,\text{m}) \sin 90°} = \boxed{5.0 \times 10^{-3}\,\text{T north to south}}$.

56. $F = ILB \sin \theta = (15\,\text{A})(0.75\,\text{m})(1.0 \times 10^{-4}\,\text{T}) \sin 30° = \boxed{5.6 \times 10^{-4}\,\text{N}}$.

57. (a) $F = ILB \sin \theta$, ☞ $\dfrac{F}{L} = IB \sin \theta = IB \sin 0° = \boxed{0}$.

   (b) $\dfrac{F}{L} = (10\,\text{A})(0.40\,\text{T}) \sin 90° = \boxed{4.0\,\text{N/m in } +z}$.

   (c) $\dfrac{F}{L} = (10\,\text{A})(0.40\,\text{T}) \sin 90° = \boxed{4.0\,\text{N/m in } -y}$.

   (d) $\dfrac{F}{L} = (10\,\text{A})(0.40\,\text{T}) \sin 90° = \boxed{4.0\,\text{N/m in } -z}$.

   (e) $\dfrac{F}{L} = (10\,\text{A})(0.40\,\text{T}) \sin 90° = \boxed{4.0\,\text{N/m in } +y}$.

58. $F = ILB \sin \theta$, ☞ $I = \dfrac{F}{LB \sin \theta} = \dfrac{0.050\,\text{N}}{(0.25\,\text{m})(0.30\,\text{T}) \sin 90°} = \boxed{0.67\,\text{A in } -z}$.

59. B_x has no contribution to force since $\sin \theta = 0°$.

   $F_z = I_x LB_y \sin \theta$, ☞ $\dfrac{F_z}{L} = I_x B_y \sin \theta = (10\,\text{A})(0.040\,\text{T}) \sin 90° = \boxed{0.40\,\text{N/m in } +z \text{ direction}}$.

60. $\dfrac{F}{L} = \dfrac{\mu_0 I_1 I_2}{2\pi d} = \dfrac{(4\pi \times 10^{-7}\,\text{T·m/A})(15\,\text{A})^2}{2\pi(0.15\,\text{m})} = \boxed{3.0 \times 10^{-4}\,\text{N/m repulsive}}$. It is repulsive because the

   currents are opposite and so the fields in between the wires are in the same direction.

61. $\dfrac{F}{L} = \dfrac{\mu_0 I_1 I_2}{2\pi d} = \dfrac{(4\pi \times 10^{-7}\,\text{T·m/A})(2.0\,\text{A})(4.0\,\text{A})}{2\pi(0.24\,\text{m})} = \boxed{6.7 \times 10^{-6}\,\text{N/m attractive}}$. It is attractive because the

   currents are in the same direction and so the fields in between the wires are in opposite directions.

62. $\dfrac{F}{L} = \dfrac{\mu_0 I_1 I_2}{2\pi d} = \dfrac{(4\pi \times 10^{-7}\,\text{T·m/A})(3.0\,\text{A})^2}{2\pi(0.10\,\text{m})} = \boxed{1.8 \times 10^{-5}\,\text{N/m repulsive}}$. It is repulsive because the

   currents are opposite and so the fields in between the wires are in the same direction.

63. $F = ILB \sin \theta = (1000\,\text{A})(15\,\text{m})(5.0 \times 10^{-5}\,\text{T}) \sin 90° = \boxed{0.75\,\text{N upward}}$.

64. $\dfrac{F}{L} = \dfrac{\mu_0 I_1 I_2}{2\pi d} = \dfrac{(4\pi \times 10^{-7}\,\text{T·m/A})(8.0\,\text{A})(2.0\,\text{A})}{2\pi(0.12\,\text{m})} = \boxed{2.7 \times 10^{-5}\,\text{N/m toward wire 2}}$,

   since the force is attractive.

65. $\dfrac{F}{L} = \dfrac{\mu_0 I_1 I_2}{2\pi d} = \dfrac{(4\pi \times 10^{-7}\ \text{T·m/A})(2.0\ \text{A})(8.0\ \text{A})}{2\pi\ (0.12\ \text{m})} = \boxed{2.7 \times 10^{-5}\ \text{N/m toward wire 1}}$,

since the force is attractive.

66. (a) The top wire must attract the lower wire so it can stay in equilibrium. For the magnetic force to attract, the $\boxed{\text{currents must be in the same direction}}$.

(b) Magnetic force cancels gravity. $\quad F = mg$.

So $\quad \dfrac{F}{L} = \dfrac{\mu_0 I_1 I_2}{2\pi d} = \dfrac{mg}{L}$. $\quad$ Therefore for a length of 1 m, we have

$I = I_1 = I_2 = \sqrt{\dfrac{2\pi d m g}{\mu_0}} = \sqrt{\dfrac{2\pi(0.020\ \text{m})(1.5 \times 10^{-3}\ \text{kg})(9.80\ \text{m/s}^2)}{4\pi \times 10^{-7}\ \text{T·m/A}}} = \boxed{38\ \text{A}}$.

67. For the left segment, $\quad F_L = ILB \sin\theta = (5.0\ \text{A})(0.50\ \text{m})(1.0\ \text{T}) \sin 90° = \boxed{2.5\ \text{N to the left}}$.

For the right segment, $\quad F_R = (5.0\ \text{A})(0.50\ \text{m})(1.0\ \text{T}) \sin 90° = \boxed{2.5\ \text{N to the right}}$.

For the top segment, $\quad F_L = (5.0\ \text{A})(3 \times 0.50\ \text{m})(1.0\ \text{T}) \sin 90° = \boxed{7.5\ \text{N upward}}$.

68. (a) $m = IA = (1.5\ \text{A})(0.20\ \text{m})(0.30\ \text{m}) = \boxed{9.0 \times 10^{-2}\ \text{A·m}^2}$.

(b) With the normal to the plane of the coil perpendicular to the field or $\boxed{\text{plane of coil parallel to field}}$.

69. $\boxed{\text{Zero}}$ net force as the magnetic field generated by one wire is parallel to the current in the other wire.

$\boxed{\text{Yes}}$, there is a net torque on each wire.

70. $\theta = 90° - 30° = 60°$ (θ is the angle between the normal to the plane and the field).

$\tau = IAB \sin\theta = (0.25\ \text{A})(0.20\ \text{m}^2)(0.30\ \text{T}) \sin 60° = \boxed{0.013\ \text{m·N}}$.

71. (d).

72. (d).

73. Pushing the button in both cases completes the circuit. The current through the wires activates the electromagnet, causing the clapper to be attracted and ring the bell. However, this breaks the armature contact and opens the circuit. Holding the button causes this to repeat and the bell rings continuously. For the chimes, when the circuit is completed, the electromagnet attracts the core and compresses the spring. Inertia causes it to hit one tone bar and the spring force then sends the core in the opposite direction to strike the other bar.

74. The magnetic force on the electron beam, which "prints" pictures, causes the deflection of the electrons.

75. $v = \dfrac{V}{Bd} = \dfrac{E}{B} = \dfrac{8.0 \times 10^3 \text{ V/m}}{0.040 \text{ T}} = \boxed{2.0 \times 10^5 \text{ m/s}}$.

76. (a) $v = \dfrac{V}{Bd}$, ☞ $V = vBd = (8.0 \times 10^4 \text{ m/s})(1.5 \text{ T})(0.015 \text{ m}) = \boxed{1.8 \times 10^3 \text{ V}}$.

   (b) The voltage is the $\boxed{\text{same}}$, 1.8×10^3 V, since it is independent of charge on the particle.

77. (a) $v = \dfrac{V}{Bd} = \dfrac{E}{B} = \dfrac{3000 \text{ N/C}}{0.030 \text{ T}} = \boxed{1.0 \times 10^5 \text{ m/s}}$.

   (b) The speed is the $\boxed{\text{same}}$, 1.0×10^5 m/s, since it is independent of charge on the particle.

78. $v = \dfrac{V}{Bd} = \dfrac{E}{B} = \dfrac{1.0 \times 10^3 \text{ V/m}}{0.10 \text{ T}} = 1.0 \times 10^4 \text{ m/s}$.

   Here the magnetic force provides centripetal force for the circular motion.

   $F = qvB \sin \theta = m \dfrac{v^2}{R}$,

   so $m = \dfrac{qBR \sin \theta}{v} = \dfrac{(1.6 \times 10^{-19} \text{ C})(0.10 \text{ T})(0.012 \text{ m}) \sin 90°}{1.0 \times 10^4 \text{ m/s}} = \boxed{1.9 \times 10^{-26} \text{ kg}}$.

79. (a) $v = \dfrac{V}{Bd} = \dfrac{E}{B} = \dfrac{1.0 \times 10^3 \text{ V/m}}{0.100 \text{ T}} = 1.0 \times 10^4 \text{ m/s}$.

   In circular motion magnetic force provides centripetal force.

   $F = qvB \sin \theta = m \dfrac{v^2}{R}$,

   so $m = \dfrac{qBR \sin \theta}{v} = \dfrac{(2 \times 1.6 \times 10^{-19} \text{ C})(0.10 \text{ T})(0.015 \text{ m}) \sin 90°}{1.0 \times 10^4 \text{ m/s}} = \boxed{4.8 \times 10^{-26} \text{ kg}}$.

   (b) $K = \frac{1}{2} mv^2 = \frac{1}{2}(4.8 \times 10^{-26} \text{ kg})(1.0 \times 10^4 \text{ m/s})^2 = \boxed{2.4 \times 10^{-18} \text{ J}}$.

   (c) $\boxed{\text{No}}$. The centripetal force (magnetic force) is perpendicular to velocity and it does no work.

80. $K = \frac{1}{2} mv^2$, ☞ $v = \sqrt{\dfrac{2K}{m}} = \sqrt{\dfrac{2(10 \times 10^3 \text{ eV})(1.6 \times 10^{-19} \text{ J/eV})}{2.25 \times 10^{-28} \text{ kg}}} = 3.77 \times 10^6 \text{ m/s}$.

   $v = \dfrac{E}{B}$, ☞ $B = \dfrac{E}{v} = \dfrac{2.0 \times 10^3 \text{ V/m}}{3.77 \times 10^6 \text{ m/s}} = \boxed{5.3 \times 10^{-4} \text{ T}}$.

81. $K = \frac{1}{2}mv^2$, ☞ $v = \sqrt{\frac{2K}{m}} = \sqrt{\frac{2(10 \times 10^3 \text{ eV})(1.6 \times 10^{-19} \text{ J/eV})}{1.67 \times 10^{-27} \text{ kg}}} = 1.38 \times 10^6$ m/s.

In this circular motion, the magnetic force provides the centripetal force.

$F = qvB \sin \theta = m\frac{v^2}{R}$, ☞ $B = \frac{mv}{qR \sin \theta} = \frac{(1.67 \times 10^{-27} \text{ kg})(1.38 \times 10^6 \text{ m/s})}{(1.6 \times 10^{-19} \text{ C})(0.50 \text{ m}) \sin 90°} = \boxed{2.9 \times 10^{-2} \text{ T}}$.

82. (d).

83. (b).

84. (a) $\boxed{\text{Zero}}$. (b) $\boxed{\text{Up}}$. (c) $\boxed{\text{East}}$.

85. It is a $\boxed{\text{north magnetic pole}}$ by definition since a south pole of a compass is attracted to it.

86. $K = \frac{1}{2}mv^2$, ☞ $v = \sqrt{\frac{2K}{m}} = \sqrt{\frac{2(3.0 \times 10^3 \text{ eV})(1.6 \times 10^{-19} \text{ J/eV})}{1.67 \times 10^{-27} \text{ kg}}} = 7.58 \times 10^5$ m/s.

$v = \frac{E}{B} = \frac{V}{Bd}$, ☞ $B = \frac{V}{vd} = \frac{250 \text{ V}}{(7.58 \times 10^5 \text{ m/s})(0.10 \text{ m})} = \boxed{3.3 \times 10^{-3} \text{ T}}$.

87. $B = \mu_0 \frac{N_1}{\ell} I_1 + \mu_0 \frac{N_2}{\ell} I_2 = \frac{4\pi \times 10^{-7} \text{ T·m/A}}{0.10 \text{ m}} [(3000)(5.0 \text{ A}) + (2000)(10 \text{ A})] = \boxed{0.44 \text{ T}}$.

88. $F = qvB \sin \theta = (1.6 \times 10^{-19} \text{ C})(10^3 \text{ m/s})(5.0 \times 10^{-5} \text{ T}) \sin 90° = \boxed{8.0 \times 10^{-21} \text{ N west}}$.

The direction is west because electron has negative charge.

89. Magnetic force provides the centripetal force.

$F = qvB \sin \theta = m\frac{v^2}{R}$, ☞ $v = \frac{qBR \sin 90°}{m}$. So

$K = \frac{1}{2}mv^2 = \frac{1}{2}m \frac{q^2 B^2 R^2}{m^2} = \frac{q^2 B^2 R^2}{2m} = \frac{(1.6 \times 10^{-19} \text{ C})^2 (0.80 \text{ T})^2 (0.046 \text{ m})^2}{2(1.67 \times 10^{-27} \text{ kg})} = \boxed{1.0 \times 10^{-14} \text{ J}}$.

90. $\tau = IAB \sin \theta = IL^2 B \sin \theta$, where θ is the angle between the normal to the plane and the field.

So $L = \sqrt{\frac{\tau}{IB \sin \theta}} = \sqrt{\frac{0.15 \text{ N·m}}{(10 \text{ A})(0.500 \text{ T}) \sin 40°}} = \boxed{0.22 \text{ m}}$.

91. (a) $K = \frac{1}{2}mv^2$, ☞ $v = \sqrt{\dfrac{2K}{m}} = \sqrt{\dfrac{2(1.0 \times 10^3 \text{ eV})(1.6 \times 10^{-19} \text{ J/eV})}{1.67 \times 10^{-27} \text{ kg}}} = 4.38 \times 10^5 \text{ m/s}.$

Magnetic force provides the necessary centripetal force.

$F = qvB \sin \theta = m\dfrac{v^2}{R}$, ☞ $R = \dfrac{mv}{qB} = \dfrac{(1.67 \times 10^{-27} \text{ kg})(4.38 \times 10^5 \text{ m/s})}{(1.6 \times 10^{-19} \text{ C})(4.5 \times 10^{-3} \text{ T})} = \boxed{1.0 \text{ m}}.$

(b) $T = \dfrac{2\pi R}{v} = \dfrac{2\pi m}{qB} = \dfrac{2\pi(1.67 \times 10^{-27} \text{ kg})}{(1.6 \times 10^{-19} \text{ C})(4.5 \times 10^{-3} \text{ T})} = \boxed{1.5 \times 10^{-5} \text{ s}}.$

92. $v = \dfrac{V}{Bd} = \dfrac{E}{B}$,

$B = \dfrac{E}{v} = \dfrac{100 \text{ V/m}}{2.0 \times 10^2 \text{ m/s}} = \boxed{0.50 \text{ T east}}$ if $\mathbf{v}$ is north and $\mathbf{E}$ is upward.

93. $F = qvB \sin \theta = mg$, ☞ $v = \dfrac{mg}{qB \sin \theta} = \dfrac{(9.11 \times 10^{-31} \text{ kg})(9.80 \text{ m/s}^2)}{(1.6 \times 10^{-19} \text{ C})(10^{-4} \text{ T}) \sin 90°} = \boxed{5.6 \times 10^{-7} \text{ m/s}}.$

94. For maximum force, $F = qvB \sin \theta = qvB$, ☞ $B = \dfrac{F}{qv} = \dfrac{1.8 \times 10^{-6} \text{ N}}{(4.0 \times 10^{-8} \text{ C})(3.0 \times 10^2 \text{ m/s})} = \boxed{0.15 \text{ T}}.$

95. $\tau = IAB \sin \theta = (10 \text{ A})(0.20 \text{ m})(0.30 \text{ m})(0.050 \text{ T}) \sin 90° = \boxed{3.0 \times 10^{-2} \text{ m·N}}$,

where θ is the angle between the normal to the loop and the field.

CHAPTER 20

ELECTROMAGNETIC INDUCTION

1.   (d).

2.   (d).

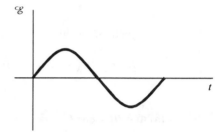

3.   (a) When the bar magnet enters the coil, the needle deflects to one side and when the magnet leaves the coil, the needle reverses direction.

       (b) $\boxed{\text{No}}$, by Lenz's law, it is repelled moving toward the loop, and attracted as it leaves the loop.

4.   (d).

5. $\boxed{\text{Counterclockwise}}$ (in head-on view).

6. $\boxed{\text{The one from the plastic tube}}$ will emerge first. When the one falls into the copper tube, a current will be induced by the changing magnetic flux in the copper tube. This current will generate a magnetic field opposite to the one of the magnet's. The two fields will generate an attractive force and slow down the falling of the magnet. There is no such current in the plastic tube because it is an insulator.

7.   Sound waves cause the resistance of the button to change as described. This results in change in the current, so the sound waves produce electrical pulses. These pulses travel through the phone lines, and to a receiver. The receiver has a coil wrapped around a magnet, and the pulses create a varying magnetic field as they pass through the coil causing the diaphragm to vibrate and thus produce sound waves as the diaphragm vibrates in the air.

8. $\Phi = BA \cos \theta$, where θ is the angle between the field and the normal to the loop.

       (a) $\Phi = BA \cos 90° = \boxed{0}$.

       (b) $\Phi = (0.30 \text{ T})(0.015 \text{ m}^2) \cos (90° - 37°) = \boxed{2.7 \times 10^{-3} \text{ T·m}^2}$.

       (c) $\Phi = (0.30 \text{ T})(0.015 \text{ m}^2) \cos 0° = \boxed{4.5 \times 10^{-3} \text{ T·m}^2}$.

9.   (a) $\Phi = BA \cos \theta = BA \cos 90° = \boxed{0}$.

      (b) $\Phi = (0.15 \text{ T})(\pi)(0.20 \text{ m})^2 \cos 0° = \boxed{1.9 \times 10^{-2} \text{ T·m}^2}$.

      (c) $\Phi = (0.15 \text{ T})(\pi)(0.20 \text{ m})^2 \cos 40° = \boxed{1.4 \times 10^{-2} \text{ T·m}^2}$.

10. $\mathscr{E} = -N\dfrac{\Delta\Phi}{\Delta t} = -N\dfrac{A\Delta B}{\Delta t} = -(1)\dfrac{(0.020 \text{ m}^2)(0 - 0.30 \text{ T})}{0.0045 \text{ s}} = \boxed{1.3 \text{ V}}$.

11.   The length of the third side of the right triangle is $\sqrt{(0.500 \text{ m})^2 - (0.400 \text{ m})^2} = 0.300 \text{ m}$.

      $\Phi = BA \cos \theta = (0.550 \text{ T})(\frac{1}{2})(0.300 \text{ m})(0.400 \text{ m}) \cos 0° = \boxed{3.3 \times 10^{-2} \text{ T·m}^2}$.

12.   (a) $\Phi = NBA \cos 6$,   ☞ $A = \dfrac{\Phi}{NB \cos 6} = \dfrac{0.50 \text{ T·m}^2}{(10)(0.25 \text{ T}) \cos 0°} = \boxed{0.20 \text{ m}^2}$.

      (b) $\theta = 90° - 60° = 30°$. $A = \dfrac{0.50 \text{ T·m}^2}{(10)(0.25 \text{ T}) \cos 30°} = \boxed{0.23 \text{ m}^2}$.

13. $\Phi = BA \cos 6 = (\mu_0 nI)A \cos 0° = (4\pi \times 10^{-7} \text{ T·m/A})(250 \text{ /m})(1.5 \text{ A})(\pi)(0.030 \text{ m})^2 = \boxed{1.3 \times 10^{-6} \text{ T·m}^2}$.

14. $\mathscr{E} = -N\dfrac{\Delta\Phi}{\Delta t} = -N\dfrac{A\Delta B}{\Delta t} = -(1)\dfrac{(0.40 \text{ m}^2)(-0.20 \text{ T})}{10^{-3} \text{ s}} = \boxed{80 \text{ V}}$.

15. $\mathscr{E} = -N\dfrac{\Delta\Phi}{\Delta t} = -N\dfrac{A\Delta B}{\Delta t} = -(1)\dfrac{(0.40 \text{ m})^2(0 - 0.100 \text{ T})}{0.010 \text{ s}} = \boxed{1.6 \text{ V}}$.

16. $\mathscr{E} = -N\dfrac{\Delta\Phi}{\Delta t} = -N\dfrac{A\Delta B}{\Delta t} = -(60)\dfrac{5.0 \text{ Wb} - 35 \text{ Wb}}{0.10 \text{ s}} = 1.8 \times 10^4 \text{ V}$.

      So $R = \dfrac{\varepsilon}{I} = \dfrac{1.8 \times 10^4 \text{ V}}{3.6 \times 10^3 \text{ A}} = \boxed{5.0 \text{ }\Omega}$.

17. $\mathscr{E} = IR = (40 \text{ A})(2.5 \text{ }\Omega) = 100 \text{ V}$.   Also $\mathscr{E} = -N\dfrac{\Delta\Phi}{\Delta t}$,

      so $\Delta t = -N\dfrac{\Delta\Phi}{\mathscr{E}} = -(1)\dfrac{-30 \text{ T·m}^2}{100 \text{ V}} = \boxed{0.30 \text{ s}}$.

18. $\mathscr{E} = -N\dfrac{\Delta\Phi}{\Delta t} = -N\dfrac{A\Delta B}{\Delta t}$,   ☞ $\Delta B = -\dfrac{\mathscr{E}\Delta t}{NA} = -\dfrac{(9.0 \text{ V})(0.20 \text{ s})}{(50)(\pi)(0.10 \text{ m})^2} = -1.15 \text{ T}$.

      So the final magnetic field is $1.5 \text{ T} + (-1.15 \text{ T}) = \boxed{0.35 \text{ T}}$.

19. $\mathscr{E} = -N\dfrac{\Delta\Phi}{\Delta t} = -N\dfrac{B\Delta A}{\Delta t} = -(1)\dfrac{(0.15\text{ T})(\pi)[(0.20\text{ m})^2 - (0.10\text{ m})^2]}{0.040\text{ s}} = -0.35\text{ V, i.e., }\boxed{0.35\text{ V}}.$

20. (a) $\mathscr{E} = -N\dfrac{\Delta\Phi}{\Delta t} = -N\dfrac{A\Delta B}{\Delta t} = -(1)\dfrac{(0.10\text{ m}^2)(1.0\text{ T} - 0)}{2.0 \times 10^{-3}\text{ s}} = \boxed{-50\text{ V}}.$

(b) $\mathscr{E} = -(10)\dfrac{(0.10\text{ m}^2)(0.6\text{ T} - 1.0\text{ T})}{5.0 \times 10^{-3}\text{ s} - 2.0 \times 10^{-3}\text{ s}} = \boxed{+13\text{ V}}.$

(c) $\mathscr{E} = -(10)\dfrac{(0.10\text{ m}^2)(0.6\text{ T} - 0.6\text{ T})}{9.0 \times 10^{-3}\text{ s} - 5.0 \times 10^{-3}\text{ s}} = \boxed{0}.$

(d) $\mathscr{E} = -(10)\dfrac{(0.10\text{ m}^2)(0\text{ T} - 0.6\text{ T})}{14 \times 10^{-3}\text{ s} - 9.0 \times 10^{-3}\text{ s}} = \boxed{+12\text{ V}}.$

21. (a) $\boxed{\text{No}}$, the emf is zero.

(b) $\boxed{\text{Near the Earth's magnetic poles}}$.

22. $v = 320\text{ km/h} = 88.9\text{ m/s}.$ From Example 20.3, the magnitude is

$\mathscr{E} = -BLv = -(5.0 \times 10^{-5}\text{ T})(30\text{ m})(88.9\text{ m/s}) = -0.13\text{ V, i.e., }\boxed{0.13\text{ V}}.$

23. (a) From Example 20.3, the magnitude is $\mathscr{E} = BLv = (0.30\text{ T})(0.20\text{ m})(10\text{ m/s}) = \boxed{0.60\text{ V}}.$

(b) But $I = \boxed{0}$ since the metal frame is connected to insulators.

24. (a) The negative flux change simply means that the final magnetic field is opposite to the initial field.

(b) $\mathscr{E} = -N\dfrac{\Delta\Phi}{\Delta t} = -(1)\dfrac{-20\text{ Wb} - 40\text{ Wb}}{1.5 \times 10^{-3}\text{ s}} = \boxed{4.0 \times 10^4\text{ V}}.$

25. When the area is parallel to the field, the flux is zero because $\theta = 90°$ ($\Phi = BA\cos\theta$).

So $\mathscr{E} = -N\dfrac{\Delta\Phi}{\Delta t} = -(10)\dfrac{(1.8\text{ T})(0.055\text{ m}^2)\cos 0° - 0}{0.25\text{ s}} = -\boxed{4.0\text{ V}}.$

26. For the lower incline, the angle between the normal to the incline and the field is

$\theta = \sin\dfrac{0.25\text{ m}}{0.30\text{ m}} = 56.4°.$

$\Phi = BA\cos\theta = (0.50\text{ T})(0.30\text{ m})(0.45\text{ m})\cos 56.4° = \boxed{0.037\text{ T·m}^2}.$

For the upper incline, the angle between the normal to the incline and the field is

$\theta = \sin\dfrac{0.20\text{ m}}{0.25\text{ m}} = 53.1°.$

$\Phi = (0.50 \text{ T})(0.45 \text{ m})(0.25 \text{ m}) \cos 53.1° = \boxed{0.034 \text{ T·m}^2}$.

For back side, $A = (0.45 \text{ m}) \left(\sqrt{(0.25 \text{ m})^2 - (0.20 \text{ m})^2} + \sqrt{(0.30 \text{ m})^2 - (0.25 \text{ m})^2} \right) = 0.142 \text{ m}^2$.

$\Phi = (0.50 \text{ T})(0.142 \text{ m}^2) \cos 0° = \boxed{0.071 \text{ T·m}^2}$.   The flux through all other surfaces is zero.

27. $\mathscr{E} = -N \dfrac{\Delta\Phi}{\Delta t} = -N \dfrac{A\Delta B}{\Delta t} = -(1) \dfrac{(\pi)(0.20 \text{ m})^2 (0 - 14 \times 10^{-3} \text{ T})}{0.25 \text{ s}} = 7.04 \times 10^{-3} \text{ V}$.

$R = \dfrac{\rho L}{A} = \dfrac{(1.70 \times 10^{-8} \ \Omega\text{·m})(2\pi)(0.20 \text{ m})}{\pi[(0.8118 \times 10^{-3} \text{ mm})/2]^2} = 0.0413 \ \Omega$.

$E = Pt = \dfrac{\mathscr{E}^2}{R} t = \dfrac{(7.04 \times 10^{-3} \text{ V})^2}{0.0413 \ \Omega} (0.25 \text{ s}) = \boxed{3.0 \times 10^{-4} \text{ J}}$.

28.   (c). The maximum induced emf is directly proportional to the area of the loop.

29.   (c).

30.   (a) When the value of emf is minimum, the plane of the loop is perpendicular to the field. At this position the magnetic flux is maximum and so when it rotates to a slightly different position the change in flux will be small.

(b) When the magnetic flux is a minimum, the plane of the loop is parallel to the field. At this position the flux is minimum and so when it rotates to a slightly different position the change in flux will be big (any change from zero is a big change).

31.   The magnet moving through the coils produces a current. As the magnet moves up and down in the coil it will induce a current in the coil which will light the bulb. However, the magnet produces the current at the expense of its kinetic energy and potential energy. The magnet's motion will therefore damp out (Lenz's law).

32.   (a) After half a period the voltage will be maximum (magnitude, the voltage is actually negative) again.

$t = \dfrac{T}{2} = \dfrac{1}{2f} = \dfrac{1}{2(60 \text{ Hz})} = \boxed{1/120 \text{ s}}$.

(b) After one-quarter of a period the voltage will be zero.

$t = \dfrac{T}{4} = \dfrac{1}{4(60 \text{ Hz})} = \boxed{1/240 \text{ s}}$.

(c) After one period, the value returns. $t = \dfrac{1}{60 \text{ Hz}} = \boxed{1/60 \text{ s}}$.

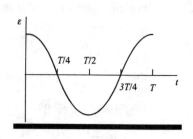

33. (a) $\mathscr{E}_0 = NBA\alpha = (1)(0.015 \text{ T})(0.10 \text{ m})^2 (2\pi)(60 \text{ Hz}) = \boxed{0.057 \text{ V}}$.

   (b) $\mathscr{E}_0 \propto N$, so $\mathscr{E}_0 = \boxed{0.57 \text{ V}}$

34. (a) $\mathscr{E} = \mathscr{E}_0 \sin 2\pi ft = \mathscr{E}_0 \sin 2\pi ft = \mathscr{E}_0 \sin 2\pi(60 \text{ Hz})t = \boxed{\mathscr{E}_0 \sin 120\pi t}$.

   (b) $\mathscr{E}_0 = NBA\alpha = 2\pi NBAf = 2\pi(10)(0.350 \text{ T})(50 \times 10^{-4} \text{ m}^2)(60 \text{ Hz}) = \boxed{6.6 \text{ V}}$.

35. From Exercise 20.34, $\mathscr{E} = \mathscr{E}_0 \sin 120\pi t = \pm(120 \text{ V}) \sin [(120\pi)(1/180 \text{ s})] = \boxed{\pm 104 \text{ V}}$.

   The initial voltage direction was not specified, so there are two possible directions.

36. $\mathscr{E}_0 = NBA\alpha = 2\pi NBAf$,

   so $N = \dfrac{\mathscr{E}_0}{2\pi BAf} = \dfrac{40 \text{ V}}{2\pi(0.200 \text{ T})(\pi)(0.15 \text{ m})^2 (60 \text{ Hz})} = \boxed{75 \text{ loops}}$.

37. (a) From Exercise 20.34, $\mathscr{E} = \mathscr{E}_0 \sin 120\pi t = (100 \text{ V}) \sin [(120\pi)(1/240 \text{ s})] = \boxed{100 \text{ V}}$.

   (b) When emf passes through zero in changing to a negative polarity, $t_1 = T/2 = 1/120$ s.

   $\mathscr{E} = (100 \text{ V}) \sin [(120\pi)(1/120 \text{ s} + 1/120 \text{ s})] = \boxed{0}$.

38. $\mathscr{E}_0 = NBA\alpha = 2\pi NBAf = 2\pi(20)(0.800 \text{ T})(\pi)(0.10 \text{ m})^2 (60 \text{ Hz}) = \boxed{1.9 \times 10^2 \text{ V}}$.

   This maximum value (positive or negative) is attained every half of a period.

   $t = \dfrac{T}{2} = \dfrac{1}{2f} = \dfrac{1}{2(60 \text{ Hz})} = \boxed{1/120 \text{ s}}$.

39. $\mathscr{E}_0 = NBA\alpha = 2\pi NBAf$, ☞ $f = \dfrac{\mathscr{E}_0}{2\pi NBA} = \dfrac{24 \text{ V}}{2\pi(100)(0.250 \text{ T})(0.080 \text{ m})(0.12 \text{ m})} = \boxed{16 \text{ Hz}}$.

40. $\mathscr{E}_0 = NBA\alpha$. $\mathscr{E}_{0A} = (1)(0.020 \text{ T})(100 \times 10^{-4} \text{ m}^2)(2\pi)(60 \text{ Hz}) = 0.075 \text{ V}$.

   $\mathscr{E}_{0B} = (1)(0.200 \text{ T})(75 \times 10^{-4} \text{ m}^2)(2\pi)(120 \text{ Hz}) = 1.1 \text{ V}$.

   So $\boxed{\text{student B's}}$ has the greater maximum emf.

41. $\mathscr{E}_b = V - IR = 110 \text{ V} - (4.00 \text{ A})(2.50 \text{ }\Omega) = \boxed{100 \text{ V}}$.

42. (a) $\mathscr{E}_b = V - IR$, ☞ $I = \dfrac{V - \mathscr{E}_b}{R} = \dfrac{12 \text{ V} - 10 \text{ V}}{0.40 \text{ }\Omega} = \boxed{5.0 \text{ A}}$.

   (b) When initially starting up, there is no back emf, so $I = \dfrac{12 \text{ V}}{0.40 \text{ }\Omega} = \boxed{30 \text{ A}}$.

43.   (a) $\mathscr{E}_b = V - IR = 240 \text{ V} - (16 \text{ A})(1.5 \text{ }\Omega) = \boxed{216 \text{ V}}$.

       (b) When initially starting up, there is no back emf,   so $I = \dfrac{240 \text{ V}}{1.5 \text{ }\Omega} = \boxed{160 \text{ A}}$.

       (c) $R_{\text{total}} = \dfrac{240 \text{ V}}{25 \text{ A}} = 9.6 \text{ }\Omega$,   so $R_s = 9.6 \text{ }\Omega - 1.5 \text{ }\Omega = \boxed{8.1 \text{ }\Omega}$.

44.   (b).

45.   (c).

46.   (c).

47.   First of all, the DC voltage has to be converted to a time varying voltage. This was achieved by the points in older cars and electronic devices in newer cars. The coil functions as a step-up transformer to give high voltage pulses. The distributor distributes the high voltage pulses to different spark plugs to ignite the gas–air mixture.

48.   (a) $\boxed{\text{Step–up}}$ since $N_s > N_p$.

       (b) $\dfrac{I_p}{I_s} = \dfrac{V_s}{V_p} = \dfrac{N_s}{N_p} = \dfrac{450}{75} = \boxed{6{:}1}$

       (c) $\dfrac{V_p}{V_s} = \dfrac{N_p}{N_s} = \dfrac{75}{450} = \boxed{1{:}6}$.

49.   (a) $\dfrac{I_p}{I_s} = \dfrac{V_s}{V_p} = \dfrac{N_s}{N_p}$,   ☞ $N_p = \dfrac{V_p}{V_s} N_s = \dfrac{8.0 \text{ V}}{2000 \text{ V}} (4000) = \boxed{16}$ turns.

       (b) $I_p = \dfrac{N_s}{N_p} I_s = \dfrac{4000}{16} (2.0 \text{ A}) = \boxed{5.0 \times 10^2 \text{ A}}$.

50.   (a) $\dfrac{I_p}{I_s} = \dfrac{V_s}{V_p} = \dfrac{N_s}{N_p}$,   ☞ $V_s = \dfrac{N_s}{N_p} V_p = \dfrac{180}{720} (120 \text{ V}) = \boxed{30 \text{ V}}$.

       (b) $I_s = \dfrac{N_p}{N_s} I_p = \dfrac{720}{180} (15 \text{ A}) = \boxed{60 \text{ A}}$.

51. $\dfrac{N_p}{N_s} = \dfrac{V_p}{V_s} = \dfrac{120 \text{ V}}{5.0 \text{ V}} = \boxed{24{:}1}$.

52.   (a) $\dfrac{I_p}{I_s} = \dfrac{V_s}{V_p} = \dfrac{N_s}{N_p} = \dfrac{10 \text{ A}}{4.0 \text{ A}} = 2.5$.   So $N_s = 2.5 (120 \text{ V}) = \boxed{3.0 \times 10^2 \text{ V}}$.

       (b) $N_p = \dfrac{4.0 \text{ A}}{10 \text{ A}} N_s = \dfrac{800}{2.5} = \boxed{3.2 \times 10^2 \text{ turns}}$.

53. (a) $\dfrac{I_p}{I_s} = \dfrac{V_s}{V_p} = \dfrac{N_s}{N_p}$, ☞ $I_s = \dfrac{N_p}{N_s} I_p = \dfrac{840}{120}(2.50\text{ A}) = \boxed{17.5\text{ A}}$.

(b) $V_s = \dfrac{110}{840}(120\text{ V}) = \boxed{15.7\text{ V}}$.

54. Since $\dfrac{I_s}{I_p} = \dfrac{V_p}{V_s}$, the efficiency $= \dfrac{I_s V_s}{I_p V_p} = \dfrac{V_p}{V_s}\dfrac{V_s}{V_p} = 1 = 100\%$, which implies the conditions are ideal and there is no loss to the wires in the windings, etc.

55. (a) $P_s = V_s I_s = (9.0\text{ V})(0.300\text{ A}) = 2.7\text{ W} < 6.0\text{ W} = P_p$. $\boxed{\text{No}}$, it is not an ideal transformer.

(b) $\varepsilon = \dfrac{P_s}{P_p} = \dfrac{2.7\text{ W}}{6.0\text{ W}} = \boxed{45\%}$.

56. (a) $\dfrac{I_p}{I_s} = \dfrac{V_s}{V_p} = \dfrac{N_s}{N_p}$, ☞ $N_s = \dfrac{V_s}{V_p} N_p = \dfrac{20\text{ V}}{120\text{ V}}(300) = \boxed{50\text{ turns}}$.

(b) $I_p = \dfrac{50}{300}(0.50\text{ A}) = \boxed{8.3 \times 10^{-2}\text{ A}}$.

57. (a) $\dfrac{N_s}{N_p} = \dfrac{V_s}{V_p} = \dfrac{6.0\text{ V}}{120\text{ V}} = \boxed{1{:}20}$.

(b) $I_p = \dfrac{1}{20}(0.50\text{ A}) = \boxed{2.5 \times 10^{-2}\text{ A}}$.

58. $\dfrac{I_p}{I_s} = \dfrac{V_s}{V_p} = \dfrac{N_s}{N_p}$, ☞ $N_s = \dfrac{V_s}{V_p} N_p = \dfrac{10\,000\text{ V}}{440\text{ V}}(150) = \boxed{3.4 \times 10^3\text{ turns}}$.

59. (a) Without stepping up, $E_o = P_o t = I_o^2 Rt = (20\text{ A})^2 (0.80\ \Omega/\text{km})(80.0\text{ km})(5.00\text{ h}) = 128\text{ kWh}$.

With stepping up, $I = I_s = \dfrac{132}{3000}(20\text{ A}) = 0.88\text{ A}$.

$E = (0.88\text{ A})^2 (0.80\ \Omega/\text{km})(80.0\text{ km})(5.00\text{ h}) = 0.248\text{ kWh}$.

So the energy saved is $128\text{ kWh} - 0.248\text{ kWh} = \boxed{128\text{ kWh}}$.

(b) The savings is $(128\text{ kWh}/5.00\text{ h})(30 \times 24\text{ h})(\$0.10/\text{kWh}) = \boxed{\$1840}$.

60. $I_s = \dfrac{P_s}{V_s} = \dfrac{10 \times 10^6\text{ W}}{20\,000\text{ V}} = 500\text{ A}$. $I_p = \dfrac{V_s}{V_p} I_s = \dfrac{20\,000\text{ V}}{100\,000\text{ V}}(500\text{ A}) = 100\text{ A}$.

So the currents in the primary and secondary are $\boxed{100\text{ A and }500\text{ A}}$.

61.   (a) At the area substation, $\dfrac{N_s}{N_p} = \dfrac{V_s}{V_p} = \dfrac{100\,000\text{ V}}{200\,000\text{ V}} = \boxed{1:2}$;

at the distributing station, $\dfrac{N_s}{N_p} = \dfrac{7200\text{ V}}{100\,000\text{ V}} = \boxed{1:14}$;

at the utility pole, $\dfrac{N_s}{N_p} = \dfrac{240\text{ V}}{7200\text{ V}} = \boxed{1:30}$.

(b) At the area substation, $\dfrac{I_s}{I_p} = \dfrac{V_p}{V_s} = \dfrac{200\,000\text{ V}}{100\,000\text{ V}} = \boxed{2.0}$;

at the distributing station, $\dfrac{I_s}{I_p} = \dfrac{100\,000\text{ V}}{7200\text{ V}} = \boxed{14}$;

at the utility pole, $\dfrac{I_s}{I_p} = \dfrac{7200\text{ V}}{240\text{ V}} = \boxed{30}$;

(c) Overall, $\dfrac{I_s}{I_p} = \dfrac{200\,000\text{ V}}{240\text{ V}} = \boxed{833}$.

62.   (a) $P_o = I^2 R = (50\text{ A})^2 (1.2\ \Omega/\text{km})(25\text{ km}) = \boxed{75\text{ kW}}$.

(b) $P = \dfrac{P_o}{15} = \dfrac{75\,000\text{ W}}{15} = 5000\text{ W}$.   So $I = \sqrt{\dfrac{P}{R}} = \sqrt{\dfrac{5000\text{ W}}{(1.2\ \Omega/\text{km})(25\text{ km})}} = 12.9\text{ A}$.

Therefore $V_s = \dfrac{I_p}{I_s} V_p = \dfrac{50\text{ A}}{12.9\text{ A}} (20\,000\text{ V}) = \boxed{77\text{ kV}}$.

63.   (a) $I_s = \dfrac{V_p}{V_s} I_p = \dfrac{440\text{ V}}{44\,000\text{ V}} (50\text{ A}) = 0.50\text{ A}$.

$P_o = I^2 R = (0.50\text{ A})^2 (1.2\ \Omega/\text{km})(175\text{ km}) = \boxed{53\text{ W}}$.

(b) $\dfrac{N_p}{N_s} = \dfrac{V_p}{V_s} = \dfrac{44\,000\text{ V}}{220\text{ V}} = \boxed{200}$.

64. $\boxed{\text{No}}$. It takes an alternating current to emit electromagnetic waves.

65.   (b).

66.   (d).

67.   Infrared (heat) radiation is absorbed by clouds (water molecules), but the sunburning ultraviolet is not.

68.   (a) $f = \dfrac{c}{\lambda} = \dfrac{3.00 \times 10^8\text{ m/s}}{2.0\text{ m}} = \boxed{1.5 \times 10^8\text{ Hz}}$.

(b) $f = \dfrac{3.00 \times 10^8\text{ m/s}}{25\text{ m}} = \boxed{1.2 \times 10^7\text{ Hz}}$.

(c) $f = \dfrac{3.00 \times 10^8\text{ m/s}}{75\text{ m}} = \boxed{4.0 \times 10^6\text{ Hz}}$.

69.   For AM: $\lambda_{min} = \dfrac{c}{f_{max}} = \dfrac{3.00 \times 10^8 \text{ m/s}}{1.7 \times 10^6 \text{ Hz}} = \boxed{1.8 \times 10^2 \text{ m}}$;

$\lambda_{max} = \dfrac{3.00 \times 10^8 \text{ m/s}}{0.53 \times 10^6 \text{ Hz}} = \boxed{5.7 \times 10^2 \text{ m}}$.

For FM: $\lambda_{min} = \dfrac{3.00 \times 10^8 \text{ m/s}}{108 \times 10^6 \text{ Hz}} = \boxed{2.8 \text{ m}}$;

$\lambda_{max} = \dfrac{3.00 \times 10^8 \text{ m/s}}{88 \times 10^6 \text{ Hz}} = \boxed{3.4 \text{ m}}$.

For TV: $\lambda_{min} = \dfrac{3.00 \times 10^8 \text{ m/s}}{890 \times 10^6 \text{ Hz}} = \boxed{0.34 \text{ m}}$,

$\lambda_{max} = \dfrac{3.00 \times 10^8 \text{ m/s}}{54 \times 10^6 \text{ Hz}} = \boxed{5.6 \text{ m}}$.

70.   The radar pulse travels twice the distance (to and from).

$d = \dfrac{ct}{2} = \dfrac{(3.00 \times 10^8 \text{ m/s})(0.24 \times 10^{-3} \text{ s})}{2} = 3.6 \times 10^4 \text{ m} = \boxed{36 \text{ km}}$.

71.   The wave travels twice the distance in the time interval.

$t = 2\dfrac{d}{c} = \dfrac{2(240\,000 \text{ mi})(1609 \text{ m/mi})}{3.00 \times 10^8 \text{ m/s}} = \boxed{2.6 \text{ s}}$.

72. $f_o = \dfrac{c}{\lambda_o} = \dfrac{3.00 \times 10^8 \text{ m/s}}{600 \times 10^{-9} \text{ m}} = 5.0 \times 10^{14} \text{ Hz}$; $f_g = \dfrac{3.00 \times 10^8 \text{ m/s}}{510 \times 10^{-9} \text{ m}} = 5.88 \times 10^{14} \text{ Hz}$.

So $\Delta f = 5.88 \times 10^{14} \text{ Hz} - 5.0 \times 10^{14} \text{ Hz} = \boxed{8.8 \times 10^{13} \text{ Hz}}$.

73.   For AM: $L = \dfrac{\lambda}{4} = \dfrac{c/f}{4} = \dfrac{c}{4f} = \dfrac{3.00 \times 10^8 \text{ m/s}}{4(0.53 \times 10^6 \text{ Hz} + 1.7 \times 10^6 \text{ Hz})/2} = \boxed{67 \text{ m}}$.

For FM, $L = \dfrac{3.00 \times 10^8 \text{ m/s}}{4(88 \times 10^6 \text{ Hz} + 108 \times 10^6 \text{ Hz})/2} = \boxed{0.77 \text{ m}}$.

74. $\lambda = 2(5.0 \text{ cm}) = 10 \text{ cm} = 0.10 \text{ m}$.

$f = \dfrac{c}{\lambda} = \dfrac{3.00 \times 10^8 \text{ m/s}}{0.10 \text{ m}} = \boxed{3.0 \times 10^9 \text{ Hz or 3.0 GHz}}$.

75.   (a) At startup, there is no back emf.

So $I_o = \dfrac{V}{R} = \dfrac{120 \text{ V}}{4.0 \ \Omega} = \boxed{30 \text{ A}}$.

(b) $\mathscr{E}_b = V - IR$,   ☞ $I = \dfrac{V - \mathscr{E}_b}{R} = \dfrac{120 \text{ V} - 110 \text{ V}}{4.0 \ \Omega} = \boxed{2.5 \text{ A}}$.

76. It is a step down transformer, so the $\boxed{\text{primary}}$ has more turns.

$$\frac{N_p}{N_s} = \frac{V_p}{V_s} = \frac{120 \text{ V}}{4.5 \text{ V}} = \boxed{27}.$$

77. $\Phi = BA \cos \theta = B\pi r^2 \cos \theta,$ ☞ $r = \sqrt{\dfrac{\Phi}{\pi B \cos 6}} = \sqrt{\dfrac{0.12 \text{ T·m}^2}{\pi(0.150 \text{ T}) \cos 45°}} = \boxed{0.60 \text{ m}}.$

78. $\dfrac{I_p}{I_s} = \dfrac{V_s}{V_p} = \dfrac{N_s}{N_p},$ ☞ $N_s = \dfrac{V_s}{V_p} N_p = \dfrac{240 \text{ V}}{1.5 \times 10^3 \text{ V}} (500) = \boxed{80 \text{ turns}}.$

79. There are two zeros in each period. So the frequency of zero emf is $2f = 2(50 \text{ Hz}) = 100 \text{ Hz}.$

Therefore the period is $\dfrac{1}{100 \text{ Hz}} = 0.01 \text{ s}$, i.e., $\boxed{\text{once every 0.01 s}}.$

80. (a) $\mathscr{E}_b = V - IR,$ ☞ $R = \dfrac{V - \mathscr{E}_b}{I} = \dfrac{120 \text{ V} - 96 \text{ V}}{6.0 \text{ A}} = 4.0 \text{ }\Omega.$

At startup, there is no back emf. So $I = \dfrac{V}{R} = \dfrac{120 \text{ V}}{4.0 \text{ }\Omega} = \boxed{30 \text{ A}}.$

(b) $R_{\text{total}} = \dfrac{120 \text{ V}}{15 \text{ A}} = 8.0 \text{ }\Omega,$ ☞ $R_s = 8.0 \text{ }\Omega - 4.0 \text{ }\Omega = \boxed{4.0 \text{ }\Omega}.$

81. (a) $\boxed{\text{Up}}.$

(b) $I = \dfrac{\mathscr{E}}{R} = \dfrac{BLv}{R} = \dfrac{(0.250 \text{ T})(0.50 \text{ m})(2.0 \text{ m/s})}{10 \text{ }\Omega} = 2.5 \times 10^{-2} = \boxed{25 \text{ mA}}.$

82. (a) $\dfrac{I_p}{I_s} = \dfrac{V_s}{V_p} = \dfrac{N_s}{N_p},$ ☞ $V_s = \dfrac{N_s}{N_p} V_p = \dfrac{840}{120} (120 \text{ V}) = \boxed{840 \text{ V}}.$

(b) $I_s = \dfrac{N_p}{N_s} I_p = \dfrac{120}{840} (14 \text{ A}) = \boxed{2.0 \text{ A}}.$

83. $\Phi = BA \cos 6 = (0.75 \text{ T})(1.0 \text{ m})^2 \cos 0° = \boxed{0.75 \text{ T·m}^2}.$

84. (a) $\dfrac{I_p}{I_s} = \dfrac{V_s}{V_p} = \dfrac{N_s}{N_p},$ ☞ $I_s = \dfrac{N_p}{N_s} I_p = \dfrac{80}{360} (3.0 \text{ A}) = \boxed{0.67 \text{ A}}.$

(b) $V_s = \dfrac{360}{80} (12 \text{ V}) = \boxed{54 \text{ V}}.$

(c) $P_s = V_s I_s = (54 \text{ V})(0.667 \text{ A}) = \boxed{36 \text{ W}}.$

85. $P = \dfrac{\mathcal{E}^2}{R}$, ☞ $\mathcal{E} = \sqrt{PR} = \sqrt{(5.0\ \text{W})(0.20\ \Omega)} = 1.0\ \text{V}.$

$\mathcal{E} = N\dfrac{\Delta\Phi}{\Delta t} = N\dfrac{A\Delta B}{\Delta t},$ ☞ $\dfrac{\Delta B}{\Delta t} = \dfrac{\mathcal{E}}{NA} = \dfrac{1.0\ \text{V}}{(1)(0.50\ \text{m})^2} = \boxed{4.0\ \text{T/s}}.$

86. There are two polarity changes in each period.

So the period is $f = \dfrac{1}{2(0.010\ \text{s})} = \boxed{50\ \text{Hz}}.$

87. $I_s = \dfrac{P_s}{V_s} = \dfrac{6.6 \times 10^3\ \text{W}}{220\ \text{V}} = 30\ \text{A}; \quad I_p = \dfrac{V_s}{V_p}I_s = \dfrac{220\ \text{V}}{20\,000\ \text{V}}(30\ \text{A}) = 0.33\ \text{A}.$

So the currents are $\boxed{0.33\ \text{A and } 30\ \text{A}}.$

88. $f = \dfrac{c}{\lambda} = \dfrac{3.00 \times 10^8\ \text{m/s}}{3 \times 10^{-15}\ \text{m}} = \boxed{1 \times 10^{23}\ \text{Hz}}.$

89. (a) $f = \boxed{50\ \text{rotations/s}}.$

(b) No, if they are ideal (lossless) the same turn ratios would work. However in reality the 50-Hz delivery would have fewer losses due to eddy currents because they are generated less frequently.

CHAPTER 21

AC CIRCUITS

1.   (c).

2. $\boxed{\text{Yes}}$, the average current in an ac circuit is zero. However, power depends on the current squared so it is nondirectional. Therefore power does not average out to zero.

3.   That means the voltage and current reach maximum at the same time, reach minimum at the same time, and are zero at the same, etc.

4. $V_{o120} = \sqrt{2} \ V_{rms1} = \sqrt{2} \ (120 \text{ V}) = \boxed{170 \text{ V}}$,   and

$V_{o240} = \sqrt{2} \ (240 \text{ V}) = \boxed{339 \text{ V}}$.

5. $I_o = \sqrt{2} \ I_{rms} = \sqrt{2} \ (5.0 \text{ A}) = \boxed{7.1 \text{ A}}$.

6. $V_{rms} = \dfrac{V_o}{\sqrt{2}} = \dfrac{156 \text{ V}}{\sqrt{2}} = \boxed{110 \text{ V}}$.

7. $\overline{P} = I_{rms}^2 R$,   ☞ $I_{rms} = \sqrt{\dfrac{\overline{P}}{R}} = \sqrt{\dfrac{15 \text{ W}}{10 \ \Omega}} = \boxed{1.2 \text{ A}}$.

8.   (a) $V_{rms} = I_{rms} R = (0.75 \text{ A})(5.0 \ \Omega) = \boxed{3.8 \text{ V}}$;

$V_o = \sqrt{2} \ V_{rms} = \sqrt{2} \ (3.75 \text{ V}) = \boxed{5.3 \text{ V}}$.

(b) $\overline{P} = I_{rms} V_{rms} = (0.75 \text{ A})(3.75 \text{ V}) = \boxed{2.8 \text{ W}}$.

9.   (a) $\overline{P} = I_{rms} V_{rms}$, $I_{rms} = \dfrac{\overline{P}}{V_{rms}} = \dfrac{1200 \text{ W}}{120 \text{ V}} = \boxed{10 \text{ A}}$.

(b) $I_o = \sqrt{2} \ I_{rms} = \sqrt{2} \ (10 \text{ A}) = \boxed{14 \text{ A}}$.

(c) $R = \dfrac{V_{rms}}{I_{rms}} = \dfrac{120 \text{ V}}{10 \text{ A}} = \boxed{12 \ \Omega}$.

10.   (a) Since $V = V_o \sin 2\pi ft$, $V_{rms} = \dfrac{V_o}{\sqrt{2}} = \dfrac{170 \text{ V}}{\sqrt{2}} = \boxed{120 \text{ V}}$.

(b) $2\pi ft = 120t$,   ☞ $T = \dfrac{1}{f} = \dfrac{2\pi}{120} = \boxed{5.2 \times 10^{-2} \text{ s}}$.

11. (a) $\bar{P} = I_{rms}^2 R$, ☞ $I_{rms} = \sqrt{\dfrac{\bar{P}}{R}} = \sqrt{\dfrac{500 \text{ W}}{25 \text{ }\Omega}} = \boxed{4.5 \text{ A}}$;

$I_o = \sqrt{2}\, I_{rms} = \sqrt{2}\ (4.47 \text{ A}) = \boxed{6.3 \text{ A}}$.

(b) $V_{rms} = I_{rms} R = (4.47 \text{ A})(25 \text{ }\Omega) = \boxed{112 \text{ V}}$; $V_o = \sqrt{2}\, V_{rms} = \sqrt{2}\ (112 \text{ V}) = \boxed{158 \text{ V}}$.

12. (a) $V = V_o \sin 2\pi f t = (85 \text{ V}) \sin 2\pi(60 \text{ Hz})t = (85 \text{ V}) \sin 120\pi t$.

So $V(2.0 \text{ s}) = (85 \text{ V}) \sin [120\pi(2.0 \text{ s})] = \boxed{0}$.

(b) $V_{rms} = \dfrac{V_o}{\sqrt{2}} = \dfrac{85 \text{ V}}{\sqrt{2}} = \boxed{60 \text{ V}}$.

13. It takes $t = \dfrac{T}{4}$ for the voltage to go from zero to its maximum value. So $T = 4(4.2 \text{ ms}) = 16.8 \text{ ms}$.

Therefore $f = \dfrac{1}{T} = \dfrac{1}{16.8 \times 10^{-3} \text{ s}} = 59.5 \text{ Hz}$.

Thus $V = V_o \sin 2\pi f t = \sqrt{2}\, V_{rms} \sin 2\pi f t = \sqrt{2}\ (120 \text{ V}) \sin [2\pi(59.5)t] = \boxed{(170 \text{ V}) \sin 119\pi t}$.

14. $\bar{P} = \dfrac{V_{rms}^2}{R}$, ☞ $R = \dfrac{V_{rms}^2}{\bar{P}} = \dfrac{(120 \text{ V})^2}{100 \text{ W}} = \boxed{144 \text{ }\Omega}$.

$I_{rms} = \dfrac{V_{rms}}{R} = \dfrac{120 \text{ V}}{144 \text{ }\Omega} = \boxed{0.833 \text{ A}}$.

15. $I_{rms} = \dfrac{\bar{P}}{V_{rms}} = \dfrac{40 \text{ W}}{120 \text{ V}} = \boxed{0.33 \text{ A}}$ and $I_o = \sqrt{2}\, I_{rms} = \sqrt{2}\ (0.333 \text{ A}) = \boxed{0.47 \text{ A}}$.

16. (a) $I_{rms} = \dfrac{\bar{P}}{V_{rms}} = \dfrac{50 \times 10^3 \text{ W}}{240 \text{ V}} = 208 \text{ A}$,   so $I_o = \sqrt{2}\, I_{rms} = \sqrt{2}\ (208 \text{ A}) = \boxed{2.9 \times 10^2 \text{ A}}$.

(b) $V_o = \sqrt{2}\, V_{rms} = \sqrt{2}\ (240 \text{ V}) = \boxed{3.4 \times 10^2 \text{ V}}$.

17. $I_{rms} = \dfrac{I_o}{\sqrt{2}} = \dfrac{8.0 \text{ A}}{\sqrt{2}} = 5.66 \text{ A}$; $V_{rms} = \dfrac{V_o}{\sqrt{2}} = \dfrac{60 \text{ V}}{\sqrt{2}} = 42.4 \text{ V}$.

So $\bar{P} = I_{rms} V_{rms} = (5.66 \text{ A})(42.4 \text{ V}) = \boxed{2.4 \times 10^2 \text{ W}}$.

18. $\bar{P} = I_{rms} V_{rms} = \dfrac{I_o}{\sqrt{2}} \dfrac{V_o}{\sqrt{2}} = \dfrac{I_o V_o}{2} = \dfrac{(2.5 \text{ A})(16 \text{ V})}{2} = \boxed{20 \text{ W}}$.

19. (a) Since $I = I_0 \sin 2\pi f t$, $\quad 2\pi f t = 380t$. $\quad$ So $\quad f = \dfrac{380}{2\pi} = \boxed{60 \text{ Hz}}$.

(b) $I_{\text{rms}} = \dfrac{I_0}{\sqrt{2}} = \dfrac{2.0 \text{ A}}{\sqrt{2}} = \boxed{1.4 \text{ A}}$.

(c) $\bar{P} = I_{\text{rms}}^2 R = (1.41 \text{ A})^2 (60 \ \Omega) = \boxed{1.2 \times 10^2 \text{ W}}$.

(d) $V_0 = I_0 R = (2.0 \text{ A})(60 \ \Omega) = 120 \text{ V}$. $\quad$ So $\quad \boxed{V = (120 \text{ V}) \sin 380t}$.

(e) $P = VI = (120 \text{ V})(2.0 \text{ A}) \sin^2 380t$. $\quad$ So $\quad \boxed{P = (240 \text{ W}) \sin^2 380t}$.

(f) $P = (240 \text{ W}) \dfrac{1 - \cos 2(380t)}{2} = 120 \text{ W} - (120 \text{ W}) \cos 2(380t)$.

The average of a sine or cosine function is zero. So $\bar{P} = 120 \text{ W}$.

20. $V_0 = \sqrt{2} \ V_{\text{rms}} = \sqrt{2} \ (50 \text{ V}) = 70.7 \text{ V}$. $\quad V_0 = \mathcal{E}_0 = NBA\omega = 2\pi NBAf$,

so $\quad B = \dfrac{\mathcal{E}_0}{2\pi NAf} = \dfrac{70.7 \text{ V}}{2\pi (40)(\pi)(0.075 \text{ m})^2 (60 \text{ Hz})} = \boxed{0.27 \text{ T}}$.

21. (b).

22. (c).

23. For a capacitor, the *lower the frequency*, the longer the charging time in each cycle. A longer charging time means more charge accumulation on the plates and therefore *more* opposition to the current (current decreases as charge accumulates).

For an inductor, the *lower the frequency*, the more slowly the current in the inductor changes, the smaller will be the rate of change in its magnetic flux, and thus the *smaller* the self-induced emf that opposes the current.

24. (b).

25. In an ac circuit, a capacitor can oppose current. This is because as the capacitor charges, the voltage across its plates increases, opposing the current. Also, an inductor can oppose current because the induced emf opposes the change in flux and thus opposes the current in the circuit.

26. One cycle is equal to 2π radians or $360°$. "The voltage across an inductor leads the current by $90°$" means the voltage leads the current by a quarter-cycle or reaches maximum a quarter-cycle ahead of the current. "The voltage across a capacitor lags the current by $90°$" means the voltage lags the current by a quarter-cycle or reaches maximum a quarter-cycle after the current.

27. $X_C = \dfrac{1}{2\pi f C}$, ☞ $C = \dfrac{1}{2\pi f X_C} = \dfrac{1}{2\pi(60\ \text{Hz})(100\ \Omega)} = \boxed{2.65 \times 10^{-5}\ \text{F}}$.

28. $X_C = \dfrac{1}{2\pi f C}$, ☞ $f = \dfrac{1}{2\pi C X_C} = \dfrac{1}{2\pi(25 \times 10^{-6}\ \text{F})(25\ \Omega)} = \boxed{2.5 \times 10^2\ \text{Hz}}$.

29. $X_C = \dfrac{1}{2\pi f C} = \dfrac{1}{2\pi(60\ \text{Hz})(2.0 \times 10^{-6}\ \text{F})} = \boxed{1.3 \times 10^3\ \Omega}$.

30. (a) $X_L = 2\pi f L = 2\pi(60\ \text{Hz})(0.050\ \text{H}) = \boxed{19\ \Omega}$.

    (b) $I_{rms} = \dfrac{V_{rms}}{X_L} = \dfrac{120\ \text{V}}{18.8\ \Omega} = \boxed{6.4\ \text{A}}$.

    (c) Voltage leads current by $\boxed{90°}$.

31. $X_C = \dfrac{1}{2\pi f C} = \dfrac{1}{2\pi(60\ \text{Hz})(50 \times 10^{-6}\ \text{F})} = 53.1\ \Omega$.   So $I_{rms} = \dfrac{V_{rms}}{X_C} = \dfrac{120\ \text{V}}{53.1\ \Omega} = \boxed{2.3\ \text{A}}$.

32. $P = IV \cos \phi = IV \cos 90° = \boxed{0}$.

33. Since $X_C = \dfrac{1}{2\pi f C}$ and $I_{rms} = \dfrac{V_{rms}}{X_C}$, $\dfrac{I_2}{I_1} = \dfrac{V/X_{C2}}{V/X_{C1}} = \dfrac{X_{C1}}{X_{C2}} = \dfrac{C_2}{C_1} = \dfrac{0.40\ \mu\text{F}}{0.25\ \mu\text{F}} = 1.6$.

    Therefore the percentage change is $\dfrac{I_2 - I_1}{I_1} = \dfrac{I_2}{I_1} - 1 = 0.60 = \boxed{60\%}$, an increase.

34. $X_L = 2\pi f L$,   ☞ $L = \dfrac{X_L}{2\pi f} = \dfrac{90\ \Omega}{2\pi(60\ \text{Hz})} = \boxed{0.24\ \text{H}}$.

35. $X_L = 2\pi f L$,   ☞ $f = \dfrac{X_L}{2\pi L} = \dfrac{400\ \Omega}{2\pi(0.250\ \text{H})} = \boxed{255\ \text{Hz}}$.

36. (a) $X_L = 2\pi f L = 2\pi(60\ \text{Hz})(0.150\ \text{H}) = 56.5\ \Omega$. $V_{rms} = I_{rms} X_L = (1.6\ \text{A})(56.5\ \Omega) = \boxed{90\ \text{V}}$.

    (b) Voltage leads current by $\boxed{90°}$.

37. $X_L = 2\pi f L = X_C = \dfrac{1}{2\pi f C}$,   ☞ $L = \dfrac{1}{4\pi^2 f^2 C} = \dfrac{1}{4\pi^2 (60\ \text{Hz})^2 (10 \times 10^{-6}\ \text{F})} = \boxed{0.70\ \text{H}}$.

38. $X_C = \dfrac{V_{rms}}{I_{rms}} = \dfrac{120\ \text{V}}{0.20\ \text{A}} = 600\ \Omega$.

    $X_C = \dfrac{1}{2\pi f C}$,   ☞ $C = \dfrac{1}{2\pi X_C f} = \dfrac{1}{2\pi(600\ \Omega)(60\ \text{Hz})} = 4.4 \times 10^{-6}\ \text{F} = \boxed{4.4\ \mu\text{F}}$.

39.   (d).

40.   (a).

41.   (d).

42.   At resonance, $X_L = X_C$, so $Z = \sqrt{R^2 + (X_L - X_C)^2} = \sqrt{R^2} = \boxed{R}$

43.   (a) $X_L = 2\pi f L = 2\pi(60 \text{ Hz})(0.45 \text{ H}) = \boxed{1.7 \times 10^2 \ \Omega}$.

        (b) $Z = \sqrt{R^2 + (X_L - X_C)^2} = \sqrt{(100 \ \Omega)^2 + (170 \ \Omega - 0)^2} = \boxed{2.0 \times 10^2 \ \Omega}$.

44.   (a) $X_C = \dfrac{1}{2\pi f C} = \dfrac{1}{2\pi(60 \text{ Hz})(25 \times 10^{-6} \text{ F})} = \boxed{1.1 \times 10^2 \ \Omega}$.

        $Z = \sqrt{R^2 + (X_L - X_C)^2} = \sqrt{(200 \ \Omega)^2 + (0 - 106 \ \Omega)^2} = 226 \ \Omega = \boxed{2.3 \times 10^2 \ \Omega}$.

        (b) $I_{rms} = \dfrac{V_{rms}}{Z} = \dfrac{120 \text{ V}}{226 \ \Omega} = \boxed{0.53 \text{ A}}$.

45.   (a) $X_L = 2\pi f L = 2\pi(60 \text{ Hz})(0.100 \text{ H}) = \boxed{38 \ \Omega}$.

        $Z = \sqrt{R^2 + (X_L - X_C)^2} = \sqrt{(100 \ \Omega)^2 + (38 \ \Omega - 0)^2} = 107 \ \Omega = \boxed{1.1 \times 10^2 \ \Omega}$.

        (b) $I_{rms} = \dfrac{V_{rms}}{Z} = \dfrac{120 \text{ V}}{107 \ \Omega} = \boxed{1.1 \text{ A}}$.

46.   (a) $X_C = \dfrac{1}{2\pi f C} = \dfrac{1}{2\pi(60 \text{ Hz})(6.0 \times 10^{-6} \text{ F})} = 442 \ \Omega = \boxed{4.4 \times 10^2 \ \Omega}$.

        (b) $Z = \sqrt{R^2 + (X_L - X_C)^2} = \sqrt{(250 \ \Omega)^2 + (0 - 442 \ \Omega)^2} = 508 \ \Omega = \boxed{5.1 \times 10^2 \ \Omega}$.

47. $\phi = \tan^{-1}\left(\dfrac{X_L - X_C}{R}\right) = \tan^{-1}\left(\dfrac{50 \ \Omega - 0}{100 \ \Omega}\right) = \boxed{+27°}$.

48.   At resonance, $f_0 = \dfrac{1}{2\pi\sqrt{LC}} = \dfrac{1}{2\pi\sqrt{(0.30 \text{ H})(8.0 \times 10^{-6} \text{ F})}} = \boxed{1.0 \times 10^2 \text{ Hz}}$.

49. If the frequency f doubles, R remains the same, X_L doubles to 80 Ω because $X_L = 2\pi f L$, and X_C halves to

20 Ω since $X_C = \dfrac{1}{2\pi f C}$.

So $\quad Z = \sqrt{R^2 + (X_L - X_C)^2} = \sqrt{(40\ \Omega)^2 + (80\ \Omega - 20\ \Omega)^2} = \boxed{72\ \Omega}$.

50. $X_L = 2\pi f L = 2\pi(60\ \text{Hz})(0.500\ \text{H}) = 188\ \Omega$;

$X_C = \dfrac{1}{2\pi f C} = \dfrac{1}{2\pi(60\ \text{Hz})(3.5 \times 10^{-6}\ \text{F})} = 758\ \Omega \neq X_L$.

So $\boxed{\text{no}}$, the circuit is not driven in resonance.

$L = \dfrac{758\ \Omega}{2\pi(60\ \text{Hz})} = \boxed{\text{2.0 H for any resistor}}$ since the condition for resonance is $X_L = X_C$.

51. $Z = \sqrt{R^2 + (X_L - X_C)^2} = \sqrt{(500\ \Omega)^2 + (188\ \Omega - 758\ \Omega)^2} = 758\ \Omega$.

$\tan\phi = \dfrac{X_L - X_C}{R} = \dfrac{188\ \Omega - 758\ \Omega}{500\ \Omega} = -1.14, \quad \text{☞} \quad \phi = -48.7°.$

So $\quad \bar{P} = \dfrac{V_{\text{rms}}^2}{Z}\cos\phi = \dfrac{(240\ \text{V})^2}{758\ \Omega}\cos(-48.7°) = \boxed{50\ \text{W}}$.

52. At resonance, $\quad f_o = \dfrac{1}{2\pi\sqrt{LC}} = \dfrac{1}{2\pi\sqrt{(0.100\ \text{H})(5.00 \times 10^{-6}\ \text{F})}} = \boxed{225\ \text{Hz}}$.

53. $f_o = \dfrac{1}{2\pi\sqrt{LC}}$, so $C = \dfrac{1}{4\pi^2 f_o^2 L} = \dfrac{1}{4\pi^2(980 \times 10^3\ \text{Hz})^2(0.50 \times 10^{-3}\ \text{H})} = \boxed{5.3 \times 10^{-11}\ \text{F}}$.

54. f_o must range from 530 kHz to 1710 kHz.

$C_1 = \dfrac{1}{4\pi^2(530 \times 10^3\ \text{Hz})^2(0.50 \times 10^{-3}\ \text{H})} = 1.8 \times 10^{-10}\ \text{F}.$

$C_2 = \dfrac{1}{4\pi^2(1710 \times 10^3\ \text{Hz})^2(0.50 \times 10^{-3}\ \text{H})} = 1.7 \times 10^{-11}\ \text{F}.$

So the range is from $\boxed{1.7 \times 10^{-11}\ \text{F to } 1.8 \times 10^{-10}\ \text{F}}$.

55. $X_L = 2\pi f L = 2\pi(60\ \text{Hz})(0.250\ \text{H}) = 94.2\ \Omega, \quad X_C = \dfrac{1}{2\pi f C} = \dfrac{1}{2\pi(60\ \text{Hz})(40 \times 10^{-6}\ \text{F})} = 66.3\ \Omega.$

ab: $\quad Z = \sqrt{R^2 + (X_L - X_C)^2} = X_L = 94.2\ \Omega, \quad I_{\text{rms}} = \dfrac{V_{\text{rms}}}{Z} = \dfrac{120\ \text{V}}{94.2\ \Omega} = \boxed{1.3\ \text{A}}.$

ac: $\quad Z = \sqrt{(30\ \Omega)^2 + (94.2\ \Omega)^2} = 98.9\ \Omega, \quad I_{\text{rms}} = \dfrac{120\ \text{V}}{98.9\ \Omega} = \boxed{1.2\ \text{A}}.$

bc: $Z = R = 30\ \Omega$, $I_{rms} = \dfrac{120\ V}{30\ \Omega} = \boxed{4.0\ A}$.

cd: $Z = X_C = 66.3\ \Omega$, $I_{rms} = \dfrac{120\ V}{66.3\ \Omega} = \boxed{1.8\ A}$.

bd: $Z = \sqrt{(30\ \Omega)^2 + (66.3\ \Omega)^2} = 72.8\ \Omega$, $I_{rms} = \dfrac{120\ V}{72.8\ \Omega} = \boxed{1.6\ A}$.

ad: $Z = \sqrt{(30\ \Omega)^2 + (94.2\ \Omega - 66.3\ \Omega)^2} = 41.0\ \Omega$, $I_{rms} = \dfrac{120\ V}{41.0\ \Omega} = \boxed{2.9\ A}$.

56.   (a) $X_L = 2\pi f L = 2\pi(60\ Hz)(0.15\ H) = 56.5\ \Omega$.

$Z = \sqrt{R^2 + (X_L - X_C)^2} = \sqrt{(30\ \Omega)^2 + (56.5\ \Omega)^2} = 64.0\ \Omega$.

So $I_{rms} = \dfrac{V_{rms}}{Z} = \dfrac{120\ V}{64.0\ \Omega} = \boxed{1.9\ A}$.

(b) $\tan \phi = \dfrac{X_L - X_C}{R} = \dfrac{56.5\ \Omega}{30\ \Omega} = 1.88$,   ☞ $\phi = \boxed{62°}$.

57. $\overline{P} = I_{rms} V_{rms} \cos \phi$,   ☞ $I_{rms} = \dfrac{\overline{P}}{V_{rms} \cos \phi} = \dfrac{1200\ W}{(120\ V)(0.75)} = \boxed{13\ A}$.

58.   (a) $Z = \sqrt{R^2 + (X_L - X_C)^2} = \sqrt{(10\ \Omega)^2 + (120\ \Omega - 120\ \Omega)^2} = 10\ \Omega$.

$I_{rms} = \dfrac{V_{rms}}{Z} = \dfrac{220\ V}{10\ \Omega} = 22\ A$.   So $(V_{rms})_R = I_{rms} R = (22\ A)(10\ \Omega) = \boxed{220\ V}$.

(b) $(V_{rms})_L = I_{rms} X_L = (22\ A)(120\ \Omega) = \boxed{2.64 \times 10^3\ V}$.

(c) $(V_{rms})_C = I_{rms} X_C = (22\ A)(120\ \Omega) = \boxed{2.64 \times 10^3\ V}$.

59. $f_o = \dfrac{1}{2\pi\sqrt{LC}} = \dfrac{1}{2\pi\sqrt{(0.250\ H)(0.80 \times 10^{-6}\ F)}} = 356\ Hz$.

$X_L = 2\pi f L = 2\pi(356\ Hz)(0.250\ H) = 559\ \Omega$,

$X_C = \dfrac{1}{2\pi f C} = \dfrac{1}{2\pi(356\ Hz)(0.80 \times 10^{-6}\ F)} = 559\ \Omega$.

$Z = R = 25\ \Omega$, $I_{rms} = \dfrac{V_{rms}}{Z} = \dfrac{12\ V}{25\ \Omega} = 0.48\ A$.

So $(V_{rms})_R = I_{rms} R = (0.48\ A)(25\ \Omega) = \boxed{12\ V}$, $(V_{rms})_L = I_{rms} X_L = (0.48\ A)(559\ \Omega) = \boxed{2.7 \times 10^2\ V}$,

and $(V_{rms})_C = I_{rms} X_C = (0.48\ A)(559\ \Omega) = \boxed{2.7 \times 10^2\ V}$.

60.   In Exercises 58 and 59, $(V_{rms})_R$, $(V_{rms})_C$, and $(V_{rms})_L$ are all rms voltages. Due to phase differences, these rms voltages are *not* reached at the same time. Instantaneously, however, $V_R + V_C + V_L$ is still equal to the source voltage.

61.　(a) $X_L = 2\pi fL = 2\pi(60 \text{ Hz})(0.450 \text{ H}) = 170 \text{ }\Omega$, $X_C = \dfrac{1}{2\pi fC} = \dfrac{1}{2\pi(60 \text{ Hz})(5.00 \times 10^{-6} \text{ F})} = 531 \text{ }\Omega$.

$Z = \sqrt{R^2 + (X_L - X_C)^2} = \sqrt{(25.0 \text{ }\Omega)^2 + (170 \text{ }\Omega - 531 \text{ }\Omega)^2} = \boxed{362 \text{ }\Omega}$.

(b) $f_0 = \dfrac{1}{2\pi\sqrt{LC}} = \dfrac{1}{2\pi\sqrt{(0.450 \text{ H})(5.00 \times 10^{-6} \text{ F})}} = 106 \text{ Hz}$;

$\boxed{\text{no}}$, the circuit is not in resonance and the resonance frequency is $\boxed{1.1 \times 10^2 \text{ Hz}}$.

62.　(a) $\tan \phi = \dfrac{X_L - X_C}{R} = \dfrac{500 \text{ }\Omega - 300 \text{ }\Omega}{400 \text{ }\Omega} = 0.50$, ☞ $\phi = 26.6°$.

So the power factor $\cos \phi = \cos (26.6°) = \boxed{0.894}$.

(b) $X_C = \dfrac{1}{2\pi fC}$, ☞ $C = \dfrac{1}{2\pi fX_C} = \dfrac{1}{2\pi(60 \text{ Hz})(300 \text{ }\Omega)} = 8.84 \times 10^{-6} \text{ F}$.

For the power factor to be 1, $\phi = 0°$ or $X_L = X_C$.

$C_{total} = \dfrac{1}{2\pi(60 \text{ Hz})(300 \text{ }\Omega)} = 5.31 \times 10^{-6} \text{ F} < 8.84 \times 10^{-6} \text{ F}$.

So a series capacitor is needed.　$\dfrac{1}{C_{total}} = \dfrac{1}{C} + \dfrac{1}{C'}$,

so　$C' = \dfrac{C \, C_{total}}{C - C_{total}} = \dfrac{(8.84 \times 10^{-6} \text{ F})(5.31 \times 10^{-6} \text{ F})}{8.84 \times 10^{-6} \text{ F} - 5.31 \times 10^{-6} \text{ F}} = 1.33 \times 10^{-5} \text{ F} = \boxed{13.3 \text{ }\mu\text{F, series}}$.

63.　In resonance,　$\overline{P}_0 = \dfrac{V_{rms}^2}{R} = \dfrac{(120 \text{ V})^2}{50 \text{ }\Omega} = 288 \text{ W}$.

Not in resonance,　$X_L = 2\pi fL = 2\pi(60 \text{ Hz})(0.15 \text{ H}) = 56.5 \text{ }\Omega$,

$X_C = \dfrac{1}{2\pi fC} = \dfrac{1}{2\pi(60 \text{ Hz})(20 \times 10^{-6} \text{ F})} = 133 \text{ }\Omega$.

$Z = \sqrt{R^2 + (X_L - X_C)^2} = \sqrt{(50 \text{ }\Omega)^2 + (56.5 \text{ }\Omega - 133 \text{ }\Omega)^2} = 91.4 \text{ }\Omega$.

$I_{rms} = \dfrac{V_{rms}}{Z} = \dfrac{120 \text{ V}}{91.4 \text{ }\Omega} = 1.31 \text{ A}$.

Only the resistor dissipates power.　So　$\overline{P} = I_{rms}^2 R = (1.31 \text{ A})^2 (50 \text{ }\Omega) = 86.2 \text{ W}$.

Therefore the percentage is $\dfrac{\overline{P}}{\overline{P}_0} = \dfrac{86.2 \text{ W}}{288 \text{ W}} = \boxed{30\%}$.

64.　(a) $V_0 = \sqrt{2} \, V_{rms} = \sqrt{2} \, (120 \text{ V}) = \boxed{170 \text{ V}}$.

(b) $\overline{P} = I_{rms} V_{rms}$, ☞ $I_{rms} = \dfrac{\overline{P}}{V_{rms}} = \dfrac{60 \text{ W}}{120 \text{ V}} = 0.50 \text{ A}$.

So　$I_0 = \sqrt{2} \, I_{rms} = \sqrt{2} \, (0.50 \text{ A}) = \boxed{0.707 \text{ A}}$.

65. $I_{p-p} = 2I_o = 2\sqrt{2}\,I_{rms} = 2\sqrt{2}\,(0.25\text{ A}) = \boxed{0.71\text{ A}}$.

66. (a) $X_L = 2\pi fL = 2\pi(60\text{ Hz})(0.40\text{ H}) = 151\ \Omega$. So $\quad I_{rms} = \dfrac{V_{rms}}{X_L} = \dfrac{120\text{ V}}{151\ \Omega} = \boxed{0.80\text{ A}}$.

(b) The voltage leads the current by $\boxed{90°}$.

67. $f_o = \dfrac{1}{2\pi\sqrt{LC}}$, $\quad \mathbb{G}\mkern-6mu= \quad C = \dfrac{1}{4\pi^2 f_o^2 L} = \dfrac{1}{4\pi^2(98.9\times10^6\text{ Hz})^2(1.50\times10^{-6}\text{ H})} = \boxed{1.7\times10^{-12}\text{ F}}$.

68. (a) $X_L = 2\pi fL = 2\pi(60\text{ Hz})(0.100\text{ H}) = \boxed{38\ \Omega}$.

(b) $Z = \sqrt{R^2 + (X_L - X_C)^2} = \sqrt{(50\ \Omega)^2 + (37.7\ \Omega)^2} = \boxed{63\ \Omega}$.

(c) $I_{rms} = \dfrac{V_{rms}}{Z} = \dfrac{110\text{ V}}{62.6\ \Omega} = \boxed{1.8\text{ A}}$.

(d) Only the resistor dissipates power. So the power dissipated in the coil is $\boxed{0}$.

69. $\tan\phi = \dfrac{X_L - X_C}{R} = \dfrac{38\ \Omega}{50\ \Omega} = 0.76$, $\quad \mathbb{G}\mkern-6mu= \quad \phi = \boxed{37°}$.

70. (a) $X_C = \dfrac{1}{2\pi fC} = \dfrac{1}{2\pi(60\text{ Hz})(1.0\times10^{-6}\text{ F})} = \boxed{2.7\times10^3\ \Omega}$.

(b) $I_{rms} = \dfrac{V_{rms}}{X_C} = \dfrac{120\text{ V}}{2650\ \Omega} = \boxed{4.5\times10^{-2}\text{ A}}$.

(c) The current leads the voltage by 90° and so the phase angle is $\boxed{-90°}$.

71. From $X_C = \dfrac{1}{2\pi fC}$ and $X_L = 2\pi fL$, we can see that the capacitor opposes current more strongly at lower frequencies and the inductor opposes current more strongly at high frequencies. In Fig. 21.18a, the inductor in series with R_L filters out the high frequency current and so only the low frequency current reaches R_L. In Fig. 21.18b, the capacitor in series with R_L filters out the low frequency current and so only the high frequency current reaches R_L.

72. $f_o = \dfrac{1}{2\pi\sqrt{LC}}$, $\quad \mathbb{G}\mkern-6mu= \quad C = \dfrac{1}{4\pi^2 f_o^2 L} = \dfrac{1}{4\pi^2(60\text{ Hz})(0.750\text{ H})} = \boxed{9.4\times10^{-6}\text{ F for any resistor}}$

since f_o is independent of R.

CHAPTER 22

GEOMETRICAL OPTICS: REFLECTION AND REFRACTION OF LIGHT

1. (c).

2. (c).

3. (d).

4. (d).

5. They are visible because of the diffuse reflections by the particulate matter in the air.

6. $\boxed{\text{Yes}}$, the angle of reflection is *always* equal to the angle of incidence in either specular or diffuse reflection. $\boxed{\text{No}}$, the angle of reflection is *never* less than the angle of incidence.

7. Since $\theta_i = \theta_r$, the angle between the beams is $35° + 35° = \boxed{70°}$.

8. $\theta_i = \theta_r = 32°$ from the normal. So the angle between the surface and the beam is $90° - \theta_r = \boxed{58°}$.

9. $\theta_r = \theta_i = 90° - 43° = \boxed{47°}$

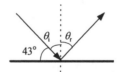

10. $\theta_i = 90° - 55° = 35°$. So $\theta_r = \theta_i = 35°$.

    Therefore the angle between the reflected ray and the surface of the mirror is $90° - 35° = \boxed{55°}$.

11. $\tan \theta_i = \dfrac{2.5 \text{ m}}{3.0 \text{ m}} = 0.833$,

    so $\theta_i = \theta_r = \tan^{-1} 0.833 = \boxed{40°}$.

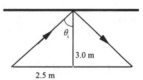

12. According to the law of reflection, the angle of reflection from the second mirror is $\boxed{20°}$.

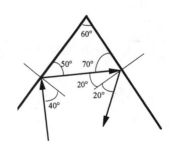

13. $\theta = \tan^{-1} \dfrac{25\ \text{cm}}{50\ \text{cm}} = \tan^{-1} 0.50 = \boxed{27^\circ}$.

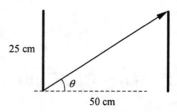

14.   After rain, water fills the unevenness of the road and the reflection off the road is specular so images of buildings, trees, and so on are formed. When the road is dry, the unevenness of the road cause diffuse reflection so there are no images of buildings, tree, etc.

15.   Use similar triangles. $\dfrac{d + 0.45\ \text{m} + 0.45\ \text{m}}{8.50\ \text{m}} = \dfrac{0.45\ \text{m}}{0.30\ \text{m}}$, ☞ $d = \boxed{12\ \text{m}}$.

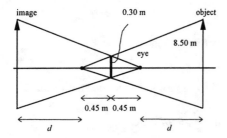

16.   According to the law of reflection,

$\beta = 180^\circ - [\alpha + (90^\circ - \theta_{i_1})] = 90^\circ - \alpha + \theta_{i_1}$.

So   the angle of reflection from the second mirror is

$\theta_{r_2} = 90^\circ - \beta = \alpha - \theta_{i_1}$.

(a) $\theta_{r_2} = 70^\circ - 35^\circ = \boxed{35^\circ}$.

(b) $\theta_{r_2} = 115^\circ - 60^\circ = \boxed{55^\circ}$.

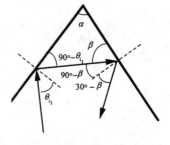

17.   If $\alpha = \boxed{90^\circ}$, $\theta_{i_1} + \theta_{r_2} = 90^\circ$ and the two normals are perpendicular to each other. So the reflected ray is parallel to the incident ray for $\boxed{\text{any } \theta_{i_1}}$.

18.   (b), because $n_1 \sin \theta_1 = n_2 \sin \theta_2$. When $n_1 > n_2$, $\theta_1 < \theta_2$, so refracted ray is bent away from the normal.

19.   (d).

20. $\boxed{\text{Yes}}$, wavelength changes. $\boxed{\text{No}}$, frequency does not change. $\boxed{\text{Yes}}$, speed changes since $v = \lambda f$.

21.   (b).

22. Total internal reflection occurs when $\boxed{n_1 > n_2 \text{ and } \theta_i > \theta_c}$.

23. The angles of refractions are different for air-glass and water-glass interfaces.

24. Initially light has to travel along a straight line to reach our eyes and the top of the container blocks the light from the bottom of the coin. When water is added, the light coming out of water is bent into the air with a larger angle of refraction and so it reaches our eyes.

25. $\boxed{\text{The laser}}$ has a better chance to hit the fish. The fish appears to the hunter at a location different from its true location due to refraction. The laser beam obeys the same law of refraction and retraces the light the hunter sees to the fish. The arrow goes into the water in a near-straight line path.

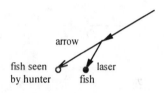

arrow

fish seen
by hunter

laser
fish

26. $n = \dfrac{c}{v} = \dfrac{3.00 \times 10^8 \text{ m/s}}{2.07 \times 10^8 \text{ m/s}} = \boxed{1.45}$.

27. $n = \dfrac{c}{v}$, ☞ $v = \dfrac{c}{n}$. So $\dfrac{v_Z}{v_D} = \dfrac{n_D}{n_Z} = \dfrac{2.42}{1.92} = 1.26$.

So the percentage difference is $\dfrac{v_Z - v_D}{v_D} = 1 - \dfrac{v_Z}{v_D} = 0.26 = \boxed{26\% \text{ greater in zircon}}$.

28. $n_1 \sin \theta_1 = n_2 \sin \theta_2$, ☞ $\sin \theta_2 = \dfrac{n_1 \sin \theta_1}{n_2} = \dfrac{(1) \sin 60°}{1.33} = 0.651$. So $\theta_2 = \boxed{41°}$.

29. $n_1 \sin \theta_1 = n_2 \sin \theta_2$, ☞ $\sin \theta_1 = \dfrac{n_2 \sin \theta_2}{n_1} = \dfrac{(1.33) \sin 20°}{1} = 0.455$. So $\theta_1 = \boxed{27°}$.

30. $n_1 \sin \theta_1 = n_2 \sin \theta_2$, ☞ $n_2 = \dfrac{n_1 \sin \theta_1}{\sin \theta_2} = \dfrac{(1) \sin 50°}{\sin 35°} = \boxed{1.34}$.

31. (a) $\theta_c = \sin^{-1} \dfrac{1}{n} = \sin^{-1} \dfrac{1}{2.42} = \boxed{24°}$.

    (b) From $\boxed{\text{diamond to air}}$ because $n_1 > n_2$.

32. $\theta_c = \sin^{-1} \dfrac{1}{n}$, ☞ $n = \dfrac{1}{\sin \theta_c} = \dfrac{1}{\sin 41.8°} = \boxed{1.50}$.

33. $n_1 \sin \theta_1 = n_2 \sin \theta_2,$ ☞ $\sin \theta_1 = \dfrac{n_2 \sin \theta_2}{n_1} = \dfrac{(1.46) \sin 30°}{1} = 0.73.$ So $\theta_1 = 47°.$

Therefore the angle of reflection is also $\boxed{47°}$ according to the law of reflection.

34. $n_1 \sin \theta_1 = n_2 \sin \theta_2,$ ☞ $\sin \theta_2 = \dfrac{n_1 \sin \theta_1}{n_2} = \dfrac{(1) \sin 55°}{1.49} = 0.550.$ So $\theta_2 = 33°.$

Therefore the angle relative to the surface is $90° - \theta_2 = \boxed{57°}.$

35. The frequency does not change and is still $\boxed{6.5 \times 10^{14} \text{ Hz}}.$

$$\lambda = \dfrac{v}{f} = \dfrac{c}{fn} = \dfrac{3.00 \times 10^8 \text{ m/s}}{(6.5 \times 10^{14} \text{ Hz})(1.66)} = \boxed{2.8 \times 10^{-7} \text{ m}}.$$

36. $\dfrac{v_\text{B}}{v_\text{A}} = \dfrac{c/n_\text{B}}{c/n_\text{A}} = \dfrac{n_\text{A}}{n_\text{B}} = \dfrac{4/3}{5/4} = \boxed{\dfrac{16}{15}}.$

37. $f_\text{A} = f_\text{B}.$ $\dfrac{\lambda_\text{B}}{\lambda_\text{A}} = \dfrac{v_\text{B}/f}{v_\text{A}/f} = \dfrac{v_\text{B}}{v_\text{A}} = \boxed{\dfrac{16}{15}}.$

38. $\lambda_\text{m} = \dfrac{\lambda}{n} = \dfrac{632.8 \text{ nm}}{1.36} = \boxed{465 \text{ nm}},$ $f = f_\text{m} = \dfrac{c}{\lambda} = \dfrac{3.00 \times 10^8 \text{ m/s}}{632.8 \times 10^{-9} \text{ m}} = \boxed{4.74 \times 10^{14} \text{ Hz}}.$

39. From the figure, the distance a is common to both d and d', and using trigonometry

$$\tan \theta_1 = \dfrac{a}{d'} \quad \text{and} \quad \tan \theta_2 = \dfrac{a}{d}.$$

Combining these two equations to form a ratio

$$\dfrac{d'}{d} = \dfrac{\tan \theta_2}{\tan \theta_1} \quad \text{or} \quad d' = \dfrac{\tan \theta_2}{\tan \theta_1} d.$$

If $\theta < 15°$, $\tan \theta \approx \sin \theta.$ So $\dfrac{d'}{d} = \dfrac{\tan \theta_2}{\tan \theta_1} \approx \dfrac{\sin \theta_2}{\sin \theta_1} = \dfrac{1}{n}$ (Snell's law).

Therefore $d' \approx \dfrac{d}{n}.$

40. The first refraction is at the air-glass interface and the second refraction is at the glass-water interface.

$n_1 \sin \theta_1 = n_2 \sin \theta_2,$ ☞ $\sin \theta_2 = \dfrac{n_1 \sin \theta_1}{n_2} = \dfrac{(1) \sin 40°}{1.50} = 0.429.$ So $\theta_2 = 25.4°.$

The critical angle at the glass-water interface is $\theta_\text{c} = \sin^{-1} \dfrac{n_3}{n_2} = \sin^{-1} \dfrac{1.33}{1.50} = \sin^{-1} 0.887 = 62.5°.$

Therefore the angle of incidence at the glass-water interface is smaller than the critical angle and thus there is no total internal reflection and $\boxed{\text{yes}}$, the fish is illuminated.

41. (a) $\theta_c \geq \sin^{-1} \dfrac{n_2}{n_1}$, ☞ $n_1 \geq \dfrac{n_2}{\sin \theta_c} = \dfrac{1}{\sin 45°} = \boxed{1.41}$.

(b) $n_1 \geq \dfrac{n_2}{\sin \theta_c} = \dfrac{1.33}{\sin 45°} = \boxed{1.88}$.

42. (a) $\theta_c = \sin^{-1} \dfrac{n_2}{n_1} = \sin^{-1} \dfrac{1}{1.85} = \sin^{-1} 0.541 = 32° < 45°$. So $\boxed{\text{yes}}$.

(b) $\theta_c = \sin^{-1} \dfrac{1.33}{1.85} = \sin^{-1} 0.719 = 46° > 45°$. So $\boxed{\text{no}}$.

43. (a) Repeat the calculation in Example 22.2. $\sin \theta_2 = \dfrac{\sin 40°}{1.65} = 0.390$, ☞ $\theta_2 = 22.9°$.

$d = y \tan \theta_2 = (10.0 \text{ cm}) \tan 22.9° = \boxed{4.2 \text{ cm}}$.

(b) The length of the ray inside the plate is $\dfrac{y}{\cos \theta_2}$, so the perpendicular distance between the two rays is

$\dfrac{y}{\cos \theta_2} \sin (\theta_1 - \theta_2) = \dfrac{10.0 \text{ cm}}{\cos 22.9°} \sin (40° - 22.9°) = \boxed{3.2 \text{ cm}}$.

44. $d' = \dfrac{d}{n} = \dfrac{3.2 \text{ m}}{1.33} = \boxed{2.4 \text{ m}}$.

45. $d' = \dfrac{d}{n}$, ☞ $\dfrac{d'}{d} = \dfrac{1}{n} = \dfrac{1}{1.33} = 0.75 = \boxed{75\%}$.

46. The setting is at zero altitude or 90° from the normal, so the angle should be equal to the critical angle of

$\theta_c = \sin^{-1} \dfrac{1}{n} = \sin^{-1} \dfrac{1}{1.33} = \sin^{-1} 0.752 = \boxed{48.8°}$.

47. $\theta_c = \sin^{-1} \dfrac{1}{n} = \sin^{-1} \dfrac{1}{1.33} = 49°$. So the 50° angle will be totally reflected and the 40° angle will refract

through. Therefore $\boxed{\text{seen for 40° and not for 50°}}$.

48. The altitude is measured from the horizon and so the angle from the normal is (90° − altitude).

$n_1 \sin \theta_1 = n_2 \sin \theta_2$, ☞ $\sin \theta_1 = \dfrac{n_2 \sin \theta_2}{n_1} = \dfrac{(1.33) \sin (90° - 45°)}{1} = 0.940$.

So $\theta_1 = 70°$. Therefore the actual altitude is $90° - 70° = \boxed{20°}$.

49. $\theta_2 = \tan^{-1} \dfrac{0.90 \text{ m}}{1.50 \text{ m}} = \tan^{-1} 0.60 = 31.0°$. $\quad n_1 \sin \theta_1 = n_2 \sin \theta_2$,

so $\quad \sin \theta_1 = = \sin \theta = \dfrac{n_2 \sin \theta_2}{n_1} = \dfrac{(1.33) \sin 31.0°}{1} = 0.685$. Therefore $\quad \theta = \boxed{43°}$.

50. We can measure the angles of incidence and refraction from the photography and calculate the index of refraction of the fluid from the law of refraction. $\quad \theta_1 \approx 65°$ and $\theta_2 \approx 43°$.

$n_1 \sin \theta_1 = n_2 \sin \theta_2$, $\quad \text{☞} \quad n_2 = \dfrac{n_1 \sin \theta_1}{\sin \theta_2} \approx \dfrac{(1) \sin 65°}{\sin 43°} = \boxed{1.3}$.

51. (a) $\theta_c = \sin^{-1} \dfrac{1}{n} = \sin^{-1} \dfrac{1}{1.60} = 38.7°$. The beam is $\boxed{\text{internally reflected}}$.

(b) $\theta_c = \sin^{-1} \dfrac{n_2}{n_1} = \sin^{-1} \dfrac{1.20}{1.60} = 48.6°$. The beam is not internally reflected and is $\boxed{\text{transmitted}}$.

52. $d' = \dfrac{d}{n} = \dfrac{2.5 \text{ cm}}{1.52} = \boxed{1.6 \text{ cm}}$.

53. $\theta_2 = \tan^{-1} \dfrac{0.50 \text{ m}}{0.75 \text{ m}} = \tan^{-1} 0.667 = 33.7°$. $\quad n_1 \sin \theta_1 = n_2 \sin \theta_2$,

so $\quad \sin \theta_1 = \dfrac{n_2 \sin \theta_2}{n_1} = \dfrac{(1.33) \sin 33.7°}{1} = 0.738$.

Therefore $\quad \theta_1 = 47.5°$.

Thus $\quad d = (1.8 \text{ m}) \tan \theta_1 = (1.8 \text{ m}) \tan 47.5° = \boxed{2.0 \text{ m}}$.

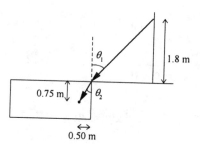

54. To see the whole newspaper print, the minimum angle of refraction is 45°.

The maximum $n_1 \sin \theta_1$ is $1 \sin 90° = 1$.

$n_2 \sin \theta_2 = 1.66 \sin 45° = 1.17 > 1$.

So $\boxed{\text{no}}$, it is impossible.

55. (a) For refraction at the prism-prism interface, $\quad (1.60) \sin 45° = (1.40) \sin \theta_2$,

so $\quad \theta_2 = \sin^{-1} 0.808 = 53.9°$.

For the prism-air interface,

$\theta_3 = 180° - [135° + (90° - \theta_2)] = \theta_2 - 45° = 53.9° - 45° = 8.9°$.

So $\quad (1.40) \sin 8.9° = (1) \sin \theta$,

therefore $\quad \theta = \sin^{-1} 0.217 = \boxed{12.5°}$.

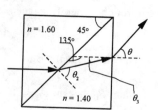

(b) $\theta_c = \sin^{-1} \dfrac{n_2}{n_1} = \sin^{-1} \dfrac{1.40}{1.60} = 61.0°$.

This is the angle required at the interface.

For the air-prism interface,

$\theta_2 = 180° - [135° + (90° - \theta_c)] = \theta_c - 45° = 61.0° - 45° = 16.0°$.

So   (1) $\sin \theta_1 = (1.60) \sin 16°$,

therefore $\theta_1 = \sin^{-1} 0.441 = \boxed{26.2°}$.

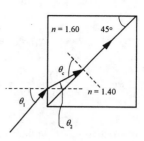

56.   (d).

57.   (b).

58.   It is due to the $\boxed{\text{different speeds of different frequencies in the material}}$. This, in turn, causes the different indices of refraction, therefore the different angles of refraction.

59. $\boxed{\text{No}}$, the light will be further dispersed by the second prism.

60. $\boxed{\text{Color B}}$ has a longer wavelength. For normal dispersion, shorter wavelength bends more than longer wavelength after refracting through a prism.

61.   (a) $\boxed{\text{The angle of incidence is approximately zero}}$ and so there is no dispersion because the angle of refraction for all colors is also zero.

(b) $\boxed{\text{No}}$ as explained in (a). $\boxed{\text{No}}$, the speeds are different.

62. $n_1 \sin \theta_1 = n_R \sin \theta_R = n_B \sin \theta_B$,   ☞ $\sin \theta_R = \dfrac{n_1 \sin \theta_1}{n_R} = \dfrac{(1) \sin 37°}{1.515} = 0.3972$.

So $\theta_R = 23.406°$. $\sin \theta_B = \dfrac{(1) \sin 37°}{1.523} = 0.3952$.   Therefore $\theta_B = 23.275°$.

Hence $\Delta\theta = 23.406° - 23.275° = \boxed{0.131°}$.

63. $\theta_{cR} = \sin^{-1} \dfrac{1}{n_R} = \sin^{-1} \dfrac{1}{1.515} = 41.30°$,   and $\theta_{cB} = \sin^{-1} \dfrac{1}{1.523} = 41.04°$.

So $\boxed{\text{red is transmitted and blue is internally reflected}}$.

64. $n_1 \sin \theta_1 = n_R \sin \theta_R = n_B \sin \theta_B$, ☞ $\sin \theta_R = \dfrac{n_1 \sin \theta_1}{n_R} = \dfrac{(1) \sin 30°}{1.4925} = 0.33501$.

So $\theta_R = 19.573°$. $\Delta \theta = \theta_R - \theta_B$, $\theta_B = \theta_R - \Delta \theta = 19.573° - (0.00131 \text{ rad}) \times \dfrac{180°}{\pi \text{ rad}} = 19.498°$.

Therefore $n_B = \dfrac{(1) \sin 30°}{\sin 18.498°} = \boxed{1.4980}$.

65. (a) For the first air-prism interface, (1) $\sin 80.0° = (1.400) \sin \theta_2$,

So $\theta_2 = \sin^{-1} 0.7034$. Therefore $\theta_2 = 44.70°$.

For the second prism-air interface,

$\theta_3 = 180° - (120° + \theta_2) = 60° - \theta_2 = 60° - 44.70° = 15.30°$.

So (1.400) $\sin 15.30° = (1) \sin \theta$,

therefore $\theta = \sin^{-1} 0.3693 = \boxed{21.7°}$.

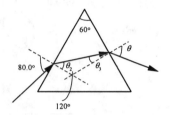

(b) For blue light, $\theta_2 = \sin^{-1} \dfrac{\sin 80.0°}{1.403} = 44.58°$. $\theta_3 = 60° - 44.58° = 15.42°$.

So $\theta = \sin^{-1} [(1.403) \sin 15.42°] = 21.90°$. Therefore $\Delta \theta = 21.90° - 21.68° = \boxed{0.22°}$.

(c) For blue light, $\theta_2 = \sin^{-1} \dfrac{\sin 80.0°}{1.405} = 44.50°$. $\theta_3 = 60° - 44.50° = 15.50°$.

So $\theta = \sin^{-1} [(1.405) \sin 15.50°] = 22.05°$. Therefore $\Delta \theta = 22.05° - 21.68° = \boxed{0.37°}$.

66. $n_1 \sin \theta_1 = n_2 \sin \theta_2$,

so $\sin \theta_2 = \dfrac{n_1 \sin \theta_1}{n_2} = \dfrac{(1) \sin 50°}{1.33} = 0.576$.

Therefore $\theta_2 = 35.2°$.

Thus $x = (15 \text{ cm}) \tan \theta_2 = (15 \text{ cm}) \tan 35.2° = \boxed{11 \text{ cm}}$.

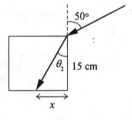

67. (a) $\theta_c = \sin^{-1} \dfrac{n_2}{n_1} = \sin^{-1} \dfrac{1.7}{2.0} = \boxed{58°}$.

(b) There must be a total internal reflection at the n_2 - air interface.

$\theta_{c2} = \sin^{-1} \dfrac{1}{n_2} = \sin^{-1} \dfrac{1}{1.7} = 36.0°$, so $\theta_2 = \theta_{c2}$.

$n_1 \sin \theta_1 = n_2 \sin \theta_2$, ☞ $\sin \theta_1 = \dfrac{n_2 \sin \theta_2}{n_1} = \dfrac{(1.7) \sin 36.0°}{2.0} = 0.50$.

Therefore $\theta_1 = \boxed{30°}$.

68. The angle of incidence is $90° - 50° = 40°$. So the angle of reflection is also $\boxed{40°}$.

69. $n_1 \sin\theta_1 = n_2 \sin\theta_2,$ ☞ $n_2 = \dfrac{n_1 \sin\theta_1}{\sin\theta_2} = \dfrac{(1.33)\sin 45°}{\sin 35°} = \boxed{1.64}.$

70. (a) $n_1 \sin\theta_1 = n_2 \sin\theta_2,$ ☞ $\sin\theta_2 = \dfrac{n_1 \sin\theta_1}{n_2} = \dfrac{(1)\sin 40°}{1.52} = 0.423.$

So $\theta_2 = \boxed{25°}.$

(b) $v = \dfrac{c}{n} = \dfrac{3.00 \times 10^8 \text{ m/s}}{1.52} = \boxed{1.97 \times 10^8 \text{ m/s}}.$

(c) $\lambda_m = \dfrac{\lambda}{n} = \dfrac{550 \text{ nm}}{1.52} = \boxed{362 \text{ nm}}.$

71. $n_1 \sin\theta_1 = n_2 \sin\theta_2,$ ☞ $\sin\theta_2 = \dfrac{n_1 \sin\theta_1}{n_2} = 0.$ So $\theta_2 = \boxed{0}$, not refracted.

CHAPTER 23

1.   (b).

2.   (c).

3.   (a) Reflections from the window are seen clearly against a dark background, During the day, light passes both ways through the pane, and although some is reflected, it is difficult to see the reflection due to the light coming through. At night, there is little light coming through the pane, so the reflections are seen much more clearly.

(b) The two images are due to reflections on both sides of the pane glass, producing two similar images.

(c) This works on a combination of half-silvering and bright light on one side and dark on the other. For example, at night people inside the house cannot see things outside because there is little light coming through the window from the outside and they see their own reflections.

4.   During the day, the reflection is mainly from the silvered back surface. During the night, when the switch is flipped, the reflection comes from the front side. and so there is a reduction of intensity and glare because the front side reflects only about 5% of the light, which is more than enough to see due to the dark background.

5.   (a) The left-right reversal is an apparent one. It is caused by the front-back reversal. Right and left are directional senses like clockwise and counterclockwise rather than fixed directions referenced to a coordinate system.

(b) No.

6.   The magnification is $\boxed{+1}$ because the image is upright and of the same size as the object.

7.   When viewed by a driver through a rear view mirror, the right-left reversal property of the image formed by a plane mirror will make it read "AMBULANCE."

8.   (a) Image distance equals object distance. The distance from object to image is $2.0\text{ m} + 2.0\text{ m} = \boxed{4.0\text{ m}}$.

(b) $\boxed{\text{Upright, virtual, and same size}}$.

9.   (a) Image distance equals object distance.

So the distance from object to image is 40 cm + 40 cm = $\boxed{0.80 \text{ m}}$.

(b) The image has the same height as the object. So it is $\boxed{5.0 \text{ cm}}$.

(c) The image is unmagnified and upright. So the magnification is $\boxed{+1.0}$.

10.   Image distance equals object distance. The distance from object to image is 2.5 m + 2.5 m = $\boxed{5.0 \text{ m}}$.

11.   (a) Image distance equals object distance and so it is $\boxed{1.5 \text{ m behind the mirror}}$.

(b) The image also moves at 0.5 m/s toward the dog and so the relative velocity of the dog to the image is

0.5 m/s + 0.5 m/s = $\boxed{1.0 \text{ m/s}}$.

12.   The image formed by the wall mirror is 0.90 m + 0.90 m = 1.80 m behind the woman or 1.80 m + 0.30 m =

2.10 m behind the hand mirror. The image formed by the hand mirror is then 2.10 m in front of the hand

mirror or 2.10 m + 0.30 m = $\boxed{2.40 \text{ m}}$ in front of the woman.

13.   The first image by the north mirror is $\boxed{3.0 \text{ m}}$ behind the *north* mirror.

This image is 3.0 m + 3.0 m + 5.0 m = 11 m from the south mirror. So the second image by the south

mirror is $\boxed{11 \text{ m}}$ behind the *south* mirror.

The first image by the south mirror is $\boxed{5.0 \text{ m}}$ behind the *south* mirror.

This image is 5.0 m + 5.0 m + 3.0 m = 13 m from the north mirror. So the second image by the north

mirror is $\boxed{13 \text{ m}}$ behind the *north* mirror.

14.   (a) The mirror needs to be half as tall as the object as explained in Example 23.2. So it is $\boxed{0.85 \text{ m}}$ tall.

(b) It is independent of object distance and it is still $\boxed{0.85 \text{ m}}$.

15.   The two triangles (with d_o and d_i as base, respectively) are similar to each other

because all three angles of one triangle are the same as those of the other triangle due

to the law of reflection. Furthermore, the two triangles share the same height, the

common vertical side. Therefore the two triangles are identical. Hence $d_o = d_i$.

16. The image I_3 is a degenerated image, i.e., two images, one is the image of I_1 by the top mirror and the other is the image of I_2 by the side mirror on top of each other. This happens when the mirrors are at 90° to each other. In Fig 23.23b, the mirrors are not at 90° to each other. So the degeneracy is lifted and the two images are not on top of each other.

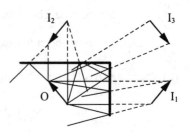

17. (d).

18. (a).

19. (a) The plane mirror gives a large view of the area immediately around that side of the truck. The small convex mirror gives a wide angle perspective of the road in back of both sides of the truck (but the image is smaller).

(b) These are convex mirrors that give a better field of view, but also images are smaller than objects (so the image distances are smaller than object distances) and hence appear closer than they actually are.

(c) Yes, it can be considered as a converging mirror, because it collects a large amount of radio waves and focuses them onto a small area.

20. (a) A spoon can behave as either a concave or a convex mirror depending on which side you use for reflection. If you use the concave side, you see an inverted image. If you use the convex side, you see an upright image.

(b) Yes, if you are very close (inside the center of curvature) to the spoon on the concave side, you can see an upright image.

21. (a) The image is smaller than the object and it is possible to "see your full body in 10 cm" in a diverging mirror.

(b) As the ball swings toward the mirror and approaches the focal point, the image enlarges. An enlarged image appears to be closer to our eyes and so it appears to move toward the observer and therefore produces the effect of appearing to "jump" out of the mirror as the ball swings through the focal point.

22. The image of a distant object (at infinity) is formed on a screen in the focal plane. The distance from the vertex of the mirror to the plane is the focal length.

23. $f = \dfrac{R}{2} = \dfrac{10 \text{ cm}}{2} = \boxed{5.0 \text{ cm}}$.

24. $d_0 = 20$ cm, $f = \dfrac{R}{2} = \dfrac{30 \text{ cm}}{2} = 15$ cm. $d_i = \dfrac{d_0 f}{d_0 - f} = \dfrac{(20 \text{ cm})(15 \text{ cm})}{20 \text{ cm} - 15 \text{ cm}} = \boxed{60 \text{ cm}}$.

$M = -\dfrac{d_i}{d_0} = -\dfrac{60 \text{ cm}}{20 \text{ cm}} = -3.0$. So $h_i = Mh_0 = -3.0 \,(3.0 \text{ cm}) = -9.0$ cm. It is $= \boxed{9.0 \text{ cm}}$ tall.

25. $d_i = \dfrac{(10 \text{ cm})(15 \text{ cm})}{10 \text{ cm} - 15 \text{ cm}} = \boxed{-30 \text{ cm}}$. $M = -\dfrac{-30 \text{ cm}}{10 \text{ cm}} = +3.0$.

So $h_i = +3.0 \,(1.5 \text{ cm}) = \boxed{9.0 \text{ cm, virtual, upright, and magnified}}$.

26. $d_0 = 30$ cm, $f = -60$ cm (convex mirror). $d_i = \dfrac{d_0 f}{d_0 - f} = \dfrac{(30 \text{ cm})(-60 \text{ cm})}{30 \text{ cm} - (-60 \text{ cm})} = \boxed{-20 \text{ cm}}$.

$M = -\dfrac{d_i}{d_0} = -\dfrac{-20 \text{ cm}}{30 \text{ cm}} = \dfrac{2}{3}$. So $h_i = Mh_0 = \boxed{\tfrac{2}{3} h_0}$.

27. (a) $d_0 = 5.0$ cm, $d_i = -10$ cm (virtual image).

$\dfrac{1}{f} = \dfrac{1}{d_0} + \dfrac{1}{d_i} = \dfrac{1}{5.0 \text{ cm}} + \dfrac{1}{-10 \text{ cm}} = \dfrac{1}{10 \text{ cm}}$,

so $f = \boxed{10 \text{ cm}}$, and $R = 2f = \boxed{20 \text{ cm}}$.

(b) $M = -\dfrac{d_i}{d_0} = -\dfrac{-10 \text{ cm}}{5.0 \text{ cm}} = +2$ So $h_i = Mh_0 = +2 \,(1.5 \text{ cm}) = \boxed{3.0 \text{ cm}}$.

28. (a) $f = \dfrac{R}{2} = \dfrac{30 \text{ cm}}{2} = 15$ cm, $d_0 = 40$ cm.

$d_i = \dfrac{d_0 f}{d_0 - f} = \dfrac{(40 \text{ cm})(15 \text{ cm})}{40 \text{ cm} - 15 \text{ cm}} = \boxed{24 \text{ cm}}$.

$M = -\dfrac{d_i}{d_0} = -\dfrac{24 \text{ cm}}{40 \text{ cm}} = -0.60$.

So $h_i = Mh_0 = -0.60 \,(3.0 \text{ cm}) = -1.8 \text{ cm} = \boxed{1.8 \text{ cm, real and inverted}}$.

(b) $d_i = \dfrac{(30 \text{ cm})(15 \text{ cm})}{30 \text{ cm} - 15 \text{ cm}} = \boxed{30 \text{ cm}}$. $M = -\dfrac{30 \text{ cm}}{30 \text{ cm}} = -1.0$.

So $h_i = -1.0 \,(3.0 \text{ cm}) = -3.0 \text{ cm} = \boxed{3.0 \text{ cm, real and inverted}}$.

(c) $d_i = \dfrac{(15 \text{ cm})(15 \text{ cm})}{15 \text{ cm} - 15 \text{ cm}} = \boxed{\infty}$. The characteristics of the image are not defined.

(d) $d_i = \dfrac{(5.0 \text{ cm})(15 \text{ cm})}{5.0 \text{ cm} - 15 \text{ cm}} = \boxed{-7.5 \text{ cm}}$. $M = -\dfrac{-7.5 \text{ cm}}{5.0 \text{ cm}} = +1.5$.

So $h_i = +1.5 \,(3.0 \text{ cm}) = \boxed{4.5 \text{ cm, virtual and upright}}$.

29.　(a)

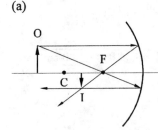

(b)

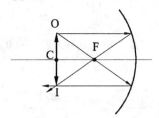

(c)

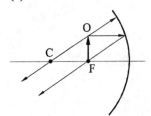

(d)

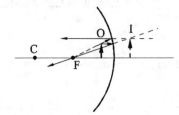

30.　Since $d_o < f$, $d_i = \dfrac{d_o f}{d_o - f} < 0$. Also $M = -\dfrac{d_i}{d_o} = -\dfrac{f}{d_o - f} = \dfrac{f}{f - d_o} > +1$.

So the image is virtual (negative d_i), upright (positive M), and magnified ($|M| > 1$).

31.　f is negative for a convex mirror. So $d_i = \dfrac{d_o f}{d_o - f} = \dfrac{d_o(-|f|)}{d_o + |f|} < 0$.

Also $M = -\dfrac{d_i}{d_o} = -\dfrac{d_o(-|f|)}{d_o(d_o + |f|)} = \dfrac{|f|}{d_o + |f|} < +1$.

Therefore the image is virtual (negative d_i), upright (positive M), and reduced ($|M| < 1$).

32.　$d_o = 18$ cm, $M = +\frac{1}{2}$ (it is a virtual and upright image). $d_i = -Md_o = -\frac{1}{2}(18 \text{ cm}) = -9.0$ cm.

$\dfrac{1}{f} = \dfrac{1}{d_o} + \dfrac{1}{d_i} = \dfrac{1}{18 \text{ cm}} + \dfrac{1}{-9.0 \text{ cm}} = -\dfrac{1}{18 \text{ cm}}$, ☞ $f = \boxed{-18 \text{ cm}}$.

33.　$d_o = 20$ cm, $M = +1.5$ (upright image). $d_i = -Md_o = -1.5 (20 \text{ cm}) = -30$ cm.

$\dfrac{1}{f} = \dfrac{1}{d_o} + \dfrac{1}{d_i} = \dfrac{1}{20 \text{ cm}} + \dfrac{1}{-30 \text{ cm}} = \dfrac{1}{60 \text{ cm}}$, ☞ $f = 60$ cm. So $R = 2f = \boxed{120 \text{ cm}}$.

34.　(a) $d_o = 50$ cm, $M = +3.0$. Since M is positive, the image is $\boxed{\text{virtual and upright}}$.

(b) $d_i = -Md_o = -3.0 (50 \text{ cm}) = -150$ cm. $\dfrac{1}{f} = \dfrac{1}{d_o} + \dfrac{1}{d_i} = \dfrac{1}{50 \text{ cm}} + \dfrac{1}{-150 \text{ cm}} = \dfrac{2}{150 \text{ cm}}$,

so $f = 75$ cm. Therefore $R = 2f = \boxed{150 \text{ cm}}$.

35. $f = \dfrac{R}{2} = \dfrac{-4.5\ \text{cm}}{2} = -2.25\ \text{cm}$ (convex surface), $M = +\frac{1}{2}$ (virtual image). $d_i = -Md_o = -\dfrac{d_o}{2}$.

So $\dfrac{1}{f} = \dfrac{1}{d_o} + \dfrac{1}{d_i} = \dfrac{1}{d_o} - \dfrac{1}{d_o/2} = -\dfrac{1}{d_o}$, ☞ $d_o = -f = \boxed{2.3\ \text{cm}}$.

36. $M = +4.0$ (upright image). $d_i = -Md_o = -4.0d_o$.

So $\dfrac{1}{f} = \dfrac{1}{d_o} + \dfrac{1}{d_i} = \dfrac{1}{d_o} + \dfrac{1}{-4.0d_o} = \dfrac{3}{4.0d_o}$, therefore it is a $\boxed{\text{concave}}$ mirror with $f = \boxed{\tfrac{4}{3}d_o}$.

37. (a) $f = \dfrac{R}{2} = \dfrac{30\ \text{cm}}{2} = 15\ \text{cm}$, $d_o = 20\ \text{cm}$. $d_i = \dfrac{d_o f}{d_o - f} = \dfrac{(20\ \text{cm})(15\ \text{cm})}{20\ \text{cm} - 15\ \text{cm}} = \boxed{60\ \text{cm}}$.

$M = -\dfrac{d_i}{d_o} = -\dfrac{60\ \text{cm}}{20\ \text{cm}} = \boxed{-3.0,\ \text{real and inverted}}$.

(b) See diagram on right.

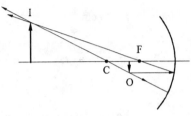

38. $d_o = 12\ \text{cm}$, $M = \dfrac{9.0\ \text{cm}}{3.0\ \text{cm}} = +3.0$.

$d_i = -Md_o = -3.0\,(12\ \text{cm}) = -36\ \text{cm}$.

So $\dfrac{1}{f} = \dfrac{1}{d_o} + \dfrac{1}{d_i} = \dfrac{1}{12\ \text{cm}} + \dfrac{1}{-36\ \text{cm}} = \dfrac{1}{18\ \text{cm}}$, ☞ $f = 18\ \text{cm}$.

So $R = 2f = 36\ \text{cm}$.

Therefore it is $\boxed{\text{concave and } R = 36\ \text{cm}}$.

39. $d_o = 2.5\ \text{m}$, $M = +2.0$. $d_i = -Md_o = -2.0\,(2.5\ \text{m}) = -5.0\ \text{m}$. So

$\dfrac{1}{f} = \dfrac{1}{d_o} + \dfrac{1}{d_i} = \dfrac{1}{2.5\ \text{m}} + \dfrac{1}{-5.0\ \text{m}} = \dfrac{1}{5.0\ \text{cm}}$, ☞ $f = 5.0\ \text{m}$

Therefore $R = 2f = \boxed{10\ \text{m}}$.

40. (a) $d_i = \dfrac{d_o f}{d_o - f} = \dfrac{f}{1 - f/d_o}$. $|M| = \dfrac{d_i}{d_o} = \dfrac{f}{d_o - f}$.

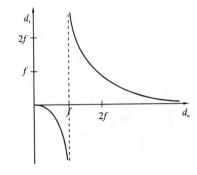

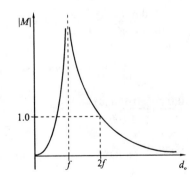

(b) $d_i = \dfrac{d_o(-f)}{d_o + f} = \dfrac{-f}{1 + f/d_o}$.

$|M| = \dfrac{d_i}{d_o} = \dfrac{-f}{d_o + f}$.

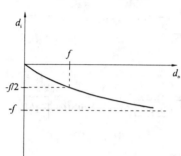

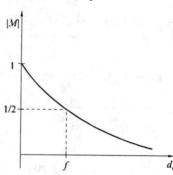

41. $d_o = 30$ cm, $f = 20$ cm. $d_i = \dfrac{d_o f}{d_o - f} = \dfrac{(30 \text{ cm})(20 \text{ cm})}{30 \text{ cm} - 20 \text{ cm}} = \boxed{60 \text{ cm}}$.

$M = -\dfrac{d_i}{d_o} = -\dfrac{60 \text{ cm}}{30 \text{ cm}} = -2.0$.   So the image is $\boxed{\text{real, inverted, and magnified}}$.

42. $d_i = \dfrac{d_o f}{d_o - f}$.   For concave, $M = -\dfrac{d_i}{d_o} = \dfrac{f}{f - d_o} = +1.8$,   ☞ $f = \dfrac{9}{4} d_o$.

For convex, we replace f with $-|f| = -f$.

So $M = \dfrac{f}{f + d_o} = \dfrac{9/4 \, d_o}{9/4 \, d_o + d_o} = \dfrac{9}{13} = \boxed{0.69}$.

43. $f = \dfrac{R}{2} = \dfrac{20 \text{ cm}}{2} = 10$ cm, $M = \pm 2.0$, the + is for a virtual image and the − is for a real image.

$d_i = -M d_o = \mp 2.0 d_o$. $\dfrac{1}{f} = \dfrac{1}{d_o} + \dfrac{1}{d_i}$,   so $\dfrac{1}{10 \text{ cm}} = \dfrac{1}{d_o} + \dfrac{1}{\mp 2.0 d_o}$,

or $\dfrac{2 \mp 1}{2 d_o} = \dfrac{1}{10 \text{ cm}}$.

Solving, $d_o = \dfrac{10 \text{ cm}}{2}(2 \mp 1) = \boxed{5.0 \text{ cm or } 15 \text{ cm}}$.

44.   (a) $d_o = 100$ m, $f = -0.400$ m.

$d_i = \dfrac{d_o f}{d_o - f} = \dfrac{(100 \text{ m})(-0.400 \text{ m})}{100 \text{ m} - (-0.400 \text{ m})} = -0.398 \text{ m} = \boxed{-39.8 \text{ cm}}$.

$M = -\dfrac{d_i}{d_o} = -\dfrac{-0.398 \text{ m}}{100 \text{ m}} = +0.00398$.   So $h_i = M h_o = +0.00398 \,(2.0 \text{ m}) = \boxed{0.80 \text{ cm}}$.

(b) $d_i = \dfrac{(10.0 \text{ m})(-0.400 \text{ m})}{10.0 \text{ m} - (-0.400 \text{ m})} = -0.385 \text{ m} = \boxed{-38.5 \text{ cm}}$.

$M = -\dfrac{-0.385 \text{ m}}{10.0 \text{ m}} = +0.0385$.   So $h_i = +0.0385 \,(2.0 \text{ m}) = \boxed{7.7 \text{ cm}}$.

45. $\boxed{\text{Yes}}$ it is possible. One is a real image and the other is a virtual image.

$f = \dfrac{R}{2} = \dfrac{40 \text{ cm}}{2} = 20 \text{ cm}, \qquad M = \pm 3.0,$ the + is for a virtual image and the − is for a real image.

$d_i = -Md_o = \mp 3.0 d_o.$ $\quad \dfrac{1}{f} = \dfrac{1}{d_o} + \dfrac{1}{d_i},$ $\quad$ so $\quad \dfrac{1}{20 \text{ cm}} = \dfrac{1}{d_o} + \dfrac{1}{\mp 3.0 d_o},$

or $\quad \dfrac{3 \mp 1}{3 d_o} = \dfrac{1}{20 \text{ cm}}.$ $\quad$ Solving, $\quad d_o = \dfrac{20 \text{ cm}}{3}(3 \mp 1) = \boxed{13 \text{ cm or } 27 \text{ cm}}.$

46. (d).

47. (c).

48. (b).

49. When the fish is inside the focal point, the image is upright, virtual, and magnified.

50. $\boxed{\text{Yes}}$. If the object is inside the focal point, the image of a real object is virtual, upright, and magnified.

51. $d_i = \dfrac{d_o f}{d_o - f} = \dfrac{(50.0 \text{ cm})(10.0 \text{ cm})}{50.0 \text{ cm} - (10.0 \text{ cm})} = \boxed{12.5 \text{ cm}}.$ $\quad M = -\dfrac{d_i}{d_o} = -\dfrac{12.5 \text{ cm}}{50.0 \text{ cm}} = \boxed{-0.25}.$

52. $\dfrac{1}{f} = \dfrac{1}{d_o} + \dfrac{1}{d_i} = \dfrac{1}{30 \text{ cm}} + \dfrac{1}{15 \text{ cm}} = \dfrac{1}{10 \text{ cm}},$ $\quad \text{☞} \quad f = \boxed{10 \text{ cm}}.$

53. $f = 20 \text{ cm}, \quad d_i = 200 \text{ cm}.$ $\quad d_o = \dfrac{d_i f}{d_i - f} = \dfrac{(200 \text{ cm})(20 \text{ cm})}{200 \text{ cm} - 20 \text{ cm}} = \boxed{22 \text{ cm}}.$

54. (a) $d_i = \dfrac{d_o f}{d_o - f} = \dfrac{(15 \text{ cm})(22 \text{ cm})}{15 \text{ cm} - 22 \text{ cm}} = \boxed{-47 \text{ cm}}.$

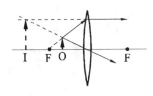

$M = -\dfrac{d_i}{d_o} = -\dfrac{-47.1 \text{ cm}}{15 \text{ cm}} = +3.14.$

So $\quad h_i = Mh_o = +3.14 \,(4.0 \text{ cm}) = \boxed{13 \text{ cm, virtual and upright}}.$

(b) $d_i = \dfrac{(36 \text{ cm})(22 \text{ cm})}{36 \text{ cm} - 22 \text{ cm}} = \boxed{57 \text{ cm}}.$ $\quad M = -\dfrac{56.6 \text{ cm}}{36 \text{ cm}} = -1.57.$

So $\quad h_i = -1.57 \,(4.0 \text{ cm}) = -6.3 \text{ cm} = \boxed{6.3 \text{ cm, real and inverted}}.$

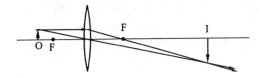

55.   (a) $f = -18.0$ cm, $d_o = 10$ cm.

$$d_i = \frac{d_o f}{d_o - f} = \frac{(10 \text{ cm})(-18.0 \text{ cm})}{10 \text{ cm} - (-18.0 \text{ cm})} = \boxed{-6.4 \text{ cm}}.$$

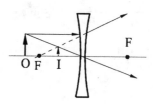

$$M = -\frac{d_i}{d_o} = -\frac{-6.43 \text{ cm}}{10 \text{ cm}} = \boxed{0.64, \text{ virtual and upright}}.$$

(b) $d_i = \dfrac{(25 \text{ cm})(-18.0 \text{ cm})}{25 \text{ cm} - (-18.0 \text{ cm})} = \boxed{-10.5 \text{ cm}}.$

$$M = -\frac{-10.5 \text{ cm}}{25 \text{ cm}} = \boxed{0.42, \text{ virtual and upright}}.$$

56.   For a diverging lens, the focal length is negative.

$$d_i = \frac{d_o f}{d_o - f} = \frac{-d_o |f|}{d_o + |f|} < 0, \text{ so the image is always virtual.}$$

$$M = -\frac{d_i}{d_o} = -\frac{-|f|}{d_o + |f|} = \frac{|f|}{d_o + |f|} < 1, \text{ since } d_o + |f| > |f|.$$

Therefore $0 < M < 1$, i.e., the image is upright and reduced.

57.   (a) $f = 12$ cm, $M = -2.0$ (real). $d_i = -M d_o = 2.0 d_o.$

$$\frac{1}{f} = \frac{1}{d_o} + \frac{1}{d_i} = \frac{1}{d_o} + \frac{1}{2.0 d_o} = \frac{3}{2 d_o}, \quad \Rightarrow \quad d_o = \frac{3}{2} f = \frac{3}{2} (12 \text{ cm}) = \boxed{18 \text{ cm}}.$$

(b) $M = +2.0$ (virtual). $d_i = -M d_o = -2.0 d_o.$

$$\frac{1}{f} = \frac{1}{d_o} + \frac{1}{-2.0 d_o} = \frac{1}{2 d_o}, \quad \Rightarrow \quad d_o = \frac{1}{2} f = \frac{1}{2} (12 \text{ cm}) = \boxed{6.0 \text{ cm}}.$$

58.   (a) $\dfrac{1}{f} = \dfrac{1}{d_o} + \dfrac{1}{d_i} = \dfrac{1}{6.0 \text{ cm}} + \dfrac{1}{400 \text{ cm}} = 0.169 \text{ m}^{-1}, \quad \Rightarrow \quad f = \boxed{5.9 \text{ cm}}.$

(b) $M = -\dfrac{d_i}{d_o} = -\dfrac{400 \text{ cm}}{6.0 \text{ cm}} = -66.7.$

So $h_i = M h_o = -66.7 (1.0 \text{ cm}) = -66.7 \text{ cm} = \boxed{67 \text{ cm, inverted}}.$

59. $d_o = 4.0$ m, $M = \dfrac{h_i}{h_o} = \dfrac{-35 \text{ mm}}{1.7 \times 10^3 \text{ mm}} = -0.0206$ (inverted).

$$d_i = -M d_o = 0.0206 (4.0 \text{ m}) = 0.0824 \text{ m}.$$

$$\frac{1}{f} = \frac{1}{d_o} + \frac{1}{d_i} = \frac{1}{4.0 \text{ m}} + \frac{1}{0.0824 \text{ m}} = 12.4 \text{ m}^{-1}, \quad \Rightarrow \quad f = 0.081 \text{ m} = \boxed{8.1 \text{ cm}}.$$

60. $d_o = 10$ cm, $M = +\frac{1}{5}$ (image by concave lens is always virtual). $d_i = -Md_o = -\frac{1}{5}d_o$.

$$\frac{1}{f} = \frac{1}{d_o} + \frac{1}{d_i} = \frac{1}{d_o} + \frac{1}{-\frac{1}{5}d_o} = \frac{-4}{d_o}, \quad \text{☞} \quad f = -\frac{d_o}{4} = -\frac{10 \text{ cm}}{4} = \boxed{-2.5 \text{ cm}}.$$

61. $d_i = \dfrac{d_o f}{d_o - f}, \quad \text{☞} \quad d = d_o + d_i = d_o + \dfrac{d_o f}{d_o - f} = \dfrac{d_o(d_o - f)}{d_o - f} + \dfrac{d_o f}{d_o - f} = \dfrac{d_o^2}{d_o - f}.$

The quantity $\dfrac{d_o^2}{d_o - f}$ reaches its minimum when $d_o = 2f$ (try it), i.e., the minimum distance between the

object and the image for sharp image to form is $d_{min} = 4f$.

$f = 10$ cm, $d = d_o + d_i = 40$ cm. So $d = 4f$, which is the minimum distance for sharp image to form.

So $d_o = d_i = \boxed{20 \text{ cm}}$, and $M = -\dfrac{d_i}{d_o} = \boxed{-1}$.

62. (a) From similar triangles, $\dfrac{d_i - f}{f} = -\dfrac{y_i}{y_o}$, where the negative is introduced because the image is inverted.

Also $-\dfrac{y_i}{y_o} = \dfrac{d_i}{d_o}$. So $\dfrac{d_i - f}{f} = \dfrac{d_i}{d_o}$, or $d_o d_i - d_o f = d_i f$, i.e., $d_i f + d_o f = d_o d_i$.

Dividing by $d_o d_i f$ on both sides gives $\dfrac{1}{d_o} + \dfrac{1}{d_i} = \dfrac{1}{f}$.

(b) $M = \dfrac{y_i}{y_o} = -\dfrac{d_i}{d_o}$ from the similar triangles in (a).

63. (a) From the result of Exercise 23.61, the minimum distance between the object and the image is $4f$ for a

sharp image to form. At this minimum distance, $d_o = d_i = 2f$. So $M = -\dfrac{d_i}{d_o} = -1$, i.e., a real image.

Therefore the minimum distance for a real image to form is also $\boxed{4f}$.

(b) For a biconvex lens, virtual image forms when $0 < d_o < f$. When d_o approaches, $d_i = \dfrac{d_o f}{d_o - f}$ also

approaches 0. So the distance between the object and the image approaches $\boxed{0}$.

64. $d_o = 3.0$ cm, $M = +3.5$ (virtual image). $d_i = -Md_o = -3.5\,(3.0 \text{ cm}) = -10.5$ cm.

$$\frac{1}{f} = \frac{1}{d_o} + \frac{1}{d_i} = \frac{1}{3.0 \text{ cm}} + \frac{1}{-10.5 \text{ cm}} = 0.238 \text{ cm}^{-1}, \quad \text{☞} \quad f = \boxed{4.2 \text{ cm}}.$$

65. (a) $d_o = 30$ cm, $f = -45$ cm. $d_i = \dfrac{d_o f}{d_o - f} = \dfrac{(30 \text{ cm})(-45 \text{ cm})}{30 \text{ cm} - (-45 \text{ cm})} = \boxed{-18 \text{ cm}}.$

(b) $d_i = \dfrac{(30 \text{ cm})(45 \text{ cm})}{30 \text{ cm} - 45 \text{ cm}} = \boxed{-90 \text{ cm}}.$

66. For the lens, $d_{i1} = \dfrac{d_{o1}f_1}{d_{o1} - f_1} = \dfrac{(0.40 \text{ m})(0.15 \text{ m})}{0.40 \text{ m} - 0.15 \text{ m}} = 0.24 \text{ m}.$

$M_1 = -\dfrac{d_{i1}}{d_{o1}} = -\dfrac{0.24 \text{ m}}{0.40 \text{ m}} = -0.60.$ The image by the lens is the object for the mirror.

For the mirror, $d_{o2} = 0.50 \text{ m} - d_{i1} = 0.50 \text{ m} - 0.24 \text{ m} = 0.26 \text{ m}.$

$d_{i2} = \dfrac{(0.26 \text{ m})(0.13 \text{ m})}{0.26 \text{ m} - 0.13 \text{ m}} = \boxed{0.26 \text{ m in front of the mirror}}.$

$M_2 = -\dfrac{0.26 \text{ m}}{0.26 \text{ m}} = -1.$ So $M_{\text{total}} = M_1 M_2 = (-0.60)(-1.0) = \boxed{0.60, \text{ real and upright}}.$

67. (a) $d_o = 1.5 \text{ m}, \quad f = 0.045 \text{ m}. \quad d_i = \dfrac{d_o f}{d_o - f} = \dfrac{(1.5 \text{ m})(0.045 \text{ m})}{1.5 \text{ m} - 0.045 \text{ m}} = 0.046 \text{ m} = \boxed{4.6 \text{ cm}}.$

(b) $M = -\dfrac{d_i}{d_o} = -\dfrac{0.046 \text{ m}}{1.5 \text{ m}} = -0.0309.$ So $h_i = Mh_o = -0.0309 \,(26 \text{ cm}) = \boxed{0.80 \text{ cm, inverted}}.$

68. For the objective, $d_{i1} = \dfrac{d_{o1} f_o}{d_{o1} - f_o} = \dfrac{(0.30 \text{ cm})(0.28 \text{ cm})}{0.30 \text{ cm} - 0.28 \text{ cm}} = 4.2 \text{ cm}.$

The image by the objective is the object for the eyepiece.

For the eyepiece, $d_{o2} = 7.0 \text{ cm} - d_{i1} = 7.0 \text{ cm} - 4.2 \text{ cm} = 2.8 \text{ cm}.$

$d_{i2} = \dfrac{d_{o2} f_e}{d_{o2} - f_e} = \dfrac{(2.8 \text{ cm})(3.3 \text{ cm})}{2.8 \text{ cm} - 3.3 \text{ cm}} = -18 \text{ cm}.$

So the image is a $\boxed{\text{virtual image 18 cm to the left of the eyepiece}}.$

69. For L_1, $d_{i1} = \dfrac{d_{o1} f_o}{d_{o1} - f_o} = \dfrac{(50 \text{ cm})(30 \text{ cm})}{50 \text{ cm} - 30 \text{ cm}} = 75 \text{ cm}.$ $M_1 = -\dfrac{d_{i1}}{d_{o1}} = -\dfrac{75 \text{ cm}}{50 \text{ cm}} = -1.5.$

The image by L_1 is the object for L_2.

For L_2, $d_{o2} = d - d_{i1} = 60 \text{ cm} - 75 \text{ cm} = -15 \text{ cm}$, where d is the distance between the lenses. A negative object means that the "object" is on the image side.

$d_{i2} = \dfrac{d_{o2} f_2}{d_{o2} - f_2} = \dfrac{(-15 \text{ cm})(20 \text{ cm})}{-15 \text{ cm} - 20 \text{ cm}} = \boxed{8.6 \text{ cm}}.$ $M_2 = -\dfrac{d_{i2}}{d_{o2}} = -\dfrac{8.57 \text{ cm}}{-15 \text{ cm}} = 0.57.$

So $M_{\text{total}} = M_1 M_2 = (-1.5)(0.57) = -0.86 = \boxed{0.86, \text{ real and inverted}}.$

70. According to the definition of lateral magnification, $M_1 = -\dfrac{h_{i1}}{h_{o1}}$, $M_2 = -\dfrac{h_{i2}}{h_{o2}}$, and $M = \dfrac{h_{i2}}{h_{o1}}.$

Since $h_{o2} = h_{i1}$ (the image formed by the first lens is the object for the second lens),

$M_1 M_2 = \dfrac{h_{i1}}{h_{o1}} \dfrac{h_{i2}}{h_{o2}} = \dfrac{h_{i2}}{h_{o1}} = M_{\text{total}}.$

71.   For f_1, $\quad \dfrac{1}{d_{o1}} + \dfrac{1}{d_{i1}} = \dfrac{1}{f_1}$.   Eq. (1)

The image by f_1 is the object for f_2.

For f_2, $\quad d_{o2} = d - d_{i1} = 0 - d_{i1}$, where $d = 0$ is the distance between the lenses.

So $\quad \dfrac{1}{d_{o2}} + \dfrac{1}{d_{i2}} = -\dfrac{1}{d_{i1}} + \dfrac{1}{d_{i2}} = \dfrac{1}{f_2}$.   Eq. (2)

Eq. (1) + Eq. (2) gives $\quad \dfrac{1}{d_{o1}} + \dfrac{1}{d_{i2}} = \dfrac{1}{f_1} + \dfrac{1}{f_2} = \dfrac{1}{f}$,

where $d_{o1} = d_o$ and $d_{i2} = d_i$ are the object and image distance for the lens system.

Therefore $\quad \dfrac{1}{f} = \dfrac{1}{f_1} + \dfrac{1}{f_2}$.

72.   (b).

73.   (a) $\dfrac{1}{f} = (n-1)\left(\dfrac{1}{R_1} - \dfrac{1}{R_2}\right)$ assumes $n_{air} = 1$. If the index of refraction of the surrounding is not air, the lens

maker's equation needs to be modified as $\dfrac{1}{f} = (n_1/n_2 - 1)\left(\dfrac{1}{R_1} - \dfrac{1}{R_2}\right)$, where n_1 is the index of refraction of

the material and n_2 is the index of refraction of the surrounding.

So $\quad \dfrac{f'}{f} = \dfrac{1.6/1.33 - 1}{1.6/1 - 1} = 0.34$, i.e., the $\boxed{\text{focal length decreases by a factor of } 0.34}$.

(b) $\dfrac{f'}{f} = \dfrac{1.3/1.33 - 1}{1.3/1 - 1} = -0.075$,

i.e., $\boxed{\text{diverging lens becomes converging lens and vice versa and } f \text{ decreases by a factor of } 0.075}$.

74. $\boxed{\text{No}}$. From Exercise 23.73(a), $\dfrac{1}{f} = (n_1/n_2 - 1)\left(\dfrac{1}{R_1} - \dfrac{1}{R_2}\right)$. So if $n_2 > n_1$, f is negative.

75.   For a rectangular glass block, $R_1 = R_2 = \infty$. So $\dfrac{1}{f} = (n-1)\left(\dfrac{1}{R_1} - \dfrac{1}{R_2}\right) = 0$.

Therefore $f = \boxed{\infty}$, i.e., it has no focusing power.

76. $P = \dfrac{1}{f} = (n-1)\left(\dfrac{1}{R_1} - \dfrac{1}{R_2}\right)$,   ☞ $\left(\dfrac{1}{R_1} - \dfrac{1}{R_2}\right) = \dfrac{P}{n-1} = \dfrac{1.5\,\text{D}}{1.6 - 1} = 2.5\,\text{D}$.

So $\quad \dfrac{1}{R_2} = \dfrac{1}{R_1} - 2.5\,\text{D} = \dfrac{1}{0.20\,\text{m}} - 2.5\,\text{D} = 2.5\,\text{D}$. Therefore $R_2 = \dfrac{1}{2.5\,\text{D}} = 0.40\,\text{m} = \boxed{40\,\text{cm}}$.

77. $P = \dfrac{1}{f} = (n-1)\left(\dfrac{1}{R_1} - \dfrac{1}{R_2}\right) = (1.35 - 1)\left(\dfrac{1}{\infty} - \dfrac{1}{0.50\ \text{m}}\right) = \boxed{-0.70\ \text{D}}$.

78. (a) $\dfrac{1}{f} = (n-1)\left(\dfrac{1}{R_1} - \dfrac{1}{R_2}\right) = (1.6 - 1)\left(\dfrac{1}{0.30\ \text{m}} - \dfrac{1}{-0.40\ \text{m}}\right) = 3.5\ \text{D},\quad \text{☞}\quad f = 0.29\ \text{m} = \boxed{29\ \text{cm}}$.

   (b) From Exercise 23.73(a), $\dfrac{1}{f} = (n_1/n_2 - 1)\left(\dfrac{1}{R_1} - \dfrac{1}{R_2}\right) = (1.6/1.33 - 1)\left(\dfrac{1}{0.30\ \text{m}} - \dfrac{1}{-0.40\ \text{m}}\right) = 1.184\ \text{D}$.

   So $\quad f = 0.84\ \text{m} = \boxed{84\ \text{cm}}$.

79. Since the Moon is so far away, its image will be at the focal plane and so $d_i = f = 60$ mm.

   $M = -\dfrac{d_i}{d_o} = -\dfrac{60 \times 10^{-3}\ \text{m}}{3.8 \times 10^8\ \text{m}} = -1.58 \times 10^{-10}$.

   So $\quad h_i = Mh_o = -1.58 \times 10^{-10}\,(3.5 \times 10^6\ \text{m}) = -5.5 \times 10^{-4}\ \text{m} = \boxed{0.55\ \text{mm}}$, inverted.

80. (a) It must be a $\boxed{\text{convex}}$ mirror since a concave mirror can only form magnified virtual images.

   (b) $M = +0.50$ (virtual), $\quad d_o = 7.0$ cm. $\quad d_i = -Md_o = -0.50\,(7.0\ \text{cm}) = -3.5$ cm.

   $\dfrac{1}{f} = \dfrac{1}{d_o} + \dfrac{1}{d_i} = \dfrac{1}{7.0\ \text{cm}} + \dfrac{1}{-3.5\ \text{cm}} = -\dfrac{1}{7.0\ \text{cm}},\quad \text{☞}\quad f = -7.0\ \text{cm}. \quad \text{So}\quad R = 2|f| = \boxed{14\ \text{cm}}$.

81. $f = \dfrac{R}{2} = \dfrac{50\ \text{cm}}{2} = 25\ \text{cm}, \quad d_o = 75\ \text{cm}. \quad d_i = \dfrac{d_o f}{d_o - f} = \dfrac{(75\ \text{cm})(25\ \text{cm})}{75\ \text{cm} - 25\ \text{cm}} = \boxed{37.5\ \text{cm}}$.

   $M = -\dfrac{d_i}{d_o} = -\dfrac{37.5\ \text{cm}}{75\ \text{cm}} = -0.50$.

   So $\quad h_i = Mh_o = -0.50\,(6.0\ \text{cm}) = -3.0\ \text{cm} = \boxed{3.0\ \text{cm, real and inverted}}$.

82. When the object distance is decreasing, the image distance decreases at the same rate, so the relative velocity of the image to the object is $2(4.5\ \text{km/h}) = 9.0\ \text{km/h} = \boxed{2.5\ \text{m/s}}$.

83. The image formed by the converging lens is at the mirror. This image is the object for the diverging lens. If the mirror is at the focal point of the diverging lens, the rays refracted after the diverging lens will be parallel to the axis. These rays will be reflected back parallel to the axis by the mirror and will form another image at the mirror. This second image is now the object for the converging lens. By reversing the rays, a sharp image is formed on the screen located where the original object is. Therefore the distance from the diverging lens to the mirror is the focal length of the diverging lens.

84. The two shaded triangles are similar to each other.

So $|M| = \dfrac{h_i}{h_o} = \dfrac{d_i}{d_o}$.

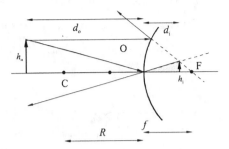

85. $d_o = 20$ cm, $M = -2.5$ (real, inverted).

$d_i = -Md_o = 2.5(20 \text{ cm}) = 50$ cm.

$\dfrac{1}{f} = \dfrac{1}{d_o} + \dfrac{1}{d_i} = \dfrac{1}{20 \text{ cm}} + \dfrac{1}{50 \text{ cm}} = \dfrac{7}{100 \text{ cm}}$,   ☞ $f = \dfrac{100 \text{ cm}}{7} = \boxed{14 \text{ cm}}$.

86. $f_1 = f_2 = \dfrac{1}{P} = \dfrac{1}{10 \text{ D}} = 0.10 \text{ m} = 10$ cm.

For the first lens, $d_{i1} = \dfrac{d_{o1} f_1}{d_{o1} - f_1} = \dfrac{(60 \text{ cm})(10 \text{ cm})}{60 \text{ cm} - 10 \text{ cm}} = 12$ cm. $M_1 = -\dfrac{d_{i1}}{d_{o1}} = -\dfrac{12 \text{ cm}}{60 \text{ cm}} = -0.20$.

The image by the first lens is the object for the second lens.   For the second lens, $d_{o2} = d - d_{i1} = 20$ cm

$-$ 12 cm = 8.0 cm, where d is the distance between the two lenses.

So $d_{i2} = \dfrac{d_{o2} f_2}{d_{o2} - f_2} = \dfrac{(8.0 \text{ cm})(10 \text{ cm})}{8.0 \text{ cm} - 10 \text{ cm}} = -40$ cm, i.e., 40 cm on the object side from lens 2. Therefore the

position of the image relative to lens 1 is 20 cm $-$ 40 cm = -20 cm = $\boxed{20 \text{ cm on object side of } L_1}$.

$M_2 = -\dfrac{d_{i2}}{d_{o2}} = -\dfrac{-40 \text{ cm}}{8.0 \text{ cm}} = +5.0$.   So $M_{\text{total}} = M_1 M_2 = (-0.20)(5.0) = \boxed{-1.0, \text{ virtual and inverted}}$.

87. Since the mirror and lens equations are the same and the definition of the lateral magnification are also the same mathematically, the graphs are exactly the same as those in Exercise 23.40.

88. For the first lens, $d_{o1} = 15$ cm, $f_1 = 10$ cm. $d_{i1} = \dfrac{d_{o1} f_1}{d_{o1} - f_1} = \dfrac{(15 \text{ cm})(10 \text{ cm})}{15 \text{ cm} - 10 \text{ cm}} = 30$ cm.

$M_1 = -\dfrac{d_{i1}}{d_{o1}} = -\dfrac{30 \text{ cm}}{15 \text{ cm}} = -2.0$.   The image of the first lens is the object for the second lens.

For the second lens, $d_{o2} = d - d_{i1} = 60$ cm $-$ 30 cm = 30 cm, where d is the distance between the lenses.

So $d_{i2} = \dfrac{d_{o2} f_2}{d_{o2} - f_2} = \dfrac{(30 \text{ cm})(20 \text{ cm})}{30 \text{ cm} - 20 \text{ cm}} = \boxed{60 \text{ cm to right of } L_2}$.

$M_2 = -\dfrac{d_{i2}}{d_{o2}} = -\dfrac{60 \text{ cm}}{30 \text{ cm}} = -2.0$.   Therefore $M_{\text{total}} = M_1 M_2 = (-2.0)(-2.0) = \boxed{4.0, \text{ real and upright}}$.

89.   (a) Since the index of refraction of the lens is greater than that of air, the angle of refraction is smaller than the angle of incidence at the air–lens interface and greater than the angle of incidence at the lens–air interface. So both refractions bend the incident light toward the axis.

(a)   (b)

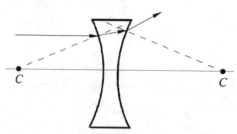

(b) For the same reason, the rays bend away from the axis due to the opposite curvatures of the surfaces.

90. $f = -25$ cm, $d_o = 15$ cm. $d_i = \dfrac{d_o f}{d_o - f} = \dfrac{(15 \text{ cm})(-25 \text{ cm})}{15 \text{ cm} - (-25 \text{ cm})} = \boxed{-9.4 \text{ cm}}$.

$M = -\dfrac{d_i}{d_o} = -\dfrac{-9.38 \text{ cm}}{15 \text{ cm}} = +0.625$.   So $h_i = Mh_o = 0.625 \,(3.0 \text{ cm}) = \boxed{1.9 \text{ cm}}$.

91.   From Exercise 23.73(a), $\dfrac{1}{f} = (n_1/n_2 - 1)\left(\dfrac{1}{R_1} - \dfrac{1}{R_2}\right)$.

So $\dfrac{f_{\text{water}}}{f_{\text{air}}} = \dfrac{1.62/1 - 1}{1.62/1.33 - 1} = 2.84$.   Therefore $f_{\text{water}} = 2.84\,(30 \text{ cm}) = \boxed{85 \text{ cm}}$.

92. $d_o = 30$ cm, $d_i = 20$ cm (real because on a screen).

$\dfrac{1}{f} = \dfrac{1}{d_o} + \dfrac{1}{d_i} = \dfrac{1}{30 \text{ cm}} + \dfrac{1}{20 \text{ cm}} = \dfrac{5}{60 \text{ cm}}$,   so $f = \dfrac{60 \text{ cm}}{5} = 12$ cm.

Therefore $R = 2f = \boxed{24 \text{ cm}}$.

93.   (a)

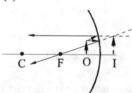

(b) $d_o = 20$ cm, $M = +1.5$ (virtual). $d_i = -Md_o = -1.5\,(20 \text{ cm}) = -30$ cm.

$\dfrac{1}{f} = \dfrac{1}{d_o} + \dfrac{1}{d_i} = \dfrac{1}{20 \text{ cm}} + \dfrac{1}{-30 \text{ cm}} = \dfrac{1}{60 \text{ cm}}$,   ☞ $f = \boxed{60 \text{ cm}}$.

CHAPTER 24

PHYSICAL OPTICS: THE WAVE NATURE OF LIGHT

1. (b), $y_n = \dfrac{n\lambda L}{d} \propto \dfrac{1}{d}$.

2. (a). Constructive interference occurs when $\Delta = n\lambda$, $n = 0, 1, 2, \ldots$

3. Since $y_n = \dfrac{n\lambda L}{d} \propto \lambda$, $\boxed{\text{blue}}$ is closer to the central maximum.

4. There will be $\boxed{\text{no interference fringes}}$, just uniform light intensity, if the light is not coherent.

5. The path difference will change because of the airplane. This change in path difference results in a change in the condition of interference, i.e., constructive is no longer constructive, etc. Therefore the pictures flutter.

6. $\boxed{\text{No}}$, the flashlights are not coherent sources.

7. We approximate $\tan \theta$ with $\sin \theta$. So the percentage difference is

   $$\frac{\tan \theta - \sin \theta}{\tan \theta} = \frac{\tan 15° - \sin 15°}{\tan 15°} = 0.034 = \boxed{3.4\%}.$$

8. $0.75 \text{ m} = 0.50 \text{ m} + 0.25 \text{ m} = 1.5(0.50 \text{ m}) = 1.5\lambda$. So the waves will interfere $\boxed{\text{destructively}}$.

9. (a) $\Delta L = r_2 - r_1$

   $$= \sqrt{(15.0 \text{ m} - 4.0 \text{ m})^2 + (20.0 \text{ m} - 3.0 \text{ m})^2} - \sqrt{(15.0 \text{ m} - 2.0 \text{ m})^2 + (20.0 \text{ m} - 5.0 \text{ m})^2}$$

   $$= 0.40 \text{ m} = \frac{(1)\lambda}{2},$$

   so $\lambda = 2(0.40 \text{ m}) = \boxed{0.80 \text{ m}}$.

   (b) $\Delta\theta = \dfrac{2\pi\Delta}{\lambda} = \dfrac{2\pi}{\lambda}(0.40 \text{ m}) = \dfrac{\pi}{4}$, ☞ $\lambda = 8(0.40 \text{ m}) = \boxed{3.2 \text{ m}}$.

10.   (a) $d \sin \theta = \dfrac{m\lambda}{2}$, where $\sin \theta \approx \tan \theta = \dfrac{y_m}{L}$,   ☞ $\boxed{y_m = \dfrac{m\lambda L}{2d} \;\; (m = 1, 3, 5, \ldots)}$.

$\Delta y = y_{m+2} - y_m = \dfrac{(m+2)\lambda L}{2d} - \dfrac{m\lambda L}{2d} = \boxed{\dfrac{\lambda L}{d}}$.

(b) The third dark fringe corresponds to $m = 5$.   So $\Delta L = \dfrac{m\lambda}{2} = \dfrac{5\lambda}{2} = \boxed{2.5\lambda}$.

11. $\lambda = \dfrac{y_n d}{nL}$,   ☞ $L = \dfrac{y_n d}{n\lambda} = \dfrac{(0.045 \text{ m})(50 \times 10^{-6} \text{ m})}{(2)(550 \times 10^{-9} \text{ m})} = \boxed{2.0 \text{ m}}$.

12.   The distance is equal to $y_3 - y_0 = 3\Delta y = \dfrac{3L\lambda}{d} = \dfrac{3(1.5 \text{ m})(680 \times 10^{-9} \text{ m})}{0.25 \times 10^{-3} \text{ m}} = \boxed{1.2 \text{ cm}}$.

13.   (a) $\lambda = \dfrac{y_n d}{nL} = \dfrac{(0.0660 \text{ m})(0.0250 \times 10^{-3} \text{ m})}{(3)(1.25 \text{ m})} = \boxed{4.40 \times 10^{-7} \text{ m}}$.

(b) $y_2 = \dfrac{(2)(1.25 \text{ m})(4.40 \times 10^{-7} \text{ m})}{0.0250 \times 10^{-3} \text{ m}} = \boxed{4.40 \text{ cm}}$.

14. $\Delta y = \dfrac{L\lambda}{d}$,   ☞ $\lambda = \dfrac{d\Delta y}{L} = \dfrac{(0.20 \times 10^{-3} \text{ m})(0.45 \times 10^{-2} \text{ m})}{1.5 \text{ m}} = \boxed{600 \text{ nm (orange-yellow)}}$.

15.   (a) $\Delta y = \dfrac{L\lambda}{d} = \dfrac{(3.00 \text{ m})(640 \times 10^{-9} \text{ m})}{1.0 \times 10^{-3} \text{ m}} = \boxed{1.9 \text{ mm}}$.

(b) Δy will decrease to $\Delta y = \dfrac{(3.00 \text{ m})(640 \times 10^{-9} \text{ m})}{1.5 \times 10^{-3} \text{ m}} = \boxed{1.2 \text{ mm}}$.

16.   (a) $\theta = \dfrac{y}{L} = \dfrac{n\lambda}{d}$,   ☞ $\Delta\theta = \dfrac{\Delta n\lambda}{d} = \dfrac{(2 - 0)(550 \times 10^{-9} \text{ m})}{1.75 \times 10^{-4} \text{ m}} = \boxed{6.29 \times 10^{-3} \text{ rad}}$.

(b) $y_2 = \Delta\theta L = (6.29 \times 10^{-3} \text{ rad})(2.00 \text{ m}) = \boxed{1.26 \text{ cm}}$.

17.   (a) $\theta = \dfrac{y}{L} = \dfrac{n\lambda}{d}$,   ☞ $\Delta\theta = \dfrac{\Delta n\lambda}{d}$.

So $\lambda = \dfrac{\Delta\theta d}{\Delta n} = \dfrac{(0.0230 \text{ rad})(0.0350 \times 10^{-3} \text{ m})}{(2 - 0)} = \boxed{4.00 \times 10^{-7} \text{ m, violet}}$.

(b) $y_2 = \Delta\theta L = (0.0230 \text{ rad})(1.50 \text{ m}) = \boxed{3.45 \text{ cm}}$.

18.   (a) In water, $\lambda' = \dfrac{\lambda}{n} = \dfrac{\lambda}{1.33}$.   So $y_n{}' = \dfrac{y_n}{1.33} = \boxed{(0.75)y_n}$.

(b) $3\Delta y' = (0.75)\, 3\Delta y = (0.75)(1.2 \times 10^{-2} \text{ m}) = \boxed{9.0 \text{ mm}}$.

19. $y_n = \dfrac{n\lambda L}{d}$, ☞ $\dfrac{(3)(600 \text{ nm}) L}{d} = \dfrac{(4)\,\lambda_2\, L}{d}$. So $\lambda_2 = \dfrac{3}{4}(600 \text{ nm}) = \boxed{450 \text{ nm}}$.

20. (a) because only the reflection at n_o–n_1 interface has 180° phase shift.

21. (a) because both reflections have 180° phase shifts.

22. The path difference in the film would be different (rather than directly down and back in terms of t alone), and the angular dependence and Snell's law would have to be used to determine the conditions for interference.

23. The wavelengths that are not visible in the reflected light are $\boxed{\text{all wavelengths except bluish purple}}$.

24. $\boxed{\text{No}}$, this is not a violation of the conservation of energy. There are regions where waves interfere constructively. The total energy is still conserved.

25. (a) $\lambda_n = \dfrac{\lambda}{n} = \dfrac{550 \text{ nm}}{1.5} = 367 \text{ nm}$. $t = 1.1 \times 10^{-5} \text{ m} = 30(367 \times 10^{-9} \text{ m}) = \boxed{30\lambda}$.

    (b) The path length difference $\Delta L = 2t = 2(30\lambda) = 60\lambda$. However, the first reflection has a 180° phase shift. So they will interfere $\boxed{\text{destructively}}$.

26. $t = \dfrac{\lambda}{4n} = \dfrac{700 \text{ nm}}{4(1.4)} = 125 \text{ nm} = \boxed{1.3 \times 10^{-7} \text{ m}}$.

27. $t = \dfrac{\lambda}{4n}$, ☞ $\Delta t = \dfrac{1}{4n} \Delta\lambda = \dfrac{1}{4(1.38)}(300 \text{ nm}) = 54 \text{ nm} = \boxed{5.4 \times 10^{-8} \text{ m}}$.

28. (a) $t = \dfrac{\lambda}{4n} = \dfrac{550 \text{ nm}}{4(1.22)} = 113 \text{ nm} = \boxed{1.13 \times 10^{-7} \text{ m}}$.

    (b) $\boxed{\text{Yes}}$, they must satisfy $n_{\text{solar}} > n_{\text{film}}$.

29. The first reflection has 180° phase shift. So the condition for destructive interference becomes

    $\Delta L = 2t = \lambda_n$, where $\lambda_n = \dfrac{\lambda}{n}$. So $t = \dfrac{\lambda}{2n}$.

    Therefore $t_1 = \dfrac{480 \text{ nm}}{2(1.5)} = \boxed{160 \text{ nm}}$ and $t_2 = \dfrac{600 \text{ nm}}{2(1.5)} = \boxed{200 \text{ nm}}$.

30. $t = \dfrac{\lambda}{4n} = \dfrac{c/f}{4n} = \dfrac{c}{4fn} = \dfrac{3.00 \times 10^8 \text{ m/s}}{4(3.75 \times 10^{14} \text{ Hz})(1.20)} = \boxed{1.67 \times 10^{-7} \text{ m}}$.

31. (a) The two rays for interference are the reflections from the bottom surface of the top plate and the top surface from the bottom plate. The reflection from the top surface of the bottom plate has 180° phase shifts, so the condition for constructive interference for reflection is $\Delta L = 2t = \frac{\lambda}{2}$,

so $t = \frac{\lambda}{4} = \frac{632.8 \text{ nm}}{4} = \boxed{158.2 \text{ nm}}$.

(b) Constructive for transmission is the same as destructive for reflection.

So $\Delta L = 2t = \lambda$, ☞ $t = \frac{\lambda}{2} = \frac{632.8 \text{ nm}}{2} = \boxed{316.4 \text{ nm}}$.

32. (a) The two rays for interference are the reflections from the bottom surface of the top plate and the top surface from the bottom plate. The reflection from the top surface of the bottom plate has 180° phase shifts (half-wave), so the condition for constructive interference for reflection is

$\Delta L = 2t + \frac{\lambda}{2} = m\lambda,\ m = 1, 2, 3, \ldots$ So $\boxed{2t = (m - \frac{1}{2})\lambda,\ m = 1, 2, 3, \ldots}$.

(b) For the dark fringes, $\Delta L = 2t = m\,\lambda,\ m = 0, 1, 2, 3, \ldots$ So $m = \frac{2t}{\lambda}$.

33. $2t = (m - \frac{1}{2})\lambda,$ ☞ $d = t = \frac{(6 - \frac{1}{2})(550 \times 10^{-9} \text{ m})}{2} = \boxed{1.51 \times 10^{-6} \text{ m}}$.

34. (b).

35. (b).

36. (a) $y_m = \frac{mL\lambda}{w}$. If $w = \lambda$, $y_m = mL$. The width of the central maximum is then $2L$. This prediction is not correct because we used the assumption $\sin\theta = \tan\theta$ to obtain the result. When $w = \lambda$, this assumption is no longer valid.

(b) If $n = 0$, $\theta = 0°$ or the angle of incidence is 90° and so there will be no interference.

37. If the slit length is comparable to the width, $\boxed{\text{a second diffraction pattern in addition to the first}}$ will also be observed. The second diffraction patters is perpendicular to the first.

38. (a) The width of the central maximum is

$y_1 - y_{-1} = 2\Delta y = \frac{2\,L\,\lambda}{w} = \frac{2(1.0 \text{ m})(480 \times 10^{-9} \text{ m})}{0.20 \times 10^{-3} \text{ m}} = \boxed{4.8 \text{ mm}}$.

(b) $y_3 - y_2 = y_4 - y_3 = \Delta y = \frac{L\,\lambda}{w} = \boxed{2.4 \text{ mm}}$.

39. (a) The width of the central maximum is

$$y_1 - y_{-1} = 2\Delta y = \frac{2L\lambda}{w} = \frac{2(1.0 \text{ m})(680 \times 10^{-9} \text{ m})}{0.025 \times 10^{-3} \text{ m}} = \boxed{5.4 \text{ cm}}.$$

(b) The width of the side maxima is half the width of the central maximum. $\Delta y = \boxed{2.7 \text{ cm}}$.

40. $d \sin \theta = n\lambda$, ☞ $\sin \theta = \dfrac{n\lambda}{d} = \dfrac{2(550 \times 10^{-9} \text{ m})}{1.25 \times 10^{-6} \text{ m}} = 0.880.$

So $\theta = \sin^{-1} 0.880 = \boxed{61.6°}$.

41. (a) $d \sin \theta = m\lambda$, ☞ $\lambda = \dfrac{d \sin \theta}{m} = (0.025 \text{ m}) \sin 10° = \boxed{4.3 \text{ mm}}$.

(b) $f = \dfrac{c}{\lambda} = \dfrac{3.00 \times 10^8 \text{ m/s}}{4.34 \times 10^{-3} \text{ m}} = 6.9 \times 10^{10} \text{ Hz}, \boxed{\text{microwave}}$.

42. (a) $w \sin \theta = m\lambda$, ☞ $\theta = \sin^{-1} \dfrac{m\lambda}{w} = \sin^{-1} \dfrac{(2)(680 \times 10^{-9} \text{ m})}{0.50 \times 10^{-3} \text{ m}} = \boxed{0.16° = 2.7 \times 10^{-3} \text{ rad}}$.

(b) $\Delta y = \theta L = (2.72 \times 10^{-3} \text{ rad})(1.80 \text{ m}) = \boxed{4.9 \text{ mm}}$.

43. The width of the central maximum is

$$y_1 - y_{-1} = 2\Delta y = \frac{2L\lambda}{w} = \frac{2(1.80 \text{ m})(680 \times 10^{-9} \text{ m})}{0.50 \times 10^{-3} \text{ m}} = \boxed{4.9 \text{ mm}}.$$

44. $\lambda = \dfrac{c}{f} = \dfrac{3.00 \times 10^8 \text{ m/s}}{5.0 \times 10^{17} \text{ Hz}} = 6.0 \times 10^{-10} \text{ m}.$

$2d \sin \theta = n\lambda$, ☞ $d = \dfrac{n\lambda}{2 \sin \theta} = \dfrac{(1)(6.0 \times 10^{-10} \text{ m})}{2 \sin 25°} = \boxed{7.1 \times 10^{-10} \text{ m}}$.

45. $d = \dfrac{1}{7500 \text{ lines/cm}} = 1.33 \times 10^{-4} \text{ cm} = 1.33 \times 10^{-6} \text{ m}.$ $d \sin \theta = m\lambda$, ☞ $\theta = \sin^{-1} \dfrac{m\lambda}{d}$.

For blue, $\theta_{1b} = \sin^{-1} \dfrac{420 \times 10^{-9} \text{ m}}{1.33 \times 10^{-6} \text{ m}} = \boxed{18.4°}$. So $x_1 = L \tan \theta_1 = (1.5 \text{ m}) \tan 18.4° = \boxed{0.50 \text{ m}}$;

$\theta_{2b} = \sin^{-1} \dfrac{(2)(420 \times 10^{-9} \text{ m})}{1.33 \times 10^{-6} \text{ m}} = \boxed{39.2°}$. So $x_2 = (1.5 \text{ m}) \tan 39.2° = \boxed{1.2 \text{ m}}$.

For red, $\theta_{1r} = \sin^{-1} \dfrac{680 \times 10^{-9} \text{ m}}{1.33 \times 10^{-6} \text{ m}} = \boxed{30.7°}$. So $x_1 = (1.5 \text{ m}) \tan 30.7° = \boxed{0.89 \text{ m}}$;

$\theta_{2r} = \sin^{-1} \dfrac{(2)(680 \times 10^{-9} \text{ m})}{1.33 \times 10^{-6} \text{ m}} = \sin^{-1} 1.02.$

Since $\sin 90° = 1$, it is impossible to locate it.

46.

$$d = \frac{1}{10\,000 \text{ lines/cm}} = 1.0 \times 10^{-4} \text{ cm} = 1.0 \times 10^{-6} \text{ m}.$$

$$d \sin \theta = m\lambda, \quad \text{☞} \quad m_{max} = \frac{d \sin 90°}{\lambda} = \frac{d}{\lambda} = \frac{1.0 \times 10^{-6} \text{ m}}{560 \times 10^{-9} \text{ m}} = 1.8.$$

So there are $\boxed{3}$ orders of maxima corresponding to $m = 0$ or ± 1.

47.

(a) $d \sin \theta = m\lambda, \quad \text{☞} \quad d = \frac{m\lambda}{\sin \theta} = \frac{(2)(700 \times 10^{-9} \text{ m})}{\sin 20°} = 4.09 \times 10^{-6} \text{ m} = 4.09 \times 10^{-4} \text{ cm}.$

So the number of lines per cm is $\frac{1}{4.09 \times 10^{-4} \text{ cm}} = \boxed{2.44 \times 10^3 \text{ lines/cm}}$.

(b) In order to see the whole spectrum, we must see red because it has the longest wavelength.

$$m_{max} = \frac{d \sin 90°}{\lambda} = \frac{d}{\lambda} = \frac{4.09 \times 10^{-6} \text{ m}}{700 \times 10^{-9} \text{ m}} = 5.8.$$

So there are $\boxed{11}$ orders of maxima for $m = 0, \pm 1, \pm 2, \pm 3, \pm 4$ or ± 5.

48.

$$d = \frac{1}{4000 \text{ lines/cm}} = 2.5 \times 10^{-4} \text{ cm} = 2.5 \times 10^{-6} \text{ m}. \quad d \sin \theta = m\lambda, \quad \text{☞} \quad \theta = \sin^{-1} \frac{m\lambda}{d}.$$

If they do overlap, it will be the first order red to the second order blue.

For blue, $\quad \theta_{2b} = \sin^{-1} \frac{(2)(400 \times 10^{-9} \text{ m})}{2.5 \times 10^{-6} \text{ m}} = 18.7°.$ For red, $\quad \theta_{1r} = \sin^{-1} \frac{700 \times 10^{-9} \text{ m}}{2.5 \times 10^{-6} \text{ m}} = 16.3°.$

So $\quad \theta_{2b} > \theta_{1r};$ they $\boxed{\text{do not overlap}}$.

49.

$$d = \frac{1}{8000 \text{ lines/cm}} = 1.25 \times 10^{-4} \text{ cm} = 1.25 \times 10^{-6} \text{ m}. \quad d \sin \theta = m\lambda, \quad \text{☞} \quad \theta = \sin^{-1} \frac{m\lambda}{d}.$$

For blue, $\quad \theta_{1b} = \sin^{-1} \frac{400 \times 10^{-9} \text{ m}}{1.25 \times 10^{-6} \text{ m}} = 18.7°.$

For red, $\quad \theta_{1r} = \sin^{-1} \frac{700 \times 10^{-9} \text{ m}}{1.25 \times 10^{-6} \text{ m}} = 34.1°.$

So $\quad \Delta \theta = \theta_{1r} - \theta_{1b} = \boxed{15.4°}.$

50.

$$d = \frac{1}{8000 \text{ cm}} = 1.25 \times 10^{-4} \text{ cm} = 1.25 \times 10^{-6} \text{ m}.$$

$$d \sin \theta = m\lambda, \quad \text{☞} \quad m_{max} = \frac{d \sin 90°}{\lambda} = \frac{d}{\lambda} = \frac{1.25 \times 10^{-6} \text{ m}}{632.8 \times 10^{-9} \text{ m}} = 1.98.$$

So $m_{max} = 1. \quad \theta = \sin^{-1} \frac{m\lambda}{d} = \sin^{-1} \frac{(1)(632.8 \times 10^{-9} \text{ m})}{1.25 \times 10^{-6} \text{ m}} = 30.4°.$

Therefore $\boxed{\text{two at} \pm 30.4°}$ for $m = \pm 1$ can be formed.

51. $d \sin \theta = m\lambda$, ☞ $\theta = \sin^{-1} \dfrac{m\lambda}{d}$.

For violet, $\theta_{3v} = \sin^{-1} \dfrac{(3)(400 \text{ nm})}{d} = \sin^{-1} \dfrac{1200 \text{ nm}}{d}$.

For yellow-orange, $\theta_{2y} = \sin^{-1} \dfrac{(2)(600 \text{ nm})}{d} = \sin^{-1} \dfrac{1200 \text{ nm}}{d}$.

So $\theta_{3v} = \theta_{2y}$, i.e., they overlap.

52. $\lambda = \dfrac{v}{f} = \dfrac{335 \text{ m/s}}{1000 \text{ Hz}} = 0.335 \text{ m}$. $w \sin \theta = m\lambda$, ☞ $\theta = \sin^{-1} \dfrac{m\lambda}{w}$.

$\theta_1 = \sin^{-1} \dfrac{0.335 \text{ m}}{1.0 \text{ m}} = 19.6°$. So there is a minimum at $19.6°$ and therefore the boys cannot hear.

Thus $\boxed{\text{yes}}$ they are telling the truth.

53. (d).

54. (a).

55. Looking through a lens of each pair, rotate one of the lenses. If the intensity changes as the glasses are rotated, both pairs are polarized.

56. We see the rainbow by the scattering of light from the water droplets. The light is partially polarized in the horizontal direction, so the axis of the analyzer should be in the horizontal direction. We can never block out the polarized light completely because it is only partially polarized.

57. When the axes are perpendicular it darkens and when the axes are parallel it lightens.

(a) $\boxed{\text{Twice}}$.   (b) $\boxed{\text{Four times}}$.   (c) $\boxed{\text{None}}$.   (d) $\boxed{\text{Six times}}$.

58. Since $\tan \theta_p = n$ when the material is in air, we can calculate n by measuring θ_p.

59. $\tan \theta_p = n$, ☞ $\theta_p = \tan^{-1} n$. So $\theta_p = \tan^{-1} 1.4$ to $\tan^{-1} 1.7 = \boxed{54° \text{ to } 60°}$.

60. $n = \tan \theta_p = \tan 58° = \boxed{1.6}$.

61. $\tan \theta_p = n$, ☞ $\theta_p = \tan^{-1} n$. So $\theta_1 = \theta_p = \tan^{-1} n = \tan^{-1} 1.62 = 58.3°$.

$n_1 \sin \theta_1 = n_2 \sin \theta_2$, ☞ $\sin \theta_2 = \dfrac{n_1 \sin \theta_1}{n_2} = \dfrac{(1) \sin 58.3°}{1.62} = 0.525$. So $\theta_2 = \boxed{31.7°}$.

62. $n = \dfrac{1}{\sin \theta_c} = \dfrac{1}{\sin 45°} = 1.41.$ $\tan \theta_p = n,$ ☞ $\theta_p = \tan^{-1} n = \tan^{-1} 1.41 = \boxed{55°}.$

63. $\tan \theta_p = n,$ ☞ $\theta_p = \tan^{-1} n.$ So $\theta_1 = \theta_p = \tan^{-1} n = \tan^{-1} 1.22 = 50.7°.$

     $n_1 \sin \theta_1 = n_2 \sin \theta_2,$ ☞ $\sin \theta_2 = \dfrac{n_1 \sin \theta_1}{n_2} = \dfrac{(1)\sin 50.7°}{1.22} = 0.634.$ So $\theta_2 = \boxed{39.3°}.$

64. $\tan \theta_p = n,$ ☞ $\theta_p = \tan^{-1} n = \tan^{-1} 1.55 = \boxed{57.2°}.$

65. Snell's law must be written as $\dfrac{\sin \theta_1}{\sin \theta_2} = \dfrac{\sin \theta_1}{\cos \theta_1} = \tan \theta_1 = \dfrac{n_2}{n_1} = n.$ So $\theta_p = \tan^{-1} \dfrac{n_2}{n_1}.$

66. From Exercise 24.65, $\theta_p = \tan^{-1} \dfrac{n_2}{n_1} = \tan^{-1} \dfrac{1.60}{1.33} = \boxed{50.3°}.$

67. From Exercise 24.65, $\theta_p = \tan^{-1} \dfrac{n_2}{n_1}.$

     The angle of incidence at the water–glass interface must be $\theta_p = \tan^{-1} \dfrac{1.52}{1.33} = 48.8°.$

     For the air–water interface, $n_1 \sin \theta_1 = n_2 \sin \theta_2,$ ☞ $\sin \theta_1 = \dfrac{n_2 \sin \theta_2}{n_1} = (1.33)\sin 48.8° > 1.$

     So the answer is $\boxed{\text{no}}$.

68. (a) since the scattering is inversely proportional to wavelength.

69. Blue scatters more efficiently than red. In the morning and evening, the blue component of the light from the Sun is scattered more in the denser atmosphere near the Earth, so we see red when we look in the direction of the rising or setting Sun. During the day, we mainly see the blue component from overhead scattering.

70. (a) This is caused by the $\boxed{\text{variable air molecule density}}$.

     (b) There is no air on the surface of the Moon, and so an astronaut would see a $\boxed{\text{black}}$ sky.

71. $n = \tan \theta_p = \tan (1.05 \text{ rad}) = \boxed{1.74}.$

72. $\Delta y = \dfrac{\lambda L}{w},$ ☞ $\dfrac{\Delta y}{\Delta y_o} = \dfrac{\lambda}{\lambda_o} \dfrac{L}{L_o} \dfrac{w_o}{w} = \dfrac{450 \text{ nm}}{600 \text{ nm}} \dfrac{2}{3} \dfrac{1}{2} = \boxed{0.25}.$

73. $n = \tan \theta_p,$ ☞ $\theta_p = \tan^{-1} n = \tan^{-1} 1.5 = \boxed{56°}.$

74. $d = \dfrac{1}{1000 \text{ lines/cm}} = 1.00 \times 10^{-3} \text{ cm} = 1.00 \times 10^{-5} \text{ m}, \quad \theta = \tan^{-1}\dfrac{0.045 \text{ cm}}{1.00 \text{ m}} = 2.58°.$

$d \sin \theta = m\lambda, \quad \text{☞} \quad \lambda = \dfrac{d \sin \theta}{m} = (1.00 \times 10^{-5} \text{ m}) \sin 2.58° = 4.50 \times 10^{-7} \text{ m} = \boxed{450 \text{ nm}}.$

75. (a) From the result of Exercise 24.32, for bright fringes, $\quad 2t = (m - \tfrac{1}{2})\lambda, \; m = 1, 2, 3, \ldots.$

So $\quad 2\,\Delta t = (m + 1 - \tfrac{1}{2})\lambda - (m - \tfrac{1}{2})\lambda = \lambda, \quad \text{☞} \quad \Delta t = \dfrac{\lambda}{2}.$

(b) Replacing λ by $\lambda_n = \dfrac{\lambda}{n}$. So the result is $\Delta t = \boxed{\dfrac{\lambda}{2n}}.$

76. $d \sin \theta = m\lambda, \quad \text{☞} \quad d = \dfrac{m\lambda}{\sin \theta} = \dfrac{(2)(700 \times 10^{-9} \text{ m})}{\sin 10°} = 8.06 \times 10^{-6} \text{ m} = 8.06 \times 10^{-4} \text{ cm}.$

So the number of lines per cm is $\dfrac{1}{8.06 \times 10^{-4} \text{ cm}} = \boxed{1.2 \times 10^3 \text{ lines/cm}}.$

77. $\Delta y = \dfrac{\lambda L}{d}, \quad \text{☞} \quad \Delta \theta = \dfrac{\Delta y}{L} = \dfrac{\lambda}{d} = \dfrac{480 \times 10^{-9} \text{ m}}{0.75 \times 10^{-3} \text{ m}} = \boxed{6.4 \times 10^{-4} \text{ rad}}.$

78. $y_3 - y_1 = 2\Delta y = \dfrac{2\lambda L}{d} = \dfrac{2(500 \times 10^{-9} \text{ m})(1.0 \text{ m})}{40 \times 10^{-6} \text{ m}} = \boxed{2.5 \text{ cm}}.$

79. $t = \dfrac{\lambda}{4n}, \quad \text{☞} \quad \lambda = 4nt = 4(1.4)(1.0 \times 10^{-7} \text{ m}) = \boxed{560 \text{ nm}}.$

80. $d = \dfrac{1}{9000 \text{ lines/cm}} = 1.11 \times 10^{-4} \text{ cm} = 1.11 \times 10^{-6} \text{ m}.$

$d \sin \theta = m\lambda, \quad \text{☞} \quad m_{max} = \dfrac{d \sin 90°}{\lambda} = \dfrac{d}{\lambda}.$

For red, $\quad m_{max} = \dfrac{1.11 \times 10^{-6} \text{ m}}{700 \times 10^{-9} \text{ m}} = 1.6.$ So $\quad m_{max} = \boxed{1 \text{ for red}}.$

For violet, $\quad m_{max} = \dfrac{1.11 \times 10^{-6} \text{ m}}{400 \times 10^{-9} \text{ m}} = 2.8.$ So $\quad m_{max} = \boxed{2 \text{ for violet}}.$

81. $d \sin \theta = m\lambda, \quad \text{☞} \quad \lambda = \dfrac{d \sin \theta}{m} = \dfrac{(0.35 \times 10^{-3} \text{ m}) \sin 0.16°}{2} = \boxed{4.9 \times 10^{-7} \text{ m}}.$

82. $t = \dfrac{\lambda}{4n} = \dfrac{450 \text{ nm}}{4(1.35)} = \boxed{83.3 \text{ nm}}.$

CHAPTER 25

1.   (b).

2.   (c).

3.   The eye focuses by changing the shape of its lens to change the focal length according to the lens maker's equation. The focal length is adjusted to form a sharp image. The image distance is fairly constant and is the distance from the lens to the retina. From the thin lens equation, the eye must have short focal length for looking at close objects and so the radius is small; the eye must have long focal length for looking at distant objects and so the radius is large.

4.   Inverted .

5.   The pre-flash occurs before the aperture is open and the film exposed. The bright light causes the iris to reduce down (giving a small pupil) so that when the second flash comes momentarily, you don't have a wide opening through which you get the red-eye reflection from the retina.

6.   Aperture, lens, and film .

7.   (a) $P = \dfrac{1}{f} = \dfrac{1}{0.20 \text{ m}} = \boxed{+5.0 \text{ D}}$.   (b) $P = \dfrac{1}{-0.50 \text{ m}} = \boxed{-2.0 \text{ D}}$.

8. $d_o = \infty$, $d_i = -300$ cm (image is on the object side).

   $$\frac{1}{f} = \frac{1}{d_o} + \frac{1}{d_i} = \frac{1}{\infty} + \frac{1}{-300 \text{ cm}} = \frac{1}{-300 \text{ cm}}.$$

   So $f = -300$ cm, $\boxed{\text{diverging}}$.

9. $d_o = 25$ cm $= 0.25$ m, $d_i = -50$ cm $= -0.50$ m (image on the object side).

   $$P = \frac{1}{f} = \frac{1}{d_o} + \frac{1}{d_i} = \frac{1}{0.25 \text{ cm}} + \frac{1}{-0.50 \text{ cm}} = +2.0 \text{ D}, \boxed{\text{converging}}.$$

10.   (a) Nearsighted .

   (b) $d_o = \infty$, $d_i = -12.5$ m (image on object side).

   $$P = \frac{1}{f} = \frac{1}{d_o} + \frac{1}{d_i} = \frac{1}{\infty} + \frac{1}{-12.5 \text{ m}} = \boxed{-0.080 \text{ D, diverging}}.$$

11. $d_o = \infty$, $d_i = -200$ cm $= -2.00$ m (image on object side).

$$P = \frac{1}{f} = \frac{1}{d_o} + \frac{1}{d_i} = \frac{1}{\infty} + \frac{1}{-2.00 \text{ m}} = \boxed{-0.50 \text{ D, diverging}}.$$

12. $d_o = 25$ cm, $d_i = -80$ cm (image on object side).

$$\frac{1}{f} = \frac{1}{d_o} + \frac{1}{d_i} = \frac{1}{25 \text{ cm}} + \frac{1}{-80 \text{ cm}} = 0.0275 \text{ cm}^{-1}, \quad ☞ \quad f = 36 \text{ cm}.$$

(a) $\boxed{\text{Converging}}$.

(b) $f = \boxed{36 \text{ cm}}$.

13. (a) $d_o = 25$ cm $= 0.25$ m, $d_i = -100$ cm $= -1.0$ m (image on object side).

$$P = \frac{1}{f} = \frac{1}{d_o} + \frac{1}{d_i} = \frac{1}{0.25 \text{ cm}} + \frac{1}{-1.0 \text{ m}} = \boxed{+3.0 \text{ D}}.$$

(b) $\frac{1}{d_i} = \frac{1}{f} - \frac{1}{d_o} = 3.0 \text{ D} - \frac{1}{\infty} = 3.0 \text{ D}, \quad ☞ \quad d_i = \frac{1}{3.0 \text{ D}} = 0.33 \text{ m} = 33 \text{ cm}.$

This image is way behind the retina and so she has to $\boxed{\text{take them out}}$.

14. $d_o = 25$ cm $= 0.25$ m, $d_i = -0.95$ m (image on object side).

$$P = \frac{1}{f} = \frac{1}{d_o} + \frac{1}{d_i} = \frac{1}{0.25 \text{ m}} + \frac{1}{-0.95 \text{ m}} = \boxed{+2.9 \text{ D}}.$$

15. $d_o = 25$ cm $= 0.25$ m, $d_i = -1.5$ m (image on object side).

$$P = \frac{1}{f} = \frac{1}{d_o} + \frac{1}{d_i} = \frac{1}{0.25 \text{ m}} + \frac{1}{-1.5 \text{ m}} = +3.3 \text{ D}.$$

(a) $\boxed{\text{Converging}}$.

(b) $P = \boxed{+3.3 \text{ D}}$.

16. (a) $d_o = \infty$, $d_i = -150$ cm $= -1.50$ m (image on object side).

$$P = \frac{1}{f} = \frac{1}{d_o} + \frac{1}{d_i} = \frac{1}{\infty} + \frac{1}{-1.50 \text{ m}} = \boxed{-0.67 \text{ D}}.$$

(b) $\frac{1}{d_i} = \frac{1}{f} - \frac{1}{d_o} = -0.667 \text{ D} - \frac{1}{0.25 \text{ m}} = -4.67 \text{ D}, \quad ☞ \quad d_i = -0.21 \text{ m} < -0.25 \text{ m}.$

Therefore the answer is $\boxed{\text{yes}}$ and the near point is $\boxed{21 \text{ cm}}$.

(c) $\boxed{\text{30–40 years old}}$ from Table 25.1.

17. First find his new near point. $d_o = 33$ cm $= 0.33$ m, $P = \dfrac{1}{f} = +2.0$ D.

$$\frac{1}{d_i} = \frac{1}{f} - \frac{1}{d_o} = +2.0\ \text{D} - \frac{1}{0.33\ \text{m}} = -1.0\ \text{D}, \quad \mathnormal{☞} \quad d_i = -1.0\ \text{m}. \quad \text{So the near point is 1.0 m.}$$

To bring this near point to 25 cm, the power of the new lenses must be

$$P' = \frac{1}{f} = \frac{1}{0.25\ \text{m}} + \frac{1}{-1.0\ \text{m}} = \boxed{+3.0\ \text{D}}.$$

18. Top: $d_o = \infty$, $d_i = -500$ cm $= -5.0$ m (image on object side).

$$P = \frac{1}{f} = \frac{1}{d_o} + \frac{1}{d_i} = \frac{1}{\infty} + \frac{1}{-5.0\ \text{m}} = \boxed{-0.20\ \text{D}}.$$

Bottom: $d_o = 25$ cm $= 0.25$ m, $d_i = -70$ cm $= -0.70$ m (image on object side).

$$P = \frac{1}{0.25\ \text{m}} + \frac{1}{-0.70\ \text{m}} = \boxed{+2.6\ \text{D}}.$$

19. First calculate the power of the lens from the far points. $d_o = \infty$, $d_i = -4.0$ m (image on object side).

$$P = \frac{1}{f} = \frac{1}{d_o} + \frac{1}{d_i} = \frac{1}{\infty} + \frac{1}{-4.0\ \text{m}} = -0.25\ \text{D}.$$

For the near points, $d_i = -0.20$ m.

$$\frac{1}{d_o} = P - \frac{1}{d_o} = -0.25\ \text{D} - \frac{1}{-0.20\ \text{m}} = 5.25\ \text{m}^{-1}, \quad \mathnormal{☞} \quad d_o = \boxed{21\ \text{cm}}.$$

20. (a) $d_o = \infty$, $d_i = -(750\ \text{cm} - 2.0\ \text{cm}) = -748$ cm $= -7.48$ m (image on object side).

$$P = \frac{1}{f} = \frac{1}{d_o} + \frac{1}{d_i} = \frac{1}{\infty} + \frac{1}{-7.48\ \text{m}} = \boxed{-0.13\ \text{D}}.$$

(b) $d_i = -7.5$ m. $\quad P = \dfrac{1}{\infty} + \dfrac{1}{-7.5\ \text{m}} = \boxed{-0.13\ \text{D}}$

21. Nearsightedness, $d_o = \infty$, $d_i = -(220\ \text{cm} - 3.0\ \text{cm}) = -2.17$ m (image on object side).

$$P = \frac{1}{f} = \frac{1}{d_o} + \frac{1}{d_i} = \frac{1}{\infty} + \frac{1}{-2.17\ \text{m}} = -0.46\ \text{D}.$$

Right farsightedness: $d_o = 25$ cm $- 3.0$ cm $= 0.22$ m, $d_i = -0.320$ m (image on object side).

$$P_r = \frac{1}{0.22\ \text{m}} + \frac{1}{-0.320\ \text{m}} = 1.42\ \text{D}.$$

Left farsightedness: $d_o = 25$ cm $- 3.0$ cm $= 0.22$ m, $d_i = -0.420$ m (image on object side).

$$P_r = \frac{1}{0.22\ \text{m}} + \frac{1}{-0.420\ \text{m}} = 2.16\ \text{D}.$$

So the prescription is $\boxed{\text{right: } +1.42\ \text{D},\ -0.46\ \text{D};\ \text{left: } +2.16\ \text{D},\ -0.46\ \text{D}}$.

22.   (d).

23.   (d).

24.   A short focal length lens has a very small radius according to the lens maker's equation. The aberration (geometrical optics or small angle approximation is no longer valid if the object is large compared with the size of the lens) will be bigger and bigger as the focal length gets smaller and smaller. This limits the magnification to about 3× to 4×.

25. $\boxed{\text{Inside}}$ the focal length. When the object in inside the focal length, the image is virtual, upright, and magnified.

26. $\theta_1 \approx \dfrac{y}{L} = \dfrac{1.0 \text{ m}}{500 \text{ m}} = \boxed{2.0 \times 10^{-3} \text{ rad}}, \qquad \theta_2 = \dfrac{1.0 \text{ m}}{1025 \text{ m}} = \boxed{9.8 \times 10^{-4} \text{ rad}}.$

27.   (a) $d_i = \dfrac{d_o f}{d_o - f} = \dfrac{(10 \text{ cm})(18 \text{ cm})}{10 \text{ cm} - 18 \text{ cm}} = -22.5 \text{ cm}. \qquad M = -\dfrac{d_i}{d_o} = -\dfrac{-22.5 \text{ cm}}{10 \text{ cm}} = \boxed{2.3\times}.$

    (b) $m = \dfrac{\theta}{\theta_o} = \dfrac{y_o/10 \text{ cm}}{y_o/25 \text{ cm}} = \boxed{2.5\times}.$

28. $m = 1 + \dfrac{25 \text{ cm}}{f} = 1 + \dfrac{25 \text{ cm}}{12 \text{ cm}} = \boxed{3.1\times}.$

29.   (a) $m = 1 + \dfrac{25 \text{ cm}}{f} = 1 + \dfrac{25 \text{ cm}}{15 \text{ cm}} = \boxed{2.7\times}.$

    (b) $m = \dfrac{25 \text{ cm}}{f} = \dfrac{25 \text{ cm}}{15 \text{ cm}} = \boxed{1.7\times}.$

30.   (a) $f = 8.0 \text{ cm}, \quad d_i = -25 \text{ cm (virtual)}. \qquad d_o = \dfrac{d_i f}{d_i - f} = \dfrac{(-25 \text{ cm})(8.0 \text{ cm})}{-25 \text{ cm} - 8.0 \text{ cm}} = \boxed{6.1 \text{ cm}}.$

    (b) $m = 1 + \dfrac{25 \text{ cm}}{f} = 1 + \dfrac{25 \text{ cm}}{8.0 \text{ cm}} = \boxed{4.1\times}.$

31. $f = \dfrac{1}{P} = \dfrac{1}{3.5 \text{ D}} = 0.286 \text{ m} = 28.6 \text{ cm}. \qquad \text{So} \qquad m = 1 + \dfrac{25 \text{ cm}}{f} = 1 + \dfrac{25 \text{ cm}}{28.6 \text{ cm}} = \boxed{1.9\times}.$

32.   (a) $f = \dfrac{1}{P} = \dfrac{1}{10 \text{ D}} = 0.10 \text{ m} = 10 \text{ cm}, \quad d_i = -25 \text{ cm}.$

    $d_o = \dfrac{d_i f}{d_i - f} = \dfrac{(-25 \text{ cm})(10 \text{ cm})}{-25 \text{ cm} - 10 \text{ cm}} = \boxed{7.1 \text{ cm}}.$

    (b) $m = 1 + \dfrac{25 \text{ cm}}{f} = 1 + \dfrac{25 \text{ cm}}{10 \text{ cm}} = \boxed{3.5\times}.$

33. (a) $f = \dfrac{1}{P} = \dfrac{1}{3.0 \text{ D}} = 0.333 \text{ m} = 33.3 \text{ cm}.$ $m = 1 + \dfrac{25 \text{ cm}}{f} = 1 + \dfrac{25 \text{ cm}}{33.3 \text{ cm}} = \boxed{1.8\times}.$

(b) $m = 1 + \dfrac{10 \text{ cm}}{33.3 \text{ cm}} = \boxed{1.3\times}.$

34. $M_{\text{total}} = \dfrac{(25 \text{ cm})L}{f_o f_e},$ ☞ $P_o = \dfrac{1}{f_o} = \dfrac{M_{\text{total}} f_e}{(0.25 \text{ m})L} = \dfrac{(360)(0.0080 \text{ cm})}{(0.25 \text{ cm})(0.15 \text{ cm})} = \boxed{+77 \text{ D}}.$

35. $M_{\text{total}} = \dfrac{(25 \text{ cm})L}{f_o f_e} = \dfrac{(25 \text{ cm})(15 \text{ cm})}{(0.35 \text{ cm})(3.0 \text{ cm})} = 357\times = \boxed{360\times}.$

36. $M_{\text{total}} = \dfrac{(25 \text{ cm})L}{f_o f_e} = \dfrac{(25 \text{ cm})(18 \text{ cm})}{(0.45 \text{ cm})(3.0 \text{ cm})} = 333\times = \boxed{330\times}.$

37. (a) $M_{\text{total}} = \dfrac{(25 \text{ cm})L}{f_o f_e} = \dfrac{(25 \text{ cm})(22 \text{ cm})}{(0.50 \text{ cm})(3.25 \text{ cm})} = 338\times = \boxed{340\times}.$

(b) $m = 1 + \dfrac{25 \text{ cm}}{f_e} = 1 + \dfrac{25 \text{ cm}}{3.25 \text{ cm}} = 8.7\times.$

So the percentage is $\dfrac{340\times}{8.7 \times} = 39 = \boxed{3900\%}.$

38. $M_{\text{total}} = \dfrac{(25 \text{ cm})L}{f_o f_e},$ ☞ $f_e = \dfrac{(25 \text{ cm})L}{f_o M_{\text{total}}} = \dfrac{(25 \text{ cm})(20 \text{ cm})}{(0.75 \text{ cm})(150)} = \boxed{4.4 \text{ cm}}.$

39. $d_i = \dfrac{d_o f}{d_o - f},$ $M_o = -\dfrac{d_i}{d_o} = \dfrac{f}{f - d_o} = \dfrac{1}{1 - d_o/f} = \dfrac{1}{1 - d_o D} = \dfrac{1}{1 - (5.0 \times 10^{-3} \text{ m})(250 \text{ D})} = -4.0\times.$

$M_{\text{total}} = M_o m_e,$ ☞ $m_e = \dfrac{M_{\text{total}}}{M_o} = \dfrac{100}{4.0} = \boxed{25\times}.$

40. From thin lens equation: $d_o = \dfrac{d_i f}{d_i - f},$ ☞ $\dfrac{d_i}{d_o} = \dfrac{d_i - f}{f} = \dfrac{-(D - d) - f}{f}.$

By small angle approximation: $m = \dfrac{\theta_i}{\theta_o} = \dfrac{y_i/D}{y_o/25 \text{ cm}} = \dfrac{y_i}{y_o} \dfrac{25 \text{ cm}}{D}.$

By similar triangles: $\dfrac{y_i}{y_o} = \dfrac{-d_i}{d_o},$ the $-$ sign is introduced because d_i is negative (virtual image).

So $m = \dfrac{(D - d) + f}{f} \dfrac{25 \text{ cm}}{D} = \dfrac{25}{f} (1 - \dfrac{d}{D}) + \dfrac{25}{D}.$

41. $d_i = \dfrac{d_o f}{d_o - f} = \dfrac{(5.0 \text{ cm})(10 \text{ cm})}{5.0 \text{ cm} - 10 \text{ cm}} = -10 \text{ cm}.$ So $D = 4.0 \text{ cm} + 10 \text{ cm} = 14 \text{ cm}.$

From Exercise 25.40, $m = \dfrac{25}{f} \left(1 - \dfrac{d}{D}\right) + \dfrac{25}{D} = \dfrac{25 \text{ cm}}{10 \text{ cm}} \left(1 - \dfrac{4.0 \text{ cm}}{14 \text{ cm}}\right) + \dfrac{25 \text{ cm}}{14 \text{ cm}} = \boxed{3.6\times}.$

42. $d_{\rm o} = \dfrac{d_{\rm i}f_{\rm o}}{d_{\rm i} - f_{\rm o}}$, ☞ $M_{\rm o} = \dfrac{d_{\rm i}}{d_{\rm o}} = \dfrac{d_{\rm i} - f_{\rm o}}{f_{\rm o}}$. So $M_1 = \dfrac{150\ {\rm mm} - 16\ {\rm mm}}{16\ {\rm mm}} = 8.38\times$,

$M_2 = \dfrac{150\ {\rm mm} - 4.0\ {\rm mm}}{4.0\ {\rm mm}} = 36.5\times$, and $M_3 = \dfrac{150\ {\rm mm} - 1.6\ {\rm mm}}{1.6\ {\rm mm}} = 92.8\times$.

Therefore $M_{\rm max} = (92.8\times)(10\times) = \boxed{930\times}$ and $M_{\rm min} = (8.38\times)(5.0\times) = \boxed{42\times}$.

43. (b).

44. (d).

45. $\boxed{\text{No}}$, the whole star can still be seen. The obstruction will reduce the intensity or brightness of the image.

46. $m = \dfrac{f_{\rm o}}{f_{\rm e}} = \dfrac{50\ {\rm cm}}{2.5\ {\rm cm}} = \boxed{20\times}$.

47. (a) $m = \dfrac{f_{\rm o}}{f_{\rm e}} = \dfrac{60\ {\rm cm}}{15\ {\rm cm}} = \boxed{4.0\times}$.

(b) $L = f_{\rm o} + f_{\rm e} = 60\ {\rm cm} + 15\ {\rm cm} = \boxed{75\ {\rm cm}}$.

48. $L = f_{\rm o} + f_{\rm e}$, ☞ $f_{\rm o} = L - f_{\rm e} = 1.5\ {\rm m} - 10 \times 10^{-3}\ {\rm m} \approx 1.49\ {\rm m}$.

$m = \dfrac{f_{\rm o}}{f_{\rm e}} = \dfrac{1.49\ {\rm m}}{10 \times 10^{-3}\ {\rm m}} = 149\times = \boxed{150\times}$.

49. (a) $m = \dfrac{f_{\rm o}}{f_{\rm e}} = \dfrac{87.5\ {\rm cm}}{0.800\ {\rm cm}} = 109\times = \boxed{110\times}$.

(b) $L = f_{\rm o} + f_{\rm e} = 87.5\ {\rm cm} + 0.800\ {\rm cm} = \boxed{88.3\ {\rm cm}}$.

50. (a) $m = \dfrac{f_{\rm o}}{f_{\rm e}} = \dfrac{40\ {\rm cm}}{15\ {\rm cm}} = \boxed{2.7\times}$.

(b) $L = f_{\rm o} + f_{\rm e} + 4f_{\rm i} = 40\ {\rm cm} + 15\ {\rm cm} + 4(20\ {\rm cm}) = \boxed{135\ {\rm cm}}$.

(c) $\boxed{\text{No}}$, all it does is create an inverted image with magnification equal to 1.

51. (a) $m_1 = \dfrac{f_{\rm o1}}{f_{\rm e1}} = \dfrac{90.0\ {\rm cm}}{0.84\ {\rm cm}} = 107\times$, $m_2 = \dfrac{85.0\ {\rm cm}}{0.77\ {\rm cm}} = 110\times$.

So the $\boxed{\text{second}}$ one has a higher magnification.

(b) The resolution depends on the diameter of the objective, so the $\boxed{\text{first}}$ one has a higher resolution.

52. $m = \dfrac{f_o}{f_e} = 50\times,$ ☞ $f_o = 50f_e.$ Eq. (1)

$L = f_o + f_e = 1.02$ m.   Eq. (2)

Solving, $f_o = \boxed{1.00 \text{ m}}$ and $f_e = \boxed{2.0 \text{ cm}}$.

53. $\theta_i \approx \tan \theta_i = \dfrac{y_i}{f_e}$ and $\theta_o = \dfrac{y_i}{f_o}.$ So $m = \dfrac{\theta_i}{\theta_o} = \dfrac{y_i/f_e}{y_i/f_o} = \dfrac{f_o}{f_e}.$

54. (c).

55. (a) since $\theta_{min} = \dfrac{1.22\lambda}{D}.$

56. (d).

57. $\boxed{\text{Smaller}}$ minimum angle of resolution corresponds to higher resolution because smaller details can be resolved.

58. The central maximum of one pattern falls on the first minimum of the other. The angular position of the first minimum is determined by $w \sin \theta \approx w\theta = m\lambda = (1)\,\lambda.$

So $\theta_{min} = \dfrac{\lambda}{w} = \dfrac{680 \times 10^{-9} \text{ m}}{0.55 \times 10^{-3} \text{ m}} = \boxed{1.2 \times 10^{-3} \text{ rad}}.$

59. From Exercise 25.58, $\lambda = \theta_{min}\, w = (0.0055 \text{ rad})(0.10 \times 10^{-3} \text{ m}) = 5.5 \times 10^{-7} \text{ m} = \boxed{550 \text{ nm}}.$

60. $\theta_{min} = \dfrac{1.22\lambda}{D} = \dfrac{1.22(550 \times 10^{-9} \text{ m})}{1.02 \text{ m}} = \boxed{6.58 \times 10^{-7} \text{ rad}}.$

61. $\theta_{min} = \dfrac{1.22\lambda}{D} = \dfrac{1.22(550 \times 10^{-9} \text{ m})}{(200 \text{ in})(0.0254 \text{ m/in})} = \boxed{1.32 \times 10^{-7} \text{ rad}}.$

$\dfrac{\text{Yerkes}}{\text{Hale}} = \dfrac{6.58 \times 10^{-7} \text{ rad}}{1.32 \times 10^{-7} \text{ rad}} = \boxed{4.98}.$

62. $\theta_{min} = \dfrac{1.22\lambda}{D} = \dfrac{1.22(550 \times 10^{-9} \text{ m})}{7.0 \times 10^{-3} \text{ m}} = \boxed{9.6 \times 10^{-5} \text{ rad}}.$

63. $\theta = \dfrac{d}{L} = \dfrac{3.0 \times 10^6 \text{ km}}{3.1 \times 10^8 \text{ km}} = 9.7 \times 10^{-3} \text{ rad} > 9.6 \times 10^{-5} \text{ rad}.$ So in theory, the answer is $\boxed{\text{yes}}$.

64. $\theta_{min} = 9.6 \times 10^{-5} \text{ rad} = \dfrac{d}{L} = \dfrac{1.7 \text{ m}}{L},$ ☞ $L = 1.8 \times 10^4 \text{ m} = \boxed{18 \text{ km}}$

65. (a) Violet light has the highest resolution. The angular separation of the stars must be larger than the minimum angle of resolution

$$\theta_{min} = \frac{1.22\lambda}{D} = \frac{1.22(400 \times 10^{-9}\ \text{m})}{0.300\ \text{m}} = \boxed{1.63 \times 10^{-6}\ \text{rad}}.$$

(b) The lateral distance is $d = \theta L = (1.63 \times 10^{-6}\ \text{rad})(6.00 \times 10^{23}\ \text{m}) = \boxed{9.76 \times 10^{17}\ \text{m}}$.

66. (a) $\theta_{min} = \dfrac{1.22\lambda}{D} = \dfrac{1.22(570 \times 10^{-9}\ \text{m})}{0.0250\ \text{m}} = \boxed{2.78 \times 10^{-5}\ \text{rad}}.$

(b) $s = f\theta_{min} = (30.0\ \text{mm})(2.78 \times 10^{-5}\ \text{rad}) = \boxed{8.34 \times 10^{-4}\ \text{mm}}.$

67. (a) $\theta_{min} = \dfrac{1.22\lambda}{D} = \dfrac{1.22(546.1 \times 10^{-9}\ \text{m})}{0.0120\ \text{m}} = \boxed{5.55 \times 10^{-5}\ \text{rad}}.$

(b) $\boxed{\text{Blue}}$, shortest λ, smallest θ_{min}, highest resolution.

(c) $\theta'_{min} = \dfrac{1.22\lambda'}{D} = \dfrac{1.22\lambda}{nD}$. So the percentage is $\dfrac{\Delta\theta}{\theta_{min}} = \dfrac{1 - 1/n}{1} = 1 - \dfrac{1}{1.50} = \boxed{33.3\%}.$

68. (d).

69. (d).

70. With red light, red and white appear red; blue appears black.

With green light, only white appears green; both red and blue appear black.

With blue light, red appears black; white and blue appear blue.

71. Since white is obtained by adding colors, it cannot be obtained by the subtractive method. That method subtracts colors, and the one we see is the one that is not absorbed.

Black objects do not absorb all wavelengths of light. We see the objects because we perceive the extremely faint light as black. (Think of twilight vision.)

72. The liquid is dark or colored because it absorbs all light except that color. The amount of light absorbed by an object always depends on how much material is absorbing the light. Foam has very low material density and it can only absorb very little light or almost all light is reflected and therefore the foam is generally white.

73. White light enters the blue filter which allows the green, blue, and violet to pass through; when it passes through the yellow filter only the green emerges.

74. $d_o = \infty$, $d_i = -130$ cm $= -1.3$ m (image on object side).

$$P = \frac{1}{f} = \frac{1}{d_o} + \frac{1}{d_i} = \frac{1}{\infty} + \frac{1}{-1.3 \text{ m}} = \boxed{-0.77 \text{ D}}.$$

75. $$\theta_{\min} = \frac{1.22\lambda}{D} = \frac{1.22(4.0 \text{ m})}{300 \text{ m}} = \boxed{1.6 \times 10^{-2} \text{ rad}}.$$

76. $L = f_o + f_e + 4f_i$, ☞ $f_i = \dfrac{L - f_o - f_e}{4} = \dfrac{80 \text{ cm} - 45 \text{ cm} - 15 \text{ cm}}{4} = \boxed{5.0 \text{ cm}}.$

77. The far point is at the image location with glasses. $d_o = \infty$, $P = \dfrac{1}{f} = -0.15$ D.

$$\frac{1}{d_o} + \frac{1}{d_i} = \frac{1}{f} = P, \quad \text{so} \quad d_i = f = \frac{1}{P} = \frac{1}{-0.15 \text{ D}} = -6.7 \text{ m}.$$

Therefore the far point is $\boxed{6.7 \text{ m}}$.

78. $$m = \frac{25 \text{ cm}}{f} = \frac{25 \text{ cm}}{15 \text{ cm}} = \boxed{1.7\times}.$$

79. $$\theta_{\min} = \theta_1 = \frac{\lambda}{w} = \frac{550 \times 10^{-9} \text{ m}}{0.050 \times 10^{-3} \text{ m}} = \boxed{1.1 \times 10^{-2} \text{ rad}}.$$

80. $$M_{\text{total}} = \frac{(25 \text{ cm})L}{f_o f_e} = \frac{L}{f_o} \frac{25 \text{ cm}}{f_e} = \frac{L}{f_o} m_e = \frac{(15.0 \text{ cm})}{0.400 \text{ cm}} (10.0) = \boxed{375\times}.$$

81. $$m = \frac{25 \text{ cm}}{f} = 1 + \frac{25 \text{ cm}}{12 \text{ cm}} = \boxed{2.1\times}.$$

82. $$m = \frac{f_o}{f_e} = \frac{50 \text{ cm}}{1.5 \text{ cm}} = 33.3. \quad \theta_o = \frac{0.10 \text{ m}}{50 \text{ m}} = 2.0 \times 10^{-3} \text{ rad}.$$

So $\theta = m\theta_o = (33.3)(2.0 \times 10^{-3} \text{ rad}) = 0.0666 \text{ rad} = \boxed{3.8°}.$

83. The near point is at the image location with glasses.

$$d_o = 25 \text{ cm} = 0.25 \text{ m}, \quad f = \frac{1}{P} = \frac{1}{2.8 \text{ D}} = 0.357 \text{ m}.$$

$$d_i = \frac{d_o f}{d_o - f} = \frac{(0.25 \text{ m})(0.357 \text{ m})}{0.25 \text{ m} - 0.357 \text{ m}} = -0.834 \text{ m}. \quad \text{So the near point is } \boxed{83 \text{ cm}}.$$

84. $m = 1 + \dfrac{25 \text{ cm}}{f}$, ☞ $f = \dfrac{25 \text{ cm}}{m - 1} = \dfrac{25 \text{ cm}}{3 - 1} = \boxed{13 \text{ cm}}.$

85. $M_{\text{total}} = \dfrac{(25 \text{ cm})L}{f_o f_e} = \dfrac{(25 \text{ cm})(15 \text{ cm})}{(0.75 \text{ cm})(1.0 \text{ cm})} = \boxed{500\times}$.

86. (a) Since the amount of light depends on the area of the aperture $A = 4\pi D^2$, the amount of light is inversely proportional to the square of the f-stop. $\quad \dfrac{A_2}{A_1} = \dfrac{(\text{f–stop})_1}{(\text{f–stop})_2}$.

So (1) $\dfrac{A_{3.2}}{A_8} = \dfrac{8^2}{(3.2)^2} = \boxed{6.3}$ (2) $\dfrac{A_{16}}{A_8} = \dfrac{8^2}{16^2} = \boxed{0.25}$.

(b) The amount of light is also proportional to the exposure time.

So $A_8 t_8 = A_{5.6} t_{5.6}, \quad \text{☞} \quad t_{5.6} = \dfrac{A_8}{A_{5.6}} t_8 = \dfrac{5.6^2}{8^2} \left(\dfrac{1}{60} \text{ s}\right) = \boxed{\dfrac{1}{120} \text{ s}}$.

87. Assume the diameter of a typical iris is 1.0 cm and use 550 nm as the wavelength.

The resolution is $\theta_{\min} = \dfrac{1.22\lambda}{D} = \dfrac{1.22(550 \times 10^{-9} \text{ m})}{0.010 \text{ m}} = 6.7 \times 10^{-5} \text{ rad}$.

The resolving power on the Earth is then $s = d\theta_{\min} = (150 \times 10^3 \text{ m})(6.7 \times 10^{-5} \text{ rad}) = 10 \text{ m} \approx 33 \text{ ft}$.

So, in theory, she is able to identify $\boxed{\text{objects as large as typical houses}}$.

CHAPTER 26

1.   (d).

2.   (a).

3.   (a).

4.   (c).

5.   (a).

6.   The centripetal acceleration due to the rotation of the Earth is very small for most purposes, so we can ignore it and therefore we can treat the Earth as an inertial frame of reference.

7.   Since the speed of light is constant in all directions for all frames of references and no ether (wind) would be present, there is no extra time difference between the two beams and no fringe shift is observed.

8.   Take eastward as positive.

(a) $v_{BA} = v_B - v_A = -65$ km/h $- 85$ km/h $= -150$ km/h $= \boxed{150 \text{ km/h westward}}$.

(b) $v_{BA} = 65$ km/h $- 85$ km/h $= -20$ km/h $= \boxed{20 \text{ km/h westward}}$.

9.   (a) The speed of sound relative to you is $v = 345$ m/s $+ 10.0$ m/s $= 355$ m/s.

So $t = \dfrac{d}{v} = \dfrac{1.20 \times 10^3 \text{ m}}{355 \text{ m/s}} = \boxed{3.38 \text{ s}}$.

(b) The speed of sound relative to you is $v = 345$ m/s $+ (-10.0$ m/s$) = 335$ m/s.

So $t = \dfrac{1.20 \times 10^3 \text{ m}}{335 \text{ m/s}} = \boxed{3.58 \text{ s}}$.

10.   (a) The velocity relative to ground is 200 km/h $+ (-35$ km/h$) = \boxed{165 \text{ km/h}}$.

(b) The velocity relative to ground is 200 km $+ 25$ km/h $= \boxed{225 \text{ km/h}}$.

11. Maximum speed occurs when the boat and water are moving in the same direction. The velocity of the boat relative to the ground is $50 \text{ m/s} + 5 \text{ m/s} = \boxed{55 \text{ m/s}}$.

Minimum speed occurs when the boat and water are moving in opposite directions. The velocity of the boat relative to the ground is $50 \text{ m/s} + (-5 \text{ m/s}) = \boxed{45 \text{ m/s}}$.

12. (a) Perpendicular to the shore, $\quad t = \dfrac{y}{v_\perp} = \dfrac{50 \text{ m}}{0.50 \text{ m/s}} = \boxed{1.0 \times 10^2 \text{ s}}$.

(b) Along the shore, $\quad x = v_\parallel t = (0.15 \text{ m/s})(100 \text{ s}) = \boxed{15 \text{ m}}$.

(c) $\theta = \sin^{-1}\left(\dfrac{0.15}{0.50}\right) = \boxed{17° \text{ upstream}}$.

13. The swimmer has to swim at an angle upstream (the art in the Exercise is incorrect).
For the swimmer across the river,

$$t_1 = \frac{2d}{\sqrt{c^2 - v^2}} = \frac{2d/c}{\sqrt{1 - (v/c)^2}}.$$

For the swimmer along the shore,

$$t_2 = \frac{d}{c - v} + \frac{d}{c + v} = \frac{2d}{c}\frac{c^2}{c^2 - v^2} = \frac{2d/c}{1 - (v/c)^2}.$$

So the time difference is not zero and the answer is $\boxed{\text{no}}$.

14. The time between adjacent gaps is $\quad t = \dfrac{\theta}{\omega} = \dfrac{2\pi/N}{2\pi f} = \dfrac{1}{Nf}$.

So the speed of light is $\quad c = \dfrac{2L}{t} = \dfrac{2L}{1/(Nf)} = 2fNL$.

15. $t_2 = \dfrac{2dc}{c^2 - v^2} = \dfrac{2\,d}{c(1 - v^2/c^2)}$. $\qquad$ If d is contracted by $\sqrt{1 - v^2/c^2}$,

we have $\quad t_2 = \dfrac{2\,d\sqrt{1 - v^2/c^2}}{c(1 - v^2/c^2)} = \dfrac{2d/c}{\sqrt{1 - (v/c)^2}} = t_1$.

16. (a).

17. (c).

18. $\boxed{c}$, since the speed of light is a constant.

19. (b) since your friend is traveling to the front, he sees the front mark occur first.

20. (c).

21. (a) 300 m/s. An inertial frame O' moving at this velocity will determine the proper time of the two events.

(b) The time interval between these two events observed by another inertial frame is $\Delta t = \dfrac{\Delta t_o}{\sqrt{1-v^2/c^2}}$,

where Δt_o is the proper time. Δt can never be negative and so the firing of the gun will always precede the hitting of the target.

22. (a) An inertial frame O' moving from A to B could see the two flashes simultaneously.
(b) From A to B.

23. (c), her friend does appear the same height because the height is perpendicular to their relative velocity.

24. $\boxed{\text{No}}$, this is not possible. From the boy's view, the barn is moving at he same speed so it would appear to contract so it is not long enough for the pole.

25. $\boxed{\text{Yes}}$. You will find yourself younger after a high speed space trip (close to c) due to time dilation.

26. We are finding the proper time in another reference frame.

$$t = \frac{t_o}{\sqrt{1-v^2/c^2}}, \quad \text{☞} \quad t_o = t\sqrt{1-v^2/c^2} = (10 \text{ min})\sqrt{1-0.90^2} = \boxed{4.4 \text{ min}}.$$

27. The proper time for one beat is $\dfrac{1}{80 \text{ beats/min}} = \dfrac{1}{80}$ min/beat.

So $\quad t = \dfrac{t_o}{\sqrt{1-v^2/c^2}} = \dfrac{1/80 \text{ min/beat}}{\sqrt{1-0.85^2}} = \dfrac{1}{42}$ min/beat.

Therefore the number of beats per min is $\boxed{42 \text{ beats/min}}$.

28. $L = L_o\sqrt{1-v^2/c^2} = (15.0 \text{ m})\sqrt{1-(1/3)^2} = \boxed{14.1 \text{ m}}$.

29. $L = L_o\sqrt{1-v^2/c^2} = (100 \text{ m})\sqrt{1-0.75^2} = \boxed{66 \text{ m}}$. $\boxed{100 \text{ m}}$ is the proper length.

30. $t = \dfrac{t_0}{\sqrt{1 - v^2/c^2}}$, ☞ $v = \sqrt{1 - t_0^2/t^2}\, c = \sqrt{1 - 2.20^2/34.8^2}\, c = \boxed{0.998c}$.

31. The one on the Earth will be $25\text{ y} + 39\text{ y} = \boxed{64\text{ y}}$ old.

$t = \dfrac{t_0}{\sqrt{1 - v^2/c^2}}$, ☞ $t_0 = t\sqrt{1 - v^2/c^2} = (39\text{ y})\sqrt{1 - 0.95^2} = 12.2\text{ y}$.

So the one on the spaceship is $25\text{ y} + 12.2\text{ y} = \boxed{37\text{ y}}$ old.

32. (a) The time observed on Earth is $t = \dfrac{4.30\text{ ly}}{0.60c} = 7.17\text{ y}$.

$t = \dfrac{t_0}{\sqrt{1 - v^2/c^2}}$, ☞ $t_0 = t\sqrt{1 - v^2/c^2} = (7.17\text{ y})\sqrt{1 - 0.60^2} = \boxed{5.7\text{ y}}$.

(b) As found in (a), $t = \boxed{7.2\text{ y}}$.

33. The diameter is still 8.25 m because it is perpendicular to the relative velocity.

$L = L_0\sqrt{1 - v^2/c^2} = (35.0\text{ m})\sqrt{1 - 2.44^2/3.00^2} = 20.4\text{ m}$.

So the dimensions are $\boxed{\text{length of } 20.4\text{ m and diameter } 8.25\text{ m}}$.

34. (a) The altitude is still 15.0 m because it is perpendicular to the relative velocity.

The base, however, is $L = L_0\sqrt{1 - v^2/c^2} = (40.0\text{ m})\sqrt{1 - 0.90^2} = 17.44\text{ m}$.

So the area is $A = \tfrac{1}{2}(17.44\text{ m})(15.0\text{ m}) = \boxed{131\text{ m}^2}$.

(b) The angle between the hypotenuse and the base is $\theta = \tan^{-1}\left(\dfrac{15.0}{17.44}\right) = \boxed{40.7^\circ}$.

35. $L = L_0\sqrt{1 - v^2/c^2}$, ☞ $v = c\sqrt{1 - L^2/L_0^2} = c\sqrt{1 - 0.50^2} = \boxed{0.87c}$.

36. The time observed by an Earth-bound observer is $\Delta t = \dfrac{1.00\text{ ly}}{0.700c} = 1.429\text{ y}$.

$\Delta t = \dfrac{\Delta t_0}{\sqrt{1 - v^2/c^2}}$, ☞ $\Delta t_0 = \Delta t\sqrt{1 - v^2/c^2} = (1.429\text{ y})\sqrt{1 - 0.700^2} = \boxed{1.02\text{ y}}$.

37. $L = L_0\sqrt{1 - v^2/c^2} = (7.0\text{ m})\sqrt{1 - 0.65^2} = \boxed{5.3\text{ m}}$.

38.
$$\frac{v}{c} = \frac{(100 \text{ km/h})(1000 \text{ m/km})(1 \text{ h/3600 s})}{3.00 \times 10^8 \text{ m/s}} = 9.26 \times 10^{-8} \ll 1.$$

So $\quad L = L_0 \sqrt{1 - v^2/c^2} \approx L_0 (1 - \frac{1}{2}v^2/c^2).$

Therefore $\quad \Delta L = L_0 - L = (5.00 \text{ m}) \left[\frac{1}{2}(9.26 \times 10^{-8})^2 \right] = \boxed{2.14 \times 10^{-14} \text{ m}}.$

39. $L = L_0 \sqrt{1 - v^2/c^2}, \quad \text{☞} \quad v = c \sqrt{1 - L^2/L_0^2} = c \sqrt{1 - (3 \times 0.3048)^2} = 0.40c.$

So $\boxed{\text{she is traveling at } 0.40c \text{ in the direction parallel to the lengths of the two sticks}}.$

40. The time observed by an Earth-bound observer is $\Delta t = \dfrac{9.0 \text{ ly}}{v} = \dfrac{9.0 \text{ y}}{v/c}.$

$\Delta t = \dfrac{\Delta t_0}{\sqrt{1 - v^2/c^2}}, \quad \text{☞} \quad \Delta t_0 = 12 \text{ y} = \Delta t \sqrt{1 - v^2/c^2} = \dfrac{9.0 \text{ y}}{v/c} \sqrt{1 - v^2/c^2}.$

Simplifying, $\quad 12^2 (v/c)^2 = 9^2 [1 - (v/c)^2] \quad \text{or} \quad 225 (v/c)^2 = 81.$

Solving, $\quad v/c = 0.60 \quad \text{or} \quad v = \boxed{0.60c}.$

41. (d).

42. (b).

43. $\boxed{\text{No}}$, there are no such limits on momentum and energy as $p = \gamma m v$ and $E = \gamma mc^2.$

44. $\boxed{\text{No}}$, since it takes an infinite amount of energy to do it. When $v = c$, $\gamma = \dfrac{1}{\sqrt{1 - v^2/c^2}} = \infty$ so $E = \infty.$

45. According to the classical theory, $\quad K = \frac{1}{2}mv^2,$

so $\quad v = \sqrt{\dfrac{2K}{m}} = \sqrt{\dfrac{2(2 \times 10^3 \text{ eV})(1.6 \times 10^{-19} \text{ J/eV})}{9.11 \times 10^{-31} \text{ kg}}} = 2.7 \times 10^7 \text{ m/s} \approx 0.10 \, c, \text{ i.e., } \boxed{\text{yes}}.$

$v' = \sqrt{\dfrac{2(2 \times 10^6 \text{ eV})(1.6 \times 10^{-19} \text{ J/eV})}{9.11 \times 10^{-31} \text{ kg}}} = 8.4 \times 10^8 \text{ m/s} > c, \text{ i.e., } \boxed{\text{no}}.$

46. $E_0 = mc^2 = (9.11 \times 10^{-31} \text{ kg})(3.00 \times 10^8 \text{ m/s})^2 = 8.20 \times 10^{-14} \text{ J} \approx 0.511 \text{ MeV}.$

$E = \gamma E_0 = \dfrac{1}{\sqrt{1 - v^2/c^2}} E_0 = \dfrac{1}{\sqrt{1 - 0.600^2}} (0.511 \text{ MeV}) = \boxed{0.639 \text{ MeV}}.$

47.   (a) $E_0 = mc^2 = (9.11 \times 10^{-31}\text{ kg})(3.00 \times 10^8\text{ m/s})^2 = 8.20 \times 10^{-14}\text{ J} \approx 0.511\text{ MeV}$.

$E = K + E_0 = 2.5\text{ MeV} + 0.511\text{ MeV} = 3.011\text{ MeV}$.

$E = \gamma E_0 = \dfrac{1}{\sqrt{1 - v^2/c^2}}\, E_0,$ ☞ $v = c\sqrt{1 - E_0^2/E^2} = c\sqrt{1 - (0.511)^2/(3.011)^2} = \boxed{0.985c}$.

(b) $K = q\Delta V = e(2.50\text{ MV}) = \boxed{2.50\text{ MeV}}$.

(c) $p = \gamma mv = \dfrac{mv}{\sqrt{1 - v^2/c^2}} = \dfrac{(9.11 \times 10^{-31}\text{ kg})(0.985)(3.00 \times 10^8\text{ m/s})}{\sqrt{1 - 0.985^2}} = \boxed{1.56 \times 10^{-21}\text{ kg·m/s}}$.

48.   (a) $E = \gamma E_0 = \dfrac{E_0}{\sqrt{1 - v^2/c^2}},$ ☞ $v = c\sqrt{1 - E_0^2/E^2} = c\sqrt{1 - 1/(1.01)^2} = \boxed{0.14c}$.

(b) $v = c\sqrt{1 - 1/(1.99)^2} = \boxed{0.86c}$.

49.   The energy required is $(250\,000)(1.5 \times 10^4\text{ kWh})(1000\text{ W/kW})(3600\text{ s/h}) = 1.35 \times 10^{16}\text{ J}$.

$E_0 = mc^2,$ ☞ $m = \dfrac{E_0}{c^2} = \dfrac{1.35 \times 10^{16}\text{ J}}{(3.00 \times 10^8\text{ m/s})^2} = \boxed{0.15\text{ kg}}$.

50.   The energy required is $(3.0 \times 10^{12}\text{ kWh})(1000\text{ W/kW})(3600\text{ s/h}) = 1.08 \times 10^{19}\text{ J}$.

$E_0 = mc^2,$ ☞ $m = \dfrac{E_0}{c^2} = \dfrac{1.08 \times 10^{19}\text{ J}}{(3.00 \times 10^8\text{ m/s})^2} = 120\text{ kg}$.

With an efficiency of 25%, the amount of mass needed is $\dfrac{120\text{ kg}}{0.25} = \boxed{4.8 \times 10^2\text{ kg}}$.

51.   From the work–energy theorem:

$$W = \Delta K = K - K_0 = K = E_0(\gamma - 1) = mc^2\left(\dfrac{1}{\sqrt{1 - v^2/c^2}} - 1\right)$$

$$= (3.0 \times 10^6\text{ kg})(3.00 \times 10^8\text{ m/s})^2\left(\dfrac{1}{\sqrt{1 - 0.99^2}} - 1\right)$$

$$= \boxed{1.6 \times 10^{24}\text{ J or } 150\,000\text{ times more}}\text{ than } 1.08 \times 10^{19}\text{ J} = 3\text{ trillion kWh}.$$

52. $E_0 = mc^2 = (9.11 \times 10^{-31}\text{ kg})(3.00 \times 10^8\text{ m/s})^2 = 8.20 \times 10^{-14}\text{ J} \approx 0.511\text{ MeV}$.

$E = \gamma E_0 = \dfrac{E_0}{\sqrt{1 - v^2/c^2}},$ ☞ $v = c\sqrt{1 - E_0^2/E^2} = c\sqrt{1 - (0.511)^2/(2.8)^2} = 0.983c$.

So $p = \dfrac{mv}{\sqrt{1 - v^2/c^2}} = \dfrac{(9.11 \times 10^{-31}\text{ kg})(0.983)(3.00 \times 10^8\text{ m/s})}{\sqrt{1 - 0.983^2}} = \boxed{1.5 \times 10^{-21}\text{ kg·m/s}}$.

53. $E_o = mc^2 = (9.11 \times 10^{-31} \text{ kg})(3.00 \times 10^8 \text{ m/s})^2 = 8.20 \times 10^{-14} \text{ J} \approx 0.511 \text{ MeV}.$

$$K = E - E_o = E_o(\gamma - 1) = E_o \left(\frac{1}{\sqrt{1 - v^2/c^2}} - 1 \right) = (0.511 \times 10^3 \text{ MeV}) \left(\frac{1}{\sqrt{1 - 0.50^2}} - 1 \right)$$

$$= \boxed{79 \text{ keV}}.$$

54. (a) $E = K + E_o = 0.60E + E_o,$ ☞ $0.40E = E_o.$

Also $E = \dfrac{E_o}{\sqrt{1 - v^2/c^2}},$ ☞ $v = c\sqrt{1 - E_o^2/E^2} = c\sqrt{1 - 0.40^2} = 0.917c \approx \boxed{0.92c}.$

(b) $p = \dfrac{mv}{\sqrt{1 - v^2/c^2}} = \dfrac{(9.11 \times 10^{-31} \text{ kg})(0.917)(3.00 \times 10^8 \text{ m/s})}{\sqrt{1 - 0.917^2}} = \boxed{6.3 \times 10^{-22} \text{ kg·m/s}}.$

55. (a)   (b)

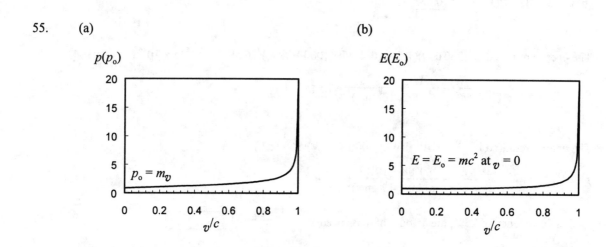

56. (a) $E_o = mc^2 = (1.67 \times 10^{-27} \text{ kg})(3.00 \times 10^8 \text{ m/s})^2 = 1.502 \times 10^{-10} \text{ J} = 939 \text{ MeV}.$

So $E = \dfrac{E_o}{\sqrt{1 - v^2/c^2}} = \dfrac{939 \text{ MeV}}{\sqrt{1 - 0.35^2}} = \boxed{1.0 \times 10^3 \text{ MeV}}.$

(b) $K = E - E_o = 1002 \text{ MeV} - 939 \text{ MeV} = \boxed{63 \text{ MeV}}.$

(c) $p = \dfrac{mv}{\sqrt{1 - v^2/c^2}} = \dfrac{(1.67 \times 10^{-27} \text{ kg})(0.35)(3.00 \times 10^8 \text{ m/s})}{\sqrt{1 - 0.35^2}} = \boxed{1.9 \times 10^{19} \text{ kg·m/s}}.$

57. (a) $E = \dfrac{E_o}{\sqrt{1 - v^2/c^2}},$ ☞ $v = c\sqrt{1 - E_o^2/E^2} = c\sqrt{1 - 1/2.5^2} = \boxed{0.92c}.$

(b) $E_o = mc^2 = (1.67 \times 10^{-27} \text{ kg})(3.00 \times 10^8 \text{ m/s})^2 = 1.502 \times 10^{-10} \text{ J} = 939 \text{ MeV}.$

$K = E - E_o = (2.5 - 1)E_o = 1.5E_o = 1.5(939 \text{ MeV}) = \boxed{1.4 \times 10^3 \text{ MeV}}.$

58.   (a) In one hour, $E = Pt = (3.827 \times 10^{26} \text{ W})(3600 \text{ s}) = 1.378 \times 10^{30} \text{ J}$.

$$E_0 = mc^2, \quad \mathbb{F} \quad m = \frac{E_0}{c^2} = \frac{1.378 \times 10^{30} \text{ J}}{(3.00 \times 10^8 \text{ m/s})^2} = \boxed{1.531 \times 10^{13} \text{ kg}}.$$

(b) One percent of the mass is $0.01(1.989 \times 10^{30} \text{ kg}) = 1.989 \times 10^{28} \text{ kg}$.

So it takes $\dfrac{1.989 \times 10^{28} \text{ kg}}{1.531 \times 10^{13} \text{ kg/h}} = 1.299 \times 10^{15} \text{ h} = \boxed{1.483 \times 10^{11} \text{ y}}$.

59.   (a) $E_0 = mc^2 = (9.11 \times 10^{-31} \text{ kg})(3.00 \times 10^8 \text{ m/s})^2 = 8.20 \times 10^{-14} \text{ J} \approx 0.511 \text{ MeV}$.

$$K = E - E_0 = E_0(\gamma - 1) = E_0 \left(\frac{1}{\sqrt{1 - v^2/c^2}} - 1 \right) = (0.511 \text{ MeV}) \left(\frac{1}{\sqrt{1 - 0.950^2}} - 1 \right)$$

$$= \boxed{1.13 \text{ MeV}}.$$

(b) $E = K + E_0 = 1.13 \text{ MeV} + 0.511 \text{ MeV} = \boxed{1.64 \text{ MeV}}$.

60. $E = mL_f = (1.0 \text{ kg})(3.33 \times 10^5 \text{ J/kg}) = 3.33 \text{ J}$.

$$E = \Delta mc^2, \quad \mathbb{F} \quad \Delta m = \frac{E}{c^2} = \frac{3.33 \times 10^5 \text{ J}}{(3.00 \times 10^8 \text{ m/s})^2} = \boxed{3.7 \times 10^{-12} \text{ kg}}.$$

61. $E_0 = mc^2 = (5.00 \times 10^{-3} \text{ kg})(3.00 \times 10^8 \text{ m/s})^2 = 4.50 \times 10^{14} \text{ J}$.

$$P = \frac{E_0}{t}, \quad \mathbb{F} \quad t = \frac{E_0}{P} = \frac{4.5 \times 10^{14} \text{ J}}{100 \text{ W}} = 4.5 \times 10^{12} \text{ s} = \boxed{1.43 \times 10^5 \text{ y}}.$$

62. $E^2 = \gamma^2 m^2 c^4 = \gamma^2 m^2 c^2 (c^2 + v^2 - v^2) = \gamma^2 m^2 v^2 c^2 + \gamma^2 m^2 c^4 \left(1 - \dfrac{v^2}{c^2} \right)$

$$= p^2 c^2 + \frac{m^2 c^4}{\left(\sqrt{1 - v^2/c^2} \right)^2} \left(1 - \frac{v^2}{c^2} \right) = p^2 c^2 + (mc^2)^2.$$

63.   (a) The minimum energy is the rest energy, which for a proton is

$E_0 = mc^2 = (1.67 \times 10^{-27} \text{ kg})(3.00 \times 10^8 \text{ m/s})^2 = 1.502 \times 10^{-10} \text{ J} = 939 \text{ MeV} > 600 \text{ MeV}$.

(b) $E = K + E_0 = 600 \text{ MeV} + 939 \text{ MeV} = 1539 \text{ MeV}$.

$$E = \frac{E_0}{\sqrt{1 - v^2/c^2}}, \quad \mathbb{F} \quad v = c\sqrt{1 - E_0^2/E^2} = c\sqrt{1 - (939)^2/(1539)^2} = \boxed{0.792c}.$$

(c) $p = \dfrac{mv}{\sqrt{1 - v^2/c^2}} = \dfrac{(1.67 \times 10^{-27} \text{ kg})(0.792)(3.00 \times 10^8 \text{ m/s})}{\sqrt{1 - 0.792^2}} = \boxed{6.50 \times 10^{-19} \text{ kg·m/s}}$.

64.   (a).

65.   (d).

66.   (c).

67.   The stick would be elongated or "stretched" by the gravity gradient (difference).

68. $R_E = \dfrac{2GM_E}{c^2} = \dfrac{2(6.67 \times 10^{11}\,\text{N·m}^2/\text{kg}^2)(6.0 \times 10^{24}\,\text{kg})}{(3.00 \times 10^8\,\text{m/s})^2} = 8.9 \times 10^{-3}\,\text{m} = \boxed{8.9\,\text{mm}}$.

$R_J = \dfrac{2GM_J}{c^2} = \dfrac{2G(318M_E)}{c^2} = 318R_E = \boxed{2.8\,\text{m}}$.

69. $\rho = \dfrac{m}{V} = \dfrac{2.0 \times 10^{30}\,\text{kg}}{4\pi(3.0 \times 10^3)^3/3} = \boxed{1.8 \times 10^{19}\,\text{kg/m}^3}$.

70. $R = \dfrac{2GM}{c^2}$,   ☞ $M = \dfrac{Rc^2}{2G} = \dfrac{(5.00 \times 10^3\,\text{m})(3.00 \times 10^8\,\text{m/s})^2}{2(6.67 \times 10^{-11}\,\text{N·m}^2/\text{kg}^2)} = \boxed{3.37 \times 10^{30}\,\text{kg}}$.

(b) $\rho = \dfrac{M}{V} = \dfrac{3.37 \times 10^{30}\,\text{kg}}{4\pi(5.0 \times 10^3)^3/3} = \boxed{6.44 \times 10^{18}\,\text{kg/m}^3}$.

71. $\boxed{\text{Drop the cup with the pole vertical}}$. By the principle of equivalence, the weight of the ball is effectively zero in the falling reference frame. The ball is then subject only to the tension force of the stretched rubber band and is pulled inside the cup.

72. $v = 7.5 \times 10^7\,\text{m/s} = 0.25c$.

$u = \dfrac{v + u'}{1 + v\,u'/c^2} = \dfrac{0.25c + 0.20c}{1 + (0.25)(0.20)} = \boxed{0.43c}$.

73. $u = \dfrac{v + u'}{1 + v\,u'/c^2} = \dfrac{0.40c + (-0.15c)}{1 + (0.40)(-0.15)} = \boxed{0.27c}$, same direction as spacecraft

74.   Use the rocket as the moving reference frame.

$u = \dfrac{v + u'}{1 + v\,u'/c^2} = \dfrac{0.100c + (-0.250c)}{1 + (0.100)(-0.250)} = -0.154\,c = \boxed{0.154\,c\text{ toward Earth}}$.

75. Take the direction to the right as positive.

(a) $u = \dfrac{v + u'}{1 + v\,u'/c^2}$,   ☞ $v = \dfrac{u - u'}{1 - u\,u'/c^2} = \dfrac{-0.800c - 0.900c}{1 - (-0.800)(0.900)} = -0.988c$

$$= \boxed{0.988c \text{ to the left}}.$$

(b) $v = \dfrac{0.900c - (-0.800c)}{1 - (0.900)(-0.800)} = +0.988c = \boxed{0.988c \text{ to the right}}$.

76. $E_o = mc^2 = (1.67 \times 10^{-27} \text{ kg})(3.00 \times 10^8 \text{ m/s})^2 = 1.503 \times 10^{-10} \text{ J} = \boxed{939 \text{ MeV}}$.

77. $t = \dfrac{t_o}{\sqrt{1 - v^2/c^2}}$,   ☞ $t_o = \sqrt{1 - v^2/c^2}\; t$.

So $\Delta t = t - t_o = \left(1 - \sqrt{1 - v^2/c^2}\right)t = \left(1 - \sqrt{1 - 0.60^2}\right)(24 \text{ h}) = \boxed{4.8 \text{ h}}$.

78. $v = 9.5 \times 10^7 \text{ m/s} = 0.317c$.

$E_o = mc^2 = (9.11 \times 10^{-31} \text{ kg})(3.00 \times 10^8 \text{ m/s})^2 = 8.20 \times 10^{-14} \text{ J} \approx 0.511 \text{ MeV}$.

$E = \dfrac{E_o}{\sqrt{1 - v^2/c^2}} = \dfrac{0.511 \text{ MeV}}{\sqrt{1 - 0.317^2}} = \boxed{0.54 \text{ MeV}}$.

79. $L = L_o \sqrt{1 - v^2/c^2} = (50 \text{ m})\sqrt{1 - 0.65^2} = 38 \text{ m}$.   The height and width are the same.

So the dimensions are $\boxed{\text{length 38 m; height 2.5 m; width 2.0 m}}$.

80. $E_o = mc^2 = (1.0 \text{ kg})(3.00 \times 10^8 \text{ m/s})^2 = 9.0 \times 10^{16} \text{ J} = (9.0 \times 10^{16} \text{ W·s})(1 \text{ kW}/1000 \text{ W})(3600 \text{ s/h})$

$$= \boxed{2.5 \times 10^{10} \text{ kWh}}.$$

81. $\Delta t = \dfrac{\Delta t_o}{\sqrt{1 - v^2/c^2}} = \dfrac{30 \text{ min}}{\sqrt{1 - 0.80^2}} = \boxed{50 \text{ min}}$.

82. The rest energy of an electron or a positron is

$E_o = mc^2 = (9.11 \times 10^{-31} \text{ kg})(3.00 \times 10^8 \text{ m/s})^2 = 8.20 \times 10^{-14} \text{ J} \approx 0.511 \text{ MeV}$.

The total energy of the radiation is $0.511 \text{ MeV} + 0.511 \text{ MeV} = \boxed{1.02 \text{ MeV}}$.

83. $L = L_o \sqrt{1 - v^2/c^2}$,   ☞ $v = c\sqrt{1 - L^2/L_o^2} = c\sqrt{1 - (110)^2/(150)^2} = \boxed{0.68c}$.

84. $\Delta t = t_2 - t_1 = \dfrac{2L_1}{c} \left[\dfrac{1}{1 - v^2/c^2} - \dfrac{1}{\sqrt{1 - v^2/c^2}} \right].$

$\Delta t' = t_1' - t_2' = -\dfrac{2L_2}{c} \left[\dfrac{1}{1 - v^2/c^2} - \dfrac{1}{\sqrt{1 - v^2/c^2}} \right].$

So $\Delta t - \Delta t' = \dfrac{2L_1}{c} \left[\dfrac{1}{1 - v^2/c^2} - \dfrac{1}{\sqrt{1 - v^2/c^2}} \right] + \dfrac{2L_2}{c} \left[\dfrac{1}{1 - v^2/c^2} - \dfrac{1}{\sqrt{1 - v^2/c^2}} \right]$

$\qquad = \dfrac{2}{c} (L_1 + L_2) \left[\dfrac{1}{1 - v^2/c^2} - \dfrac{1}{\sqrt{1 - v^2/c^2}} \right].$

85. $E_o = Pt = \dfrac{1.2 \times 10^9 \text{ W}}{0.33} (18)(30)(86400 \text{ s}) = 1.70 \times 10^{17} \text{ J}.$

$E_o = mc^2, \quad \text{☞} \quad m = \dfrac{E_o}{c^2} = \dfrac{1.70 \times 10^{17} \text{ J}}{(3.00 \times 10^8 \text{ m/s})^2} = \boxed{1.9 \text{ kg}}.$

CHAPTER 27

1. (d).

2. (c).

3. No, it is actually $2^4 = 16$ times since it depends on T^4.

4. The red ones have the lower temperatures because red has a longer wavelength and the wavelength of the most intense radiation is inversely proportional to temperature ($\lambda_{max} T = 2.9 \times 10^{-3}$ m·K).

5. (a) $\lambda_{max} T = 2.9 \times 10^{-3}$ m·K, ☞ $T = \dfrac{2.9 \times 10^{-3} \text{ m·K}}{\lambda_{max}} = \dfrac{2.9 \times 10^{-3} \text{ m·K}}{c} f \propto f$.

   (b) $T = \dfrac{2.9 \times 10^{-3} \text{ m·K}}{\lambda_{max}} \propto \dfrac{1}{\lambda_{max}}$.

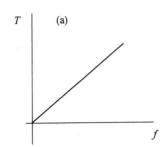
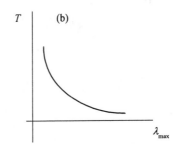

6. $\lambda_{max} T = 2.9 \times 10^{-3}$ m·K, ☞ $T = \dfrac{2.9 \times 10^{-3} \text{ m·K}}{\lambda_{max}} = \dfrac{2.9 \times 10^{-3} \text{ m·K}}{700 \times 10^{-9} \text{ m}} = \boxed{4.1 \times 10^{3} \text{ K}}$.

7. $\lambda_{max} T = 2.9 \times 10^{-3}$ m·K, ☞ $\lambda_{max} = \dfrac{2.9 \times 10^{-3} \text{ m·K}}{T} = \dfrac{2.9 \times 10^{-3} \text{ m·K}}{273 \text{ K}} = \boxed{1.06 \times 10^{-5} \text{ m}}$.

   $f = \dfrac{c}{\lambda_{max}} = \dfrac{3.00 \times 10^{8} \text{ m/s}}{1.06 \times 10^{-5} \text{ m}} = \boxed{2.83 \times 10^{13} \text{ Hz}}$.

8. $\lambda_{max} T = 2.9 \times 10^{-3}$ m·K, ☞ $\lambda_{max} = \dfrac{2.9 \times 10^{-3} \text{ m·K}}{T} = \dfrac{2.9 \times 10^{-3} \text{ m·K}}{(273 + 37) \text{ K}} = \boxed{9.4 \times 10^{-6} \text{ m; infrared}}$.

9. $\lambda_{max} T = 2.9 \times 10^{-3}$ m·K, ☞ $\lambda_{max} = \dfrac{2.9 \times 10^{-3} \text{ m·K}}{T} = \dfrac{2.9 \times 10^{-3} \text{ m·K}}{(273 + 27) \text{ K}} = 9.67 \times 10^{-6}$ m.

   So $f = \dfrac{c}{\lambda_{max}} = \dfrac{3.00 \times 10^{8} \text{ m/s}}{9.67 \times 10^{-6} \text{ m}} = \boxed{3.1 \times 10^{13} \text{ Hz}}$.

10. $\lambda_{max}T = 2.9 \times 10^{-3}$ m·K, ☞ $\lambda_{max} = \dfrac{2.9 \times 10^{-3} \text{ m·K}}{T}$.

So $\Delta f = f_2 - f_1 = \dfrac{c}{\lambda_1} - \dfrac{c}{\lambda_2} = \dfrac{c\,T_2}{2.9 \times 10^{-3} \text{ m·K}} - \dfrac{c\,T_1}{2.9 \times 10^{-3} \text{ m·K}} = \dfrac{c}{2.9 \times 10^{-3} \text{ m·K}} \Delta T$

$= \dfrac{3.00 \times 10^8 \text{ m/s}}{2.9 \times 10^{-3} \text{ m·K}} (200 \text{ K}) = \boxed{2.1 \times 10^{13} \text{ Hz}}$.

11. $\lambda_{max}T = 2.9 \times 10^{-3}$ m·K, ☞ $\lambda_{max} = \dfrac{2.9 \times 10^{-3} \text{ m·K}}{T} = \dfrac{2.9 \times 10^{-3} \text{ m·K}}{373 \text{ K}} = 7.77 \times 10^{-6}$ m.

So $f = \dfrac{c}{\lambda_{max}} = \dfrac{3.00 \times 10^8 \text{ m/s}}{7.77 \times 10^{-6} \text{ m}} = 3.86 \times 10^{13}$ Hz.

Therefore $E = hf = (6.63 \times 10^{-34} \text{ J·s})(3.86 \times 10^{13} \text{ Hz}) = \boxed{2.56 \times 10^{-20} \text{ J}}$.

12. $\lambda_{max}T = 2.9 \times 10^{-3}$ m·K, ☞ $\lambda_{max} = \dfrac{2.9 \times 10^{-3} \text{ m·K}}{T} = \dfrac{2.9 \times 10^{-3} \text{ m·K}}{1000 \text{ K}} = 2.9 \times 10^{-6}$ m.

So $f = \dfrac{c}{\lambda_{max}} = \dfrac{3.00 \times 10^8 \text{ m/s}}{2.9 \times 10^{-6} \text{ m}} = 1.03 \times 10^{14}$ Hz.

Therefore $E = hf = (6.63 \times 10^{-34} \text{ J·s})(1.03 \times 10^{14} \text{ Hz}) = 6.83 \times 10^{-20}$ J/quantum.

The number of quanta per square meter per second is

$n = \dfrac{I}{E} = \dfrac{2.0 \text{ W/m}^2}{6.83 \times 10^{-20} \text{ J/quantum}} = \boxed{2.9 \times 10^{19} \text{ quanta/(s·m}^2)}$.

13. (b).

14. (d).

15. The energy packets of radio photons arrive in such quantity and so quickly that when they are converted to sound our ear cannot distinguish between discrete arrivals. It is similar to a movie, where the picture is actually single frames passing in front of us at a rapid speed, but we see it as a smooth and continuous moving picture. Likewise, although the radio signals are single frames, we hear them continuously.

16. The X–ray photon has much more energy than the red-light photon ($E = hf$).

17. The energy of radiation is proportional to its intensity, according to the wave theory, and its frequency, according to the particle theory. It takes a certain amount of energy to eject a photoelectron. Since only the frequency, not the intensity, matters in this case, it favors the particle theory.

18. $E = hf = (6.63 \times 10^{-34} \text{ J·s})(5.0 \times 10^{14} \text{ Hz}) = \boxed{3.3 \times 10^{-19} \text{ J}}$.

19. $E = hf$,   ☞ $f = \dfrac{E}{h} = \dfrac{3.3 \times 10^{-15} \text{ J}}{6.63 \times 10^{-34} \text{ J·s}} = 4.98 \times 10^{18}$ Hz.

      So $\lambda = \dfrac{c}{f} = \dfrac{3.00 \times 10^8 \text{ m/s}}{4.98 \times 10^{19} \text{ Hz}} = \boxed{6.0 \times 10^{-11} \text{ m; X–ray}}$.

20. $E = hf$,   ☞ $\dfrac{E_v}{E_r} = \dfrac{f_v}{f_r} = \dfrac{\lambda_r}{\lambda_v} = \dfrac{700 \text{ nm}}{400 \text{ nm}} = 1.75$.   So $\boxed{\text{violet by 1.75 times more}}$.

21.   (a) $E = hf = \dfrac{hc}{\lambda} = \dfrac{1.24 \times 10^3 \text{ eV·nm}}{150 \text{ nm}} = 8.27 \text{ eV} = \boxed{1.32 \times 10^{-18} \text{ J}}$.

      (b) As in (a), $E = \boxed{8.27 \text{ eV}}$.

22.   The current is also $\boxed{\text{doubled}}$ since it is directly proportional to the intensity.

23.   The kinetic energy is still $\boxed{3.0 \text{ eV}}$ since it is independent of the intensity.

24.   In one minute, $E = Pt = 0.025(100 \text{ W})(60 \text{ s}) = 150$ J.

      $E_o = hf = \dfrac{hc}{\lambda} = \dfrac{(6.63 \times 10^{-34} \text{ J·s})(3.00 \times 10^8 \text{ m/s})}{550 \times 10^{-9} \text{ m}} = 3.616 \times 10^{-19}$ J/quantum.

      So $n = \dfrac{E}{E_o} = \dfrac{150 \text{ J}}{3.616 \times 10^{-19} \text{ J/quantum}} = \boxed{4.15 \times 10^{20} \text{ quanta}}$.

25.   (a) Since $eV_o = hf + \phi_o$, the slope of the graph is equal to Planck's constant.

      $h = \dfrac{[(3-1) \text{ eV}](1.6 \times 10^{-19} \text{ J/eV})}{(115 - 67) \times 10^{13} \text{ Hz}} = \boxed{6.7 \times 10^{-34} \text{ J·s}}$.

      (b) $\phi_o = hf_o = (6.63 \times 10^{-34} \text{ J·s})(43.9 \times 10^{13} \text{ Hz}) = \boxed{2.9 \times 10^{-19} \text{ J}}$.

26. $hf = eV_o + \phi_o = 2.50 \text{ eV} + 2.40 \text{ eV} = 4.90 \text{ eV} = 7.84 \times 10^{-19}$ J.

      So $f = \dfrac{7.84 \times 10^{-19} \text{ J}}{6.63 \times 10^{-34} \text{ J·s}} = 1.183 \times 10^{15}$ Hz.

      Therefore $\lambda = \dfrac{c}{f} = \dfrac{3.00 \times 10^8 \text{ m/s}}{1.183 \times 10^{15} \text{ Hz}} = 2.54 \times 10^{-7} \text{ m} = \boxed{254 \text{ nm}}$.

27. $hf_o = \phi_o$,   ☞ $f_o = \dfrac{\phi_o}{h} = \dfrac{(2.8 \text{ eV})(1.6 \times 10^{-19} \text{ J/eV})}{6.63 \times 10^{-34} \text{ J·s}} = \boxed{6.8 \times 10^{14} \text{ Hz}}$.

28.   (a) $K_{max} = \frac{1}{2}mv^2_{max} = hf - \phi_0 = h(f - f_0) = hc \left(\frac{1}{\lambda} - \frac{1}{\lambda_0}\right)$,   ☞ $v_{max} = \sqrt{\frac{2hc}{m}\left(\frac{1}{\lambda} - \frac{1}{\lambda_0}\right)}$.

$$v_{max} = \sqrt{\frac{2(6.63 \times 10^{-34} \text{ J·s})(3.00 \times 10^8 \text{ m/s})}{9.11 \times 10^{-31} \text{ kg}} \left(\frac{1}{400 \times 10^{-9} \text{ m}} - \frac{1}{500 \times 10^{-9} \text{ m}}\right)}$$

$$= \boxed{4.7 \times 10^5 \text{ m/s}}.$$

(b) Since $\lambda = \lambda_0$, $v_{max} = \boxed{0}$.   (c) Since $\lambda > \lambda_0$ ($f < f_0$), there is $\boxed{\text{no emission}}$ of electrons.

29. $\phi_0 = hf_0 = \frac{hc}{\lambda_0} = \frac{1240 \text{ eV·nm}}{500 \text{ nm}} = \boxed{2.48 \text{ eV}}$.

30.   (a) $eV_0 = K_{max} = hf - \phi_0 = \frac{hc}{\lambda} - \phi_0 = \frac{1.24 \times 10^3 \text{ eV·nm}}{300 \text{ nm}} - 3.5 \text{ eV} = 0.63 \text{ eV}$.

So $V = \boxed{0.63 \text{ V}}$.

(b) $f_0 = \frac{\phi_0}{h} = \frac{(3.5 \text{ eV})(1.6 \times 10^{-19} \text{ J/eV})}{6.63 \times 10^{-34} \text{ J·s}} = \boxed{8.4 \times 10^{14} \text{ Hz}}$.

31. $K_{max} = hf - \phi_0 = \frac{hc}{\lambda} - \phi_0$,

so $\phi_0 = \frac{hc}{\lambda} - K_{max} = \frac{(6.63 \times 10^{-34} \text{ J·s})(3.00 \times 10^8 \text{ m/s})}{420 \times 10^{-9} \text{ m}} - 1.0 \times 10^{-19} \text{ J} = 3.74 \times 10^{-19} \text{ J}$.

$hf = \frac{hc}{\lambda} = \frac{(6.63 \times 10^{-34} \text{ J·s})(3.00 \times 10^8 \text{ m/s})}{700 \times 10^{-9} \text{ m}} = 2.84 \times 10^{-19} \text{ J} < \phi_0$. Therefore the answer is $\boxed{\text{no}}$.

32.   (a) $K_{max} = hf - \phi_0 = \frac{hc}{\lambda} - \phi_0 = \frac{1.24 \times 10^3 \text{ eV·nm}}{160 \text{ nm}} - 4.82 \text{ eV} = \boxed{2.93 \text{ eV}}$.

(b) $f_0 = \frac{\phi_0}{h} = \frac{(4.82 \text{ eV})(1.60 \times 10^{-19} \text{ J/eV})}{6.63 \times 10^{-34} \text{ J·s}} = \boxed{1.16 \times 10^{15} \text{ Hz}}$.

33.   (a) $K_{max} = hf - \phi_0$. The photoelectrons from $\boxed{\text{sodium}}$ will have a greater speed since it has a smaller ϕ_0.

(b) $\lambda_0 = \frac{c}{f_0} = \frac{c}{\phi_0/h} = \frac{hc}{\phi_0}$.

So $\lambda_{silver} < \frac{1240 \text{ eV·nm}}{4.73 \text{ eV}} = \boxed{262 \text{ nm}}$,   and $\lambda_{sodium} < \frac{1240 \text{ eV·nm}}{2.46 \text{ eV}} = \boxed{504 \text{ nm}}$.

34. $K_{max} = hf - \phi_0 = \frac{hc}{\lambda} - \phi_0$.

For red, $K_{red} = \frac{hc}{700 \text{ nm}} - \phi_0$;   for blue, $K_{blue} = \frac{hc}{400 \text{ nm}} - \phi_0$.

Dividing the two equations yields $2 = \dfrac{K_{blue}}{K_{red}} = \dfrac{\dfrac{hc}{400\ nm} - \phi_o}{\dfrac{hc}{700\ nm} - \phi_o}$.

So $\quad \phi_o = hc \left(\dfrac{2}{700\ nm} - \dfrac{1}{400\ nm} \right) = (1.24 \times 10^3\ eV \cdot nm) \left(\dfrac{2}{700\ nm} - \dfrac{1}{400\ nm} \right) = \boxed{0.44\ eV}$.

35.   Since $K_{max} = hf - \phi_o$, the slope is equal to Planck's constant.

The slope of the line is $4.1 \times 10^{-15}\ eV/Hz = 4.1 \times 10^{-15}\ eV \cdot s$.

$h \approx (4.1 \times 10^{-15}\ eV \cdot s)(1.6 \times 10^{-19}\ J/eV) = \boxed{6.6 \times 10^{-34}\ J \cdot s}$.

From the graph, $f_o \approx 3.7 \times 10^{14}\ Hz$.

So $\quad \phi_o = hf_o = (6.63 \times 10^{-34}\ J \cdot s)(3.7 \times 10^{14}\ Hz) = 2.45 \times 10^{-19}\ J = \boxed{1.5\ eV}$.

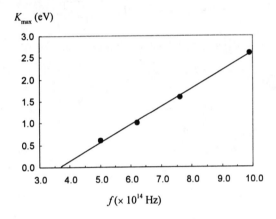

36.   (d).

37.   (d).

38.   The maximum wavelength shift for Compton scattering from a molecule is $\boxed{\text{smaller}}$ compared to that from a free electron because the Compton wavelength is inversely proportional to the mass of the scattering particle and $\Delta\lambda_{max} = 2\lambda_C = 2\dfrac{h}{mc} \propto \dfrac{1}{m}$.

39.   For each scattering the wavelength shift is approximately equal to $\Delta\lambda = \lambda_c = 0.00243\ nm$.

The wavelength change from x–ray to visible light is in the order of $550\ nm - 0.01\ nm = 550\ nm$.

So after approximately $\dfrac{550\ nm}{0.00243\ nm} = 200\,000$ scatterings, X–ray becomes visible light.

40.   From energy conservation, the scattered photon has less energy after scattering because the free electron receives part of the incident energy. Since the energy of a photon is proportional to the frequency of the light or inversely proportional to wavelength, the scattered photon always has a longer wavelength.

41. $\Delta\lambda = \lambda_c (1 - \cos\theta)$, ☞ $\Delta\lambda_{max} = (0.00243 \text{ nm})(1 - \cos 180°) = (0.00243 \text{ nm})(2) = \boxed{4.86 \times 10^{-3} \text{ nm}}$.

42. $\Delta\lambda = \lambda_c (1 - \cos\theta) = (0.00243 \text{ nm})(1 - \cos 30°) = \boxed{3.26 \times 10^{-4} \text{ nm}}$.

43. $\Delta\lambda = \lambda_c (1 - \cos\theta) = (2.43 \times 10^{-12} \text{ m})(1 - \cos 45°) = 7.12 \times 10^{-13} \text{ m}$.

So $\lambda = \lambda_0 + \Delta\lambda = 2.80 \times 10^{-10} \text{ m} + 7.12 \times 10^{-13} \text{ m} = 2.81 \times 10^{-10} \text{ m} = \boxed{0.281 \text{ nm}}$.

44. $\Delta\lambda = \lambda_c (1 - \cos\theta) = (2.43 \times 10^{-12} \text{ m})(1 - \cos 53°) = 9.68 \times 10^{-13} \text{ m}$.

So $\lambda = \lambda_0 + \Delta\lambda = 0.0045 \times 10^{-9} \text{ m} + 9.68 \times 10^{-13} \text{ m} = 5.47 \times 10^{-12} \text{ m} = \boxed{0.0055 \text{ nm}}$.

45.   According to energy conservation, the photon has energy of 10.0 keV − 0.200 keV = 9.80 keV.

$\lambda = \dfrac{c}{f} = \dfrac{c}{E/h} = \dfrac{hc}{E} = \dfrac{1.24 \times 10^3 \text{ eV·nm}}{9.80 \times 10^3 \text{ eV}} = \boxed{0.127 \text{ nm}}$.

46. $\Delta\lambda = \lambda_c (1 - \cos\theta)$, ☞ $\cos\theta = 1 - \dfrac{\Delta\lambda}{\lambda_c} = 1 - \dfrac{0.000326 \text{ nm}}{0.00243 \text{ nm}} = 0.866$.

So $\theta = \boxed{30°}$.

47. $\Delta\lambda = \lambda_c (1 - \cos\theta)$, ☞ $\cos\theta = 1 - \dfrac{\Delta\lambda}{\lambda_c} = 1 - \dfrac{1.25 \times 10^{-4} \text{ nm}}{0.00243 \text{ nm}} = 0.9486$. :

So $\theta = \boxed{18.5°}$.

48.   (a) $\lambda_c = \dfrac{h}{m_p c^2} = \dfrac{6.63 \times 10^{-34} \text{ J·s}}{(1.67 \times 10^{-27} \text{ kg})(3.00 \times 10^8 \text{ m/s})} = \boxed{1.32 \times 10^{-15} \text{ m}}$.

(b) $\dfrac{\Delta\lambda_e}{\Delta\lambda_p}\bigg|_{max} = \dfrac{2\lambda_{ce}}{2\lambda_{cp}} = \dfrac{2.43 \times 10^{-12} \text{ m}}{1.32 \times 10^{-15} \text{ m}} = \boxed{1.84 \times 10^3}$.

49.   (d).

50.   (a).

51.   The theory applies only to atoms with a single electron because it does not include electron-electron interactions.

52. $\boxed{\text{No}}$, it does not take more energy to ionize the electron that is in an excited state than in the ground state. Actually it takes less energy since the excited state has more energy than the ground state.

53. According to momentum conservation, the atom must recoil, so it carries some kinetic energy and therefore the energy of the photon is smaller than expected. Thus the wavelength of the photon is longer.

54. (a) $\Delta E = (-13.6 \text{ eV}) \left(\frac{1}{n_f^2} - \frac{1}{n_i^2} \right) = (-13.6 \text{ eV}) \left(\frac{1}{2^2} - \frac{1}{1^2} \right) = \boxed{10.2 \text{ eV}}$.

(b) $\Delta E = (-13.6 \text{ eV}) \left(\frac{1}{3^2} - \frac{1}{2^2} \right) = \boxed{1.89 \text{ eV}}$.

55. (a) $\lambda = \dfrac{1.24 \times 10^3}{\Delta E \text{ (in eV)}} \text{ nm} = \dfrac{1.24 \times 10^3}{10.2} = 122 \text{ nm}$, i.e., $\boxed{\text{ultraviolet}}$.

(b) $\lambda = \dfrac{1.24 \times 10^3}{1.89} \text{ nm} = 656 \text{ nm}$, i.e., $\boxed{\text{visible (red)}}$.

56. (a) $\Delta E = (-13.6 \text{ eV}) \left(\frac{1}{n_f^2} - \frac{1}{n_i^2} \right) = (-13.6 \text{ eV}) \left(\frac{1}{\infty} - \frac{1}{2^2} \right) = \boxed{3.40 \text{ eV}}$.

(b) $\Delta E = (-13.6 \text{ eV}) \left(\frac{1}{\infty} - \frac{1}{3^2} \right) = \boxed{1.51 \text{ eV}}$.

57. (a) $\Delta E = (-13.6 \text{ eV}) \left(\frac{1}{n_f^2} - \frac{1}{n_i^2} \right) = (-13.6 \text{ eV}) \left(\frac{1}{5^2} - \frac{1}{2^2} \right) = 2.856 \text{ eV}$.

$f = \dfrac{\Delta E}{h} = \dfrac{(2.856 \text{ eV})(1.60 \times 10^{-19} \text{ J/eV})}{6.63 \times 10^{-34} \text{ J} \cdot \text{s}} = \boxed{6.89 \times 10^{14} \text{ Hz}}$.

(b) $\Delta E = (-13.6 \text{ eV}) \left(\frac{1}{\infty} - \frac{1}{2^2} \right) = 3.40 \text{ eV}$.

$f = \dfrac{(3.40 \text{ eV})(1.60 \times 10^{-19} \text{ J/eV})}{6.63 \times 10^{-34} \text{ J} \cdot \text{s}} = \boxed{8.21 \times 10^{14} \text{ Hz}}$.

58. (a) $r_n = 0.0529 n^2 \text{ nm}$.　$r_3 = (0.0529)(2)^2 \text{ nm} = \boxed{0.212 \text{ nm}}$.

(b) $r_6 = 0.0529(4)^2 = \boxed{0.846 \text{ nm}}$.

(c) $r_{10} = 0.0529(5)^2 \text{ nm} = \boxed{1.32 \text{ nm}}$.

59. $r_n = 0.053 n^2 \text{ nm}$.　☞　$n = \sqrt{\dfrac{r_n}{0.053}} = \sqrt{\dfrac{0.5 \times 10^3 \text{ nm}}{0.053}} \boxed{\approx 100}$.

60. $$\frac{1}{\lambda} = \frac{1}{c/f} = \frac{f}{c} = \frac{\Delta E/h}{c} = \frac{\Delta E}{hc} = \frac{(-13.6 \text{ eV}) \left(\frac{1}{n_f^2} - \frac{1}{n_i^2}\right)}{hc} = \frac{13.6 \text{ eV}}{hc} \left(\frac{1}{n_i^2} - \frac{1}{n_f^2}\right).$$

So $$R = \frac{13.6 \text{ eV}}{hc} = \frac{(13.6 \text{ eV})(1.60 \times 10^{-19} \text{ C})}{(6.626 \times 10^{-34} \text{ J·s})(3.00 \times 10^8 \text{ m/s})} = \boxed{1.095 \times 10^{-2} \text{ nm}^{-1}}.$$

61. (a) $E_n = \dfrac{-13.6 \text{ eV}}{n^2}$. $E_3 = \dfrac{-13.6 \text{ eV}}{3^2} = \boxed{-1.51 \text{ eV}}$.

(b) $E_6 = \dfrac{-13.6 \text{ eV}}{6^2} = \boxed{-0.378 \text{ eV}}$.

(c) $E_{10} = \dfrac{-13.6 \text{ eV}}{10^2} = \boxed{-0.136 \text{ eV}}$.

62. (a) $\Delta E = (-13.6 \text{ eV}) \left(\dfrac{1}{n_f^2} - \dfrac{1}{n_i^2}\right) = (-13.6 \text{ eV}) \left(\dfrac{1}{\infty} - \dfrac{1}{3^2}\right) = \boxed{1.51 \text{ eV}}$.

(b) $\Delta E = (-13.6 \text{ eV}) \left(\dfrac{1}{\infty} - \dfrac{1}{5^2}\right) = \boxed{0.544 \text{ eV}}$.

(c) $\Delta E = (-13.6 \text{ eV}) \left(\dfrac{1}{\infty} - \dfrac{1}{10^2}\right) = \boxed{0.136 \text{ eV}}$.

63. $E = hf = (6.63 \times 10^{-34} \text{ J·s})(7.00 \times 10^{15} \text{ Hz}) = 4.64 \times 10^{-18} \text{ J} = 29.0 \text{ eV}$.

So $\boxed{\text{yes}}$, the atom can be ionized.

The kinetic energy of the emitted electron would be $K = 29.0 \text{ eV} - 13.6 \text{ eV} = \boxed{15.4 \text{ eV}}$.

64. (a) $\Delta E = (-13.6 \text{ eV}) \left(\dfrac{1}{n_f^2} - \dfrac{1}{n_i^2}\right)$.

$\Delta E_{52} = (13.6 \text{ eV}) \left(\dfrac{1}{2^2} - \dfrac{1}{5^2}\right) = 2.856 \text{ eV}$. $\lambda_{52} = \dfrac{1.24 \times 10^3}{\Delta E \text{ (in eV)}} \text{ nm} = \dfrac{1.24 \times 10^3}{2.856} \text{ nm} = \boxed{434 \text{ nm}}$.

$\Delta E_{21} = (13.6 \text{ eV}) \left(\dfrac{1}{1^2} - \dfrac{1}{2^2}\right) = 10.2 \text{ eV}$. $\lambda_{21} = \dfrac{1.24 \times 10^3}{10.2} \text{ nm} = \boxed{122 \text{ nm}}$.

(b) $\boxed{\text{Yes}}$, 5 to 2 is in the visible region (violet).

65. (a) $\Delta E = (-13.6 \text{ eV}) \left(\dfrac{1}{n_f^2} - \dfrac{1}{n_i^2}\right)$. $\Delta E_{53} = (13.6 \text{ eV}) \left(\dfrac{1}{3^2} - \dfrac{1}{5^2}\right) = 0.967 \text{ eV}$.

(b) $\Delta E_{62} = (13.6 \text{ eV}) \left(\dfrac{1}{2^2} - \dfrac{1}{6^2}\right) = 2.97 \text{ eV}$. 3.02 eV

(c) $\Delta E_{21} = (13.6 \text{ eV}) \left(\dfrac{1}{1^2} - \dfrac{1}{2^2}\right) = 10.2 \text{ eV}$. So the answer is (c).

66. The longest wavelength corresponds to the transition from $n = 2$ to 1.

$$\Delta E = (-13.6 \text{ eV}) \left(\frac{1}{n_f^2} - \frac{1}{n_i^2} \right) = (13.6 \text{ eV}) \left(\frac{1}{1^2} - \frac{1}{2^2} \right) = 10.2 \text{ eV}.$$

$$\lambda = \frac{1.24 \times 10^3}{\Delta E \text{ (in eV)}} \text{ nm} = \frac{1.24 \times 10^3}{10.2} \text{ nm} = \boxed{122 \text{ nm; ultraviolet}}.$$

67. (a) $E = -\dfrac{(13.6 \text{ eV})Z^2}{n^2}$, where Z is the atomic number (number of protons).

The binding energy is $\Delta E = E_\infty - E_1 = -E_1 \dfrac{(13.6 \text{ eV})(2)^2}{1^2} = \boxed{54.4 \text{ eV}}$.

(b) The binding energy is $-E_1 = \dfrac{(13.6 \text{ eV})(3)^2}{1^2} = \boxed{122 \text{ eV}}$.

68. (a) $E = hf = \dfrac{hc}{\lambda} = \dfrac{1.24 \times 10^3}{\lambda \text{ (in nm)}} \text{ eV} = \dfrac{1.24 \times 10^3}{486 \text{ nm}} \text{ eV} = \boxed{2.55 \text{ eV}}$.

(b) $\Delta E = (-13.6 \text{ eV}) \left(\dfrac{1}{n_f^2} - \dfrac{1}{n_i^2} \right) = 2.55 \text{ eV}.$

Using trial and error we find $\boxed{n_i = 2 \text{ and } n_f = 4}$.

69. $v = \dfrac{nh}{2\pi m r} = \dfrac{(6.63 \times 10^{-34} \text{ J·s})n}{2\pi(9.11 \times 10^{-31} \text{ kg})(0.0529 \times 10^{-9} \text{ m})n^2} = \boxed{(2.2 \times 10^6 \text{ m/s})/n}.$

70. $E = -\dfrac{ke^2}{2r} = -\dfrac{(9.0 \times 10^9 \text{ N·m}^2/\text{C}^2)(1.6 \times 10^{-19} \text{ C})^2}{2(0.0529 \times 10^{-9} \text{ m})} = -2.18 \times 10^{-18} \text{ J} = -13.6 \text{ eV}.$

71. (a) $U = -\dfrac{ke^2}{r} = \boxed{-27.2 \text{ eV}}$ and $K = \dfrac{ke^2}{2r} = \boxed{+13.6 \text{ eV}}$.

(b) $\boxed{|U| = 2K}$, potential energy is twice as large in magnitude.

72. (b).

73. Through stimulated emission, the photon from a laser is caused by electron transitions between two discrete energy levels and so there are only a few colors (frequencies). A light bulb emits thermal radiation at many different frequencies.

74. The photon emitted by a electron in an excited state "stimulates" the emission of another photon by a different electron in the same excited state. So the emission of one photon results in two photons and so on, four, eight, sixteen, etc. However, it takes energy to pump the electrons from a lower energy level to a higher energy level in the first place, so the pump is ultimately providing the amplification.

75.   Each second $E = Pt = (750 \times 10^3 \text{ W})(1.0 \text{ s}) = 750 \times 10^3 \text{ J}$.

$$E = nhf, \quad \text{☞} \quad n = \frac{E}{hf} = \frac{750 \times 10^3 \text{ J}}{(6.63 \times 10^{-34} \text{ J·s})(98.9 \times 10^6 \text{ Hz})} = \boxed{1.14 \times 10^{31} \text{ photons}}.$$

76. $E^2 = p^2 c^2 + (mc^2)^2 = p^2 c^2, \quad \text{☞} \quad p = \dfrac{E}{c} = \dfrac{hf}{c} = \dfrac{h}{c/f} = \dfrac{h}{\lambda}.$

77.   For photon: $E = \dfrac{hc}{\lambda}$ and $p = \dfrac{h}{\lambda}.$

Energy conservation: $E_0 + mc^2 = E_1 + (K + mc^2), \quad$ or $\quad K = \dfrac{hc}{\lambda_0} - \dfrac{hc}{\lambda}.$ Eq. (1)

Momentum conservation: (in x) $\dfrac{h}{\lambda_0} = \dfrac{h}{\lambda} \cos\theta + p_e \cos\phi;$ Eq. (2)

(in y) $0 = \dfrac{h}{\lambda} \sin\theta - p_e \sin\phi.$ Eq. (3)

Also $E_e^2 = (K + m_0 c^2)^2 = p_e^2 c^2, \quad$ or $\quad p_e^2 = \dfrac{1}{c^2}(K^2 + 2 m_0 c^2 K).$ Eq. (4)

To eliminate ϕ, we isolate the term with ϕ on one side, square Eqs. (2) and (3), and add them together.

$$\frac{h^2}{\lambda_0^2} - \frac{2h^2}{\lambda_0 \lambda} \cos\theta + \frac{h^2}{\lambda^2} = p_e^2 \qquad\qquad \text{Eq. (5)}$$

Substitute Eq. (1) into (4), then Eq. (4) into Eq. (5), simplify, and we have

$$\frac{2h^2}{\lambda_0 \lambda}(1 - \cos\theta) = 2hmc \frac{\lambda - \lambda_0}{\lambda_0 \lambda}. \qquad \text{Therefore} \quad \Delta\lambda = \lambda - \lambda_0 = \frac{h}{mc}(1 - \cos\theta) = \lambda_c(1 - \cos\theta).$$

78. $K_{\text{max}} = eV_0 = \frac{1}{2}mv^2 = \frac{1}{2}(9.11 \times 10^{-31} \text{ kg})(3.5 \times 10^5 \text{ m/s})^2 = 5.58 \times 10^{-20} \text{ J} = 0.349 \text{ eV}.$

$$hf = eV_0 + \phi_0, \quad \text{☞} \quad \phi_0 = hf - eV_0 = \frac{hc}{\lambda} - eV_0 = \frac{1.24 \times 10^3 \text{ eV·nm}}{340 \text{ nm}} - 0.349 \text{ eV} = \boxed{3.3 \text{ eV}}.$$

79.   (a) $\Delta E = (-13.6 \text{ eV})\left(\dfrac{1}{n_f^2} - \dfrac{1}{n_i^2}\right).$ $\Delta E_{13} = (-13.6 \text{ eV})\left(\dfrac{1}{3^2} - \dfrac{1}{1^2}\right) = \boxed{12.1 \text{ eV}}.$

(b) $\Delta E_{15} = (-13.6 \text{ eV})\left(\dfrac{1}{5^2} - \dfrac{1}{1^2}\right) = \boxed{13.1 \text{ eV}}.$

80. $E_0 = hf = \dfrac{hc}{\lambda} = \dfrac{(6.63 \times 10^{-34} \text{ J·s})(3.00 \times 10^8 \text{ m/s})}{700 \times 10^{-9} \text{ m}} = 2.94 \times 10^{-19} \text{ J}.$

So $n = \dfrac{E}{E_0} = \dfrac{1.0 \text{ J}}{2.94 \times 10^{-19} \text{ J/quantum}} = \boxed{3.5 \times 10^{18} \text{ quanta}}.$

81. $\Delta\lambda = \lambda_c\,(1 - \cos\theta) = (2.43 \times 10^{-12}\ \text{m})(1 - \cos 37°) = 4.89 \times 10^{-13}\ \text{m}.$

So $\quad \lambda_o = \lambda - \Delta\lambda = 4.5 \times 10^{-10}\ \text{m} - 4.89 \times 10^{-13}\ \text{m} = 4.495 \times 10^{-10}\ \text{m}.$

$E = hf_o = \dfrac{hc}{\lambda_o} = \dfrac{(6.63 \times 10^{-34}\ \text{J·s})(3.00 \times 10^8\ \text{m/s})}{4.495 \times 10^{-10}\ \text{m}} = \boxed{4.4 \times 10^{-16}\ \text{J}}.$

82. $\lambda_{max}\,T = 2.90 \times 10^{-3}\ \text{m·K}, \quad \text{☞} \quad \lambda_{max} = \dfrac{2.90 \times 10^{-3}\ \text{m·K}}{T} = \dfrac{2.90 \times 10^{-3}\ \text{m·K}}{293\ \text{K}} = 1.0 \times 10^{-5}\ \text{m}.$

So $\quad f = \dfrac{c}{\lambda_{max}} = \dfrac{3.00 \times 10^8\ \text{m/s}}{1.0 \times 10^{-5}\ \text{m}} = \boxed{3.0 \times 10^{13}\ \text{Hz}}.$

83. (a) $hf = K_{max} + \phi_o = 2.0 \times 10^{-19}\ \text{J} + (5.0\ \text{eV})(1.6 \times 10^{-19}\ \text{J/eV}) = 1.0 \times 10^{-18}\ \text{J}.$

So $\quad f = \dfrac{1.0 \times 10^{-18}\ \text{J}}{6.63 \times 10^{-34}\ \text{J·s}} = \boxed{1.5 \times 10^{15}\ \text{Hz}}.$

(b) $eV_o = K_{max} = 2.0 \times 10^{-19}\ \text{J} = 1.25\ \text{eV}. \quad$ So $\quad V_o = \boxed{1.3\ \text{V}}.$

84. $\Delta\lambda = \lambda_c\,(1 - \cos\theta), \quad \text{☞} \quad \cos\theta = 1 - \dfrac{\Delta\lambda}{\lambda_o} = 1 - 0.25 = 0.75. \quad$ So $\quad \theta = \boxed{41°}.$

85. The energy of a typical photon in the visible region is about

$E_{min} = hf = \dfrac{hc}{\lambda} = \dfrac{1.24 \times 10^3}{700}\ \text{eV} = 1.77\ \text{eV (red)}.$

$E_{max} = \dfrac{1.24 \times 10^3}{400}\ \text{eV} = 3.1\ \text{eV (violet)}.$

Since $\quad \Delta E = (-13.6\ \text{eV})\left(\dfrac{1}{n_f^2} - \dfrac{1}{n_i^2}\right)$, the electron has to be in the $n = 2$ state, because $\Delta E_{32} = 1.89\ \text{eV}$,

$\Delta E_{42} = 2.55\ \text{eV}, \Delta E_{52} = 2.86\ \text{eV}, \Delta E_{62} = 3.02\ \text{eV}. \quad$ Therefore, there are $\boxed{\text{four}}$ transitions.

86. The electrons emitted have a wide range of kinetic energies. When a retarding voltage V is applied, only those electrons which have a kinetic energy higher than eV will reach the anode. So the photocurrent decreases from its maximum (when $V = 0$). When the stopping voltage V_o is finally applied, no electron can reach the anode and so the photocurrent drops to zero.

87. $f = \dfrac{1}{T} = \dfrac{1}{2\pi r/v} = \dfrac{v}{2\pi r} = \dfrac{mvr}{2\pi mr^2} = \dfrac{nh/(2\pi)}{2\pi mr^2} = \dfrac{nh}{4\pi^2 mr^2}$

$= \dfrac{(1)(6.63 \times 10^{-34}\ \text{J·s})}{4\pi^2 (9.11 \times 10^{-31}\ \text{kg})(0.0529 \times 10^{-9}\ \text{m})^2} = \boxed{6.59 \times 10^{15}\ \text{Hz}}.$

Here we used the Bohr assumption: $mvr = nh/(2\pi), \quad$ for $n = 1, 2, 3, 4, \ldots$

CHAPTER 28

1.   (c).

2.   (d).

3.   The wavelength associated with a moving car is too short for us to observe.

4. $\lambda = \dfrac{h}{mv} = \dfrac{6.63 \times 10^{-34} \text{ J·s}}{(1000 \text{ kg})(25 \text{ m/s})} = \boxed{2.7 \times 10^{-38} \text{ m}}$.

5.   (a) $\lambda = \dfrac{h}{mv} = \dfrac{6.63 \times 10^{-34} \text{ J·s}}{(9.11 \times 10^{-31} \text{ kg})(100 \text{ m/s})} = \boxed{7.28 \times 10^{-6} \text{ m}}$.

         (b) $\lambda = \dfrac{6.63 \times 10^{-34} \text{ J·s}}{(1.67 \times 10^{-27} \text{ kg})(100 \text{ m/s})} = \boxed{3.97 \times 10^{-9} \text{ m}}$.

6. $\lambda = \dfrac{h}{mv} = \dfrac{6.63 \times 10^{-34} \text{ J·s}}{(70 \text{ kg})(2.0 \text{ m/s})} = \boxed{4.7 \times 10^{-36} \text{ m}}$.

7. $K = \frac{1}{2}mv^2 = eV$,   ☞ $v \propto \dfrac{1}{\sqrt{m}}$,   so $\lambda = \dfrac{h}{mv} \propto \dfrac{1}{\sqrt{m}}$.

     Therefore $\dfrac{\lambda_e}{\lambda_p} = \sqrt{\dfrac{m_p}{m_e}} = \sqrt{\dfrac{1.67 \times 10^{-27} \text{ kg}}{9.11 \times 10^{-31} \text{ kg}}} = \boxed{43}$.

8.   From Eq. 28.3: $\lambda = \sqrt{\dfrac{1.50}{V}}$ nm,   so $\lambda \propto \dfrac{1}{\sqrt{V}}$.

     Therefore $\dfrac{\lambda_2}{\lambda_1} = \sqrt{\dfrac{V_1}{V_2}} = \sqrt{\dfrac{250 \text{ kV}}{600 \text{ kV}}} = \boxed{0.645}$.

9.   From Eq. 28.3: $\lambda = \sqrt{\dfrac{1.50}{V}}$ nm,   ☞ $V = \dfrac{1.50}{\lambda^2} = \dfrac{1.50}{(0.010)^2} = \boxed{1.5 \times 10^4 \text{ V}}$.

10.   From Eq. 28.3: $\lambda = \sqrt{\dfrac{1.50}{V}}$ nm,   so $\lambda \propto \dfrac{1}{\sqrt{V}}$.

     Therefore $\dfrac{\lambda_2}{\lambda_1} = \sqrt{\dfrac{V_1}{V_2}} = \sqrt{\dfrac{V_1}{2V_1}} = \dfrac{1}{\sqrt{2}} = \boxed{0.71}$.

340   Chapter 28   Quantum Mechanics

11.   The initial kinetic energy of the proton is

$K_o = \frac{1}{2}mv_o^2 = \frac{1}{2}(1.67 \times 10^{-27} \text{ kg})(4.5 \times 10^4 \text{ m/s})^2 = 1.69 \times 10^{-18} \text{ J} = 10.6 \text{ eV}.$

If the proton accelerates through 10.6 V, it will have a speed of 4.5×10^4 m/s.

So $V_1 = 10.6$ V and $V_2 = 10.6$ V $+ 37$ V $= 47.6$ V.

From Eq. 28.3: $\lambda = \sqrt{\dfrac{1.50}{V}}$ nm, so $\lambda \propto \dfrac{1}{\sqrt{V}}$. So the percentage difference is

$\dfrac{\lambda_2 - \lambda_1}{\lambda_1} = \dfrac{\lambda_2}{\lambda_1} - 1 = \sqrt{\dfrac{V_1}{V_2}} - 1 = \sqrt{\dfrac{10.6 \text{ V}}{37.6 \text{ V}}} - 1 = -0.53 = \boxed{-53\% \text{ (a decrease)}}.$

12. $d \sin\theta = m\lambda$, ☞ $\lambda = \dfrac{d \sin\theta}{m} = \dfrac{(0.15 \times 10^{-9} \text{ m}) \sin 25°}{1} = 6.34 \times 10^{-11} \text{ m} = 0.0634 \text{ nm}.$

From Eq. 28.3: $\lambda = \sqrt{\dfrac{1.50}{V}}$ nm, ☞ $V = \dfrac{1.50}{\lambda^2} = \dfrac{1.50}{(0.0634)^2} = 3.7 \times 10^2 \text{ V}.$

Therefore it is $= \boxed{3.7 \times 10^2 \text{ eV}}.$

13.   The Earth revolves once a year, so $v = \dfrac{d}{t} = \dfrac{2\pi(1.5 \times 10^{11} \text{ m})}{365 \times 86400 \text{ s}} = 2.99 \times 10^4 \text{ m/s}.$

$\lambda = \dfrac{h}{mv} = \dfrac{6.63 \times 10^{-34} \text{ J·s}}{(5.98 \times 10^{24} \text{ kg})(2.99 \times 10^4 \text{ m/s})} = \boxed{3.7 \times 10^{-63} \text{ m}}.$

14.   (a) $\lambda = \dfrac{h}{mv} = \dfrac{6.63 \times 10^{-34} \text{ J·s}}{(9.11 \times 10^{-31} \text{ kg})(2.19 \times 10^6 \text{ m/s})} = \boxed{3.32 \times 10^{-10} \text{ m}}.$

(b) $2\pi r_1 = 2\pi(0.529 \times 10^{-10} \text{ m}) = \lambda.$ So they are the $\boxed{\text{same}}$, since it is a standing wave.

15.   From Eq. 28.3: $\lambda = \sqrt{\dfrac{1.50}{V}}$ nm, ☞ $V = \dfrac{1.50}{\lambda^2} = \sqrt{\dfrac{1.50}{(0.25)^2}} = \boxed{24 \text{ V}}.$

16.   (c).

17.   (b).

18.   (a) The following standing waves can be set up in the well:

$L = \dfrac{n\lambda}{2}$, $n = 1, 2, 3, \ldots$ or $\lambda = \dfrac{2L}{n}.$

Also the wave function must be zero at $x = 0$ and $x = L$.

So $\psi_n = A \sin \dfrac{2\pi}{\lambda} x = A \sin \dfrac{n\pi x}{L}$ for $n = 1, 2, 3, \ldots$

(b) $K_n = \dfrac{p^2}{2m} = \dfrac{(h/\lambda)^2}{2m} = \dfrac{h^2}{2m\lambda^2} = \dfrac{h^2}{2m(2L/n)^2} = n^2 \dfrac{h^2}{8mL^2}.$

'19.   (a) Wave functions.   (b) Probability.

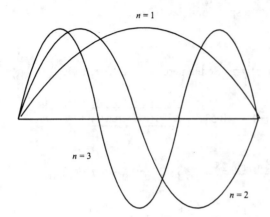

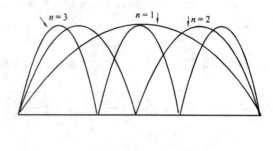

20.   (b).

21.   (c).

22.   The principle quantum number, n, gives information of the total energy and the orbit radius of an orbit in a hydrogen atom.

23.   (a).

24.   When quantum numbers are large (> 1000), the transitions between energy levels are effectively continuous, and in agreement with classical predictions.

25.   The periodical table groups elements according to the values of quantum numbers n and l. Within a group, the elements have the same or very similar electronic configurations for the outmost electrons.

26.   (a) $2n^2 = 2(2)^2 = \boxed{8}$ and $2(3)^2 = \boxed{18}$.

(b) For $n = 2$:

(2, 1, 1, +1/2);   (2, 1, 1, –1/2);   (2, 1, 0, +1/2);   (2, 1, 0, –1/2);

(2, 1, –1, +1/2); (2, 1, –1, –1/2); (2, 0, 0, +1);   (2, 0, 0, –1/2).

For $n = 3$:

(3, 2, 2, +1/2);   (3, 2, 2, –1/2);   (3, 2, 1, +1/2);   (3, 2, 1, –1/2);

(3, 2, 0, +1/2);   (3, 2, 0, –1/2);   (3, 2, –1, +1/2); (3, 2, –1, –1/2);

(3, 2, –2, +1/2); (3, 2, –2, –1/2); (3, 1, 1, +1);   (3, 1, 1, –1/2);

(3, 1, –1, +1/2); (3, 1, –1, –1/2); (3, 1, 0, +1/2);   (3, 1, 0, –1/2);

(3, 0, 0, +1/2);   (3, 0, 0, –1/2).

27.   (a) $2(2\ell + 1) = 2(0 + 1) = \boxed{2}$.

(b) $2[(2(3) + 1] = \boxed{14}$.

28.   For $n = 2$, there are $2n^2 = 2(2)^2 = 8$ sets of quantum numbers;

for $\ell = 2$, there are $2(2\ell + 1) = 2[2(2) + 1] = 10$ sets of quantum numbers.

So $\boxed{\ell = 2}$ has more sets of quantum numbers.

29.   (a) Since m_ℓ could be $0, \pm 1, \ldots, \pm \ell$, the minimum ℓ is $\boxed{2}$.

(b) Since $\ell = 0, 1, \ldots, n - 1$, the minimum n is $\boxed{3}$.

30.

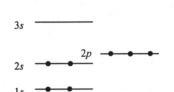

31.   (a) $\boxed{Be}$.   (b) $\boxed{N}$.

(c) $\boxed{Ne}$.   (d) $\boxed{S}$.

32.   (a)   (b)

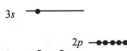

33.   (a) $\boxed{1s^2\, 2s^2\, 2p^1}$.   (b) $\boxed{1s^2\, 2s^2\, 2p^6\, 3s^2\, 3p^6\, 4s^2}$.

(c) $\boxed{1s^2\, 2s^2\, 2p^6\, 3s^2\, 3p^6\, 3d^{10}\, 4s^2}$.   (d) $\boxed{1s^2\, 2s^2\, 2p^6\, 3s^2\, 3p^6\, 3d^{10}\, 4s^2\, 4p^6\, 4d^{10}\, 5s^2\, 5p^2}$.

34. $1s^1$ is $\boxed{\text{hydrogen}}$ and $1s^2\, 2s^2\, 2p^1$ is $\boxed{\text{boron}}$.

35. $\boxed{1s^3}$ since the first state can contain three electrons now without violating the Pauli exclusion principle.

36. (b).

37. (b).

38. Due to the uncertainty principle, the product of the uncertainty in position and the uncertainty in momentum (or mass times the uncertainty in velocity) cannot be zero. So there will always be uncertainly in both position and velocity.

39. $\Delta p \Delta x \geq \dfrac{h}{2\pi}$, ☞ $\Delta x \geq \dfrac{h}{2\pi \Delta p} = \dfrac{6.63 \times 10^{-34} \text{ J·s}}{2\pi(2 \times 0.00025 \times 10^{-30} \text{ kg·m/s})} = \boxed{0.21 \text{ m}}$.

40. $\Delta p \Delta x \geq \dfrac{h}{2\pi}$, ☞ $\Delta v \geq \dfrac{\Delta p}{m} \geq \dfrac{h}{2\pi \Delta x m} = \dfrac{6.63 \times 10^{-34} \text{ J·s}}{2\pi[(0.10 - 0.050) \times 10^{-9} \text{ m}](9.11 \times 10^{-31} \text{ kg})}$

$$= \boxed{2.3 \times 10^6 \text{ m/s}}.$$

41. $\Delta p \Delta x \geq \dfrac{h}{2\pi}$, ☞ $\Delta v \geq \dfrac{\Delta p}{m} \geq \dfrac{h}{2\pi \Delta x m} = \dfrac{6.63 \times 10^{-34} \text{ J·s}}{2\pi(2 \times 0.0005 \times 10^{-2} \text{ m})(0.50 \text{ kg})}$

$$= \boxed{2.1 \times 10^{-29} \text{ m/s}}.$$

42. $K_+ = 1.03(2.00 \text{ keV}) = 2.06 \text{ keV} = 3.30 \times 10^{-16} \text{ J}$; $K_- = 0.97(2.00 \text{ keV}) = 1.94 \text{ keV} = 3.10 \times 10^{-16} \text{ J}$.

So $p_+ = \sqrt{2mK} = \sqrt{2(9.11 \times 10^{-31} \text{ kg})(3.30 \times 10^{-16} \text{ J})} = 2.45 \times 10^{-23} \text{ kg·m/s}$;

and $p_- = \sqrt{2(9.11 \times 10^{-31} \text{ kg})(3.10 \times 10^{-16} \text{ J})} = 2.38 \times 10^{-23} \text{ kg·m/s}$.

Therefore $\Delta p = p_+ - p_- = 7.00 \times 10^{-25} \text{ kg·m/s}$.

Hence $\Delta p \Delta x \geq \dfrac{h}{2\pi}$, ☞ $\Delta x \geq \dfrac{h}{2\pi \Delta p} = \dfrac{6.63 \times 10^{-34} \text{ J·s}}{2\pi(7.00 \times 10^{-25} \text{ kg·m/s})} = \boxed{1.5 \times 10^{-10} \text{ m}}$.

43. $\Delta E \Delta t \geq \dfrac{h}{2\pi}$, ☞ $\Delta E \geq \dfrac{h}{2\pi \Delta t} = \dfrac{6.63 \times 10^{-34} \text{ J·s}}{2\pi(10^{-7} \text{ s})} = \boxed{1.1 \times 10^{-27} \text{ J}}$.

44. $\Delta E \Delta t \geq \dfrac{h}{2\pi}$, ☞ $\Delta t \geq \dfrac{h}{2\pi \Delta E} = \dfrac{6.63 \times 10^{-34} \text{ J·s}}{2\pi(2 \times 0.0003 \text{ eV})(1.6 \times 10^{-19} \text{ J/eV})} = \boxed{1.1 \times 10^{-12} \text{ s}}$.

45. $\Delta E \Delta t \geq \dfrac{h}{2\pi}$, ☞ $\Delta E \geq \dfrac{h}{2\pi \Delta t}$. So $\dfrac{\Delta E_1}{\Delta E_2} = \dfrac{\Delta t_2}{\Delta t_1} = \dfrac{10^{-8} \text{ s}}{10^{-12} \text{ s}} = \boxed{10^4 \text{ times}}$.

46. (d).

47. (a).

48. When matter and antimatter meet, they will annihilate each other and energy will be converted from mass into electromagnetic energy.

49. The rest energy of the electron-positron pair is 2×0.511 MeV = 1.022 MeV.

$E = hf = (6.63 \times 10^{-34} \text{ J·s})(2.5 \times 10^{20} \text{ Hz}) = 1.66 \times 10^{-13} \text{ J} = 1.04 \text{ MeV} > 1.022 \text{ MeV}$. So $\boxed{\text{yes}}$.

50. The rest energy of the electron pair is 2×0.511 MeV = 1.022 MeV.

From the conservation of energy and momentum, each photon will move in opposite direction with the energy. So each will carry half the total energy or $\boxed{0.511 \text{ MeV}}$.

51. $E = hf \geq 2m_p c^2 = 2(1.67 \times 10^{-27} \text{ kg})(3.00 \times 10^8 \text{ m/s})^2 = 3.01 \times 10^{-10} \text{ J} = \boxed{1.9 \text{ GeV}}$.

52. $E = hf \geq 2m_\mu c^2 = 207(2m_e c^2) = 207(1.022 \text{ MeV}) = \boxed{212 \text{ MeV}}$.

53. $d \sin \theta = m\lambda$, ☞ $\lambda = \dfrac{d \sin \theta}{m} = \dfrac{(0.190 \times 10^{-9} \text{ m}) \sin 45°}{1} = 1.34 \times 10^{-10} \text{ m} = 0.144$ nm.

From Eq. 28.3: $\lambda = \sqrt{\dfrac{1.50}{V}}$ nm, ☞ $V = \dfrac{1.50}{\lambda^2} = \dfrac{1.50}{(0.134)^2} = \boxed{83.5 \text{ V}}$.

54. $\Delta p \Delta x \geq \dfrac{h}{2\pi}$, ☞ $\Delta x \geq \dfrac{h}{2\pi \Delta p} = \dfrac{h}{2\pi m \Delta v} = \dfrac{6.63 \times 10^{-34} \text{ J·s}}{2\pi(9.11 \times 10^{-31} \text{ kg})(0.00500 \text{ m/s})} = \boxed{2.32 \text{ cm}}$.

55. (a) $p = \dfrac{h}{\lambda} = \dfrac{hf}{c} = \dfrac{E}{c} = \dfrac{(7.5 \times 10^6 \text{ eV})(1.6 \times 10^{-19} \text{ J/eV})}{3.00 \times 10^8 \text{ m/s}} = \boxed{4.0 \times 10^{-21} \text{ kg·m/s}}$.

(b) $\lambda = \dfrac{h}{p} = \dfrac{6.63 \times 10^{-34} \text{ J·s}}{4.0 \times 10^{-21} \text{ kg·m/s}} = \boxed{1.7 \times 10^{-13} \text{ m}}$.

56. $K_+ = 1.03(5.00 \text{ keV}) = 5.15 \text{ keV} = 8.24 \times 10^{-16}$ J;

$K_- = 0.97(5.00 \text{ keV}) = 4.85 \text{ keV} = 7.76 \times 10^{-16}$ J.

So $p_+ = \sqrt{2mK} = \sqrt{2(9.11 \times 10^{-31} \text{ kg})(8.24 \times 10^{-16} \text{ J})} = 3.87 \times 10^{-23}$ kg·m/s;

and $p_- = \sqrt{2(9.11 \times 10^{-31} \text{ kg})(7.76 \times 10^{-16} \text{ J})} = 3.76 \times 10^{-23}$ kg·m/s.

Therefore $\Delta p = p_+ - p_- = 1.10 \times 10^{-24}$ kg·m/s.

Hence $\Delta p \, \Delta x \geq \dfrac{h}{2\pi}$, ☞ $\Delta x \geq \dfrac{h}{2\pi \Delta p} = \dfrac{6.63 \times 10^{-34} \text{ J·s}}{2\pi(1.10 \times 10^{-24} \text{ kg·m/s})} = \boxed{9.59 \times 10^{-11} \text{ m}}$.

57. The following standing waves can be set up in the well: $2L = \dfrac{n\lambda}{2}$, $n = 1, 2, 3, \ldots$,

or $\quad \lambda = \dfrac{4L}{n}$. Also the wave function must be zero at $x = \pm L$.

So $\quad \psi_n = A\cos\dfrac{2\pi}{\lambda}x = A\cos\dfrac{n\pi x}{2L}$, $n = 1, 3, 5, \ldots$,

and $\quad \psi_n = A\dfrac{2\pi}{\lambda} = A\sin\dfrac{n\pi x}{2L}$ for $n = 2, 4, 6, \ldots\ldots$

58. $K_n = \dfrac{p^2}{2m} = \dfrac{(h/\lambda)^2}{2m} = \dfrac{h^2}{2m\lambda^2} = \dfrac{h^2}{2m(4L/n)^2} = n^2\dfrac{h^2}{32mL^2}$, which is four times smaller than those in Exercise 28.18 because the well is twice as wide.

59. The $\cos\theta$ function has a maximum at $\theta = 0$. So the particle is most likely to be found at $\boxed{x = 0}$.

The probability at $x = 0$ is $|\psi_n|^2 = A^2\cos^2 0 = A^2$.

60. (a) $\lambda = \dfrac{h}{mv} = \dfrac{6.63 \times 10^{-34}\ \text{J·s}}{(0.150\ \text{kg})(20\ \text{m/s})} = \boxed{2.21 \times 10^{-34}\ \text{m}}$.

(b) 90 km/h = 25 m/s. $\quad \lambda = \dfrac{6.63 \times 10^{-34}\ \text{J·s}}{(1200\ \text{kg})(25\ \text{m/s})} = \boxed{2.21 \times 10^{-38}\ \text{m}}$.

61. $2n^2 = 2(2\ell + 1)$. So $\boxed{\text{yes when } n = 1 \text{ and } \ell = 0}$.

62. (a) $2E = 2hf = 2m_p c^2 = 2(1.67 \times 10^{-27}\ \text{kg})(3.00 \times 10^8\ \text{m/s})^2 = 3.01 \times 10^{-10}\ \text{J} = 1.88\ \text{GeV}$.

So $\quad E = \dfrac{1.88\ \text{GeV}}{2} = \boxed{0.94\ \text{GeV}}$.

(b) $f = \dfrac{3.01 \times 10^{-10}\ \text{J}}{2(6.63 \times 10^{-34}\ \text{J·s})} = \boxed{2.3 \times 10^{23}\ \text{Hz}}$.

63. $\boxed{\text{No}}$, muons are not identical particles to electrons.

64. They do not have to go off back to back according to momentum conservation, in fact, they have to go off as shown ($\theta < 90°$).

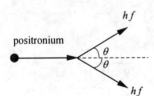

CHAPTER 29

THE NUCLEUS

The result of Exercise 29.37 is used in some exercises.

1.   (c).

2.   (d).

3.   (d).

4.   The nuclear force is an $\boxed{\text{attractive}}$ force. It acts between nucleons ($\boxed{\text{protons or neutrons}}$). It is a $\boxed{\text{short-range force}}$.

5.   The isotopes of an element have the $\boxed{\text{same number of protons}}$ but $\boxed{\text{different number of neutrons}}$.

6.   (a) For ^{24}Mg: $\boxed{12\ p}$, $24 - 12 = \boxed{12\ n}$, and $\boxed{12\ e}$.

   For ^{25}Mg: $\boxed{12\ p}$, $25 - 12 = \boxed{13\ n}$, and $\boxed{12\ e}$.

   (b) For ^{24}Mg: $\boxed{12\ p}$, $24 - 12 = \boxed{12\ n}$, and $\boxed{14\ e}$.

   For ^{25}Mg: $\boxed{12\ p}$, $25 - 12 = \boxed{13\ n}$, and $\boxed{14\ e}$.

   (c) For ^{24}Mg: $\boxed{12\ p}$, $24 - 12 = \boxed{12\ n}$, and $\boxed{11\ e}$.

   For ^{25}Mg: $\boxed{12\ p}$, $25 - 12 = \boxed{13\ n}$, and $\boxed{11\ e}$.

7.   (a) $\boxed{^{1}\text{H},\ ^{2}\text{D},\ ^{3}\text{T}}$.

   (b) $\boxed{H_2O,\ D_2O,\ T_2O,\ HDO,\ HTO,\ DTO}$.

   (c) $\boxed{T_2O,\ HTO,\ DTO}$.

8.   The mass number is $8 + 8 = 16$, $8 + 9 = 17$, and $8 + 10 = 18$, respectively. They are $\boxed{^{16}_{8}O,\ ^{17}_{8}O,\ ^{18}_{8}O}$.

9.   For argon, the number of neutrons is $N = A - Z = 40 - 18 = 22$.

   So for potassium, $A = Z + N = 19 + 22 = 41$, i.e., $\boxed{^{41}_{19}K}$.

10. There are 92 protons and 92 electrons in each U atom. The number of neutrons is $238 - 92 = 146$. So the answer is $\boxed{92 \text{ p, } 146 \text{ n, and } 92 \text{ e}}$.

11. (a) $R_{He} = (1.2 \times 10^{-15} \text{ m})(4)^{1/3} = \boxed{1.9 \times 10^{-15} \text{ m}}$; $\quad R_{Ne} = (1.2 \times 10^{-15} \text{ m})(20)^{1/3} = \boxed{3.3 \times 10^{-15} \text{ m}}$;

    $R_{Ar} = (1.2 \times 10^{-15} \text{ m})(40)^{1/3} = \boxed{4.1 \times 10^{-15} \text{ m}}$; $\quad R_{Kr} = (1.2 \times 10^{-15} \text{ m})(84)^{1/3} = \boxed{5.3 \times 10^{-15} \text{ m}}$;

    $R_{Xe} = (1.2 \times 10^{-15} \text{ m})(132)^{1/3} = \boxed{6.1 \times 10^{-15} \text{ m}}$; $\quad R_{Rn} = (1.2 \times 10^{-15} \text{ m})(222)^{1/3} = \boxed{7.3 \times 10^{-15} \text{ m}}$.

    (b) They are roughly from ten thousand to fifty thousand times smaller than an atom.

12. (d).

13. $\boxed{\text{No}}$, this is not a violation. In a negative beta decay for example, a proton, which is a nucleon, is created to make up for the loss of a neutron.

14. (a) $\boxed{^{60}_{27}\text{Co} \rightarrow \, ^{60}_{28}\text{Ni} + \, ^{0}_{-1}\text{e}}$. $\qquad\qquad$ (b) $\boxed{^{226}_{88}\text{Ra} \rightarrow \, ^{222}_{86}\text{Rn} + \, ^{4}_{2}\text{He}}$.

15. (a) $\boxed{^{237}_{93}\text{Np} \rightarrow \, ^{233}_{91}\text{Pa} + \, ^{4}_{2}\text{He}}$. $\qquad\qquad$ (b) $\boxed{^{32}_{15}\text{P} \rightarrow \, ^{32}_{16}\text{S} + \, ^{0}_{-1}\text{e}}$.

    (c) $\boxed{^{56}_{27}\text{Co} \rightarrow \, ^{56}_{26}\text{Fe} + \, ^{0}_{+1}\text{e}}$. $\qquad\qquad$ (d) $\boxed{^{56}_{27}\text{Co} + \, ^{0}_{-1}\text{e} \rightarrow \, ^{56}_{26}\text{Fe}}$.

    (e) $\boxed{^{42}_{19}\text{K}^{*} \rightarrow \, ^{42}_{19}\text{K} + \gamma}$.

16. (a) For β^{-}: $\quad ^{3}_{1}\text{T} \rightarrow \, ^{3}_{2}\text{He} + \, ^{0}_{-1}\text{e}$; $\quad$ for β^{+}: $\quad ^{3}_{1}\text{T} \rightarrow \, ^{3}_{0}\text{X} + \, ^{0}_{+1}\text{e}$.

    Since there is no element with zero protons, you expect $\boxed{\beta^{-} \text{ decay}}$.

    (b) As in (a), the daughter nucleus is $\boxed{\text{Helium-3; yes it is stable}}$.

17. α–decay: $\boxed{^{214}_{84}\text{Po} \rightarrow \, ^{210}_{82}\text{Pb} + \, ^{4}_{2}\text{He}}$; $\quad \beta$–decay: $\boxed{^{210}_{82}\text{Pb} \rightarrow \, ^{210}_{83}\text{Bi} + \, ^{0}_{-1}\text{e}}$

18. Charge: α relatively is positive; β is negative; γ is neutral.

    Mass: $\quad \alpha$ is massive; β is less massive; γ is massless.

19. α–β: $\quad ^{209}_{82}\text{Pb} + \, ^{0}_{-1}\text{e} \leftarrow \, ^{209}_{81}\text{Tl}$; $\quad ^{209}_{81}\text{Tl} + \, ^{4}_{2}\text{He} \leftarrow \boxed{^{213}_{83}\text{Bi}}$.

    β–α: $\quad ^{209}_{82}\text{Pb} + \, ^{4}_{2}\text{He} \leftarrow \, ^{213}_{84}\text{Po}$; $\quad ^{213}_{84}\text{Po} + \, ^{0}_{-1}\text{e} \leftarrow \boxed{^{213}_{83}\text{Bi}}$.

20. (a) $\boxed{^4_2\text{He}}$. (b) $\boxed{4(^1_0\text{n})}$. (c) $\boxed{\gamma}$. (d) $\boxed{^{29}_{12}\text{Mg}}$.

21. (a) $\boxed{^4_2\text{He}}$. (b) $\boxed{^0_{-1}\text{e}}$. (c) $\boxed{^{102}_{39}\text{Y}}$. (d) $\boxed{^{23}_{11}\text{Na}^*}$. (e) $\boxed{^{22}_{10}\text{Ne}}$.

22. α–series: $\boxed{^{227}_{89}\text{Ac} \rightarrow {}^{223}_{87}\text{Fr} + {}^4_2\text{He}}$; $\boxed{^{223}_{87}\text{Fr} \rightarrow {}^{223}_{88}\text{Ra} + {}^0_{-1}\text{e}}$;

$\boxed{^{223}_{88}\text{Ra} \rightarrow {}^{219}_{86}\text{Rn} + {}^4_2\text{He}}$; $\boxed{^{219}_{86}\text{Rn} \rightarrow {}^{215}_{84}\text{Po} + {}^4_2\text{He}}$.

β–series: $\boxed{^{227}_{89}\text{Ac} \rightarrow {}^{227}_{90}\text{Th} + {}^0_{-1}\text{e}}$; $\boxed{^{227}_{90}\text{Th} \rightarrow {}^{223}_{88}\text{Ra} + {}^4_2\text{He}}$;

$\boxed{^{223}_{88}\text{Ra} \rightarrow {}^{219}_{86}\text{Rn} + {}^4_2\text{He}}$; $\boxed{^{219}_{86}\text{Rn} \rightarrow {}^{215}_{84}\text{Po} + {}^4_2\text{He}}$.

23. (a) α to ^{233}Pa; β to ^{233}U; α to ^{229}Th; α to ^{225}Ra; β to ^{225}Ac; α to ^{221}Fr; α to ^{217}At; α to ^{213}Bi; α to ^{209}Tl or β to ^{213}Po; β to ^{209}Pb or α to ^{209}Pb; β to ^{209}Bi.

(b) They decay because there are $\boxed{\text{too many neutrons}}$ in the nucleus.

24. (d).

25. $\dfrac{1}{2^2} = \dfrac{1}{4} = 25\%$. So it will have decreased by $100\% - 25\% = 75\%$. (c).

26. $\boxed{\text{None}}$, it is totally independent of temperature, environment, and chemistry.

27. $\boxed{\text{No}}$, decay is exponential, not linear.

28. (a) It would be $\boxed{\text{infinite}}$.

(b) $\lambda = \dfrac{0.693}{t_{1/2}} = \boxed{0}$.

29. (a) $(2.50 \times 10^6 \text{ decays/s}) \dfrac{1 \text{ Ci}}{3.70 \times 10^{10} \text{ decays/s}} = \boxed{6.76 \times 10^{-5} \text{ Ci}}$.

(b) $\boxed{2.50 \times 10^6 \text{ Bq}}$.

30. (a) $20 \text{ mCi} = (20 \times 10^{-3} \text{ Ci}) \dfrac{3.70 \times 10^{10} \text{ decays/s}}{1 \text{ Ci}} = \boxed{7.4 \times 10^{\times 108} \text{ decays/s}}$.

(b) $7.4 \times 10^8 \text{ decays/s} = (7.4 \times 10^8 \text{ betas/s}) \dfrac{60 \text{ s}}{1 \text{ min}} = \boxed{4.4 \times 10^{10} \text{ betas/min}}$.

31. (a) 3 h = 3 $t_{1/2}$, so $\dfrac{1}{2^3} = \boxed{\dfrac{1}{8}}$ would be left.

(b) 1 d = 24 $t_{1/2}$, so $\dfrac{1}{2^{24}} = \boxed{6 \times 10^{-6}\,\%}$ of the original.

32. $\lambda = \dfrac{0.693}{t_{1/2}} = \dfrac{0.693}{18 \times 60\text{ s}} = 6.42 \times 10^{-4}\text{ s}^{-1};\quad \lambda t = (5.92 \times 10^{-4}\text{ s}^{-1})(3600\text{ s}) = 2.31.$

So $\dfrac{\Delta N}{\Delta t} = \lambda N = \lambda N_0\, e^{-\lambda t} = \dfrac{\Delta N_0}{\Delta t}\, e^{-\lambda t} = (10\text{ mCi})\, e^{-2.31} = \boxed{1\text{ mCi}}.$

33. $\dfrac{\Delta N}{\Delta t} = \lambda N = \lambda N_0\, e^{-\lambda t} = \dfrac{\Delta N_0}{\Delta t}\, e^{-\lambda t},\quad \raisebox{-0.3ex}{☞}\quad e^{-\lambda t} = 0.20.$

So $t = -\dfrac{\ln 0.20}{\lambda} = -\dfrac{t_{1/2}\ln 0.20}{0.693} = -\dfrac{(12.3\text{ y})\ln 0.20}{0.693} = \boxed{28.6\text{ y}}.$

34. $\lambda = \dfrac{0.693}{t_{1/2}},\quad \raisebox{-0.3ex}{☞}\quad \dfrac{\lambda_{Tc}}{\lambda_{Mg}} = \dfrac{(t_{1/2})_{Mg}}{(t_{1/2})_{Tc}} = \dfrac{21\text{ h}}{18/60\text{ h}} = 70.$ So $\boxed{\text{Tc is greater by 70 times}}.$

35. $\lambda = \dfrac{0.693}{t_{1/2}} = \dfrac{0.693}{8.04\text{ d}} = 0.0862\text{ d}^{-1},\quad \lambda t = (0.0862\text{ d}^{-1})(1\text{ d}) = 0.0862.$

So $N = N_0\, e^{-\lambda t},\quad \raisebox{-0.3ex}{☞}\quad \dfrac{N}{N_0} = e^{-\lambda t} = e^{-0.0862} = 0.917 = \boxed{91.7\%}.$

36. From Example 29.4, the initial activity is $\dfrac{\Delta N_0}{\Delta t} = 16$ decays/g·min.

$\dfrac{4}{16} = \dfrac{1}{4} = \dfrac{1}{2^2}$, i.e., after 2 half-lives. So $t = 2\,t_{1/2} = 2(5730\text{ y}) = \boxed{1.1 \times 10^4\text{ y}}.$

37. After n half-lives, $\lambda t = \dfrac{0.693}{t_{1/2}}\, n t_{1/2} = 0.693n.$

So $N = N_0\, e^{-\lambda t} = N_0\, e^{-0.693n} = \dfrac{N_0}{(e^{0.693})^n} = \dfrac{N_0}{2^n} = \left(\dfrac{1}{2}\right)^n N_0.$

38. $t_{1/2} = 5730$ y. $\dfrac{28\,650\text{ y}}{5730\text{ y}} = 5$, i.e., after 5 half-lives.

So $\dfrac{N}{N_0} = \dfrac{1}{2^5} = 0.031 = \boxed{3.1\%}.$

39. $1 - 0.875 = 0.125 = \dfrac{1}{8} = \dfrac{1}{2^3}$, i.e., after 3 half-lives.

So $t_{1/2} = \dfrac{t}{3} = \dfrac{54\text{ min}}{3} = 18$ min. Therefore it is $\boxed{{}^{104}\text{Tc}}$ from Table 29.1.

40. $$\frac{\Delta N}{\Delta t} = \lambda N = \lambda N_0\, e^{-\lambda t} = \frac{\Delta N_0}{\Delta t}\, e^{-\lambda t}, \qquad \raisebox{-2pt}{☞} \qquad \frac{\Delta N/\Delta t}{\Delta N_0/\Delta t} = 0.20 = e^{-\lambda t}.$$

So $\quad t = -\dfrac{\ln 0.20}{\lambda} = -\dfrac{t_{1/2}\ln 0.20}{0.693} = -\dfrac{(5.3\text{ y})\ln 0.20}{0.693} = \boxed{12\text{ y}}.$

41. $$\lambda t = \frac{0.693}{t_{1/2}}\, t = \frac{0.693}{28\text{ y}}(150\text{ y}) = 3.7125.$$

$N = N_0\, e^{-\lambda t}, \qquad \raisebox{-2pt}{☞} \qquad \dfrac{N}{N_0} = e^{-\lambda t} = e^{-3.7125} = 0.02442.$

So the amount that will be in the sample is $(0.02442)(40\ \mu\text{g}) = \boxed{0.98\ \mu\text{g}}.$

42. (a) $\lambda = \dfrac{0.693}{t_{1/2}} = \dfrac{0.693}{66.0\text{ s}} = \boxed{1.05 \times 10^{-2}\text{ s}^{-1}}.$

(b) $\dfrac{\Delta N}{\Delta t} = \lambda N = \lambda N_0\, e^{-\lambda t} = \dfrac{\Delta N_0}{\Delta t}\, e^{-\lambda t}, \qquad \raisebox{-2pt}{☞} \qquad \dfrac{\Delta N/\Delta t}{\Delta N_0/\Delta t} = 0.10 = e^{-\lambda t}.$

So $\quad t = -\dfrac{\ln 0.10}{\lambda} = -\dfrac{t_{1/2}\ln 0.10}{0.693} = -\dfrac{(66.0\text{ s})\ln 0.10}{0.693} = \boxed{219\text{ s}}.$

43. (a) The mass of one nuclei is $(223\text{ u})(1.66 \times 10^{-27}\text{ kg/u}).$

So there were $\quad \dfrac{25.0 \times 10^{-6}\text{ kg}}{(223\text{ u})(1.66 \times 10^{-27}\text{ kg/u})} = \boxed{6.75 \times 10^{19}\text{ nuclei}}.$

(b) $\lambda t = \dfrac{0.693}{t_{1/2}}\, t = \dfrac{0.693}{21.8\text{ min}}(60\text{ min} + 49\text{ min}) = 3.465.$

So $\quad N = N_0\, e^{-\lambda t}, \qquad \raisebox{-2pt}{☞} \qquad \dfrac{N}{N_0} = e^{-\lambda t} = e^{-3.465} = 0.0313.$

Therefore there are $(0.0313)(6.75 \times 10^{19}\text{ nuclei}) = \boxed{2.11 \times 10^{18}\text{ nuclei}}.$

44. (a) $\dfrac{7\text{ d}}{3.82\text{ d}} = 1.83.$ So $\quad N \approx \dfrac{N_0}{2^{1.83}} = \dfrac{7.50 \times 10^{10}\text{ atoms}}{2^{1.83}} = \boxed{2.11 \times 10^{10}\text{ atoms}}.$

(c) $\boxed{\text{No}}$, the daughters are also radioactive, giving rise to granddaughters, etc., down the chain to lead (Pb).

45. $$\lambda t = \frac{0.693}{t_{1/2}}\, t = \frac{0.693}{1600\text{ y}}(2100\text{ y} - 1898\text{ y}) = 0.0875.$$

$N = N_0\, e^{-\lambda t}, \qquad \raisebox{-2pt}{☞} \qquad \dfrac{N}{N_0} = e^{-\lambda t} = e^{-0.0875} = 0.916.$

So the amount of radium that would remain is $(0.916)(10\text{ mg}) = \boxed{9.2\text{ mg}}.$

46. $\dfrac{\Delta N}{\Delta t} = \dfrac{475 \text{ decays/min}}{250 \text{ g}} = 1.9 \text{ decays/g·min}.$

From Example 29.4, $\dfrac{\Delta N_0}{\Delta t} = 16 \text{ decays/g·min}.$

$\dfrac{\Delta N/\Delta t}{\Delta N_0/\Delta t} = \dfrac{1.9}{16} \approx \dfrac{1}{8} = \dfrac{1}{2^3},$ i.e., slightly longer than 3 half-lives.

So $\quad t \approx 3t_{1/2} = 3(5730 \text{ y}) = 17\,190 \text{ y}.$ Therefore it is about $\boxed{17\,000 \text{ y}}$.

47. The mass of U_3O_8 is $3(238 \text{ u}) + 8(16 \text{ u}) = \boxed{942 \text{ u.}}$ $\quad 842_u$

So the fraction of U by mass is $\dfrac{3 \times 238}{942} = \boxed{0.758.}$ $\quad 0.848$

In 500 000 tons of U_3O_8, there are $(0.758)(500\,000 \text{ tons})(10 \text{ kg/ton}) = 3.8 \times 10^6 \text{ kg}$ of U today.

4.6 billion years is about 1 half-life.

Therefore there were $2(3.8 \times 10^6 \text{ kg}) = \boxed{7.6 \times 10^6 \text{ kg}}$ of U.

$8.\,{}^{65}\times 10^6 \ kg$

48. (a) $\boxed{{}^{13}_{7}\text{N} \rightarrow {}^{13}_{6}\text{C} + {}^{0}_{+1}\text{e}}$.

(b) There were $N_0 = \dfrac{0.0015 \text{ kg}}{(13 \text{ u})(1.66 \times 10^{-27} \text{ kg/u})} = 6.95 \times 10^{22}$ nuclei.

$\lambda = \dfrac{0.693}{t_{1/2}} = \dfrac{0.693}{10 \text{ min}} = 0.0693 \text{ min}^{-1}.$ $\quad \lambda t = (0.0693 \text{ min}^{-1})(35 \text{ min}) = 2.43.$

$\dfrac{\Delta N_0}{\Delta t} = \lambda N_0 = (0.0693 \text{ min}^{-1})(6.95 \times 10^{22} \text{ nuclei}) = 4.82 \times 10^{21} \text{ decays/min}.$

$\dfrac{\Delta N}{\Delta t} = \dfrac{\Delta N_0}{\Delta t} e^{-\lambda t} = (4.82 \times 10^{21} \text{ decays/min}) e^{-2.43} = \boxed{4.2 \times 10^{20} \text{ decays/min}}.$

(c) $N = \dfrac{\Delta N/\Delta t}{\lambda} = \dfrac{4.23 \times 10^{20} \text{ decays/min}}{0.0693 \text{ min}^{-1}} = 6.10 \times 10^{21}$ nuclei.

So the percentage of ^{13}N is $\dfrac{6.10 \times 10^{21}}{6.95 \times 10^{22}} = \boxed{8.8\%}.$

49. (d).

50. (a).

51. $\boxed{^{1}\text{H and }^{2}\text{H are stable and }^{3}\text{H is unstable}}$ because there are too many neutrons in ^{3}T.

52. $\boxed{{}^{4}_{2}\text{He}, {}^{16}_{8}\text{O}, {}^{40}_{20}\text{Ca}, {}^{48}_{20}\text{Ca}, {}^{208}_{82}\text{Pb}}$.

53.   (a) $\boxed{^{17}_{8}\text{O}}$ because of an unpaired neutron beyond a magic number.

      (b) $\boxed{^{42}_{20}\text{Ca}}$ because of a magic number difference making $^{40}_{20}\text{Ca}$ more stable (both are paired).

      (c) $\boxed{^{10}_{5}\text{B}}$ because of lack of pairing.

      (d) $\boxed{\text{Approximately the same}}$ as both have 126 neutrons (paired and magic) and the different number of protons does not affect neutrons.

54. $\boxed{^{58}_{28}\text{Ni}}$.

55. $\boxed{\text{(b) and (d)}}$, others are odd–odd.

56. $\boxed{\text{(b) and (d)}}$ are unstable.

57. $E_b = \Delta mc^2 = (m_n + m_p - m_D)c^2$,

      so $m_D = m_p + m_n - E_b/c^2 = 1.007276 \text{ u} + 1.008665 \text{ u} + \dfrac{2.224 \text{ MeV}}{931.5 \text{ MeV/u}} = \boxed{2.013553 \text{ u}}$.

58.   For C, 1 mole $(6.02 \times 10^{23}$ atoms) has a mass of 12 g.

      So $(6.02 \times 10^{23})(12 \text{ u}) = 12 \times 10^{-3}$ kg,   ☞ $1 \text{ u} = \dfrac{12 \times 10^{-3} \text{ kg}}{12(6.02 \times 10^{23})} = 1.66 \times 10^{-27}$ kg.

59.   (a) $E_b = \Delta mc^2 = (6m_H + 6m_n - m_C)c^2 = [6(1.007825 \text{ u}) + 6(1.008665 \text{ u}) - 12.000000 \text{ u}](931.5 \text{ MeV/u})$

         $= \boxed{92.2 \text{ MeV}}$.

      (b) $\dfrac{E_b}{A} = \dfrac{92.2 \text{ MeV}}{12 \text{ nucleon}} = \boxed{7.68 \text{ MeV/nucleon}}$.

60. $E_b = \Delta mc^2 = (8m_H + 8m_n - m_O)c^2 = [8(1.007825 \text{ u}) + 8(1.008665 \text{ u}) - 15.994915 \text{ u}](931.5 \text{ MeV/u})$

      $= 127.6 \text{ MeV}$.

      $\dfrac{E_b}{A} = \dfrac{127.6 \text{ MeV}}{16 \text{ nucleon}} = \boxed{7.98 \text{ MeV/nucleon}}$

61.   For deuterium:

      $E_b = (m_H + m_n - m_D)c^2 = (1.007825 \text{ u} + 1.008665 \text{ u} - 2.014102 \text{ u})(931.5 \text{ MeV/u}) = 2.22 \text{ MeV}$.

      So $\dfrac{E_b}{A} = \dfrac{2.22 \text{ MeV}}{2 \text{ nucleon}} = 1.11 \text{ MeV}$.

For tritium:

$E_b = (m_H + 2m_n - m_T)c^2 = [1.007825 \text{ u} + 2(1.008665 \text{ u}) - 3.016049 \text{ u}](931.5 \text{ MeV/u}) = 8.48 \text{ MeV}$.

So $\dfrac{E_b}{A} = \dfrac{8.48 \text{ MeV}}{3 \text{ nucleon}} = 2.83 \text{ MeV}$.

Therefore $\boxed{\text{deuterium}}$ has the lower average binding energy per nucleon.

62. $E_b = (m_H + m_n - m_D)c^2 = (1.007825 \text{ u} + 1.008665 \text{ u} - 2.014102 \text{ u})(931.5 \text{ MeV/u}) = \boxed{2.22 \text{ MeV}}$.

63. Energy required $= E_b = (7m_H + 7m_n - m_N)c^2$

$= [7(1.007825 \text{ u}) + 7(1.008665 \text{ u}) - 14.003074 \text{ u}](931.5 \text{ MeV/u}) = \boxed{104.7 \text{ MeV}}$.

64. $E_b = (m_n + m_{K\text{-}39} - m_{K\text{-}40})c^2 = (1.008665 \text{ u} + 38.963708 \text{ u} - 39.964000 \text{ u})(931.5 \text{ MeV/u}) = \boxed{7.80 \text{ MeV}}$.

65. Energy required $= E_b = (m_{He} + m_{Na} - m_{Al})c^2 = (4.002603 \text{ u} + 22.989770 \text{ u} - 26.981541 \text{ u})(931.5 \text{ MeV/u})$

$= \boxed{10.1 \text{ MeV}}$.

66. For Al: $E_b = (13m_H + 14m_n - m_{Al})c^2 = [13(1.007825 \text{ u}) + 14(1.008665 \text{ u}) - 26.981541 \text{ u}](931.5 \text{ MeV/u})$

$= 225.0 \text{ MeV}$. So $\dfrac{E_b}{A} = \dfrac{225.0 \text{ MeV}}{27 \text{ nucleon}} = 8.33 \text{ MeV/nucleon}$.

For Na: $E_b = (11m_H + 12m_n - m_{Na})c^2 = [11(1.007825 \text{ u}) + 12(1.008665 \text{ u}) - 22.989770 \text{ u}](931.5 \text{ MeV/u})$

$= 186.6 \text{ MeV}$. So $\dfrac{E_b}{A} = \dfrac{186.6 \text{ MeV}}{23 \text{ nucleon}} = 8.11 \text{ MeV/nucleon}$.

So the nucleons are more tightly bound in $\boxed{\text{in Al}}$ on average.

67. $E_b = (92m_H + 146m_n - m_U) c^2 = [92(1.007825 \text{ u}) + 143(1.008665 \text{ u}) - 235.043925 \text{ u}](931.5 \text{ MeV/u})$

$= 1784 \text{ MeV}$. So $\dfrac{E_b}{A} = \dfrac{1784 \text{ MeV}}{235 \text{ nucleon}} = \boxed{7.59 \text{ MeV/nucleon}}$.

68. $E_b = (3m_p + 3m_n - m_{Li})c^2$,

so $m_{Li} = 3m_p + 3m_n - \dfrac{E_b}{c^2} = 3(1.007276 \text{ u}) + 3(1.008665 \text{ u}) - \dfrac{32.0 \text{ MeV}}{931.5 \text{ MeV/u}} = \boxed{6.013470 \text{ u}}$.

69. (a) $2m_{He} = 2(4.002603 \text{ u}) = 8.005206 \text{ u}$. So the mass of $\boxed{\text{two alpha}}$ particles is less.

(b) For Be:

$E_b = (4m_H + 4m_n - m_{Be})c^2 = [4(1.007825 \text{ u}) + 4(1.008665 \text{ u}) - 8.005305 \text{ u}](931.5 \text{ MeV/u}) = 56.5 \text{ MeV}$.

For 2 He:

$E_b = 2(2m_H + 2m_n - m_{He})c^2 = 2[2(1.007825 \text{ u}) + 2(1.008665 \text{ u}) - 4.002603 \text{ u}](931.5 \text{ MeV/u}) = 56.6 \text{ MeV}.$

So the binding energy of $\boxed{\text{two alphas}}$ is greater.

(c) $\boxed{\text{Yes}}$, since two alphas is more stable.

70. (b).

71. (d).

72. Less ^{14}C would have been produced. A sample measured now would have its age over estimated.

73. (a) $\boxed{\alpha \text{ particles}}$.

(b) For X-rays: Dose (in rem) = Dose (in rad) × RBE = (1.0 rad) × (1) = $\boxed{1.0 \text{ rem}}$;

for α particles: Dose (in rem) = (1.0 rad) × (20) = $\boxed{20 \text{ rem}}$.

74. (a) $E = m \times$ Dose = (0.20 kg)(1.25 rad) = $\boxed{0.25 \text{ J}}$.

(b) Dose (in rem) = Dose (in rad) × RBE = (1.25 rad)(4) = 5.0 rem, which exceeds the maximum

permissible radiation dosage with background radiation included. So the answer is $\boxed{\text{yes}}$.

75. Dose (in rem) = Σ [Dose (in rad) × RBE] = (0.5 rad)(1) + (0.3 rad)(4) + (0.1 rad)(20) = 3.7 rem in three

months. So $\boxed{\text{yes}}$, the maximum permissible radiation dosage is exceeded.

76. $\lambda t = \dfrac{0.693}{t_{1/2}} t = \dfrac{0.693}{2.7 \text{ d}} (30 \text{ d}) = 7.7.$

$\dfrac{\Delta N}{\Delta t} = \dfrac{\Delta N_0}{\Delta t} e^{-\lambda t} = (80 \text{ mCi}) e^{-7.7} = \boxed{36 \ \mu\text{Ci}}.$

77. The isotope in the hair was $\boxed{^{75}_{33}\text{As}}$.   The decay is $^{76}_{33}\text{As} \rightarrow \boxed{^{76}_{34}\text{Se}} + ^{0}_{-1}\text{e}.$

78. By $\boxed{^{14}\text{C dating}}$.

79. (a) E_b = (7.075 MeV/nucleon)(4 nucleon) = $\boxed{28.3 \text{ MeV}}$.

(b) $E_b = (2m_p + 2m_n - m_{He})c^2,$

so $m_{He} = 2m_p + 2m_n - E_b/c^2 = 2(1.007276 \text{ u}) + 2(1.008665 \text{ u}) - \dfrac{28.3 \text{ MeV}}{931.5 \text{ MeV/u}} = \boxed{4.001501 \text{ u}}.$

80. The first α decay to $^{230}_{90}$Th; the second α decay to $^{226}_{88}$Ra; the third α decay to $^{222}_{86}$Rn; the fourth α decay to $^{218}_{84}$Po; the first β decay to $^{222}_{85}$At; the second β decay to $\boxed{^{218}_{86}\text{Rn}}$.

81. (a) $\lambda = \dfrac{0.693}{t_{1/2}} = 0.28875$ min^{-1}, $\quad \lambda t = (0.28875$ min$^{-1})(10$ min$) = 2.8875$.

$N = N_o\, e^{-\lambda t} = (6.02 \times 10^{23}$ nuclei$)\, e^{-2.8875} = \boxed{3.4 \times 10^{22} \text{ nuclei}}$.

(b) $\lambda t = (0.28875$ min$^{-1})(60$ min$) = 17.325$.

$N = (6.02 \times 10^{23}$ nuclei$)\, e^{-17.325} = \boxed{1.8 \times 10^{16} \text{ nuclei}}$.

(c) After 10 min: $\quad \dfrac{\Delta N}{\Delta t} = \lambda N = (0.28875$ min$^{-1})(3.35 \times 10^{22}$ nuclei$) = \boxed{9.7 \times 10^{19} \text{ decays/min}}$;

after 1 h, $\quad \dfrac{\Delta N}{\Delta t} = (0.28875$ min$^{-1})(1.80 \times 10^{16}$ nuclei$) = \boxed{5.2 \times 10^{15} \text{ decays/min}}$.

$\boxed{\text{No}}$, it is not a realistic laboratory radioactive source.

82. From Example 29.3, $\dfrac{1}{16} = \dfrac{1}{2^4}$, i.e., after 4 half-lives.

So $\quad t = 4t_{1/2} = 4(5730$ y$) = \boxed{2.29 \times 10^4 \text{ y}}$.

83. (a) $\boxed{^{\ 0}_{-1}\text{e}}$. (b) $\boxed{^{222}_{86}\text{Rn}}$. (c) $\boxed{^{237}_{94}\text{Pu}}$. (d) $\boxed{\gamma}$. (e) $\boxed{^{\ 0}_{+1}\text{e}}$.

84. (a) See Figure 29.24.

(b) Before over 700 million years, after (one route) 30 days; (the other route) 67 min.

85. (a) $E_b = (7.58$ MeV/nucleon$)(238$ nucleon$) = \boxed{1.80 \times 10^3 \text{ MeV}}$.

(b) $E_b = (92m_p + 146m_n - m_U)c^2$, so

$m_U = 92m_p + 146m_U - E_b/c^2 = 92(1.007276$ u$) + 146(1.008665$ u$) - \dfrac{1804 \text{ MeV}}{931.5 \text{ MeV/u}} = \boxed{237.997821 \text{ u}}$.

86. (a) $E = m\,c^2 = (12$ u$)(931.5$ MeV/u$) = \boxed{1.118 \times 10^4 \text{ MeV}}$.

(b) $E = (4.002603$ u$)(931.5$ MeV/u$) = \boxed{3.728 \times 10^3 \text{ MeV}}$.

87. (1) All nuclei with $Z > 83$ are unstable.

(2) All odd–odd nuclei are unstable except for ^{2}H, ^{6}Li, ^{10}B, and ^{14}N.

(3) Stable nuclei with $A < 40$ have about equal numbers of protons and neutrons.

(4) Stable nuclei with $A > 40$ have an excess number of neutrons which becomes more obvious as A increases.

So (c) and (d) are stable.

88. (a) $^{229}_{90}\text{Th} \rightarrow \boxed{^{225}_{88}\text{Ra}} + {}^{4}_{2}\text{He}$.   (b) $^{225}_{88}\text{Ra} \rightarrow \boxed{^{225}_{89}\text{Ac}} + {}^{0}_{-1}\text{e}$.

89. $^{6}_{3}\text{Li} + {}^{1}_{1}\text{H} \rightarrow {}^{4}_{2}\text{He} + \boxed{{}^{3}_{2}\text{He}}$.

90. (a) $N_o = \dfrac{1.0 \times 10^{-3}\ \text{kg}}{(198\ \text{u})(1.66 \times 10^{-27}\ \text{kg/u})} = 3.04 \times 10^{21}$ nuclei.

  $\lambda = \dfrac{0.693}{t_{1/2}} = \dfrac{0.693}{2.7 \times 24 \times 60\ \text{min}} = 1.78 \times 10^{-4}\ \text{min}^{-1}$.

  So $\dfrac{\Delta N_o}{\Delta t} = \lambda N_o = (1.78 \times 10^{-4}\ \text{min}^{-1})(3.04 \times 10^{21}\ \text{nuclei}) = \boxed{5.4 \times 10^{17}\ \text{decays/min}}$.

  (b) $\lambda t = (1.78 \times 10^{-4}\ \text{min}^{-1})(30 \times 24 \times 60\ \text{min}) = 7.69$.

  $\dfrac{\Delta N}{\Delta t} = \dfrac{\Delta N_o}{\Delta t}\ e^{-\lambda t} = (5.41 \times 10^{17}\ \text{decays/min})\ e^{-7.69} = \boxed{2.5 \times 10^{14}\ \text{decays/min}}$.

91. (a) $\dfrac{\text{nucleon}}{\text{volume}} = \dfrac{A}{4\pi R^3/3} = \dfrac{3A}{4\pi R^3} = \dfrac{3A}{4\pi R_o^{\ 3} A} = \dfrac{3}{4\pi R_o^{\ 3}} = \dfrac{3}{4\pi (1.2 \times 10^{-15}\ \text{m})^3}$

    $\approx 1.4 \times 10^{44}$ nucleons/m^3.

  (b) 1 nucleon has a mass of 1.66×10^{-27} kg.

  So $\rho = (1.4 \times 10^{44}\ \text{nucleon/m}^3)\ \dfrac{1.66 \times 10^{-27}\ \text{kg}}{1\ \text{nucleon}} = \boxed{2.3 \times 10^{17}\ \text{kg/m}^3}$.

92. $\lambda = \dfrac{0.693}{t_{1/2}} = \dfrac{0.693}{12.33\ \text{y}} = 0.0562\ \text{y}^{-1}$, $\lambda t = (0.0562\ \text{y}^{-1})(6.00\ \text{y}) = 0.337$.

  So $N = N_o\ e^{-\lambda t}$,   ☞ $\dfrac{N}{N_o} = e^{-\lambda t} = e^{-0.337} = 0.714 = \boxed{71.4\%}$.

93. (a) For H: $\rho = \dfrac{1.67 \times 10^{-27}\ \text{kg}}{4\pi (0.053 \times 10^{-9}\ \text{m})^3/3} = 2.7 \times 10^3\ \text{kg/m}^3$.

  So $\dfrac{2.3 \times 10^{17}\ \text{kg/m}^3}{2.7 \times 10^3\ \text{kg/m}^3} = 9 \times 10^{13} \approx 10^{14}$,

  i.e., the $\boxed{\text{atomic density is about } 10^{14} \text{ times less than the nuclear density}}$.

(b) This is because the mass is the same but averaged over a $\boxed{\text{much larger volume}}$.

(c) $\boxed{\text{No}}$. The average atomic density is much higher than hydrogen gas (most gases are typically

$\approx 2 \text{ kg/m}^3$) because the gas density includes mostly empty space between gas molecules

94. $^{232}_{92}\text{U} \rightarrow {}^{228}_{90}\text{Th} + {}^{4}_{2}\text{He}$.

$E = \Delta mc^2 = (m_{\text{U}} - m_{\text{Th}} - m_{\text{He}})(931.5 \text{ MeV/u}) = (232.03714 \text{ u } - 228.02873 \text{ u} - 4.002603 \text{ u})((31.5 \text{ MeV/u})$

$= \boxed{5.41 \text{ MeV}}$.

CHAPTER 30

NUCLEAR REACTIONS AND ELEMENTARY PARTICLES

1. (d).

2. (d).

3. $K_{min} = \left(1 + \dfrac{m_a}{M_A}\right)|Q|$.

   As the target mass M_A becomes very large, $K_{min} \to |Q|$.
   If $Q = 0$, the incident particle would not need any kinetic
   energy to start the reaction.

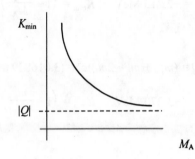

4. (a) $\boxed{^{41}_{19}\text{K}}$. (b) $\boxed{^{135}_{52}\text{Te}}$.

   (c) $\boxed{4(^1_0\text{n})}$. (d) $\boxed{^{14}_{7}\text{N}}$. (e) $\boxed{\text{n}}$.

5. (a) $\boxed{^{14}_{7}\text{N}}$. (b) $\boxed{^2_1\text{H}}$. (c) $\boxed{^{30}_{15}\text{P}}$. (d) $\boxed{^{17}_{8}\text{O}}$. (e) $\boxed{^{10}_{5}\text{B}}$.

6. (a) $\boxed{^{41}_{18}\text{Ar}^*}$. (b) $\boxed{^{236}_{92}\text{U}^*}$. (c) $\boxed{^{236}_{92}\text{U}^*}$. (d) $\boxed{^{18}_{9}\text{F}^*}$. (e) $\boxed{^{138}_{56}\text{Ba}^*}$.

7. (a) $\boxed{^{14}_{7}\text{N}^*}$. (b) $\boxed{^{14}_{7}\text{N}^*}$. (c) $\boxed{^{31}_{15}\text{P}^*}$. (d) $\boxed{^{18}_{9}\text{F}^*}$. (e) $\boxed{^{14}_{7}\text{N}^*}$.

8. $Q = (m_C + m_p - m_{He} - m_B)c^2 = (13.003355\text{ u} + 1.007825\text{ u} - 4.002603 - 10.012938\text{ u})(931.5\text{ MeV/u})$

   $= -\boxed{4.06\text{ MeV}}$. It requires 4.06 MeV.

9. (a) $\boxed{^{22}_{11}\text{Na}}$. $Q = (21.991384\text{ u} - 21.994435\text{ u} - m_e)\, c^2 < 0$. So $\boxed{\text{no}}$.

   (b) $\boxed{^{222}_{86}\text{Rn}}$. $Q = (226.025406\text{ u} - 222.017574\text{ u} - 4.002603\text{ u})\, c^2 > 0$. So $\boxed{\text{yes}}$.

   (c) $\boxed{^{12}_{6}\text{C}}$. $Q = (15.994915\text{ u} - 12.000000 - 4.002603\text{ u})\, c^2 < 0$. So $\boxed{\text{no}}$.

10. $Q = (m_p + m_H - m_{He})c^2 = (1.007825\text{ u} + 2.014102\text{ u} - 3.016029\text{ u})(931.5\text{ MeV/u}) = +5.49\text{ MeV}$.

11. $Q = (m_U - m_{Th} - m_{He})c^2 = (238.050786 \text{ u} - 234.043583 \text{ u} - 4.002603 \text{ u})(931.5 \text{ MeV/u})$

$= \boxed{+4.28 \text{ MeV}}$. We expect Q to be positive because it is a decay.

12. $Q = (m_O + m_n - m_C - m_{He})c^2 = (15.994915 \text{ u} + 1.008665 \text{ u} - 13.003355 \text{ u} - 4.002603 \text{ u})(931.5 \text{ MeV/u})$

$= -2.215 \text{ MeV}.$ $K_{min} = \left(1 + \dfrac{m_a}{M_A}\right)|Q| = \left(1 + \dfrac{1.008665}{15.994915}\right)(2.215 \text{ MeV}) = \boxed{2.35 \text{ MeV}}.$

13. $Q = (m_{He} + m_n - 2m_H)c^2 = (3.016029 \text{ u} + 1.008665 \text{ u} - 2.014102 \text{ u} - 2.014102 \text{ u})(931.5 \text{ MeV/u})$

$= -3.270 \text{ MeV}.$ $K_{min} = \left(1 + \dfrac{m_a}{M_A}\right)|Q| = \left(1 + \dfrac{1.008665}{3.016029}\right)(3.270 \text{ MeV}) = \boxed{4.36 \text{ MeV}}.$

14. $Q = (m_C + m_p - m_n - m_N)c^2 = (13.003355 \text{ u} + 1.007825 \text{ u} - 1.008665 \text{ u} - 13.005739 \text{ u})(931.5 \text{ MeV/u})$

$= -3.003 \text{ MeV}.$ $K_{min} = \left(1 + \dfrac{m_a}{M_A}\right)|Q| = \left(1 + \dfrac{1.007825}{13.003355}\right)(3.003 \text{ MeV}) = \boxed{3.24 \text{ MeV}}.$

15. $Q = (m_N + m_{He} - m_O - m_H)c^2 = (14.003074 \text{ u} + 4.002603 \text{ u} - 16.999131 \text{ u} - 1.007825 \text{ u})(931.5 \text{ MeV/u})$

$= -1.191 \text{ MeV}.$ $K_{min} = \left(1 + \dfrac{m_a}{M_A}\right)|Q| = \left(1 + \dfrac{4.002603}{14.003074}\right)(1.191 \text{ MeV}) = \boxed{1.53 \text{ MeV}}.$

16. $Q = (m_{Li} + m_p - 2m_{He})c^2 = (7.016005 \text{ u} + 1.007825 \text{ u} - 4.002603 \text{ u} - 4.002603 \text{ u})(931.5 \text{ MeV/u})$

$= +17.3 \text{ MeV}.$ So it is $\boxed{\text{exoergic}}$.

17. $Q = (m_{Hg} + m_p - m_{Au} - m_{He})c^2 \; (199.968321 \text{ u} + 1.007825 \text{ u} - 196.96656 \text{ u} - 4.002603 \text{ u})(931.5 \text{ MeV})$

$= +6.50 \text{ MeV}.$ So it is $\boxed{\text{exoergic}}$.

18. $Q = (m_{Be} + m_{He} - m_C - m_n)c^2 \; (9.012183 \text{ u} + 4.002603 \text{ u} - 12.000000 \text{ u} - 1.008665 \text{ u})(931.5 \text{ MeV/u})$

$= \boxed{5.70 \text{ MeV}}.$

19. $Q = (m_{H\text{-}3} + m_p - m_{H\text{-}2} - m_d)c^2 = (3.016049 \text{ u} + 1.007825 \text{ u} - 2.014102 \text{ u} - 2.014102 \text{ u})(931.5 \text{ MeV/u})$

$= -4.033 \text{ MeV}.$ $K_{min} = \left(1 + \dfrac{m_a}{M_A}\right)|Q| = \left(1 + \dfrac{1.007825}{3.016049}\right)(4.033 \text{ MeV}) = \boxed{5.38 \text{ MeV}}.$

20. $^{226}\text{Ra} \rightarrow \,^{222}\text{Rn} + \,^4\text{He}$.

$Q = (m_{\text{Ra}} - m_{\text{Rn}} - m_{\text{He}})c^2 = (226.025406 \text{ u} - 222.017574 \text{ u} - 4.002603 \text{ u})(931.5 \text{ MeV/u})$

$= 4.871 \text{ MeV}.$ So the kinetic energy of the recoiling daughter nucleus is

$K = 4.871 \text{ MeV} - 4.706 \text{ MeV} = \boxed{0.165 \text{ MeV}}$, according to conservation of energy.

21. For the first reaction: $(K_1)_{\text{min}} = \left(1 + \dfrac{m_a}{M_A}\right)|Q| = \left(1 + \dfrac{1}{15}\right)|Q_1|,$

For the second reaction: $(K_2)_{\text{min}} = \left(1 + \dfrac{1}{20}\right)|Q_2|.$

So $\dfrac{(K_1)_{\text{min}}}{(K_2)_{\text{min}}} = \dfrac{16/15}{21/20}\dfrac{|Q_1|}{|Q_2|} = \dfrac{16/15}{21/20} \, 3 = 3.05.$

Therefore $\boxed{\text{the first reaction by 3.05 times}}$.

22. The total area of all the plates is $A = n\pi R^2$ and the area of the wall is $A_o = LW$.

So the probability is $\dfrac{A}{A_o} = \boxed{\dfrac{n\pi R^2}{LW}}$.

23. (a) $\pi R^2 = \pi R_o^2 (A)^{2/3} = \pi(1.2 \times 10^{-15} \text{ m})^2 (12)^{2/3} = 2.37 \times 10^{-29} \text{ m}^2 = (2.37 \times 10^{-29} \text{ m}^2)\dfrac{1 \text{ b}}{10^{-28} \text{ m}^2} = \boxed{0.24 \text{ b}}.$

(b) $\pi R^2 = \pi R_o^2 (A)^{2/3} = \pi(1.2 \times 10^{-15} \text{ m})^2 (56)^{2/3} = 6.62 \times 10^{-29} \text{ m}^2 = \boxed{0.66 \text{ b}}.$

(c) $\pi R^2 = \pi R_o^2 (A)^{2/3} = \pi(1.2 \times 10^{-15} \text{ m})^2 (208)^{2/3} = 1.59 \times 10^{-28} \text{ m}^2 = \boxed{1.6 \text{ b}}.$

(d) $\pi R^2 = \pi R_o^2 (A)^{2/3} = \pi(1.2 \times 10^{-15} \text{ m})^2 (238)^{2/3} = 1.74 \times 10^{-28} \text{ m}^2 = \boxed{1.7 \text{ b}}.$

24. The electric potential energy is $U_e = \dfrac{kq_1 q_2}{r}$. The total kinetic energy is $K_{\text{total}} = 2 \left(\tfrac{3}{2} k_B T\right) = U_e.$

So $T = \dfrac{U_e}{3k_B} = \dfrac{kq_1 q_2}{3rk_B} = \dfrac{(9.0 \times 10^9 \text{ N·m}^2/\text{C}^2)(1.6 \times 10^{-19} \text{ C})^2}{3(10^{-14} \text{ m})(1.38 \times 10^{-23} \text{ J/K})} = \boxed{5.6 \times 10^8 \text{ K}}.$

25. (d).

26. (d).

27. (d).

28. (d).

29.   The reaction products collide with the core materials and coolant and in the process produce heat which converts water to steam that powers a turbine.

30.   (a) 231 nucleons are involved in the fission process.

So the energy released is (1 MeV/nucleon)(231 nucleon) = $\boxed{231 \text{ MeV}}$.

(b) 238 nucleons are involved in the fission process.

So the energy released is (1 MeV/nucleon)(238 nucleon) = $\boxed{238 \text{ MeV}}$.

31.   (a) $Q = (m_p + m_n - m_H)c^2 = (1.007825 \text{ u} + 1.008665 \text{ u} - 2.014102 \text{ u})(931.5 \text{ MeV/u}) = \boxed{2.22 \text{ MeV}}$.

(b) $Q = (2m_{He-3} - m_{He-4} - 2m_p)c^2 = [2(3.016029 \text{ u}) - 4.002603 \text{ u} - 2(1.007825 \text{ u})](931.5 \text{ MeV/u})$

$= \boxed{12.9 \text{ MeV}}$.

32.   (a) $Q = (2m_{H-2} - m_{H-3} - m_n)c^2 = [2(2.014102 \text{ u}) - 3.016029 \text{ u} - 1.008665 \text{ u}](931.5 \text{ MeV/u}) = \boxed{.27 \text{ MeV}}$.

(b) $Q = (m_{H-2} + m_{H-3} - m_{He} - m_n)c^2 = (2.014102 \text{ u} + 3.016029 \text{ u} - 4.002603 \text{ u} - 1.008665 \text{ u})(931.5 \text{ MeV/u})$

$= \boxed{17.6 \text{ MeV}}$.

33. $0.02 \text{ eV} = 0.60'' (2.0 \times 10^6 \text{ eV})$,   ☞ $n = -\dfrac{\log \dfrac{0.02}{2.0 \times 10^6}}{\log 0.60} = \boxed{36}$.

34.   (d).

35.   (c).

36.   Neutrinos interact very, very weakly with matter and so they can pass through huge quantities of matter without being detected.

37.   Neutrino has zero mass and so $E = pc = \dfrac{hc}{\lambda}$.

Therefore $\lambda = \dfrac{hc}{E} = \dfrac{(6.63 \times 10^{-34} \text{ J·})(3.00 \times 10^8 \text{ m/s})}{(2.65 \times 10^6 \text{ eV})(1.6 \times 10^{-19} \text{ J/eV})} = \boxed{4.69 \times 10^{-13} \text{ m}}$.

38.   According to momentum conservation, the momentum of the beta particle plus the daughter nucleus is equal in magnitude and opposite in direction to the momentum of the neutrino.

$p = \dfrac{E}{c} = \dfrac{(2.65 \times 10^6 \text{ eV})(1.6 \times 10^{-19} \text{ J/eV})}{3.00 \times 10^8 \text{ m/s}} = \boxed{1.41 \times 10^{-21} \text{ kg·m/s opposite to neutrino's}}$.

39.   (a) $K_{max} = 3.51$ MeV $- 2.65$ MeV $= \boxed{0.86 \text{ MeV}}$.

     (b) Since the daughter nucleus has zero kinetic energy in this case, the momentum of the beta particle is

     $\boxed{1.41 \times 10^{-21} \text{ kg·m/s opposite to neutrino's}}$.

     (c) When the kinetic energy of the beta particle is maximum, the kinetic energy and momentum of the

     daughter nucleus are $\boxed{\text{both zero}}$.

40.   In a β^- decay: $^A_Z\text{p} \rightarrow ^A_{Z+1}\text{d} + ^0_{-1}\text{e}$.

     So $Q = (m_P - m_D - m_e)c^2 = \{(m_P + Zm_e) - [m_D + (Z+1)m_e]\}c^2 = (M_P - M_D)c^2$.

41.   The daughter is ^{12}C. From Exercise 30.40, we have

     $K_{max} = Q = (M_P - M_D)c^2 = (12.014353 \text{ u} - 12.000000 \text{ u})(931.5 \text{ MeV/u}) = \boxed{13.37 \text{ MeV}}$.

42.   The maximum energy released in the decay is

     $Q = (M_P - M_D)c^2 = (31.973908 \text{ u} - 31.972072 \text{ u})(931.5 \text{ MeV/u}) = 1.710 \text{ MeV}$.

     So the energy of the neutrino is 1.710 MeV $- 1$ MeV $= \boxed{0.71 \text{ MeV}}$.

43.   In a β^+ decay: $^A_Z\text{p} \rightarrow ^A_{Z-1}\text{d} + ^0_{+1}\text{e}$.

     So $Q = (m_P - m_D - m_e)c^2 = \{(m_P + Zm_e) - [m_D + (Z-1)m_e] - 2m_e\}c^2 = (M_P - M_D - 2m_e)c^2$.

44.   The maximum energy released in the decay is

     $Q = (M_P - M_D - 2m_e)\,c^2 = (13.005739 \text{ u} - 13.003355 \text{ u})(931.5 \text{ MeV/u}) - 2(0.511 \text{ MeV}) = 1.199 \text{ MeV}$.

     So the energy of the neutrino is 1.199 MeV $- 0.250$ MeV $= \boxed{0.949 \text{ MeV}}$.

45.   The Q value has to be positive for the decays to be energetically possible and so for

     $\boxed{\beta^-: M_P > M_D \text{ and for } \beta^+: M_P > M_D + 2m_e}$.

46.   (b).

47.   (b).

48.   The effects of the existence of virtual exchange particles can be predicted and these predictions confirmed experimentally (scientific method).

49. $R = \dfrac{h}{2\pi mc}$,   ☞ $m = \dfrac{h}{2\pi Rc} = \dfrac{6.63 \times 10^{-34} \text{ J·s}}{2\pi(10^{-15} \text{ m})(3.00 \times 10^8 \text{ m/s})} = \boxed{3.5 \times 10^{-28} \text{ kg}}$.

50. It is $\boxed{\text{strong nuclear}}$ interaction. $R = c\Delta t$, ☞ $\Delta t = \dfrac{R}{c} = \dfrac{5.0 \times 10^{-16}\ \text{m}}{3.00 \times 10^8\ \text{m/s}} = \boxed{1.7 \times 10^{-24}\ \text{s}}$.

51. $m_{\text{m}} = 264 m_{\text{e}}$, so $\Delta E = m_{\text{m}} c^2 = 264(0.511\ \text{MeV}) = \boxed{135\ \text{MeV}}$.

52. $(\Delta E)(\Delta t) \geq \dfrac{h}{2\pi}$, ☞ $\Delta t \geq \dfrac{h}{2\pi \Delta E} = \dfrac{6.63 \times 10^{-34}\ \text{J·s}}{2\pi(140 \times 10^6\ \text{eV})(1.6 \times 10^{-19}\ \text{J/eV})} = \boxed{4.71 \times 10^{-24}\ \text{s}}$.

53. $R = \dfrac{h}{2\pi mc} = \dfrac{hc}{2\pi mc^2} = \dfrac{hc}{2\pi E_\text{o}} = \dfrac{(6.63 \times 10^{-34}\ \text{J·s})(3.00 \times 10^8\ \text{m/s})}{2\pi(1.00 \times 10^9\ \text{eV})(1.6 \times 10^{-19}\ \text{J/eV})} = \boxed{1.98 \times 10^{-16}\ \text{m}}$.

54. (b).

55. (a).

56. Quark flavor has one of six values. It can be changed by a weak interaction.
    Quark color has one of three values. It can be changed by gluons.

57. All hadrons contain quarks and/or antiquarks. Quarks are not believed to exist freely outside the nucleus.

58. Baryons ("heavy ones") have half-integer intrinsic spin (1/2 or 3/2), and decay into products that eventually include a proton (except a proton). Mesons have integer spin values (0 or 1) and eventually decay into leptons and photons.

59. From Table 30.3:   (a) $\boxed{\pi^+}$.   (b) $\boxed{K^0}$ (c) $\boxed{\Sigma^0}$.   (d) $\boxed{\Xi^-}$.

60. Charge: $\frac{2}{3}e + \frac{2}{3}e - \frac{1}{3}e = +e$.

61. The quark combination for a neutron is $\boxed{udd}$.
    Charge: $\frac{2}{3}e - \frac{1}{3}e - \frac{1}{3}e = 0$.

62. (b).

63. (a).

64. (a) $\boxed{{}^4_2\text{He}}$.   (b) $\boxed{{}^1_1\text{H}}$.   (c) $\boxed{{}^{93}_{38}\text{Sr}}$.   (d) $\boxed{{}^{12}_6\text{C}}$.   (e) $\boxed{{}^{16}_7\text{N}}$.

65. (a) $\boxed{{}^7_4\text{Be}^*}$.   (b) $\boxed{{}^{60}_{29}\text{Cu}^*}$.   (c) $\boxed{{}^{236}_{92}\text{U}^*}$.   (d) $\boxed{{}^{13}_6\text{C}^*}$.   (e) $\boxed{{}^{17}_8\text{O}^*}$.

66. (a) $Q = (m_{H-2} + m_{H-3} - m_{He} - m_n)c^2 = (2.014102\ u + 3.016049\ u - 4.002603\ u - 1.008665\ u)(931.5\ MeV/u)$

   $= \boxed{17.6\ MeV}$.

   (b) $Q = (2m_{H-2} - m_{H-3} - m_p)c^2 = [2(2.014102\ u) - 3.016049\ u - 1.007825\ u](931.5\ MeV/u) = \boxed{4.03\ MeV}$.

67. $^{14}_{6}C \rightarrow ^{14}_{7}N + ^{0}_{-1}e$.

   $Q = (m_C - m_N)c^2 = (14.003242\ u - 14.003074\ u)(931.5\ MeV/u) = \boxed{0.156\ MeV}$.

   The mass of the electron in the products is not included in the calculation because it is already included in the mass of the N atom (See Exercise 30.40).

68. In an electron capture: $^{A}_{Z}P + ^{0}_{-1}e \rightarrow ^{A}_{Z-1}D$.

   So $Q = (m_p + m_e - m_d)c^2 = \{(m_p + Zm_e) - [m_d + (Z-1)m_e]\}c^2 = (M_p - M_d)c^2$.

69. (a) From Exercise 68,

   $Q = (m_{Be} - m_{Li})c^2 = (7.016930\ u - 7.016005\ u)(931.5\ MeV/u) = \boxed{0.86\ MeV}$.

   (b) From Exercise 30.43,

   $Q = (M_p - M_d - 2m_e)c^2 = (7.016930\ u - 7.016005\ u)(931.5\ MeV/u) - 2(0.511\ MeV) = -0.16\ MeV$.

   So the decay is $\boxed{\text{not possible}}$.

70. (a) $\boxed{^{1}_{1}H}$.

   (b) $\boxed{^{10}_{5}B}$.

   (c) $\boxed{^{89}_{39}Y}$.

   (d) $\boxed{^{2}_{1}H}$.

College Physics

4/e — 3/e

Comparative Review

N = New
M = 3/e exercise number (modified for 4/e)
X = 3/e exercise number (unchanged)

Chapter 1

4/e	3/e	4/e	3/e	4/e	3/e
1.	1.	36.	47.	71.	74.
2.	2. M	37.	48.	72.	75.
3. N		38. N		73.	76.
4.	3. M	39. N		74. N	
5.	5.	40. N		75. N	
6.	4.	41.	38. M	76.	78.
7. N		42.	41. M	77.	79.
8.	6.	43.	42. M	78. N	
9.	7.	44.	43. M	79.	81. M
10.	8.	45.	44. M	80.	82.
11. N		46.	46. M	81. N	
12.	11.	47.	49.	82. N	
13. N		48.	50. M	83. N	
14.	15. M	49. N		84.	83.
15.	12.	50.	52.	85.	85. M
16.	13.	51.	53.	86.	86.
17.	14.	52.	54.	87.	87.
18.	16.	53.	55. M	88.	89.
19.	17.	54.	56.	89.	90.
20.	18.	55.	57.	90.	92.
21.	19.	56.	58.	91.	93.
22.	20.	57.	59.	92.	94.
23.	24.	58.	60.	93.	95.
24.	25.	59.	61.	94. N	
25. N		60. N			
26.	27.	61. N			
27.	28. M	62.	64.		
28. N		63.	65.		
29.	30.	64.	66.		
30.	31. M	65.	67.		
31. N		66.	68.		
32. N		67.	69.		
33.	36.	68.	71.		
34.	39.	69.	72. M		
35.	40. M	70.	73.		

Wilson/Buffa, Physics 4/e – 3/e   COMPARISON GRID

N = New
M = 3/e exercise number (modified for 4/e)
X = 3/e exercise number (unchanged)

Chapter 2

4/e	3/e	4/e	3/e	4/e	3/e	4/e	3/e
1.	1.	36.	33.	71.	66.	106.	109.
2.	3. M	37. N		72.	68.		
3.	6.	38.	35. M	73.	69.		
4.	4.	39.	36.	74. N			
5.	5.	40.	37.	75. N			
6.	8.	41.	38.	76.	73. M		
7. N		42.	39. M	77.	74.		
8. N		43.	40.	78.	70.		
9. N		44.	41.	79.	75. M		
10.	10. M	45.	34.	80.	76. M		
11.	11. M	46.	44. M	81. N			
12.	12.	47. N		82.	83.		
13.	13.	48.	42. M	83.	84.		
14. N		49.	45.	84. N			
15. N		50.	46.	85.	88.		
16.	15. M	51.	47.	86.	86.		
17. N		52. N		87.	87.		
18.	16. M	53.	54.	88.	89.		
19.	17. M	54.	49.	89.	91.		
20.	18.	55.	50.	90.	92.		
21.	19.	56. N		91.	93. M		
22. N		57.	55.	92.	94.		
23. N		58.	52.	93.	95.		
24.	21. M	59.	53. M	94. N			
25.	24.	60.	56.	95. N			
26.	25.	61.	57.	96. N			
27.	26.	62.	58.	97.	71. M		
28.	27. M	63.	59.	98.	98.		
29. N		64.	60.	99.	99.		
30.	28.	65.	63.	100.	97.		
31.	29.	66.	62	101. N			
32.	30. M	67. N		102.	101.		
33.	31. M	68.	64.	103.	102.		
34. N		69.	67.	104.	104.		
35. N		70.	65.	105.	106.		

N = New
M = 3/e exercise number (modified for 4/e)
X = 3/e exercise number (unchanged)

Chapter 3

4/e	3/e	4/e	3/e	4/e	3/e
1.	1. M	36. N		71. N	
2.	2.	37. N		72. N	
3.	3.	38.	34.	73. N	
4. N		39.	35.	74.	67.
5. N		40.	37. M	75.	68.
6. N		41.	39. M	76.	70.
7.	9. M	42.	40.	77.	75. M
8.	6. M	43. N		78.	71.
9.	7. M	44. N		79. N	
10.	10.	45. N		80. N	
11.	11.	46. N		81. N	
12.	12.	47. N		82.	78. M
13. N		48. N		83. N	
14.	13. M	49. N		84.	76.
15.	14.	50.	46. M	85.	77.
16.	15. M	51. N		86.	79.
17.	16.	52.	47. M	87.	80.
18. N		53. N		88.	82
19. N		54. N		89.	84. M
20.	18.	55. N		90.	87.
21.	19. M	56.	55.	91. N	
22.	20.	57.	56.	92.	8.
23.	21	58. N		93.	42.
24.	22.	59.	48.	94.	51.
25.	23.	60. N		95.	69.
26.	24.	61.	4.	96.	73.
27. N		62.	52.	97.	90.
28. N		63.	58.	98.	92.
29. N		64.	59.	99.	93. M
30. N		65.	62.	100.	95.
31.	25.	66. N		101.	96.
32.	26. M	67. N		102.	98.
33.	27.	68.	63. M	103.	100.
34.	28.	69.	65.	104.	101.
35. N		70. N		105.	102. M

N = New
M = 3/e exercise number (modified for 4/e)
X = 3/e exercise number (unchanged)

Chapter 4

4/e	3/e	4/e	3/e	4/e	3/e
1. N		36.	34. M	71. N	
2.	1.	37. N		72.	67.
3. N		38.	51.	73. N	
4.	2. M	39.	53. M	74.	68.
5.	3.	40. N		75.	69.
6.	6.	41. N		76. N	
7.	7.	42.	54. M	77. N	
8. N		43. N		78.	77.
9. N		44.	58. M	79.	81.
10. N		45. N		80.	71.
11.	8. M	46. N		81.	72. M
12. N		47. N		82.	65.
13.	11.	48.	38.	83.	70.
14.	12.	49.	39. M	84.	73.
15.	14.	50. N		85.	74. M
16.	15.	51. N		86.	79.
17. N		52. N		87.	80.
18. N		53. N		88. N	
19. N		54.	44.	89.	83.
20.	18. M	55. N		90.	84.
21.	19.	56.	35. M	91. N	
22. N		57. N		92.	86. M
23. N		58.	42.	93. N	
24.	23. M	59.	43.	94.	89. M
25. N		60.	36. M	95.	90.
26. N		61.	37.	96.	91.
27. N		62.	45.	97.	92.
28.	22. M	63. N		98.	94.
29.	24. M	64. N		99.	95.
30. N		65. N		100.	96.
31.	25. M	66.	60.	101.	97.
32.	28.	67. N		102. N	
33.	29. M	68.	61.	103.	78. M
34.	30. M	69. N		104.	100. M
35.	32.	70.	63.		

N = New
M = 3/e exercise number (modified for 4/e)
X = 3/e exercise number (unchanged)

Chapter 5

4/e	3/e	4/e	3/e	4/e	3/e
1.	2.	36.	33.	71. N	
2. N		37.	34.	72.	71.
3.	3.	38.	35.	73.	73.
4. N		39.	36.	74. N	
5.	5.	40.	37.	75.	74.
6. N		41.	40.	76.	77. M
7. N		42.	38. M	77. N	
8. N		43. N		78.	78.
9.	9.	44.	43.	79.	81.
10.	10.	45.	44.	80. N	
11.	11.	46.	46.	81.	85.
12.	12.	47. N		82.	86.
13.	13.	48.	45.	83. N	
14.	16. M	49.	47.	84.	87.
15.	17. M	50.	49.	85.	88.
16. N		51.	52.	86.	89.
17. N		52. N		87.	90.
18.	18.	53.	50. M	88.	91.
19.	19.	54.	54.	89.	94.
20.	20.	55.	55.	90.	27.
21. N		56.	56.	91.	95.
22. N		57. N		92.	66.
23. N		58.	57.	93.	69.
24.	21. M	59.	70.	94.	96.
25. N		60.	58.	95.	97.
26.	22. M	61. N		96.	98.
27.	23.	62. N		97.	101.
28.	24.	63.	60.	98.	102.
29.	25.	64.	62.	99.	103. M
30.	26. M	65.	63.		
31.	28.	66. N			
32. N		67. N			
33. N		68.	64.		
34.	32. M	69.	65.		
35. N		70.	67. M		

N = New
M = 3/e exercise number (modified for 4/e)
X = 3/e exercise number (unchanged)

Chapter 6

4/e	3/e	4/e	3/e	4/e	3/e
1.	1.	36.	60.	71.	73.
2.	2.	37. N		72.	74.
3. N		38.	22.	73.	75.
4.	5. M	39.	3. M	74.	76.
5. N		40.	23.	75. N	
6.	6. M	41.	25.	76.	77.
7. N		42. N		77.	78.
8.	10. M	43.	27. M	78.	79.
9. N		44.	28.	79.	80.
10.	11.	45.	100.	80.	81.
11. N		46.	30.	81.	84.
12.	12. M	47.	31.	82.	82.
13.	13. M	48.	32. M	83.	83.
14.	16. M	49. N		84. N	
15. N		50. N		85.	86. M
16.	18.	51.	33.	86.	88.
17.	19.	52.	35.	87.	89.
18. N		53.	36.	88.	90. M
19.	14.	54.	38.	89.	91. M
20. N		55.	39.	90.	87.
21.	21.	56.	40. M	91.	4.
22.	37.	57.	43.	92. N	
23. N		58.	54.	93.	94.
24.	41.	59.	55.	94.	95.
25.	42.	60.	57.	95.	17.
26.	46. M	61. N		96.	96.
27.	47. M	62.	62.	97.	97. M
28.	48. M	63. N		98.	99.
29. N		64.	63. M	99.	34. M
30.	15. M	65.	64.	100.	49. M
31.	50. M	66.	65.	101.	102.
32.	51. M	67.	66.	102.	103. M
33.	52. M	68.	68. M	103. N	
34.	58. M	69.	70.	104.	104.
35.	59. M	70.	72.	105.	106.

N = New
M = 3/e exercise number (modified for 4/e)
X = 3/e exercise number (unchanged)

Chapter 7

4/e	3/e	4/e	3/e	4/e	3/e
1.	1.	36.	36.	71.	71.
2.	2.	37.	37.	72.	72. M
3.	3. M	38. N		73. N	
4.	4.	39.	39.	74.	74.
5.	5. M	40.	40.	75.	75. M
6.	6. M	41.	41.	76. N	
7.	7.	42. N		77.	77.
8. N		43. N		78. N	
9.	8.	44.	43.	79.	81.
10.	10. M	45. N		80.	78.
11.	11.	46.	44.	81.	79.
12. N		47.	45.	82.	82.
13.	13.	48.	48. M	83.	83.
14. N		49.	49. M	84.	86.
15.	14.	50.	50. M	85.	90.
16.	15.	51. N		86.	92.
17.	16.	52.	53. M	87. N	
18.	17.	53.	54.	88.	94.
19.	19.	54.	55.	89.	95.
20.	20.	55.	56.	90.	97.
21. N		56. N		91.	99.
22.	22.	57.	57.	92.	100.
23. N		58. N		93.	101
24. N		59. N		94.	102.
25.	25.	60. N		95.	106.
26.	23. M	61.	61.M	96.	107.
27.N		62.	62.	97.	108.
28.	26. M	63.	63.	98.	109.
29.	27. M	64.	64.	99.	104.
30. N		65.	65.	100.	111.
31.	28.	66. N		101.	114.
32.	29. M	67.	67.	102.	115.
33. N		68.	68. M	103	116.
34.	31.	69.	69. M	104	119
35.	34. M	70.	70.		

N = New
M = 3/e exercise number (modified for 4/e)
X = 3/e exercise number (unchanged)

Chapter 8

4/e	3/e	4/e	3/e	4/e	3/e	4/e	3/e
1.	1.	36.	36.	71.	70. M	106.	110.
2.	2.	37. N		72.	57. M	107.	111.
3.	3.	38.	38.	73.	61.	108.	112.
4.	4.	39.	39.	74. N		109.	113.
5. N		40.	40.	75.	71. M		
6.	6. M	41.	41.	76.	72.		
7. N		42.	42.	77.	73.		
8.	5.	43. N		78.	77.		
9.	7. M	44.	46.	79.	79		
10.	10.	45. N		80.	80. M		
11.	11.	46.	48. M	81.	44.		
12.	8.	47. N		82.	47.		
13.	13.	48.	49. M	83. N			
14.	14.	49. N		84.	82.		
15.	15.	50.	53. M	85.	84.		
16.	17.	51.	54.	86.	88. M		
17. N		52. N		87. N			
18. N		53.	52. M	88.	90.		
19. N		54.	55.	89.	91.		
20. N		55.	56.	90. N			
21.	18.	56.	58.	91.	92.		
22.	22.	57.	59. M	92.	94.		
23.	21.	58.	60. M	93.	95. M		
24.	23.	59. N		94.	97.		
25.	24.	60. N		95.	98.		
26.	27.	61.	64.	96. N			
27.	28.	62.	62	97.	102.		
28.	29.	63.	63.	98.	103.		
29.	30. M	64.	65.	99. N			
30. N		65. N		100.	104.		
31.	37.	66.	67.M	101.	105.		
32.	32.	67.	68.M	102.	106.		
33.	33.	68. N		103.	107		
34.	31. M	69. N		104.	108.		
35.	35.	70.	69.	105. N			

Wilson/Buffa, Physics 4/e – 3/e   COMPARISON GRID

N = New
M = 3/e exercise number (modified for 4/e)
X = 3/e exercise number (unchanged)

Chapter 9

4/e	3/e	4/e	3/e	4/e	3/e
1.	1.	36.	36. M	71. N	
2.	2.	37.	37.	72.	84.
3.	3.	38. N		73.	88.
4.	4.	39.	38.	74.	89. M
5.	5.	40.	39. M	75.	90.
6.	6. M	41.	40.	76.	91.
7. N		42. N		77.	92.
8.	7. M	43. N		78.	93.
9.	9.	44. N		79. N	
10. N		45.	45.	80. N	
11. N		46. N		81. N	
12.	10.	47.	47.	82. N	
13.	12. M	48.	48.	83.	98.
14.	13.	49.	49.	84.	100.
15.	14. M	50.	50.	85.	108.
16.	15.	51.	53.	86. N	
17.	16.	52.	51.	87. N	
18. N		53.	54.	88.	106.
19.	19.	54.	56.	89.	107.
20.	20. M	55. N		90.	109.
21.	21.	56. N		91.	111. M
22. N		57.	55. M	92.	112.
23.	22.	58.	57. M	93.	113.
24.	23.	59.	58.	94.	114.
25.	24.	60.	60.	95.	115.
26.	25.	61.	61.	96.	116.
27.	26.	62.	62.	97.	117.
28.	27.	63.	63. M	98.	118.
29.	28. M	64.	67.	99.	119.
30. N		65.	77.	100.	120.
31. N		66.	78.		
32.	32.	67. N			
33.	35.	68. N			
34.	33.	69.	83. M		
35. N		70. N			

N = New
M = 3/e exercise number (modified for 4/e)
X = 3/e exercise number (unchanged)

Chapter 10

4/e	3/e	4/e	3/e	4/e	3/e
1. N		36.	33.	71.	76.
2. N		37.	92. M.	72. N	
3.	3.	38. N		73. N	
4.	4.	39.	39.	74. N	
5.	6.	40.	40.	75. N	
6.	7.	41.	41.	76. N	
7. N		42.	42.	77. N	
8.	8.	43. N		78.	78.
9.	10.	44.	43.	79.	79.
10.	9. M	45.	47. M	80. N	
11.	11.	46. N		81.	81.
12.	5.	47.	44. M	82.	58. M
13.	13.	48.	51. M	83.	83.
14.	14.	49.	53.	84.	84.
15.	15.	50.	49.	85.	85.
16.	16.	51.	50.	86. N	
17.	17. M	52.	52.	87.	87.
18.	18.	53. N		88.	89.
19.	19.	54. N		89. N	
20.	20.	55.	59. M.	90.	38.
21. N		56.	55.	91.	93. M
22.	21.	57. N		92.	94.
23.	22.	58.	57.	93.	95.
24.	23.	59.	54.	94. N	
25.	24. M	60.	60.	95.	97.
26.	25.	61. N		96.	98.
27.	27.	62.	62.		
28.	28. M	63.	63.		
29. N		64. N			
30. N		65.	65.		
31. N		66. N			
32.	34.	67.	67.		
33.	32.	68.	68. M		
34.	30.	69.	69.		
35.	31.	70.	66.		

Wilson/Buffa, Physics 4/e – 3/e   COMPARISON GRID

N = New
M = 3/e exercise number (modified for 4/e)
X = 3/e exercise number (unchanged)

Chapter 11

4/e	3/e	4/e	3/e	4/e	3/e
1.	1.	36.	36.	71.	70. M
2.	2.	37.	37.	72.	71.
3.	3. M	38. N		73.	75. M
4.	4. M	39.	38.	74.	76.
5.	5.	40.	39. M	75.	74.
6.	7.	41.	40.	76. N	
7. N		42.	41.	77.	77.
8.	8.	43.	24.	78.	78.
9.	11.	44.	43.	79.	80.
10.	12.	45.	44.	80.	82.
11. N		46. N		81.	84.
12. N		47.	47. M	82.	85.
13. N		48.	48.	83.	87.
14. N		49.	49.	84.	89. M
15. N		50.	51.	85. N	
16.	14. M	51. N			
17.	15.	52. N			
18.	18.	53.	53.		
19. N		54.	54.		
20.	23.	55.	55.		
21.	20.	56.	56.		
22.	21.	57.	57.		
23.	22	58. N	.		
24.	25.	59.	58.		
25.	26.	60.	59. M		
26.	27.	61.	61.		
27.	17.	62.	62.		
28.	28.	63.	63.		
29.	29.	64.	64.		
30.	30. M	65.N			
31.	31.	66.	65.		
32. N		67.	66.		
33. N		68.	67.		
34.	34. M	69.	68. M		
35.	35. M	70.	69. M		

Wilson/Buffa, Physics 4/e – 3/e   COMPARISON GRID

N = New
X.M = 3/e exercise number (modified for 4/e)
X = 3/e exercise number (unchanged)

Chapter 12

4/e	3/e	4/e	3/e	4/e	3/e
1.	1.	36.	34.	71. N	
2.	2.	37.	37. M	72. N	
3. N		38. N		73.	74.
4.	3. M	39.	40.	74. N	
5.	6.	40.	42.	75.	93.
6.	4. M	41.	43.	76.	80.
7. N		42.	44.	77.	75. M
8.	9.	43.	45	78.	76.
9.	10.	44.	46.	79.	77.
10.	11.	45.	47.	80.	78. M
11. N		46. N		81.	83. M
12.	12. M	47.	49. M	82.	81. M
13.	13.	48. N		83.	88. M
14. N		49.	50.	84.	85.
15.	14.	50. N		85.	86. M
16. N		51. N		86.	87.
17.	16. M	52.	51.	87.	89. M
18.	17.	53.	52.	88.	90.
19.	19.	54.	53.	89.	91.
20.	20.	55.	56. M	90.	92. M
21.	21.	56.	58.	91.	94.
22.	22.	57.	59. M	92.	95. M
23.	23.	58.	60. M	93.	96.
24.	24.	59.	61.	94.	97.
25.	26.	60.	62.	95.	98. M
26.	27. M	61.	63. M	96.	100. M
27.	28.	62.	64.	97.	102. M
28. N		63.	65.	98.	103.
29.	29.	64.	66.	99. N	
30.	30.	65. N		100.	106. M
31.	31.	66.	68.	101.	107. M
32.	32.	67.	69.	102. N	
33.	38.	68.	70.	103. N	
34.	33. M	69.	71.		
35.	41.	70.	72.		

Wilson/Buffa, Physics 4/e – 3/e   COMPARISON GRID

N = New
X.M = 3/e exercise number (modified for 4/e)
X = 3/e exercise number (unchanged)

Chapter 13

4/e	3/e	4/e	3/e	4/e	3/e
1.	1.	36. N		71. N	
2.	2.	37.	32. M	72. N	
3.	3.	38. N		73.	72.
4.	4.	39.	10.	74.	73.
5. N		40.	11.	75.	74. M
6. N		41.	33.	76. N	
7.	5. M	42.	37.	77.	76. M
8.	6. M	43.	38.	78. N	
9.	7.	44.	45.	79.	77.
10.	8.	45. N		80.	81.
11.	12.	46.	46.	81.	82.
12. N		47.	41. M	82.	79.
13.	13.	48.	48.	83.	80.
14.	14. M	49.	49.	84.	83.
15. N		50.	50.	85.	84.
16.	15.	51.	51.	86.	86.
17.	16. M	52.	52. M	87.	87.
18. N		53.	53.	88.	88. M
19. N		54. N		89.	90.
20.	17.	55.	54. M	90. N	
21.	19.	56.	55. M	91. N	
22.	20.	57.	56.	92.	93.
23.	21.	58.	57. M	93.	95.
24.	23. M	59. N		94.	96.
25.	24.	60.	59.	95. N	
26.	25. M	61.	60.	96. N	
27. N		62.	61. M	97.	99.
28.	27.	63.	62. M	98. N	
29.	28.	64.	63.	99.	101.
30.	29. M	65.	65.		
31. N		66.	66.		
32.	30. M	67.	67.		
33. N		68.	69.		
34. N		69.	70.		
35.	31.	70.	71.		

N = New
M = 3/e exercise number (modified for 4/e)
X = 3/e exercise number (unchanged)

Chapter 14

4/e	3/e	4/e	3/e	4/e	3/e
1.	1.	36.	32.	71.	73.
2.	2. M	37.	33.	72.	74. M
3.	3.	38.	34.	73. N	
4.	4.	39.	36.	74.	72. M
5.	5.	40. N		75.	75.
6. N		41.	38.	76. N	
7. N		42.	39.	77.	77.
8.	8.	43.	40.	78.	78.
9.	9. M	44.	43.	79.	81.
10.	10. M	45.	44.	80.	82.
11. N		46.	46.	81.	83.
12.	11.	47.	47. M	82.	84.
13. N		48. N		83.	86.
14.	13.	49. N		84.	88.
15.	15. M	50.	50.	85.	89.
16.	14. M	51.	51. M	86. N	
17.	16.	52.	52.	87. N	
18.	17. M	53. N		88.	93.
19.	18.	54.	53.	89.	94.
20.	19. M	55.	54. M	90.	85.
21.	20. M	56.	55.	91.	96.
22.	21.	57.	56.	92.	97.
23.	23. M	58. N		93. N	
24.	24.	59.	60.	94.	99. M
25.	25.	60.	59.	95.	76.
26.	26.	61.	58.		
27.	27.	62.	62. M		
28. N		63.	63.		
29. N		64.	64.		
30.	28. M	65.	65. M		
31. N		66.	66.		
32.	29. M	67.	61.		
33.	31.	68.	69.		
34. N		69.	70.		
35.	30. M	70.	71.		

N = New
M = 3/e exercise number (modified for 4/e)
X = 3/e exercise number (unchanged)

Chapter 15

4/e	3/e	4/e	3/e	4/e	3/e
1.	1. M	36.	36.	71.	70.
2.	2.	37.	37. M	72.	71.
3.	3.	38.	38.	73.	72. M
4.	4.	39.	39.	74.	73.
5. N		40. N		75.	74.
6.	5. M	41.	41. M	76.	75. M
7.	8. M	42. N		77.	76.
8.	6.	43.	44. M	78.	77.
9.	7. M	44.	46. M	79.	78.
10.	9. M	45. N		80. N	
11.	11.	46.	47.	81.	80.
12.	12.	47. N		82.	81.
13. N		48.	48.	83.	82.
14.	14. M	49.	49.	84.	83.
15.	15.	50.	50.	85.	84.
16.	16.	51.	51.	86.	85.
17.	17.	52.	52.	87.	86.
18. N		53.	53.	88.	87.
19.	21.	54.	54. M	89. N	
20.	18. M	55. N		90. N	
21.	19. M	56. N			
22.	22.	57.	56.		
23.	23. M	58.	57.		
24.	24.	59.	58.		
25.	25.	60. N			
26.	26. M	61. N			
27.	27. M	62.	60.		
28.	28.	63.	61.		
29.	29.	64.	62.		
30.	30.	65.	63.		
31. N		66.	64. M		
32.	32.	67.	67.		
33.	33.	68.	68.		
34.	34.	69.	69. M		
35.	35.	70. N			

N = New
M = 3/e exercise number (modified for 4/e)
X = 3/e exercise number (unchanged)

Chapter 16

4/e	3/e	4/e	3/e	4/e	3/e
1.	1.	36.	39.	71.	76.
2.	2.	37.	40.	72.	77.
3.	3.	38.	41. M	73. N	
4.	4. M	39.	42.	74.	79.
5.	5. M	40.	43. M	75.	80.
6. N		41.	44.	76.	81. M
7. N		42.	46. M	77.	82.
8.	7.	43.	47.	78. N	
9.	8. M	44.	48.	79.	84.
10.	9. M	45.	49.	80. N	
11.	10.	46. N		81.	86.
12.	11. M	47.	51. M	82.	87.
13. N		48.	52.	83.	88.
14.	12.	49.	53. M	84.	90. M
15.	13.	50.	54. M	85.	91.
16.	16. M	51.	55.	86.	92. M
17.	17. M	52. N		87.	93.
18.	18.	53.	57. M	88 N	
19.	19.	54.	58.	89.	96.
20.	20. M	55.	59.	90.	95.
21.	21. M	56.	60.	91.	97.
22.	22.	57.	61.	92.	98.
23. N		58. N		93.	100.
24. N		59. N		94.	101.
25.	25.	60.	65.	95.	104
26.	26.	61.	66.	96.	105.
27.	27.	62.	67.	97.	107.
28.	28.	63. N		98.	108.
29.	31.	64.	69. M	99.	109.
30.	32.	65.	71. M		
31.	33.	66. N			
32.	34.	67. N			
33.	35. M	68. N			
34.	36.	69.	73.		
35.	38.	70.	74. M		

Wilson/Buffa, Physics 4/e – 3/e COMPARISON GRID

N = New
M = 3/e exercise number (modified for 4/e)
X = 3/e exercise number (unchanged)

Chapter 17

4/e	3/e	4/e	3/e	4/e	3/e
1.	1.	36.	40.	71.	77.
2. N		37.	41.	72. N	
3.	3. M	38.	42.	73.	79.
4.	5.	39.	43.	74.	80.
5. N		40. N		75.	85. M
6. N		41.	45. M	76.	52.
7.	9. M	42.	46.	77.	87.
8.	10.	43.	47.	78.	88.
9.	11. M	44.	48. M	79.	89. M
10.	12.	45. N		80.	90. M
11.	13.	46. N		81.	93.
12.	14.	47.	51.	82.	94.
13.	15.	48.	53.	83.	95. M
14.	16.	49.	54.	84. N	
15. N		50.	56.	85. N	
16.	18.	51. N		86.	98.
17.	19. M	52.	57.	87.	99.
18.	21. M	53.	58.	88.	100.
19.	22.	54. N		89.	103.
20.	23. M	55. N		90.	104.
21.	24.	56. N		91. N	
22.	26.	57.	62.	92.	106.
23.	27.	68.	63.	93	107.
24.	28.	59.	64.	94.	108.
25.	29.	60. N		95.	109.
26.	30.	61.	66.		
27.	31.	62.	67. M		
28.	32. M	63.	68. M		
29.	33.	64. N			
30. N		65.	70. M		
31.	35. M	66.	71.		
32.	36. M	67.	72.		
33.	37.	68.	73.		
34.	38.	69. N			
35.	39.	70.	76.		

Wilson/Buffa, Physics 4/e – 3/e   COMPARISON GRID

N = New
M = 3/e exercise number (modified for 4/e)
X = 3/e exercise number (unchanged)

Chapter 18

4/e	3/e	4/e	3/e	4/e	3/e
1. N		36.	34.	71.	73.
2. N		37.	35. M	72.	74.
3.	3.	38.	36.	73.	75. M
4.	4.	39.	37.	74.	76.
5.	5. M	40.	38. M	75.	77.
6.	6. M	41.	39. M	76.	78.
7.	7. M	42.	40.	77.	79.
8. N		43.	41.	78.	80.
9.	8.	44. N		79.	81.
10.	9.	45.	46.	80.	82.
11.	10.	46.	44.	81.	83.
12.	11.	47.	45.	82.	84.
13. N		48.	47.	83. N	
14.	12. M	49.	48.	84. N	
15.	13.	50.	49.	85.	87.
16. N		51.	50.	86.	88.
17.	15.	52. N		87.	89. M
18.	16.	53.	54. M	88.	90. M
19.	17.	54. N		89.	91.
20.	18.	55.	55. M	90.	92.
21.	19.	56.	58.	91.	93. M
22.	20. M	57. N		92.	97.
23.	22.	58.	61.	93.	98.
24.	23.	59.	62.	94.	99. M
25.	24.	60.	63.	95.	100.
26.	25.	61.	64.	96.	103.
27.	26.	62.	65.	97.	104.
28.	27. M	63.	66.	98.	105. M
29. N		64.	67.	99.	106. M
30.	28.	65. N			
31. N		66.	68.		
32.	30.	67.	69.		
33.	31.	68.	70. M		
34.	32.	69.	71. M		
35.	33.	70.	72.		

Wilson/Buffa, Physics 4/e – 3/e   COMPARISON GRID

N = New
M = 3/e exercise number (modified for 4/e)
X = 3/e exercise number (unchanged)

Chapter 19

4/e	3/e	4/e	3/e	4/e	3/e
1.	1. M	36.	34.	71.	80.
2.	2. M	37.	35. M	72. N	
3.	3.	38.	40. M	73.	81.
4.	4.	39.	38.	74. N	
5. N		40.	39.	75.	83. M
6. N		41.	41.	76.	85.
7.	6.	42.	43.	77.	86. M
8.	7.	43.	44.	78.	88.
9. N		44.	47. M	79.	89.
10.	21.	45.	51. M	80. N	
11.	22.	46.	52. M	81.	91.
12.	10.	47.	50.	82.	92.
13.	11.	48.	53. M	83.	93.
14.	9.	49. N		84. N	
15.	12.	50. N		85.	94. M
16.	13. M	51. N		86.	96.
17.	14.	52.	58.	87.	98.
18.	15.	53.	59.	88.	99.
19.	17.	54.	60.	89.	100.
20. N		55.	61. M	90.	101.
21. N		56.	62. M	91.	102.
22. N		57.	63.	92.	103.
23. N		58.	64. M	93.	105.
24.	18.	59.	65.	94.	106.
25. N		60.	66.	95.	107.
26.	19. M	61.	67.		
27.	23. M	62.	68.		
28.	24.	63.	74. M		
29.	26.	64.	70.		
30.	27.	65.	71.		
31.	29.	66.	72. M		
32.	30.	67.	73. M		
33.	31. M	68.	75.		
34.	32.	69. N	.		
35.	33.	70.	77. M		

N = New
M = 3/e exercise number (modified for 4/e)
X = 3/e exercise number (unchanged)

Chapter 20

4/e	3/e		4/e	3/e		4/e	3/e
1.	1.		36.	36. M		71.	70.
2. N			37.	37. M		72.	72.
3.	3.		38.	38.		73.	73.
4. N			39.	39.		74.	90.
5. N			40. N			75.	74. M
6. N			41.	41. M		76.	75.
7.	4.		42.	42.		77.	76. M
8.	5. M		43.	43.		78.	55. M
9.	7.		44. N			79.	78.
10.	6. M		45. N			80.	79.
11.	8.		46.	45.		81. N	
12.	9.		47.	46.		82.	81.
13.	10.		48.	48.		83.	82.
14.	11.		49.	49.		84.	83.
15.	12. M		50.	50.		85.	84.
16.	13. M		51.	51. M		86.	85.
17.	14.		52.	52.		87.	86.
18.	15.		53.	53. M		88.	87.
19.	16.		54.	77.		89.	88.
20.	17.		55. N				
21. N			56.	56.			
22.	27.		57.	57. M			
23.	20. M		58.	58. M			
24.	21.		59.	59.			
25.	23.		60.	60. M			
26.	25.		61.	61.			
27.	26. M		62.	62.			
28. N			63.	63.			
29.	29.		64. N				
30.	30. M		65.	64. M			
31.	31.		66.	65. M			
32.	32. M		67.	66.			
33. N			68.	67.			
34.	34.		69.	68.			
35.	35.		70. N				

N = New
M = 3/e exercise number (modified for 4/e)
X = 3/e exercise number (unchanged)

Chapter 21

4/e	3/e	4/e	3/e	4/e	3/e
1.	1.	36.	38.	71.	77.
2.	4.	37.	39.	72.	78.
3. N		38. N			
4.	5.	39.	41.		
5.	6. M	40.	42.		
6.	7.	41.	44.		
7.	8. M	42. N			
8.	9.	43.	50.		
9.	10.	44.	46. M		
10.	11. M	45. N			
11.	12.	46. N			
12.	14.	47. N			
13.	15. M	48.	51.		
14. N		49.	52.		
15.	18.	50.	53.		
16.	19.	51.	54.		
17.	16.	52. N			
18.	20. M	53.	56.		
19.	13.	54.	57.		
20.	22. M	55.	55.		
21.	23. M	56.	58.		
22.	24.	57.	64. M		
23. N		58.	60.		
24.	26.	59.	61.		
25.	27.	60. N			
26. N		61.	59. M		
27.	29. M	62.	63.		
28.	30.	63.	66.		
29.	31.	64.	68.		
30.	32.	65.	69. M		
31.	33. M	66.	70.		
32.	34.	67.	71.		
33.	35.	68.	74.		
34.	36.	69.	75.		
35.	37. M	70.	76.		

N = New
M = 3/e exercise number (modified for 4/e)
X = 3/e exercise number (unchanged)

Chapter 22

4/e	3/e	4/e	3/e	4/e	3/e
1.	1.	36.	34.	71.	72.
2.	2.	37. N			
3.	3.	38.	36.		
4.	4.	39. N			
5.	5.	40.	38.		
6. N		41.	40.		
7.	6. M	42.	42.		
8.	7.	43.	41.		
9. N		44.	43. M		
10.	8. M	45.	44.		
11.	9.	46.	49.		
12.	12. M	47.	47.		
13.	13.	48.	48. M		
14. N		49.	50.		
15.	14.	50. N			
16.	15.	51.	54.		
17.	16.	52.	51.		
18. N		53.	53.		
19.	19.	54.	55.		
20. N		55.	56.		
21.	20.	56. N	57.		
22. N		57.	58.		
23.	22. M	58. N			
24.	23.	59.	59.		
25. N		60. N			
26.	24. M	61.	62.		
27.	31.	62.	60.		
28.	26.	63.	61.		
29.	28.	64.	63.		
30.	30. M	65.	65.		
31. N		66.	66.		
32. N		67.	67. M		
33.	27.	68.	69. M		
34.	29.	69.	70. M		
35.	32. M	70.	71		

Wilson/Buffa, Physics 4/e – 3/e   COMPARISON GRID

N = New
M = 3/e exercise number (modified for 4/e)
X = 3/e exercise number (unchanged)

Chapter 23

4/e	3/e	4/e	3/e	4/e	3/e
1.	1.	36.	35.	71.	71.
2.	2.	37.	36.	72.	73.
3.	3.	38.	37. M	73.	74.
4.	4.	39.	38. M	74. N	
5.	5.	40.	39.	75. N	
6. N		41.	40.	76.	76.
7. N		42.	41.	77.	77.
8.	7. M	43.	42.	78. N	
9.	8. M	44.	44.	79.	79.
10. N		45.	45. M	80.	80.
11.	10.	46.	46.	81.	81.
12. N		47. N		82.	82. M
13.	13.	48.	48.	83.	83.
14.	11. M	49.	49.	84.	84.
15. N		50. N		85.	85.
16.	16.	51. N		86.	86.
17.	18.	52. N		87.	87.
18. N		53.	61. M	88.	88.
19.	19.	54.	52.	89.	89.
20.	20.	55.	53.	90.	90.
21.	21.	56.	54.	91.	91.
22. N		57.	56. M	92.	92.
23. N		58.	58.	93.	93.
24.	23	59.	59.		
25.	24.	60.	57.		
26.	31. M	61.	60.		
27.	22.	62.	62.		
28.	28.	63.	63.		
29.	29.	64.	64. M		
30.	27.	65.	65. M		
31. N		66.	66.		
32.	26.	67.	67.		
33.	30.	68.	69.		
34.	32.	69.	70.		
35.	33.	70. N			

N = New
M = 3/e exercise number (modified for 4/e)
X = 3/e exercise number (unchanged)

Chapter 24

4/e	3/e		4/e	3/e		4/e	3/e
1. N			36.	36.		71.	71. M
2. N			37. N			72.	73.
3.	3.		38.	37. M		73.	74.
4.	4.		39.	38.		74.	75.
5.	5.		40. N			75.	76.
6. N			41.	46. M		76.	77. M
7.	8. M		42.	49. M		77.	78.
8. N			43.	50. M		78.	79.
9.	7.		44.	47.		79.	80.
10. N			45.	42.		80.	81.
11.	9. M		46.	40.		81.	82.
12.	14.		47.	41.		82.	83.
13.	15.		48.	43.			
14.	10.		49.	44.			
15.	12. M		50.	48.			
16.	16.		51.	51.			
17.	17.		52.	52.			
18.	18.		53.	53.			
19.	19.		54.	54.			
20.	20.		55.	55.			
21.	21.		56.	56.			
22.	22.		57.	57.			
23. N			58. N				
24. N			59.	59.			
25.	24. M		60. N				
26.	25.		61.	60. M			
27.	26.		62.	61. M			
28.	27. M		63.	62.			
29.	28.		64.	63.			
30.	29.		65.	64.			
31.	30. M		66.	66.			
32.	32.		67.	67.			
33.	33.		68.	68. M			
34. N			69. N				
35.	35.		70.	70.			

N = New
M = 3/e exercise number (modified for 4/e)
X = 3/e exercise number (unchanged)

Chapter 25

4/e	3/e	4/e	3/e	4/e	3/e
1.	1.	36.	33.	71.	70.
2.	2.	37.	36.	72.	71.
3.	3.	38.	37. M	73.	72.
4. N		39.	38.	74.	73.
5.	5.	40.	39.	75. N	
6. N		41.	40.	76.	48. M
7. N		42.	42.	77.	76.
8.	6. M	43.	43.	78.	77. M
9.	7. M	44.	44.	79.	78.
10.	9.	45. N		80.	79.
11.	13.	46.	45. M	81.	80.
12.	10. M	47.	46.	82.	81.
13.	11.	48.	47.	83.	82.
14.	12. M	49.	49. M	84.	83.
15.	14. M	50.	50.	85.	84.
16.	15.	51.	51.	86.	85.
17.	16.	52. N		87.	86.
18.	18.	53.	52.		
19. N		54.	53.		
20.	17.	55.	54.		
21.	20.	56.	55. M		
22.	22.	57. N			
23.	23.	58.	56. M		
24.	24.	59.	57.		
25. N		60.	58.		
26.	26. M	61.	59.		
27.	27. M	62.	60. M		
28.	25. M	63.	61. M		
29.	28.	64. N			
30.	29.	65.	63.		
31.	30. M	66.	64.		
32.	31.	67.	66. M		
33.	32.	68.	67.		
34.	34.	69.	68.		
35.	35. M	70.	69.		

N = New
M = 3/e exercise number (modified for 4/e)
X = 3/e exercise number (unchanged)

Chapter 26

4/e	3/e	4/e	3/e	4/e	3/e
1.	1.	36.	36. M	71.	72.
2.	2.	37.	37.	72.	73.
3.	3.	38.	38.	73.	74.
4.	5. M	39.	39.	74.	75.
5. N		40. N		75.	76. M
6.	6.	41.	41.	76.	77. M
7.	7. M	42.	42. M	77.	79. M
8.	8. M	43. N		78.	80.
9.	9. M	44. N		79.	81. M
10.	10.	45.	43.	80.	82.
11.	11.	46.	44. M	81.	83.
12.	12. M	47.	45.	82. N	
13.	15.	48.	47. M	83.	85.
14.	13.	49.	46. M	84.	86.
15.	14.	50.	48. M	85.	87.
16.	16.	51.	49.		
17. N		52.	52.		
18. N		53.	53.		
19.	19.	54.	51.		
20.	20.	55.	54. M		
21.	21.	56.	55.		
22.	22.	57.	56.		
23.	23.	58.	57.		
24. N		59.	58.		
25. N		60.	59.		
26.	24. M	61.	60. M		
27.	25. M	62.	62. M		
28. N	26.	63.	64.		
29. N	27.	64.	65. M		
30.	30.	65.	66.		
31.	29.	66. N			
32.	28.	67.	67.		
33.	32.	68.	69.		
34.	33.	69.	68.		
35.	34.	70.	70.		

N = New
M = 3/e exercise number (modified for 4/e)
X = 3/e exercise number (unchanged)

Chapter 27

4/e	3/e	4/e	3/e	4/e	3/e
1.	1. M	36.	36.	71.	69.
2.	2.	37.	37.	72.	72.
3.	3. M	38. N		73. N	
4. N		39.	39.	74.	74.
5.	5.	40. N		75.	75.
6.	6.	41.	40.	76.	76.
7.	4.	42.	42. M	77.	77.
8.	7.	43.	46.	78. N	
9.	8. M	44.	47.	79.	79. M
10.	10.	45.	43.	80.	80.
11.	11.	46.	45. M	81.	81.
12.	12. M	47. N		82.	82.
13.	13.	48.	48.	83.	83.
14.	14.	49.	49.	84.	84.
15.	15.	50.	50.	85.	85.
16.	16. M	51.	51.	86.	86.
17. N		52. N		87. N	
18.	17. M	53.	52.		
19.	18.	54.	53. M		
20.	19.	55.	54.		
21.	20.	56.	55. M		
22.	21. M	57.	56.		
23.	22. M	58.	58. M		
24.	23.	59.	59.		
25.	25.	60.	57.		
26.	26. M	61.	60.		
27. N		62.	61.		
28.	28.	63.	62.		
29.	29.	64.	64.		
30.	30.	65.	65.		
31.	31.	66.	63. M		
32.	32.	67.	66.		
33.	33.	68.	67. M		
34.	34. M	69.	70.		
35.	35. M	70.	68.		

N = New
M = 3/e exercise number (modified for 4/e)
X = 3/e exercise number (unchanged)

Chapter 28

4/e	3/e		4/e	3/e
1.	1.		36.	36.
2.	2.		37.	37.
3. N			38. N	
4. N			39.	40. M
5.	4.		40.	38.
6.	5.		41.	39.
7.	6.		42.	41.
8.	8.		43.	43.
9.	7. M		44.	44.
10.	9.		45.	45.
11.	10.		46.	46.
12.	11. M		47.	47.
13.	12.		48.	48. M
14.	14.		49.	49. M
15.	15. M		50.	50. M
16.	16.		51.	51.
17.	17.		52.	52.
18.	18.		53.	53. M
19.	19.		54.	54. M
20.	21.		55.	55.
21.	22.		56.	56.
22. N			57.	57.
23.	23.		58.	58.
24.	24.		59.	59.
25.	25.		60.	60. M
26.	26.		61.	61.
27.	27.		62.	62.
28.	28. M		63.	63.
29.	29. M		64.	64.
30.	30.			
31.	31.			
32.	33.			
33.	32.			
34.	34.			
35.	35.			

N = New
M = 3/e exercise number (modified for 4/e)
X = 3/e exercise number (unchanged)

Chapter 29

4/e	3/e	4/e	3/e	4/e	3/e
1.	1.	36.	36.	71.	71.
2.	2.	37.	37.	72.	72.
3.	3.	38.	38.	73.	73. M
4. N		39.	39.	74.	74.
5. N		40.	40. M	75.	75.
6.	5.	41.	41. M	76.	76. M
7.	6.	42.	42. M	77.	77.
8.	8.	43.	43.	78.	78.
9.	9.	44.	44. M	79.	79. M
10.	7. M	45.	47. M	80.	80.
11.	11.	46.	45.	81.	81.
12.	12.	47.	46.	82.	82.
13. N		48.	48.	83.	83.
14.	14.	49.	49.	84.	84.
15.	15.	50.	50.	85.	85.
16.	16.	51.	51.	86.	86.
17. N		52.	52.	87.	87.
18. N		53.	53.	88.	88.
19.	19.	54.	54.	89. N	
20.	20.	55.	55.	90.	90. M
21.	21.	56.	56.	91.	91.
22.	22.	57.	57.	92. N	
23.	23.	58.	58.	93.	93.
24.	24.	59.	59. M	94. N	
25.	25. M	60. N			
26.	26.	61.	61. M		
27.	27.	62.	62.		
28.	28.	63. N			
29.	29. M	64. N			
30.	30. M	65.	65.		
31.	31. M	66.	66.		
32.	32.	67.	67. M		
33.	33.	68.	68.		
34.	34.	69.	69.		
35.	35. M	70.	70. M		

N = New
M = 3/e exercise number (modified for 4/e)
X = 3/e exercise number (unchanged)

Chapter 30

4/e	3/e	4/e	3/e
1.	1.	36.	36.
2.	2.	37.	37.
3.	3.	38.	38.
4.	4. M	39.	39.
5.	6.	40.	40.
6.	5. M.	41.	41.
7.	7.	42.	42.
8. N		43.	43.
9.	9.	44.	44.
10.	10. M	45.	45.
11.	11.	46.	46.
12.	12.	47.	47. M
13.	17.	48.	48.
14.	18.	49.	51. M
15.	13.	50.	52.
16.	15.	51.	53.
17.	14.	52.	54.
18.	16.	53.	55. M
19.	19.	54.	56.
20.	20.	55.	57. M
21.	21. M	56.	58.
22.	22.	57.	59.
23.	23.	58. N	
24.	24.	59. N	
25.	25.	60. N	
26.	26.	61. N	
27.	27.	62. N	
28.	28.	63. N	
29.	29.	64.	60.
30.	30.	65.	61.
31.	31. M	66.	62.
32. N		67. N	
33.	33. M	68.	65.
34.	34.	69.	66.
35.	35.	70.	67. M